PARALLELOGRAM

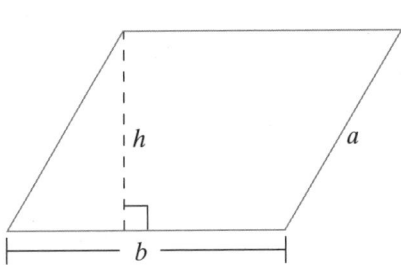

Perimeter: $P = 2a + 2b$
Area: $A = bh$

CIRCLE

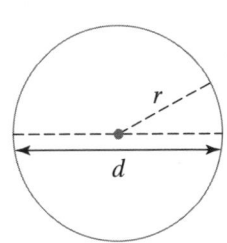

Circumference: $C = \pi d$
$C = 2\pi r$
Area: $A = \pi r^2$

RECTANGULAR SOLID

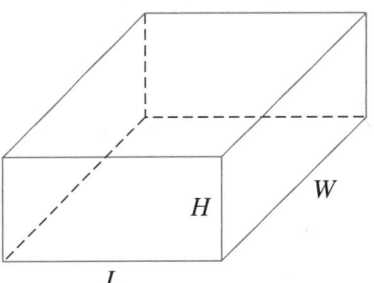

Volume: $V = LWH$
Surface Area: $A = 2HW + 2LW + 2LH$

CUBE

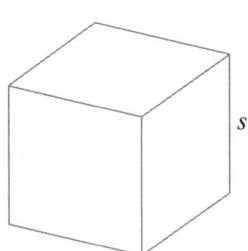

Volume: $V = s^3$
Surface Area: $A = 6s^2$

CONE

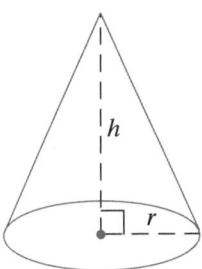

Volume: $V = \dfrac{1}{3}\pi r^2 h$
Lateral Surface Area: $A = \pi r \sqrt{r^2 + h^2}$

RIGHT CIRCULAR CYLINDER

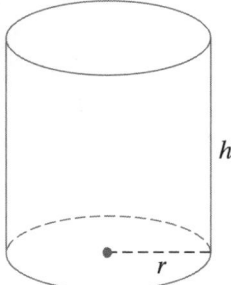

Volume: $V = \pi r^2 h$
Surface Area:
$A = 2\pi rh + 2\pi r^2$

OTHER FORMULAS

Distance: $d = rt$ (r = rate, t = time)

Temperature: $F = \dfrac{9}{5}C + 32 \qquad C = \dfrac{5}{9}(F - 32)$

Simple Interest: $I = Prt$
(P = principal, r = annual interest rate, t = time in years)

Compound Interest: $A = P\left(1 + \dfrac{r}{n}\right)^{nt}$

(P = principal, r = annual interest rate, t = time in years, n = number of compoundings per year)

Intermediate
ALGEBRA

K. Elayn Martin-Gay

Custom Edition for University of Maryland Eastern Shore

Taken from:

Intermediate Algebra, Fourth Edition
by K. Elayn Martin-Gay

Taken from:

Intermediate Algebra, Fourth Edition
by K. Elayn Martin-Gay
Copyright © 2005 1996 by Prentice-Hall, Inc.
A Pearson Education Company
Upper Saddle River, New Jersey 07458

This special edition published in cooperation with Pearson Custom Publishing.

Printed in the United States of America

10   9   8   7   6   5

ISBN 0-536-98414-X

2005360559

AK

Please visit our web site at *www.pearsoncustom.com*

PEARSON CUSTOM PUBLISHING
75 Arlington Street, Suite 300, Boston, MA 02116
A Pearson Education Company

CONTENTS

5 EXPONENTS, POLYNOMIALS, AND POLYNOMIAL FUNCTIONS   273

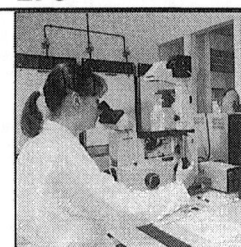

6 RATIONAL EXPRESSIONS   363

7

RATIONAL EXPONENTS, RADICALS, AND COMPLEX NUMBERS 445

8

QUADRATIC EQUATIONS AND FUNCTIONS 517

APPENDICES 735

Real Numbers and Algebraic Expressions

In arithmetic, we add, subtract, multiply, divide, raise to powers, and take roots of numbers. In algebra, we add, subtract, multiply, divide, raise to powers, and take roots of variables. Letters, such as x, that represent numbers are called **variables**. Understanding these algebraic expressions depends on your understanding of arithmetic expressions. This chapter reviews the arithmetic operations on real numbers and the corresponding algebraic expressions.

The travel industry is the third largest retail industry in the United States, accounting for the employment of over 16 million people. One segment of this ever-growing population is made up of travel agents. Travel agents are professionals trained to search for and book airline fares, rail tickets, hotel reservations, car rentals, cruise packages, tours and much more. They also address topics important to travelers, including special events, climate conditions, and travel and safety regulations for domestic and international travel.

Successful travel agents need good communication and business skills. Because the job involves searching for competitive prices, basic computer skills are also a must as well as mathematics and number sense.

In the Spotlight on Decision Making feature on page 26, you will have the opportunity to compare tour packages as a travel agent.

Link: www.astanet.com *(American Society of Travel Agents)*
Source of text: (same)

1.1 TIPS FOR SUCCESS IN MATHEMATICS

Objectives

1. Get ready for this course.
2. Understand some general tips for success.
3. Understand how to use this text.
4. Get help as soon as you need it.
5. Learn how to prepare for and take a test.
6. Develop good time management.

Before reading this section, remember that your instructor is your best source for information. Please see your instructor for any additional help or information.

1 Getting Ready for This Course

Now that you have decided to take this course, remember that a *positive attitude* will make all the difference in the world. Your belief that you can succeed is just as important as your commitment to this course. Make sure that you are ready for this course by having the time and positive attitude that it takes to succeed.

Next make sure that you have scheduled your math course at a time that will give you the best chance for success. For example, if you are also working, you may want to check with your employer to make sure that your work hours will not conflict with your course schedule. Also, schedule your class during a time of day when you are more attentive and do your best work.

On the day of your first class period, double-check your schedule and allow yourself extra time to arrive in case of traffic problems or difficulty locating your classroom. Make sure that you bring at least your textbook, paper, and a writing instrument. Are you required to have a lab manual, graph paper, calculator, or other supplies besides this text? If so, also bring this material with you.

2 General Tips for Success

Below are some general tips that will increase your chance for success in a mathematics class. Many of these tips will also help you in other courses you may be taking.

Exchange names and phone numbers with at least one other person in class. This contact person can be a great help if you miss an assignment or want to discuss math concepts or exercises that you find difficult.

Choose to attend all class periods and be on time. If possible, sit near the front of the classroom. This way, you will see and hear the presentation better. It may also be easier for you to participate in classroom activities.

Do your homework. You've probably heard the phrase "practice makes perfect" in relation to music and sports. It also applies to mathematics. You will find that the more time you spend solving mathematics problems, the easier the process becomes. Be sure to schedule enough time to complete your assignments before the next class period.

Check your work. Review the steps you made while working a problem. Learn to check your answers in the original problems. You may also compare your answers with the answers to selected exercises section in the back of the book. If you have made a mistake, try to figure out what went wrong. Then cor-

rect your mistake. If you can't find what went wrong, don't erase your work or throw it away. Bring your work to your instructor, a tutor in a math lab, or a classmate. It is easier for someone to find where you had trouble if they look at your original work.

Learn from your mistakes and be patient with yourself. Everyone, even your instructor, makes mistakes. Use your errors to learn and to become a better math student. The key is finding and understanding your errors.

Was your mistake a careless one, or did you make it because you can't read your own math writing? If so, try to work more slowly or write more neatly and make a conscious effort to carefully check your work.

Did you make a mistake because you don't understand a concept? Take the time to review the concept or ask questions to better understand it.

Did you skip too many steps? Skipping steps or trying to do too many steps mentally may lead to preventable mistakes.

Know how to get help if you need it. It's OK to ask for help. In fact, it's a good idea to ask for help whenever there is something that you don't understand. Make sure you know when your instructor has office hours and how to find his or her office. Find out whether math tutoring services are available on your campus. Check out the hours, location, and requirements of the tutoring service. Videotapes and software are available with this text. Learn how to access these resources.

Organize your class materials, including homework assignments, graded quizzes and tests, and notes from your class or lab. All of these items will make valuable references throughout your course especially when studying for upcoming tests and the final exam. Make sure that you can locate these materials when you need them.

Read your textbook before class. Reading a mathematics textbook is unlike leisure reading such as reading a book or newspaper. Your pace will be much slower. It is helpful to have a pencil and paper with you when you read. Try to work out examples on your own as you encounter them in your text. You may also write down any questions that you want to ask in class. When you read a mathematics textbook, some of the information in a section may be unclear. But after you hear a lecture or watch a videotape on that section, you will understand it much more easily than if you had not read your text beforehand.

Don't be afraid to ask questions. Instructors are not mind readers. Many times we do not know a concept is unclear until a student asks a question. You are not the only person in class with questions. Other students are normally grateful that someone has spoken up.

Hand in assignments on time. This way you can be sure that you will not lose points for being late. Show every step of a problem and be neat and organized. Also be sure that you understand which problems are assigned for homework. You can always double-check this assignment with another student in your class.

 **Using This Text**

There are many helpful resources that are available to you in this text. It is important that you become familiar with and use these resources. This should increase your chances for success in this course.

- The main section of exercises in each exercise set is referenced by examples. Use this referencing if you have trouble completing an assignment from the exercise set.

- If you need extra help in a particular section, look at the beginning of the section to see what videotapes and software are available.

- Make sure that you understand the meaning of the icons that are beside many exercises. The video icon 🔒 tells you that the corresponding exercise may be viewed on the videotape that corresponds to that section. The pencil icon ✎ tells you that this exercise is a writing exercise in which you should answer in complete sentences. The △ icon tells you that the exercise involves geometry.

- Integrated Reviews in each chapter offer you a chance to practice—in one place— the many concepts that you have learned separately over several sections.

- There are many opportunities at the end of each chapter to help you understand the concepts of the chapter.

  Chapter Highlights contain chapter summaries and examples.

  Chapter Reviews contain review problems organized by section.

  Chapter Tests are sample tests to help you prepare for an exam.

  Cumulative Reviews are reviews consisting of material from the beginning of the book to the end of that particular chapter.

See the preface at the beginning of this text for a more thorough explanation of the features of this text.

④ Getting Help

If you have trouble completing assignments or understanding the mathematics, get help as soon as you need it! This tip is presented as an objective on its own because it is so important. In mathematics, usually the material presented in one section builds on your understanding of the previous section. What does this mean? It means that if you don't understand the concepts covered during a class period, there is a good chance that you will not understand the concepts covered during the next class period. If this happens to you, get help as soon as you can.

Where can you get help? Many suggestions have been made in this section on where to get help, and now it is up to you to do it. Try your instructor, a tutoring center, or math lab, or you may want to form a study group with fellow classmates. If you do decide to see your instructor or go to a tutoring center, make sure that you have a neat notebook and be ready with your questions.

⑤ Preparing for and Taking a Test

Make sure that you allow yourself plenty of time to prepare for a test. If you think that you are a little "math anxious," it may be that you are not preparing for a test in a way that will ensure success. The way that you prepare for a test in mathematics is important. To prepare for a test,

1. Review your previous homework assignments.

2. Review any notes from class and section-level quizzes you may have taken. (If this is a final exam, also review chapter tests you have taken.)

3. Review concepts and definitions by reading the Highlights at the end of each chapter.

4. Practice working exercises by completing the Chapter Review found at the end of each chapter. (If this is a final exam, go through a Cumulative Review. There is one found at the end of each chapter (except Chapter 1). Choose the review found at the end of the latest chapter that you have covered in your course.) *Don't stop here!*

5. It is important that you place yourself in conditions similar to test conditions to find out how you will perform. In other words, as soon as you feel that you know the material, get a few blank sheets of paper and take a sample test.

There is a Chapter Test available at the end of each chapter. During this sample test, do not use your notes or your textbook. Once you complete the Chapter Test, check your answers in the back of the book. If any answer is incorrect, there is a CD available with each exercise of each chapter test worked. Use this CD or your instructor to correct your sample test. Your instructor may also provide you with a review sheet. If you are not satisfied with the results, study the areas that you are weak in and try again.

6. Get a good night's sleep before the exam.

7. On the day of the actual test, allow yourself plenty of time to arrive at where you will be taking your test.

When taking your test,

1. Read the directions on the test carefully.

2. Read each problem carefully as you take the test. Make sure that you answer the question asked.

3. Watch your time and pace yourself so that you can attempt each problem on your test.

4. If you have time, check your work and answers.

5. Do not turn your test in early. If you have extra time, spend it double-checking your work.

6   **Managing Your Time**

As a college student, you know the demands that classes, homework, work, and family place on your time. Some days you probably wonder how you'll ever get everything done. One key to managing your time is developing a schedule. Here are some hints for making a schedule:

1. Make a list of all of your weekly commitments for the term. Include classes, work, regular meetings, extracurricular activities, etc. You may also find it helpful to list such things as laundry, regular workouts, grocery shopping, etc.

2. Next, estimate the time needed for each item on the list. Also make a note of how often you will need to do each item. Don't forget to include time estimates for reading, studying, and homework you do outside of your classes. You may want to ask your instructor for help estimating the time needed.

3. In the following Exercise Set, you are asked to block out a typical week on the schedule grid given. Start with items with fixed time slots like classes and work.

4. Next, include the items on your list with flexible time slots. Think carefully about how best to schedule some items such as study time.

5. Don't fill up every time slot on the schedule. Remember that you need to allow time for eating, sleeping, and relaxing! You should also allow a little extra time in case some items take longer than planned.

6. If you find that your weekly schedule is too full for you to handle, you may need to make some changes in your workload, classload, or in other areas of your life. You may want to talk to your advisor, manager or supervisor at work, or someone in your college's academic counseling center for help with such decisions.

Note: In this chapter, we begin a feature called Study Skills Reminder. The purpose of this feature is to remind you of some of the information given in this section and to further expand on some topics in this section.

EXERCISE SET 1.1

STUDY GUIDE/SSM   CD/VIDEO   PH MATH TUTOR CENTER   MathXL®Tutorials ON CD   MathXL®   MyMathLab®

1. What is your instructor's name?

2. What are your instructor's office location and office hours?

3. What is the best way to contact your instructor?

4. What does the ＼ icon mean?

5. What does the 🔒 icon mean?

6. What does the △ icon mean?

7. Where are answers located in this text?

8. What Exercise Set answers are available to you in the answers section?

9. What Chapter Review, Chapter Test, and Cumulative Test answers are available to you in the answer section?

10. Are there worked-out solutions to exercises in this text?

11. If the answer to Exercise 10 is yes, what worked-out solutions are available to you in this text?

12. Go to the Highlights section at the end of this chapter. Describe how this section may be helpful to you when preparing for a test.

13. Do you have the name and contact information of at least one other student in class?

14. Will your instructor allow you to use a calculator in this class?

15. Are videotapes, CDs, and/or tutorial software available to you? If so, where?

16. Is there a tutoring service available? If so, what are its hours?

17. Have you attempted this course before? If so, write down ways that you might improve your chances of success during this next attempt.

18. List some steps that you can take if you begin having trouble understanding the material or completing an assignment.

19. Read or reread objective ⑥ and fill out the schedule grid below.

	Monday	Tuesday	Wednesday	Thursday	Friday	Saturday	Sunday
7:00 a.m.							
8:00 a.m.							
9:00 a.m.							
10:00 a.m.							
11:00 a.m.							
12:00 a.m.							
1:00 p.m.							
2:00 p.m.							
3:00 p.m.							
4:00 p.m.							
5:00 p.m.							
6:00 p.m.							
7:00 p.m.							
8:00 p.m.							
9:00 p.m.							

20. Study your filled-out grid from Exercise 19. Decide whether you have the time necessary to successfully complete this course and any other courses you may be registered for.

1.2   ALGEBRAIC EXPRESSIONS AND SETS OF NUMBERS

Objectives

1. Identify and evaluate algebraic expressions.
2. Identify natural numbers, whole numbers, integers, and rational and irrational real numbers.
3. Find the absolute value of a number.
4. Find the opposite of a number.
5. Write phrases as algebraic expressions.

1 Recall that letters that represent numbers are called **variables**. An **algebraic expression** is formed by numbers and variables connected by the operations of addition, subtraction, multiplication, division, raising to powers, and/or taking roots. For example,

$$2x + 3, \quad \frac{x + 5}{6} - \frac{z^2}{y^2}, \quad \text{and} \quad \sqrt{y} - 1.6$$

are algebraic expressions or, more simply, expressions.

Algebraic expressions occur often during problem solving. For example, the B747-400 aircraft costs \$8158 per hour to operate. The algebraic expression $8158t$

Copyright The Boeing Company

gives the total cost to operate the aircraft for t hours. (*Source: The World Almanac, 2003*) To find the cost to operate the aircraft for 5.2 hours, for example, we replace the variable t with 5.2 and perform the indicated operation. This process is called **evaluating** an expression, and the result is called the **value** of the expression for the given replacement value.

In our example, when $t = 5.2$ hours,

$$8158t = 8158(5.2) = 42{,}421.60$$

Thus, it costs \$42,421.60 to operate the B747-400 aircraft for 5.2 hours.

> **Helpful Hint**
>
> Recall that $8158t$ means $8158 \cdot t$.

EXAMPLE 1

FINDING THE AREA OF A TILE

The research department of a flooring company is considering a new flooring design that contains parallelograms. The area of a parallelogram with base b and height h is bh. Find the area of a parallelogram with base 10 centimeters and height 8.2 centimeters.

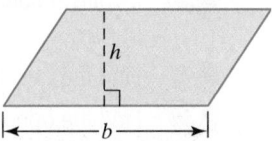

Solution   We replace b with 10 and h with 8.2 in the algebraic expression bh.

$$bh = 10 \cdot 8.2 = 82$$

The area is 82 square centimeters

Algebraic expressions simplify to different values depending on replacement values.

EXAMPLE 2

Evaluate: $3x - y$ when $x = 15$ and $y = 4$.

Solution   We replace x with 15 and y with 4 in the expression.

$$3x - y = 3 \cdot 15 - 4 = 45 - 4 = 41$$

When evaluating an expression to solve a problem, we often need to think about the kind of number that is appropriate for the solution. For example, if we are asked to determine the maximum number of parking spaces for a parking lot to be constructed, an answer of $98\frac{1}{10}$ is not appropriate because $\frac{1}{10}$ of a parking space is not realistic.

2   Let's review some common sets of numbers and their graphs on a number line. To construct a number line, we draw a line and label a point 0 with which we associate the number 0. This point is called the **origin**. Choose a point to the right of 0 and label it 1. The distance from 0 to 1 is called the **unit distance** and can be used to locate more points. The **positive numbers** lie to the right of the origin, and the **negative numbers** lie to the left of the origin. The number 0 is neither positive nor negative.

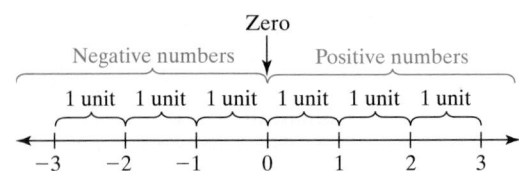

 CONCEPT CHECK

Use the definitions of positive numbers, negative numbers, and zero to describe the meaning of *nonnegative numbers.*

A number is **graphed** on a number line by shading the point on the number line that corresponds to the number. Some common sets of numbers and their graphs include:

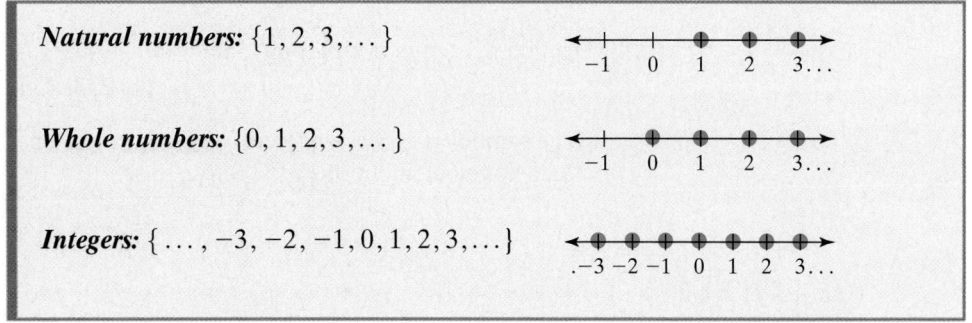

Natural numbers: $\{1, 2, 3, \dots\}$

Whole numbers: $\{0, 1, 2, 3, \dots\}$

Integers: $\{\dots, -3, -2, -1, 0, 1, 2, 3, \dots\}$

The symbol $\dots$ is used in each set above. This symbol, consisting of three dots, is called an **ellipsis** and means to continue in the same pattern.

The members of a set are called its **elements**. When the elements of a set are listed, such as those displayed in the previous paragraph, the set is written in **roster** form. A set can also be written in **set builder notation**, which describes the members of a set but does not list them. The following set is written in set builder notation.

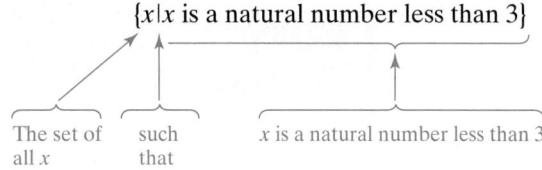

$\{x \mid x$ is a natural number less than 3$\}$

The set of all x such that x is a natural number less than 3

This same set written in roster form is $\{1, 2\}$.

A set that contains *no* elements is called the **empty set** (or **null set**) symbolized by $\{\ \}$ or $\emptyset$. The set

$$\{x \mid x \text{ is a month with 32 days}\} \text{ is } \emptyset \text{ or } \{\ \}$$

because no month has 32 days. The set has no elements.

> **Helpful Hint**
>
> Use $\{\ \}$ or $\emptyset$ to write the empty set. $\{\emptyset\}$ is **not** the empty set because it has one element: $\emptyset$.

EXAMPLE 3

List the elements in each set.

a. $\{x \mid x$ is a whole number between 1 and 6$\}$

b. $\{x \mid x$ is a natural number greater than 100$\}$

Solution   **a.** $\{2, 3, 4, 5\}$ **b.** $\{101, 102, 103, \dots\}$

The symbol $\in$ is used to denote that an element is in a particular set. The symbol $\in$ is read as "is an element of." For example, the true statement

$$3 \text{ is an element of } \{1, 2, 3, 4, 5\}$$

can be written in symbols as

$$3 \in \{1, 2, 3, 4, 5\}$$

The symbol $\notin$ is read as "is not an element of." In symbols, we write the true statement "p is not an element of $\{a, 5, g, j, q\}$" as

$$p \notin \{a, 5, g, j, q\}$$

EXAMPLE 4

Determine whether each statement is true or false.

a. $3 \in \{x \mid x \text{ is a natural number}\}$ **b.** $7 \notin \{1, 2, 3\}$

Solution **a.** True, since 3 is a natural number and therefore an element of the set.

      b. True, since 7 is not an element of the set $\{1, 2, 3\}$.

We can use set builder notation to describe three other common sets of numbers.

Identifying Numbers

Real Numbers: $\{x \mid x \text{ corresponds to a point on the number line}\}$

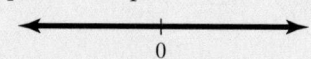

Rational numbers: $\left\{ \dfrac{a}{b} \,\middle|\, a \text{ and } b \text{ are integers and } b \neq 0 \right\}$

Irrational numbers: $\{x \mid x \text{ is a real number and } x \text{ is not a rational number}\}$

> **Helpful Hint**
>
> Notice from the definition that all real numbers are either rational or irrational.

Every rational number can be written as a decimal that either repeats or terminates. For example,

Rational Numbers

$$\frac{1}{2} = 0.5 \qquad\qquad \frac{5}{4} = 1.25$$

$$\frac{2}{3} = 0.6666666\ldots = 0.\overline{6} \qquad \frac{1}{11} = 0.090909\ldots = 0.\overline{09}$$

An irrational number written as a decimal neither terminates nor repeats. For example, π and $\sqrt{2}$ are irrational numbers. Their decimal form neither terminates nor repeats. Decimal approximations of each are below:

Irrational Numbers

$$\pi \approx 3.141592\ldots \qquad \sqrt{2} \approx 1.414213\ldots$$

Notice that every integer is also a rational number since each integer can be written as the quotient of itself and 1:

$$3 = \frac{3}{1}, \quad 0 = \frac{0}{1}, \quad -8 = \frac{-8}{1}$$

Not every rational number, however, is an integer. The rational number $\frac{2}{3}$, for example, is not an integer. Some square roots are rational numbers and some are irrational numbers. For example, $\sqrt{2}$, $\sqrt{3}$ and $\sqrt{7}$ are irrational numbers while $\sqrt{25}$ is a rational number because $\sqrt{25} = 5 = \frac{5}{1}$. The set of rational numbers together with the set of irrational numbers make up the set of real numbers. To help you make the distinction between rational and irrational numbers, here are a few examples of each.

Real Numbers		
Rational Numbers		*Irrational Numbers*
Numbers	*Equivalent Quotient of Integers, $\frac{a}{b}$* *(Decimal Form Terminates or Repeats)*	*(Decimal Form neither Terminates nor repeats)*
$-\dfrac{2}{3}$	$\dfrac{-2}{3}$ or $\dfrac{2}{-3}$	$\sqrt{5}$
$\sqrt{36}$	$\dfrac{6}{1}$	$\dfrac{\sqrt{6}}{7}$
5	$\dfrac{5}{1}$	$-\sqrt{13}$
0	$\dfrac{0}{1}$	π
1.2	$\dfrac{12}{10}$	$\dfrac{2}{\sqrt{3}}$
$3\dfrac{7}{8}$	$\dfrac{31}{8}$	

Some rational and irrational numbers are graphed below.

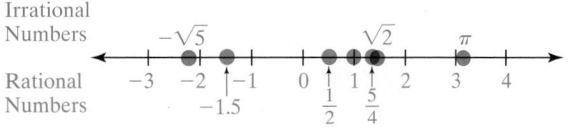

Earlier we mentioned that every integer is also a rational number. In other words, all the elements of the set of integers are also elements of the set of rational numbers. When this happens, we say that the set of integers, set Z, is a subset of the set of rational numbers, set Q. In symbols,

$$\underbrace{Z \subseteq Q}_{\text{is a subset of}}$$

The natural numbers, whole numbers, integers, rational numbers, and irrational numbers are each a subset of the set of real numbers. The relationships among these sets of numbers are shown in the following diagram.

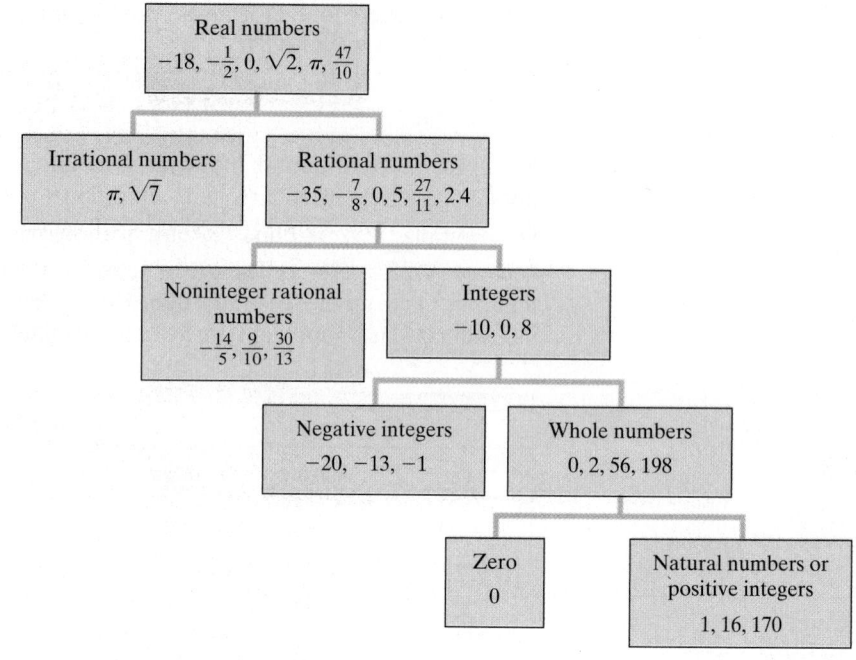

EXAMPLE 5

Determine whether the following statements are true or false.

a. 3 is a real number.

b. $\frac{1}{5}$ is an irrational number.

c. Every rational number is an integer.

d. $\{1, 5\} \subseteq \{2, 3, 4, 5\}$

Solution
a. True. Every whole number is a real number.

b. False. The number $\frac{1}{5}$ is a rational number, since it is in the form $\frac{a}{b}$ with a and b integers and $b \neq 0$.

c. False. The number $\frac{2}{3}$, for example, is a rational number, but it is not an integer.

d. False since the element 1 in the first set is not an element of the second set.

3 The number line can also be used to visualize distance, which leads to the concept of absolute value. The **absolute value** of a real number a, written as $|a|$, is the distance between a and 0 on the number line. Since distance is always positive or zero, $|a|$ is always positive or zero.

Using the number line, we see that

$$|4| = 4 \quad \text{and also} \quad |-4| = 4.$$

Why? Because both 4 and -4 are a distance of 4 units from 0.

An equivalent definition of the absolute value of a real number a is given next.

Absolute Value

The absolute value of a, written as $|a|$, is

$$|a| = \begin{cases} a \text{ if } a \text{ is } 0 \text{ or a positive number} \\ -a \text{ if } a \text{ is a negative number} \end{cases}$$

the opposite of

EXAMPLE 6

Find each absolute value.

a. $|3|$ **b.** $|-5|$ **c.** $-|2|$ **d.** $-|-8|$ **e.** $|0|$

Solution   **a.** $|3| = 3$ since 3 is located 3 units from 0 on the number line.

b. $|-5| = 5$ since -5 is 5 units from 0 on the number line.

c. $-|2| = -2$. The negative sign outside the absolute value bars means to take the opposite of the absolute value of 2.

d. $-|-8| = -8$. Since $|-8|$ is 8, $-|-8| = -8$.

e. $|0| = 0$ since 0 is located 0 units from 0 on the number line.

✔ CONCEPT CHECK

Explain how you know that $|14| = -14$ is a false statement.

4   The number line can also help us visualize opposites. Two numbers that are the same distance from 0 on the number line but are on opposite sides of 0 are called **opposites**.

See the definition illustrated on the number lines below.

The opposite of 6 is -6

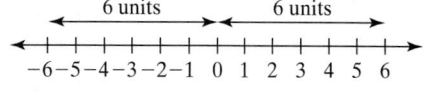

The opposite of $\dfrac{2}{3}$ is $-\dfrac{2}{3}$.

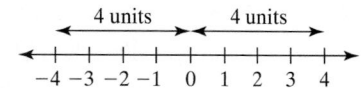

The opposite of -4 is 4.

Helpful Hint

The opposite of 0 is 0.

Opposite

The opposite of a number a is the number $-a$.

Concept Check Answer:
$|14| = 14$ since the absolute value of a number is the distance between the number and 0 and distance cannot be negative.

Above we state that the opposite of a number a is $-a$. This means that the opposite of -4 is $-(-4)$. But from the number line above, the opposite of -4 is 4. This means that $-(-4) = 4$, and in general, we have the following property.

> **Double Negative Property**
>
> For every real number a, $-(-a) = a$.

EXAMPLE 7

Write the opposite of each.

a. 8 **b.** $\dfrac{1}{5}$ **c.** -9.6

Solution   **a.** The opposite of 8 is -8.

b. The opposite of $\dfrac{1}{5}$ is $-\dfrac{1}{5}$.

c. The opposite of -9.6 is $-(-9.6) = 9.6$.

5   Often, solving problems involves translating a phrase to an algebraic expression. The following is a partial list of key words and phrases and their usual direct translations.

ADDITION	SUBTRACTION	MULTIPLICATION	DIVISION
sum	difference of	product	quotient
plus	minus	times	divide
added to	subtracted from	multiply	into
more than	less than	twice	ratio
increased by	decreased by	of	
total	less		

EXAMPLE 8

Translate each phrase to an algebraic expression. Use the variable x to represent each unknown number.

a. Eight times a number

b. Three more than eight times a number

c. The quotient of a number and -7

d. One and six-tenths subtracted from twice a number

Solution   **a.** $8 \cdot x$ or $8x$ **b.** $8x + 3$ **c.** $x \div -7$ or $\dfrac{x}{-7}$ **d.** $2x - 1.6$

Spotlight on
DECISION
MAKING

Suppose you work for an auto insurance company. Your company has just announced a new partnership with an automobile club that will allow club members to receive a 5% discount on their auto insurance. In addition, any auto club members who are safe drivers (rated 1 or 2 on the safety scale) will receive an additional 10% safe-driver discount. Your supervisor has asked you to compile a master mailing list of all current insurance clients who already belong to the auto club so they may be notified of their eligibility for the 5% discount. You must also identify the subset of auto club members who should receive a separate mailing about the additional 10% discount.

Using the given list of current insurance clients, decide who should be included in the master mailing list for notification of the 5% discount. Which of these clients should also be sent information about the 10% safe-driver discount?

Current Client Database

Client Name	Age (years)	Safety Rating (1–5)	Airbags (0 = no, 1 = yes)	Annual Mileage (miles)	Auto Club (0 = no, 1 = yes)
Alvarez, Wendy	29	1	1	5000	1
Brown, Keisha	19	2	0	5000	0
Cardoni, Anthony	43	1	0	10,000	0
Darden, Clay	35	3	1	7500	1
Evans, Gabriella	26	2	1	5000	1
Fonteneau, Monique	38	4	1	7500	0
Greenberg, Ira	49	1	0	5000	1
Hakkinen, Mika	31	1	1	15,000	0
Issacson, Maude	55	2	0	2000	1
Jones, Harold	47	1	0	7500	1
Khalosef, Avi	52	3	1	5000	1
Lee, Feng	33	2	1	10,000	0
Martinez, Ricardo	25	4	0	5000	1
Nunn, Destiny	21	4	1	5000	0

EXERCISE SET 1.2

STUDY GUIDE/SSM   CD/ VIDEO   PH MATH TUTOR CENTER   MathXL®Tutorials ON CD   MathXL®   MyMathLab®

Find the value of each algebraic expression at the given replacement values. See Examples 1 and 2.

1. $5x$ when $x = 7$

2. $3y$ when $y = 45$

3. $9.8z$ when $z = 3.1$

4. $7.1a$ when $a = 1.5$

5. ab when $a = \dfrac{1}{2}$ and $b = \dfrac{3}{4}$

6. yz when $y = \dfrac{2}{3}$ and $z = \dfrac{1}{5}$

7. $3x + y$ when $x = 6$ and $y = 4$

8. $2a - b$ when $a = 12$ and $b = 7$

9. The aircraft B737-400 flies an average speed of 400 miles per hour.

The expression $400t$ gives the distance traveled by the aircraft in t hours. Find the distance traveled by the B737-400 in 5 hours.

10. The algebraic expression $1.5x$ gives the total length of shelf space needed in inches for x encyclopedias. Find the length of shelf space needed for a set of 30 encyclopedias.

△ **11.** Employees at Wal-Mart constantly reorganize and reshelve merchandise. In doing so, they calculate floor space needed for displays. The algebraic expression $l \cdot w$ gives the floor space needed in square units for a display that measures length l units and width w units. Calculate the floor space needed for a display whose length is 5.1 feet and whose width is 4 feet.

12. The algebraic expression $\frac{x}{5}$ can be used to calculate the distance in miles that you are from a flash of lightning, where x is the number of seconds between the time you see a flash of lightning and the time you hear the thunder. Calculate the distance that you are from the flash of lightning if you hear the thunder 2 seconds after you see the lightning.

13. The B737-400 aircraft costs $2948 dollars per hour to operate. The algebraic expression $2948t$ gives the total cost to operate the aircraft for t hours. Find the total cost to operate the B737-400 for 3.6 hours.

14. Flying the SR-71A jet, Capt. Elden W. Joersz, USAF, set a record speed of 2193.16 miles per hour. At this speed, the algebraic expression $2193.16t$ gives the total distance flown in t hours. Find the distance flown by the SR-71A in 1.7 hours.

List the elements in each set. See Example 3.

15. $\{x \mid x$ is a natural number less than $6\}$

16. $\{x \mid x$ is a natural number greater than $6\}$

17. $\{x \mid x$ is a natural number between 10 and 17$\}$

18. $\{x \mid x$ is an odd natural number$\}$

19. $\{x \mid x$ is a whole number that is not a natural number$\}$

20. $\{x \mid x$ is a natural number less than $1\}$

21. $\{x \mid x$ is an even whole number less than $9\}$

22. $\{x \mid x$ is an odd whole number less than $9\}$

Graph each set on a number line.

23. $\{0, 2, 4, 6\}$

24. $\{-1, -2, -3\}$

25. $\left\{\frac{1}{2}, \frac{2}{3}\right\}$

26. $\{1, 3, 5, 7\}$

27. $\{-2, -6, -10\}$

28. $\left\{\frac{1}{4}, \frac{1}{3}\right\}$

29. In your own words, explain why the empty set is a subset of every set.

30. In your own words, explain why every set is a subset of itself.

List the elements of the set $\left\{3, 0, \sqrt{7}, \sqrt{36}, \frac{2}{5}, -134\right\}$ that are also elements of the given set. See Example 4.

31. Whole numbers

32. Integers

33. Natural numbers

34. Rational numbers

35. Irrational numbers

36. Real numbers

Place $\in$ or $\notin$ in the space provided to make each statement true. See Example 4.

37. -11 ___ $\{x \mid x$ is an integer$\}$

38. -6 ___ $\{2, 4, 6, \ldots\}$

39. 0 ___ $\{x \mid x$ is a positive integer$\}$

40. 12 ___ $\{1, 2, 3, \ldots\}$

41. 12 ___ $\{1, 3, 5, \ldots\}$

42. $\frac{1}{2}$ ___ $\{x \mid x$ is an irrational number$\}$

43. 0 ___ $\{1, 2, 3, \ldots\}$

44. 0 ___ $\{x \mid x$ is a natural number$\}$

Determine whether each statement is true or false. See Examples 4 and 5. Use the following sets of numbers.

N = set of natural numbers
Z = set of integers
I = set of irrational numbers
Q = set of rational numbers
$\mathbb{R}$ = set of real numbers

45. $Z \subseteq \mathbb{R}$

46. $\mathbb{R} \subseteq N$

47. $-1 \in Z$

48. $\frac{1}{2} \in Q$

49. $0 \in N$

50. $Z \subseteq Q$

51. $\sqrt{5} \notin I$

52. $\pi \notin \mathbb{R}$

53. $N \subseteq Z$

54. $I \subseteq N$

55. $\mathbb{R} \subseteq Q$

56. $N \subseteq Q$

57. In your own words, explain why every natural number is also a rational number but not every rational number is a natural number.

58. In your own words, explain why every irrational number is a real number but not every real number is an irrational number.

Find each absolute value. See Example 6.

59. $-|2|$

60. $|8|$

61. $|-4|$

62. $|-6|$

63. $|0|$

64. $|-1|$

65. $-|-3|$

66. $-|-11|$

67. Explain why $-(-2)$ and $-|-2|$ simplify to different numbers.

68. The boxed definition of absolute value states that $|a| = -a$ if a is a negative number. Explain why $|a|$ is always nonnegative, even though $|a| = -a$ for negative values of a.

Write the opposite of each number. See Example 7.

69. -6.2

70. -7.8

71. $\dfrac{4}{7}$

72. $\dfrac{9}{5}$

73. $-\dfrac{2}{3}$

74. $-\dfrac{14}{3}$

75. 0

76. 10.3

Write each phrase as an algebraic expression. Use the variable x to represent each unknown number. See Example 8.

77. Twice a number.

78. Six times a number.

79. Five more than twice a number.

80. One more than six times a number.

81. Ten less than a number.

82. A number minus seven.

83. The sum of a number and two.

84. The difference of twenty-five and a number.

85. A number divided by eleven.

86. The quotient of twice a number and thirteen.

87. Twelve added to three times a number.

88. Four subtracted from a number.

89. Seventeen subtracted from a number.

90. Four subtracted from three times a number.

91. Twice the sum of a number and three.

Concept Extensions

Write each phrase as an algebraic expression. Use the variable x to represent each unknown number.

92. The quotient of four and the sum of a number and one.

93. The quotient of five and the difference of four and a number.

94. Eight times the difference of a number and 9.

95. The following bar graph shows the top five countries with the projected number of tourists visiting in 2020.

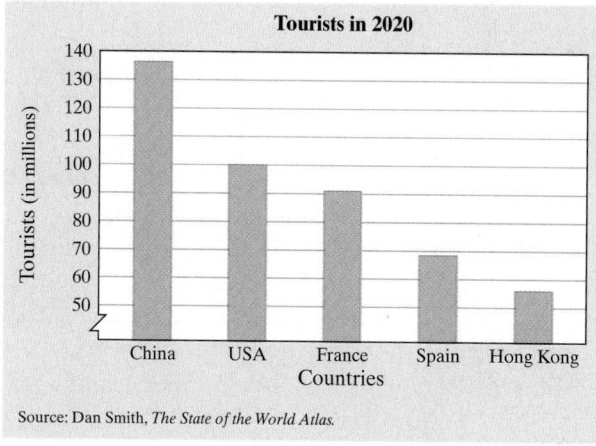

Source: Dan Smith, *The State of the World Atlas.*

Use the height of each bar to estimate the millions of tourists for each country. (Use whole numbers.)

China	
USA	
France	
Spain	
Hong Kong	

96. In your own words, explain why every natural number is also a rational number but not every rational number is a natural number.

97. In your own words, explain why every irrational number is a real number but not every real number is an irrational number.

1.3 *OPERATIONS ON REAL NUMBERS*

Objectives

1 Add and subtract real numbers.

2 Multiply and divide real numbers.

3 Simplify expressions containing exponents.

4 Find roots of numbers.

5 Use the order of operations.

6 Evaluate algebraic expressions.

1 When solving problems, we often have to add real numbers. For example, if the New Orleans Saints lose 5 yards in one play, then lose another 7 yards in the next play, their total loss may be described by $-5 + (-7)$.

The addition of two real numbers may be summarized by the following.

Adding Real Numbers

1. To add two numbers with the *same sign*, add their absolute values and attach their common sign.

2. To add two numbers with *different signs*, subtract the smaller absolute value from the larger absolute value and attach the sign of the number with the larger absolute value.

For example, to add $-5 + (-7)$, first add their absolute values.

$$|-5| = 5, |-7| = 7, \quad \text{and} \quad 5 + 7 = 12$$

Next, attach their common negative sign.

$$-5 + (-7) = -12$$

(This represents a total loss of 12 yards for the New Orleans Saints in the example above.)

To find $(-4) + 3$, first subtract their absolute values.

$$|-4| = 4, |3| = 3, \quad \text{and} \quad 4 - 3 = 1$$

Next, attach the sign of the number with the larger absolute value.

$$(-4) + 3 = -1$$

EXAMPLE 1

Add.

a. $-3 + (-11)$ **b.** $3 + (-7)$ **c.** $-10 + 15$

d. $-8.3 + (-1.9)$ **e.** $-\dfrac{2}{3} + \dfrac{3}{7}$

Solution **a.** $-3 + (-11) = -(3 + 11) = -14$ **b.** $3 + (-7) = -4$

c. $-10 + 15 = 5$ **d.** $-8.3 + (-1.9) = -10.2$

e. $-\dfrac{2}{3} + \dfrac{3}{7} = -\dfrac{14}{21} + \dfrac{9}{21} = -\dfrac{5}{21}$

Subtraction of two real numbers may be defined in terms of addition.

> ## Subtracting Real Numbers
>
> If a and b are real numbers,
> $$a - b = a + (-b)$$

In other words, to subtract a real number, we add its opposite.

EXAMPLE 2

Subtract.

a. $2 - 8$ **b.** $-8 - (-1)$ **c.** $-11 - 5$ **d.** $10.7 - (-9.8)$

e. $\dfrac{2}{3} - \dfrac{1}{2}$ **f.** $1 - 0.06$ **g.** Subtract 7 from 4.

Solution

Add the opposite

a. $2 - 8 = 2 + (-8) = -6$ **b.** $-8 - (-1) = -8 + (1) = -7$

c. $-11 - 5 = -11 + (-5) = -16$ **d.** $10.7 - (-9.8) = 10.7 + 9.8 = 20.5$

e. $\dfrac{2}{3} - \dfrac{1}{2} = \dfrac{2 \cdot 2}{3 \cdot 2} - \dfrac{1 \cdot 3}{2 \cdot 3} = \dfrac{4}{6} + \left(-\dfrac{3}{6}\right) = \dfrac{1}{6}$

f. $1 - 0.06 = 1 + (-0.06) = 0.94$ **g.** $4 - 7 = 4 + (-7) = -3$

To add or subtract three or more real numbers, add or subtract from left to right.

EXAMPLE 3

Simplify the following expressions.

a. $11 + 2 - 7$ **b.** $-5 - 4 + 2$

Solution **a.** $11 + 2 - 7 = 13 - 7 = 6$ **b.** $-5 - 4 + 2 = -9 + 2 = -7$

2   In order to discover sign patterns when you multiply real numbers, recall that multiplication by a positive integer is the same as repeated addition. For example,

$$3(2) = 2 + 2 + 2 = 6$$
$$3(-2) = (-2) + (-2) + (-2) = -6$$

Notice here that $3(-2) = -6$. This illustrates that the product of two numbers with different signs is negative. We summarize sign patterns for multiplying any two real numbers as follows.

> ### Multiplying Two Real Numbers
>
> The product of two numbers with the *same* sign is positive.
> The product of two numbers with *different* signs is negative.

Also recall that the product of zero and any real number is zero.

$$0 \cdot a = 0$$

EXAMPLE 4

Multiply.

a. $(-8)(-1)$ **b.** $(-2)\dfrac{1}{6}$ **c.** $3(-3)$ **d.** $0(11)$

e. $\left(\dfrac{1}{5}\right)\left(-\dfrac{10}{11}\right)$ **f.** $(7)(1)(-2)(-3)$ **g.** $8(-2)(0)$

Solution   **a.** Since the signs of the two numbers are the same, the product is positive. Thus $(-8)(-1) = +8$, or 8.

b. Since the signs of the two numbers are different or unlike, the product is negative. Thus $(-2)\dfrac{1}{6} = -\dfrac{2}{6} = -\dfrac{1}{3}$.

c. $3(-3) = -9$

d. $0(11) = 0$

e. $\left(\dfrac{1}{5}\right)\left(-\dfrac{10}{11}\right) = -\dfrac{10}{55} = -\dfrac{2}{11}$

f. To multiply three or more real numbers, you may multiply from left to right.

$$
\begin{aligned}
(7)(1)(-2)(-3) &= 7(-2)(-3) \\
&= -14(-3) \\
&= 42
\end{aligned}
$$

g. Since zero is a factor, the product is zero.

$$(8)(-2)(0) = 0$$

> ### Helpful Hint
> The following sign patterns may be helpful when we are multiplying.
>
> **1.** An odd number of negative factors gives a negative product.
> **2.** An even number of negative factors gives a positive product.

Recall that $\dfrac{8}{4} = 2$ because $2 \cdot 4 = 8$. Likewise, $\dfrac{8}{-4} = -2$ because $(-2)(-4) = 8$. Also, $\dfrac{-8}{4} = -2$ because $(-2)4 = -8$, and $\dfrac{-8}{-4} = 2$ because $2(-4) = -8$. From these examples, we can see that the sign patterns for division are the same as for multiplication.

> ## Dividing Two Real Numbers
>
> The quotient of two numbers with the *same* sign is positive.
> The quotient of two numbers with *different* signs is negative.

Also recall that division by a nonzero real number b is the same as multiplication by $\dfrac{1}{b}$. In other words,

$$\frac{a}{b} = a \cdot \frac{1}{b}$$

This means that to simplify $\dfrac{a}{b}$, we can divide by b or multiply by $\dfrac{1}{b}$. The nonzero numbers b and $\dfrac{1}{b}$ are called **reciprocals**. Notice that b *must* be a nonzero number. We do not define division by 0. For example, $5 \div 0$, or $\frac{5}{0}$, is undefined. To see why, recall that if $5 \div 0 = n$, a number, then $n \cdot 0 = 5$. This is not possible since $n \cdot 0 = 0$ for any number n, and never 5. Thus far we have learned that we cannot divide 5 or any other nonzero number by 0.

Can we divide 0 by 0? By the same reasoning, if $0 \div 0 = n$, a number, then $n \cdot 0 = 0$. This is true for any number n so that the quotient $0 \div 0$ would not be a single number. To avoid this, we say that

> Division by 0 is undefined.

EXAMPLE 5

Divide.

a. $\dfrac{20}{-4}$ **b.** $\dfrac{-9}{-3}$ **c.** $-\dfrac{3}{8} \div 3$ **d.** $\dfrac{-40}{10}$ **e.** $\dfrac{-1}{10} \div \dfrac{-2}{5}$ **f.** $\dfrac{8}{0}$

Solution   **a.** Since the signs are different or unlike, the quotient is negative and $\dfrac{20}{-4} = -5$.

b. Since the signs are the same, the quotient is positive and $\dfrac{-9}{-3} = 3$.

c. $-\dfrac{3}{8} \div 3 = -\dfrac{3}{8} \cdot \dfrac{1}{3} = -\dfrac{1}{8}$ **d.** $\dfrac{-40}{10} = -4$

e. $\dfrac{-1}{10} \div \dfrac{-2}{5} = -\dfrac{1}{10} \cdot -\dfrac{5}{2} = \dfrac{1}{4}$ **f.** $\dfrac{8}{0}$ is undefined.

With sign rules for division, we can understand why the positioning of the negative sign in a fraction does not change the value of the fraction. For example,

$$\frac{-12}{3} = -4, \quad \frac{12}{-3} = -4, \quad \text{and} \quad -\frac{12}{3} = -4$$

Since all the fractions equal -4, we can say that

$$\frac{-12}{3} = \frac{12}{-3} = -\frac{12}{3}$$

In general, the following holds true.

If a and b are real numbers and $b \neq 0$, then $\dfrac{a}{-b} = \dfrac{-a}{b} = -\dfrac{a}{b}$.

3 Recall that when two numbers are multiplied, they are called **factors**. For example, in $3 \cdot 5 = 15$, the 3 and 5 are called factors.

A natural number *exponent* is a shorthand notation for repeated multiplication of the same factor. This repeated factor is called the **base**, and the number of times it is used as a factor is indicated by the **exponent**. For example,

$$\overset{\text{exponent}}{\underset{\substack{\downarrow \\ 4 \text{ is a factor } 3 \text{ times}}}{\text{base} \rightarrow 4^3 = \underbrace{4 \cdot 4 \cdot 4}}} = 64$$

Also,

$$\text{base} \rightarrow 2^5 = \underbrace{2 \cdot 2 \cdot 2 \cdot 2 \cdot 2}_{2 \text{ is a factor } 5 \text{ times}} = 32$$

Exponents

If a is a real number and n is a natural number, then the **nth power of a**, or **a raised to the nth power**, written as a^n, is the product of n factors, each of which is a.

$$\text{base} \rightarrow a^n = \underbrace{a \cdot a \cdot a \cdot a \cdot \ldots \cdot a}_{a \text{ is a factor } n \text{ times}}$$

It is not necessary to write an exponent of 1. For example, 3 is assumed to be 3^1.

EXAMPLE 6

Simplify each expression.

a. 3^2 **b.** $\left(\dfrac{1}{2}\right)^4$ **c.** -5^2

d. $(-5)^2$ **e.** -5^3 **f.** $(-5)^3$

Solution

a. $3^2 = 3 \cdot 3 = 9$ **b.** $\left(\dfrac{1}{2}\right)^4 = \left(\dfrac{1}{2}\right)\left(\dfrac{1}{2}\right)\left(\dfrac{1}{2}\right)\left(\dfrac{1}{2}\right) = \dfrac{1}{16}$

c. $-5^2 = -(5 \cdot 5) = -25$ **d.** $(-5)^2 = (-5)(-5) = 25$

e. $-5^3 = -(5 \cdot 5 \cdot 5) = -125$ **f.** $(-5)^3 = (-5)(-5)(-5) = -125$

> **Helpful Hint**
>
> Be very careful when simplifying expressions such as -5^2 and $(-5)^2$.
>
> $$-5^2 = -(5 \cdot 5) = -25 \quad \text{and} \quad (-5)^2 = (-5)(-5) = 25$$
>
> Without parentheses, the base to square is 5, not -5.

4   The opposite of squaring a number is taking the **square root** of a number. For example, since the square of 4, or 4^2, is 16, we say that a square root of 16 is 4. The notation $\sqrt{a}$ is used to denote the **positive, or principal, square root** of a nonnegative number a. We then have in symbols that $\sqrt{16} = 4$. The negative square root of 16 is written $-\sqrt{16} = -4$. The square root of a negative number, such as $\sqrt{-16}$ is not a real number. Why? There is no real number, that when squared gives a negative number.

EXAMPLE 7

Find the square roots.

a. $\sqrt{9}$ **b.** $\sqrt{25}$ **c.** $\sqrt{\dfrac{1}{4}}$ **d.** $-\sqrt{36}$ **e.** $\sqrt{-36}$

Solution   **a.** $\sqrt{9} = 3$ since 3 is positive and $3^2 = 9$.

b. $\sqrt{25} = 5$ since $5^2 = 25$.   **c.** $\sqrt{\dfrac{1}{4}} = \dfrac{1}{2}$ since $\left(\dfrac{1}{2}\right)^2 = \dfrac{1}{4}$.

d. $-\sqrt{36} = -6$ **e.** $\sqrt{-36}$ is not a real number.

We can find roots other than square roots. Since 2 cubed, written as 2^3, is 8, we say that the **cube root** of 8 is 2. This is written as

$$\sqrt[3]{8} = 2.$$

Also, since $3^4 = 81$ and 3 is positive,

$$\sqrt[4]{81} = 3.$$

EXAMPLE 8

Find the roots.

a. $\sqrt[3]{27}$ **b.** $\sqrt[5]{1}$ **c.** $\sqrt[4]{16}$

Solution   **a.** $\sqrt[3]{27} = 3$ since $3^3 = 27$.

b. $\sqrt[5]{1} = 1$ since $1^5 = 1$.

c. $\sqrt[4]{16} = 2$ since 2 is positive and $2^4 = 16$.

Of course, as mentioned in Section 1.2, not all roots simplify to rational numbers. We study radicals further in Chapter 7.

5   Expressions containing more than one operation are written to follow a particular agreed-upon **order of operations.** For example, when we write $3 + 2 \cdot 10$, we mean to multiply first, and then add.

Order of Operations

Simplify expressions using the order that follows. If grouping symbols such as parentheses are present, simplify expressions within those first, starting with the innermost set. If fraction bars are present, simplify the numerator and denominator separately.

1. Raise to powers or take roots in order from left to right.
2. Multiply or divide in order from left to right.
3. Add or subtract in order from left to right.

EXAMPLE 9

Simplify.

a. $3 + 2 \cdot 10$ **b.** $2(1-4)^2$ **c.** $\dfrac{|-2|^3 + 1}{-7 - \sqrt{4}}$ **d.** $\dfrac{(6+2)-(-4)}{2-(-3)}$

Solution **a.** First multiply; then add.

$$3 + 2 \cdot 10 = 3 + 20 = 23$$

b. $2(1-4)^2 = 2(-3)^2$ Simplify inside grouping symbols first.

$$= 2(9) \qquad \text{Write } (-3)^2 \text{ as } 9.$$
$$= 18 \qquad \text{Multiply.}$$

c. Simplify the numerator and the denominator separately; then divide.

$$\frac{|-2|^3 + 1}{-7 - \sqrt{4}} = \frac{2^3 + 1}{-7 - 2} \qquad \text{Write } |-2| \text{ as } 2 \text{ and } \sqrt{4} \text{ as } 2.$$

$$= \frac{8 + 1}{-9} \qquad \text{Write } 2^3 \text{ as } 8.$$

$$= \frac{9}{-9} = -1 \qquad \text{Simplify the numerator, then divide.}$$

d. $\dfrac{(6+2)-(-4)}{2-(-3)} = \dfrac{8-(-4)}{2-(-3)}$ Simplify inside grouping symbols first.

$$= \frac{8 + 4}{2 + 3} \qquad \text{Write subtractions as equivalent additions.}$$

$$= \frac{12}{5} \qquad \text{Add in both the numerator and denominator.}$$

Besides parentheses, other symbols used for grouping expressions are brackets [ ] and braces { }. These other grouping symbols are commonly used when we group expressions that already contain parentheses.

EXAMPLE 10

Simplify: $3 - [(4-6) + 2(5-9)]$

Solution $3 - [(4-6) + 2(5-9)] = 3 - [-2 + 2(-4)]$ Simplify within the innermost sets of parentheses.

$$= 3 - [-2 + (-8)]$$
$$= 3 - [-10]$$
$$= 13$$

> **Helpful Hint**
> When grouping symbols occur within grouping symbols, remember to perform operations on the innermost set first.

✔ **CONCEPT CHECK**

True or false? If two different people use the order of operations to simplify a numerical expression and neither makes a calculation error, it is not possible that they each obtain a different result. Explain.

6   Recall from Section 1.2 that an algebraic expression is formed by numbers and variables connected by the operations of addition, subtraction, multiplication, division, raising to powers, and/or taking roots. Also, if numbers are substituted for the variables in an algebraic expression and the operations performed, the result is called **the value of the expression** for the given replacement values. This entire process is called **evaluating an expression**.

EXAMPLE 11

Evaluate each algebraic expression when $x = 2$, $y = -1$, and $z = -3$.

a. $z - y$ **b.** z^2 **c.** $\dfrac{2x + y}{z}$

Solution   **a.** $z - y = -3 - (-1) = -3 + 1 = -2$

b. $z^2 = (-3)^2 = 9$

c. $\dfrac{2x + y}{z} = \dfrac{2(2) + (-1)}{-3} = \dfrac{4 + (-1)}{-3} = \dfrac{3}{-3} = -1$

Sometimes variables such as x_1 and x_2 will be used in this book. The small 1 and 2 are called **subscripts.** The variable x_1 can be read as "x sub 1," and the variable x_2 can be read as "x sub 2." The important thing to remember is that they are two different variables. For example, if $x_1 = -5$ and $x_2 = 7$, then

$$x_1 - x_2 = -5 - 7 = -12.$$

EXAMPLE 12

The algebraic expression $\dfrac{5(x - 32)}{9}$ represents the equivalent temperature in degrees Celsius when x is the temperature in degrees Fahrenheit. Complete the following table by evaluating this expression at the given values of x.

Degrees Fahrenheit	x	-4	10	32
Degrees Celsius	$\dfrac{5(x - 32)}{9}$			

Solution   To complete the table, evaluate $\dfrac{5(x-32)}{9}$ at each given replacement value.

When $x = -4$,

$$\frac{5(x-32)}{9} = \frac{5(-4-32)}{9} = \frac{5(-36)}{9} = -20$$

When $x = 10$,

$$\frac{5(x-32)}{9} = \frac{5(10-32)}{9} = \frac{5(-22)}{9} = -\frac{110}{9}$$

When $x = 32$,

$$\frac{5(x-32)}{9} = \frac{5(32-32)}{9} = \frac{5\cdot 0}{9} = 0$$

The completed table is

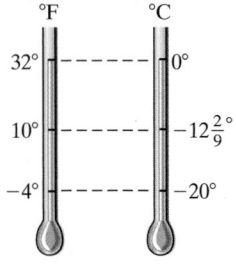

Degrees Fahrenheit	x	-4	10	32
Degrees Celsius	$\dfrac{5(x-32)}{9}$	-20	$-\dfrac{110}{9}$	0

Thus, $-4°$F is equivalent to $-20°$C, $10°$F is equivalent to $-\frac{110°}{9}$C, and $32°$F is equivalent to $0°$C.

Spotlight on DECISION ✈ MAKING

Suppose you are a travel agent. A tour company is offering bonuses to travel agents booking clients on selected tour packages for a limited time. However, prior to participating in this bonus program, you must select only one type of tour package for which you will receive the bonus. Information about the selected tour packages is shown in the table.

Based on client inquiries during the past week, you estimate that you could probably interest 30 clients in a cruise to Alaska, 60 in a Bermuda package, 50 in a trip to Cancun, and 40 in a Hawaii package. However, you also estimate that in each case, only half of the clients would book the trip if it cost over $1000 per person.

Which one of the tour packages would you choose for participating in the tour company's bonus program? Why?

Selected Tour Packages

Destination	Cost per person	Bonus per person booked
Alaska cruise	$2029	$100
Bermuda	$ 699	$ 25
Cancun, Mexico	$1349	$ 75
Hawaii	$ 840	$ 50

MENTAL MATH

Choose the fraction(s) equivalent to the given fraction. (There may sometimes be more than one correct choice.)

1. $-\dfrac{1}{7}$ **a.** $\dfrac{-1}{-7}$ **b.** $\dfrac{-1}{7}$ **c.** $\dfrac{1}{-7}$ **d.** $\dfrac{1}{7}$

2. $\dfrac{-x}{y}$ **a.** $\dfrac{x}{-y}$ **b.** $-\dfrac{x}{y}$ **c.** $\dfrac{x}{y}$ **d.** $\dfrac{-x}{-y}$

3. $\dfrac{5}{-(x+y)}$ **a.** $\dfrac{5}{(x+y)}$ **b.** $\dfrac{-5}{(x+y)}$ **c.** $\dfrac{-5}{-(x+y)}$ **d.** $-\dfrac{5}{(x+y)}$

4. $-\dfrac{(y+z)}{3y}$ **a.** $\dfrac{-(y+z)}{3y}$ **b.** $\dfrac{-(y+z)}{-3y}$ **c.** $\dfrac{(y+z)}{3y}$ **d.** $\dfrac{(y+z)}{-3y}$

5. $\dfrac{-9x}{-2y}$ **a.** $\dfrac{-9x}{2y}$ **b.** $\dfrac{9x}{2y}$ **c.** $\dfrac{9x}{-2y}$ **d.** $-\dfrac{9x}{2y}$

6. $\dfrac{-a}{-b}$ **a.** $\dfrac{a}{b}$ **b.** $\dfrac{a}{-b}$ **c.** $\dfrac{-a}{b}$ **d.** $-\dfrac{a}{b}$

EXERCISE SET 1.3

STUDY GUIDE/SSM   CD/VIDEO   PH MATH TUTOR CENTER   MathXL®Tutorials ON CD   MathXL®   MyMathLab®

Find each sum or difference. See Examples 1 through 3.

 1. $-3+8$ **2.** $-5+(-9)$

 3. $-14+(-10)$ **4.** $12+(-7)$

5. $-4.3-6.7$ **6.** $-8.2-(-6.6)$

 7. $13-17$ **8.** $15-(-1)$

9. $\dfrac{11}{15}-\left(-\dfrac{3}{5}\right)$ **10.** $\dfrac{7}{10}-\dfrac{4}{5}$

11. $19-10-11$ **12.** $-13-4+9$

Find each product or quotient. See Examples 4 and 5.

 13. $(-5)(12)$ **14.** $6(-3)$

15. $(-8)(-10)$ **16.** $7(0)$

 **17.** $\dfrac{-12}{-4}$ **18.** $\dfrac{60}{-6}$

19. $\dfrac{0}{-2}$ **20.** $\dfrac{-2}{0}$

21. $(-4)(-2)(-1)$ **22.** $5(-3)(-2)$

23. $\dfrac{-6}{7}\div 2$ **24.** $\dfrac{-9}{13}\div(-3)$

25. $\left(-\dfrac{2}{7}\right)\left(-\dfrac{1}{6}\right)$ **26.** $\dfrac{5}{9}\left(-\dfrac{3}{5}\right)$

Evaluate. See Example 6.

 27. -7^2 **28.** $(-7)^2$

29. $(-6)^2$ **30.** -6^2

31. $(-2)^3$ **32.** -2^3

Find the following roots. See Examples 7 and 8.

33. $\sqrt{49}$ **34.** $\sqrt{81}$

35. $-\sqrt{\dfrac{1}{9}}$ **36.** $-\sqrt{\dfrac{1}{25}}$

37. $\sqrt[3]{64}$ **38.** $\sqrt[5]{32}$

39. $\sqrt[4]{81}$ **40.** $\sqrt[3]{1}$

41. $\sqrt{-100}$ **42.** $\sqrt{-25}$

MIXED PRACTICE

Simplify each expression. See Examples 9 and 10.

43. $3(5 - 7)^4$

44. $7(3 - 8)^2$

45. $-3^2 + 2^3$

46. $-5^2 - 2^4$

47. $\dfrac{3 - (-12)}{-5}$

48. $\dfrac{-4 - (-8)}{-4}$

49. $|3.6 - 7.2| + |3.6 + 7.2|$

50. $|8.6 - 1.9| - |2.1 + 5.3|$

51. $\dfrac{(3 - \sqrt{9}) - (-5 - 1.3)}{-3}$

52. $\dfrac{-\sqrt{16} - (6 - 2.4)}{-2}$

53. $\dfrac{|3 - 9| - |-5|}{-3}$

54. $\dfrac{|-14| - |2 - 7|}{-15}$

55. $(-3)^2 + 2^3$

56. $(-15)^2 - 2^4$

57. $4[8 - (2 - 4)]$

58. $3[11 - (1 - 3)]$

59. $2 - [(7 - 6) + (9 - 19)]$

60. $8 - [(4 - 7) + (8 - 1)]$

61. $\dfrac{(-9 + 6)(-1^2)}{-2 - 2}$

62. $\dfrac{(-1 - 2)(-3^2)}{-6 - 3}$

63. $(\sqrt[3]{8})(-4) - (\sqrt{9})(-5)$

64. $(\sqrt[3]{27})(-5) - (\sqrt{25})(-3)$

65. $25 - [(3 - 5) + (14 - 18)]^2$

66. $10 - [(4 - 5)^2 + (12 - 14)]^4$

67. $\dfrac{\frac{1}{3} \cdot 9 - 7}{3 + \frac{1}{2} \cdot 4}$

68. $\dfrac{\frac{1}{5} \cdot 20 - 6}{10 + \frac{1}{4} \cdot 12}$

69. $\dfrac{3(-2 + 1)}{5} - \dfrac{-7(2 - 4)}{1 - (-2)}$

70. $\dfrac{-1 - 2}{2(-3) + 10} - \dfrac{2(-5)}{-1(8) + 1}$

71. $\dfrac{\frac{-3}{10}}{\frac{42}{50}}$

72. $\dfrac{\frac{-5}{21}}{\frac{-6}{42}}$

Find the value of each expression when $x = -2$, $y = -5$, and $z = 3$. See Example 11.

73. $x^2 + z^2$

74. $y^2 - z^2$

75. $-5(-x + 3y)$

76. $-7(-y - 4z)$

77. $\dfrac{3z - y}{2x - z}$

78. $\dfrac{5x - z}{-2y + z}$

Find the value of the expression when $x_1 = 2$, $x_2 = 4$, $y_1 = -3$, $y_2 = 2$. See Example 11.

79. $\dfrac{y_2 - y_1}{x_2 - x_1}$

80. $\sqrt{(x_2 - x_1)^2 + (y_2 - y_1)^2}$

See Example 12.

△ **81.** The algebraic expression $8 + 2y$ represents the perimeter of a rectangle with width 4 and length y.

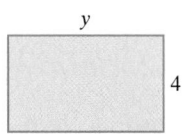

    a. Complete the table that follows by evaluating this expression at the given values of y.

Length	y	5	7	10	100
Perimeter	$8 + 2y$				

    b. Use the results of the table in **a** to answer the following question. As the width of a rectangle remains the same and the length increases, does the perimeter increase or decrease? Explain how you arrived at your answer.

△ **82.** The algebraic expression πr^2 represents the area of a circle with radius r.

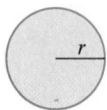

    a. Complete the table below by evaluating this expression at given values of r. (Use 3.14 for π.)

Radius	r	2	3	7	10
Area	πr^2				

    b. As the radius of a circle increases, does its area increase or decrease? Explain your answer.

83. The algebraic expression $\dfrac{100x + 5000}{x}$ represents the cost per bookshelf (in dollars) of producing x bookshelves.

a. Complete the table below.

Number of Bookshelves	x	10	100	1000
Cost per Bookshelf	$\dfrac{100x + 5000}{x}$			

b. As the number of bookshelves manufactured increases, does the cost per bookshelf increase or decrease? Why do you think that this is so?

84. If c is degrees Celsius, the algebraic expression $1.8c + 32$ represents the equivalent temperature in degrees Fahrenheit.
a. Complete the table below.

Degrees Celsius	c	-10	0	50
Degrees Fahrenheit	$1.8c + 32$			

b. As degrees Celsius increase, do degrees Fahrenheit increase or decrease?

Concept Extensions

Each circle below represents a whole, or 1. Determine the unknown fractional part of each circle.

85.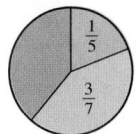

$\frac{1}{5}$ $\frac{3}{7}$

86.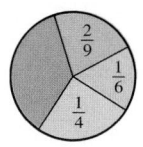

$\frac{2}{9}$ $\frac{1}{6}$ $\frac{1}{4}$

87. Most of Mauna Kea, a volcano on Hawaii, lies below sea level. If this volcano begins at 5998 meters below sea level and then rises 10,203 meters, find the height of the volcano above sea level.

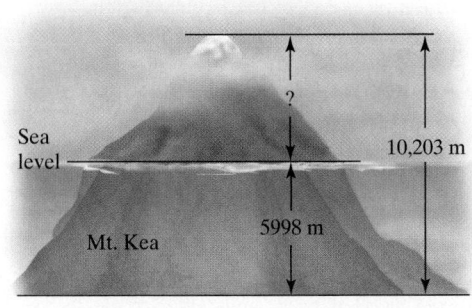

Sea level

?

10,203 m

5998 m

Mt. Kea

88. The highest point on land on Earth is the top of Mt. Everest in the Himalayas, at an elevation of 29,028 feet above sea level. The lowest point on land is the Dead Sea, between Israel and Jordan, at 1319 feet below sea level. Find the difference in elevations.

89. The following bar graph shows the U.S. life expectancy at birth for females born in the years shown. Use the graph to fill in the table below by calculating the *increase* in life expectancy over each ten-year period shown.

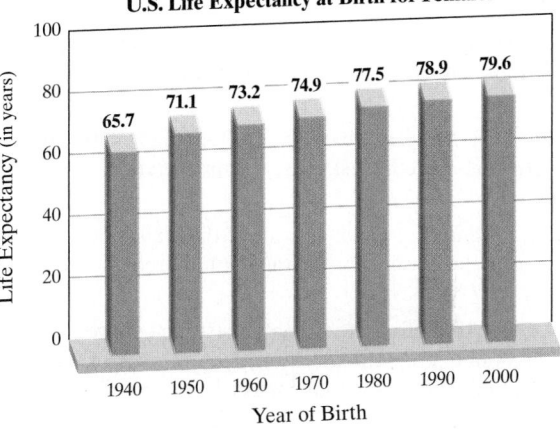

U.S. Life Expectancy at Birth for Females

Life Expectancy (in years)

65.7   71.1   73.2   74.9   77.5   78.9   79.6

1940   1950   1960   1970   1980   1990   2000

Year of Birth

Source: Social Security Administration

Year	Increase in Life Expectancy (in years) from 10 Years Earlier
1950	
1960	
1970	
1980	
1990	
2000	

Insert parentheses so that each expression simplifies to the given number.

90. $2 + 7 \cdot 1 + 3$; 36   **91.** $6 - 5 \cdot 2 + 2$; -6

92. Explain why -3^2 and $(-3)^2$ simplify to different numbers.

93. Explain why -3^3 and $(-3)^3$ simplify to the same number.

Use a calculator to approximate each square root. For exercises 98 and 99, simplify the expression. Round answers to four decimal places.

94. $\sqrt{10}$ **95.** $\sqrt{273}$

96. $\sqrt{7.9}$ **97.** $\sqrt{19.6}$

98. $\dfrac{-1.682 - 17.895}{(-7.102)(-4.691)}$ **99.** $\dfrac{(-5.161)(3.222)}{7.955 - 19.676}$

Investment firms often advertise their gains and losses in the form of bar graphs such as the one that follows. This graph shows investment risk over time for the S&P 500 Index by showing average annual compound returns for 1 year, 5 years, 15 years, and 25 years. For example, after one year, the annual compound return in percent for an investor is anywhere from a gain of 181.5% to a loss of 64%. Use this graph to answer the questions below.

100. A person investing in the S&P 500 Index may expect at most an average annual gain of what percent after 15 years?

101. A person investing in the S&P 500 Index may expect to lose at most an average per year of what percent after 5 years?

102. Find the difference in percent of the highest average annual return and the lowest average annual return after 15 years.

103. Find the difference in percent of the highest average annual return and the lowest average annual return after 25 years.

104. Do you think that the type of investment shown in the figure is recommended for short-term investments or long-term investments? Explain your answer.

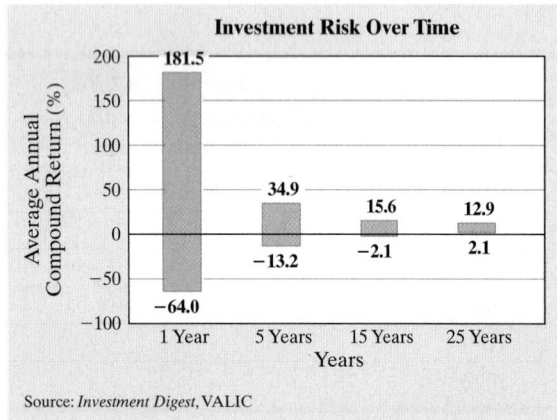

Investment Risk Over Time

Source: *Investment Digest*, VALIC

A fair game is one in which each team or player has the same chance of winning. Suppose that a game consists of three players taking turns spinning a spinner. If the spinner lands on yellow, player 1 gets a point. If the spinner lands on red, player 2 gets a point, and if the spinner lands on blue, player 3 gets a point. After 12 spins, the player with the most points wins.

a. 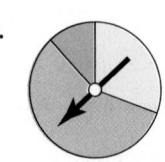 b.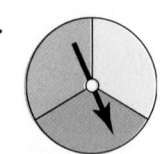

c. 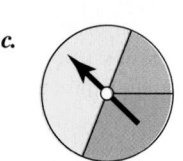 d.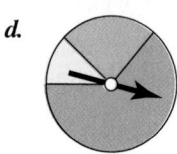

105. Which spinner would lead to a fair game?

106. If you are player 2 and want to win the game, which spinner would you choose?

107. If you are player 1 and want to lose the game, which spinner would you choose?

108. Is it possible for the game to end in a three-way tie? If so, list the possible ending scores.

109. Is it possible for the game to end in a two-way tie? If so, list the possible ending scores.

INTEGRATED REVIEW

ALGEBRAIC EXPRESSIONS AND OPERATIONS ON WHOLE NUMBERS

Fine the value of each expression when $x = -1$, $y = 3$, and $z = -4$.

1. z^2

2. $-z^2$

3. $\dfrac{4x - z}{2y}$

4. $x(y - 2z)$

Perform indicated operations.

5. $-7 - (-2)$

6. $\dfrac{9}{10} - \dfrac{11}{12}$

7. $\dfrac{-13}{2 - 2}$

8. $(1.2)^2 - (2.1)^2$

9. $\sqrt{64} - \sqrt[3]{64}$

10. $-5^2 - (-5)^2$

11. $9 + 2[(8 - 10)^2 + (-3)^2]$

12. $8 - 6[\sqrt[3]{8}(-2) + \sqrt{4}(-5)]$

Write each phrase as an algebraic expression. Use x to represent each unknown number.

13. Subtract twice a number from -15.

14. Five more than three times a number.

15. Name the whole number that is not a natural number.

16. True or false: A real number is either a rational number or an irrational number, but never both.

1.4   PROPERTIES OF REAL NUMBERS

Objectives

1 Use operation and order symbols to write mathematical sentences.
2 Identify identity numbers and inverses.
3 Identify and use the commutative, associative, and distributive properties.
4 Write algebraic expressions.
5 Simplify algebraic expressions.

1   In Section 1.2, we used the symbol $=$ to mean "is equal to." All of the following key words and phrases also imply equality.

Equality			
equals	is/was	represents	is the same as
gives	yields	amounts to	is equal to

EXAMPLE 1

Write each sentence using mathematical symbols.

a. The sum of x and 5 is 20.

b. Two times the sum of 3 and y amounts to 4.

c. Subtract 8 from x, and the difference is the same as twice x.

d. The quotient of z and 9 is 3 times the difference of z and 5.

Solution **a.**

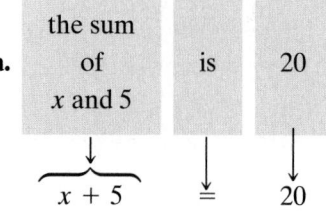

b. $2(3 + y) = 4$

c. $x - 8 = 2x$

d. $\dfrac{z}{9} = 3(z - 5)$

If we want to write in symbols that two numbers are not equal, we can use the symbol $\neq$, which means "**is not equal to.**" For example,

$$3 \neq 2$$

Graphing two numbers on a number line gives us a way to compare two numbers. For two real numbers a and b, we say **a is less than b** if on the number line a lies to the left of b. Also, if b is to the right of a on the number line, then **b is greater than a**. The symbol $<$ means "**is less than.**" Since a is less than b, we write

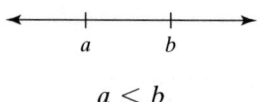

$$a < b$$

The symbol $>$ means "**is greater than.**" Since b is greater than a, we write

$$b > a$$

> **Helpful Hint**
> Notice that if $a < b$, then $b > a$.

EXAMPLE 2

Insert $<$, $>$, or $=$ between each pair of numbers to form a true statement.

a. $-1 \quad -2$ **b.** $\dfrac{12}{4} \quad 3$ **c.** $-5 \quad 0$ **d.** $-3.5 \quad -3.05$

Solution **a.** $-1 > -2$ since -1 lies to the right of -2 on the number line.

$$\begin{array}{ccccccc} & & \bullet & \bullet & & & \\ \hline -3 & -2 & -1 & 0 & 1 & & \end{array}$$

b. $\dfrac{12}{4} = 3$.

c. $-5 < 0$ since -5 lies to the left of 0 on the number line.

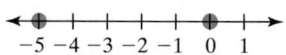

d. $-3.5 < -3.05$ since -3.5 lies to the left of -3.05 on the number line.

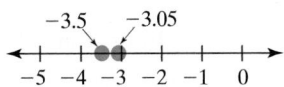

> ### Helpful Hint
>
> When inserting the $>$ or $<$ symbol, think of the symbols as arrowheads that "point" toward the smaller number when the statement is true.

In addition to $<$ and $>$, there are the inequality symbols $\leq$ and $\geq$. The symbol

$$\leq \text{ means "\textbf{is less than or equal to}"}$$

and the symbol

$$\geq \text{ means "\textbf{is greater than or equal to}"}$$

For example, the following are true statements.

$10 \leq 10$	since	$10 = 10$
$-8 \leq 13$	since	$-8 < 13$
$-5 \geq -5$	since	$-5 = -5$
$-7 \geq -9$	since	$-7 > -9$

EXAMPLE 3

Write each sentence using mathematical symbols.

a. The sum of 5 and y is greater than or equal to 7.

b. 11 is not equal to z.

c. 20 is less than the difference of 5 and twice x.

Solution   **a.** $5 + y \geq 7$ **b.** $11 \neq z$ **c.** $20 < 5 - 2x$

2   Of all the real numbers, two of them stand out as extraordinary: 0 and 1. Zero is the only number that when *added* to any real number, the result is the same real number. Zero is thus called the **additive identity**. Also, one is the only number that when *multiplied* by any real number, the result is the same real number. One is thus called the **multiplicative identity**.

	Addition	Multiplication
Identity Properties	The additive identity is 0.	The multiplicative identity is 1.
	$a + 0 = 0 + a = a$	$a \cdot 1 = 1 \cdot a = a$

In section 1.2, we learned that a and $-a$ are opposites.

Another name for opposite is **additive inverse.** For example, the additive inverse of 3 is -3. Notice that the sum of a number and its opposite is always 0.

In section 1.3, we learned that, for a nonzero number, b and $\frac{1}{b}$ are reciprocals.

Another name for reciprocal is **multiplicative inverse.** For example, the multiplicative inverse of $-\frac{2}{3}$ is $-\frac{3}{2}$. Notice that the product of a number and its reciprocal is always 1.

	Opposite or Additive Inverse	*Reciprocal or Multiplicative Inverse*
Inverse Properties	For each number a, there is a unique number $-a$ called the **additive inverse** or **opposite** of a such that $$a + (-a) = (-a) + a = 0$$	For each nonzero a, there is a unique number $\frac{1}{a}$ called the **multiplicative inverse** or **reciprocal** of a such that $$a \cdot \frac{1}{a} = \frac{1}{a} \cdot a = 1$$

 EXAMPLE 4

Write the additive inverse, or opposite, of each.

a. 8   **b.** $\frac{1}{5}$ **c.** -9.6

Solution   **a.** The opposite of 8 is -8.

b. The opposite of $\frac{1}{5}$ is $-\frac{1}{5}$.

c. The opposite of -9.6 is $-(-9.6) = 9.6$.

 EXAMPLE 5

Write the multiplicative inverse, or reciprocal, of each.

a. 11   **b.** -9 **c.** $\frac{7}{4}$

Solution   **a.** The reciprocal of 11 is $\frac{1}{11}$.

b. The reciprocal of -9 is $-\frac{1}{9}$.

c. The reciprocal of $\frac{7}{4}$ is $\frac{4}{7}$ because $\frac{7}{4} \cdot \frac{4}{7} = 1$.

> **Helpful Hint**
>
> The number 0 has no reciprocal. Why? There is no number that when multiplied by 0 gives a product of 1.

✔ **CONCEPT CHECK**

Can a number's additive inverse and multiplicative inverse ever be the same? Explain.

3   In addition to these special real numbers, all real numbers have certain properties that allow us to write equivalent expressions—that is, expressions that have the same value. These properties will be especially useful in Chapter 2 when we solve equations.

The **commutative properties** state that the order in which two real numbers are added or multiplied does not affect their sum or product.

Commutative Properties

For real numbers a and b,

$$Addition \quad a + b = b + a$$
$$Multiplication \quad a \cdot b = b \cdot a$$

The **associative properties** state that regrouping numbers that are added or multiplied does not affect their sum or product.

Associative Properties

For real numbers a, b, and c,

$$Addition \quad (a + b) + c = a + (b + c)$$
$$Multiplication \quad (a \cdot b) \cdot c = a \cdot (b \cdot c)$$

EXAMPLE 6

Use the commutative property of addition to write an expression equivalent to $7x + 5$.

Solution $7x + 5 = 5 + 7x$.

EXAMPLE 7

Use the associative property of multiplication to write an expression equivalent to $4 \cdot (9y)$. Then simplify this equivalent expression.

Solution $4 \cdot (9y) = (4 \cdot 9)y = 36y$.

Concept Check Answer:
no; answers may vary

The **distributive property** states that multiplication distributes over addition.

> **Distributive Property**
>
> For real numbers a, b, and c,
> $$a(b + c) = ab + ac$$

EXAMPLE 8

Use the distributive property to multiply.

a. $3(2x + y)$ **b.** $-(3x - 1)$ **c.** $0.7a(b - 2)$

Solution   **a.** $3(2x + y) = 3 \cdot 2x + 3 \cdot y$ Apply the distributive property.

$\qquad\qquad\qquad = 6x + 3y$ Apply the associative property of multiplication.

b. Recall that $-(3x - 1)$ means $-1(3x - 1)$.

$$-1(3x - 1) = -1(3x) + (-1)(-1)$$

$$= -3x + 1$$

c. $0.7a(b - 2) = 0.7a \cdot b - 0.7a \cdot 2 = 0.7ab - 1.4a$

✔ **CONCEPT CHECK**

Is the statement below true? Why or why not?
$6(2a)(3b) = 6(2a) \cdot 6(3b)$

4   As mentioned earlier, an important step in problem solving is to be able to write algebraic expressions from word phrases. Sometimes this involves a direct translation, but often an indicated operation is not directly stated but rather implied.

EXAMPLE 9

Write each as an algebraic expression.

a. A vending machine contains x quarters. Write an expression for the *value* of the quarters.

b. The number of grams of fat in x pieces of bread if each piece of bread contains 2 grams of fat.

c. The cost of x desks if each desk costs $156.

d. Sales tax on a purchase of x dollars if the tax rate is 9%.

Each of these examples implies finding a product.

a. The value of the quarters is found by multiplying the value of a quarter (0.25 dollar) by the number of quarters.

In words:

Value of a quarter	·	Number of quarters

Translate: 0.25   · x,   or $0.25x$

Solution   **b.** In words:

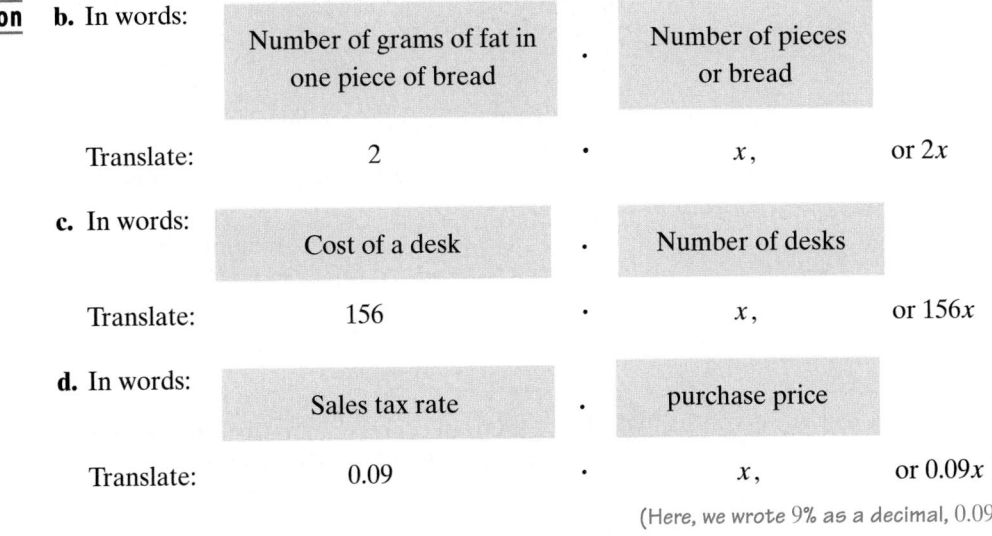

Number of grams of fat in one piece of bread	·	Number of pieces or bread	
Translate:	2	·	x,	or $2x$

c. In words:

Cost of a desk	·	Number of desks	
Translate:	156	·	x,	or $156x$

d. In words:

Sales tax rate	·	purchase price	
Translate:	0.09	·	x,	or $0.09x$

(Here, we wrote 9% as a decimal, 0.09.)

Two or more unknown numbers in a problem may sometimes be related. If so, try letting a variable represent one unknown number and then represent the other unknown number or numbers as expressions containing the same variable.

EXAMPLE 10

Write each as an algebraic expression.

a. Two numbers have a sum of 20. If one number is x, represent the other number as an expression in x.

b. The older sister is 8 years older than her younger sister. If the age of the younger sister is x, represent the age of the older sister as an expression in x.

△ **c.** Two angles are complementary if the sum of their measures is 90°. If the measure of one angle is x degrees, represent the measure of the other angle as an expression in x.

d. If x is the first of two consecutive integers, represent the second integer as an expression in x.

Solution   **a.** If two numbers have a sum of 20 and one number is x, the other number is "the rest of 20."

In words:

Twenty	minus	x
Translate: 20	—	x

b. The older sister's age is

In words:

Eight years	added to	younger sister's age
Translate: 8	+	x

c. In words:

| Ninety | minus | x |

Translate: 90 $-$ x

d. The next consecutive integer is always one more than the previous integer.

In words:

| The first integer | plus | one |

Translate: x $+$ 1

5   Often, an expression may be **simplified** by removing grouping symbols and combining any like terms. The **terms** of an expression are the addends of the expression. For example, in the expression $3x^2 + 4x$, the terms are $3x^2$ and $4x$.

Expression	**Terms**
$-2x + y$	$-2x, y$
$3x^2 - \dfrac{y}{5} + 7$	$3x^2, -\dfrac{y}{5}, 7$

Terms with the same variable(s) raised to the same power are called **like terms.** We can add or subtract like terms by using the distributive property. This process is called **combining like terms.**

EXAMPLE 11

Use the distributive property to simplify each expression.

a. $3x - 5x + 4$ **b.** $7yz + yz$ **c.** $4z + 6.1$

Solution   **a.** $3x - 5x + 4 = (3 - 5)x + 4$ *Apply the distributive property.*

$= -2x + 4$

b. $7yz + yz = (7 + 1)yz = 8yz$

c. $4z + 6.1$ cannot be simplified further since $4z$ and 6.1 are not like terms.

Let's continue to use properties of real numbers to simplify expressions. Recall that the distributive property can also be used to multiply. For example,

$$-2(x + 3) = -2(x) + (-2)(3) = -2x - 6$$

The associative and commutative properties may sometimes be needed to rearrange and group like terms when we simplify expressions.

$$-7x^2 + 5 + 3x^2 - 2 = -7x^2 + 3x^2 + 5 - 2$$
$$= (-7 + 3)x^2 + (5 - 2)$$
$$= -4x^2 + 3$$

EXAMPLE 12

Simplify each expression.

a. $3xy - 2xy + 5 - 7 + xy$

b. $7x^2 + 3 - 5(x^2 - 4)$

c. $(2.1x - 5.6) - (-x - 5.3)$

d. $\frac{1}{2}(4a - 6b) - \frac{1}{3}(9a + 12b - 1) + \frac{1}{4}$

Solution

a. $3xy - 2xy + 5 - 7 + xy = 3xy - 2xy + xy + 5 - 7$ *Apply the commutative property.*

$= (3 - 2 + 1)xy + (5 - 7)$ *Apply the distributive property.*

$= 2xy - 2$ *Simplify.*

b. $7x^2 + 3 - 5(x^2 - 4) = 7x^2 + 3 - 5x^2 + 20$ *Apply the distributive property.*

$= 2x^2 + 23$ *Simplify.*

c. Think of $-(-x - 5.3)$ as $-1(-x - 5.3)$ and use the distributive property.

$(2.1x - 5.6) - 1(-x - 5.3) = 2.1x - 5.6 + 1x + 5.3$

$= 3.1x - 0.3$ *Combine like terms.*

d. $\frac{1}{2}(4a - 6b) - \frac{1}{3}(9a + 12b - 1) + \frac{1}{4}$

$= 2a - 3b - 3a - 4b + \frac{1}{3} + \frac{1}{4}$ *Use the distributive property.*

$= -a - 7b + \frac{7}{12}$ *Combine like terms.*

✔ **CONCEPT CHECK**

Find and correct the error in the following

$x - 4(x - 5) = x - 4x - 20$

$= -3x - 20$

Concept Check Answer:

$x - 4(x - 5) = x - 4x + 20$

$= -3x + 20$

Spotlight on
DECISION
MAKING

Suppose you are a geologist studying Hawaiian volcanoes. When lava from a volcano flows into the ocean, it heats the water around it. You are color-coding a map of ocean water temperatures around a lava flow. If the water temperature is less than or equal to 22°C, the map will be colored dark blue. If the water temperature is greater than 29°C, the map will be colored tan. Otherwise, the map will be colored green. Decide what color on the map should be used for the following temperatures.

a. 25°C   **b.** 18°C   **c.** 29°C   **d.** 22°C   **e.** 31°C

EXERCISE SET 1.4

  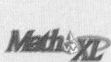

STUDY GUIDE/SSM · CD/VIDEO · PH MATH TUTOR CENTER · MathXL®Tutorials ON CD · MathXL® · MyMathLab®

Insert $<, >,$ *or* $=$ *in the space provided to form a true statement. See Example 2.*

1. $0 \quad -2$

2. $-5 \quad 0$

 3. $7.4 \quad 7.40$

 4. $\dfrac{7}{11} \quad \dfrac{9}{11}$

5. $-7.9 \quad -7.09$

6. $-13.07 \quad -13.7$

MIXED PRACTICE

Write each sentence using mathematical symbols. See Examples 1 and 3.

7. Twice x plus 5 is the same as -14.

8. The sum of 10 and x is -12.

9. 3 times the sum of x and 1 amounts to 7.

10. 9 times the difference of 4 and m amounts to 1.

11. The quotient of n and 5 is 4 times n.

12. The quotient of 8 and y is 3 more than y.

13. The difference of z and 2 is the same as the product of z and 2.

14. Five added to twice q is the same as 4 more than q.

15. The product of 7 and x is less than or equal to -21.

16. 10 subtracted from the reciprocal of x is greater than 0.

17. The sum of -2 and x is not equal to 10.

18. Twice the quotient of y and 3 is less than or equal to y.

19. Twice the difference of x and 6 is greater than the reciprocal of 11.

20. Four times the sum of 5 and x is not equal to the opposite of 15.

21. 7 subtracted from the product of 5 and y is 6.

22. The sum of z and w, divided by 2, is 12.

23. Twice the difference of x and 6 is -27

24. 5 times the sum of 6 and y is -35.

Fill in the chart. See Example 4 and 5.

	Number	*Opposite*	*Reciprocal*
25.	5		
26.	7		
27.		8	
28.			$-\dfrac{1}{4}$
29.	$-\dfrac{1}{7}$		
30.	$\dfrac{1}{11}$		
31.	0		
32.	1		
33.			$\dfrac{8}{7}$
34.		$\dfrac{23}{5}$	

35. Name the only real number that has no reciprocal, and explain why this is so.

36. Name the only real number that is its own opposite, and explain why this is so.

Use a commutative property to write an equivalent expression. See Example 6.

37. $7x + y$

38. $3a + 2b$

39. $z \cdot w$

40. $r \cdot s$

41. $\dfrac{1}{3} \cdot \dfrac{x}{5}$

42. $\dfrac{x}{2} \cdot \dfrac{9}{10}$

43. Is subtraction commutative? Explain why or why not.

44. Is division commutative? Explain why or why not.

Use an associative property to write an equivalent expression. See Example 7.

45. $5 \cdot (7x)$

46. $3 \cdot (10z)$

47. $(x + 1.2) + y$

48. $5q + (2r + s)$

49. $(14z) \cdot y$

50. $(9.2x) \cdot y$

51. Evaluate $12 - (5 - 3)$ and $(12 - 5) - 3$. Use these two expressions and discuss whether subtraction is associative.

52. Evaluate $24 \div (6 \div 3)$ and $(24 \div 6) \div 3$. Use these two expressions and discuss whether division is associative.

Use the distributive property to find the product. See Example 8.

53. $3(x + 5)$

54. $7(y + 2)$

55. $-(2a + b)$

56. $-(c + 7d)$

57. $2(6x + 5y + 2z)$

58. $5(3a + b + 9c)$

59. $-4(x - 2y + 7)$

60. $-10(2a - 3b - 4)$

61. $0.5x(6y - 3)$

62. $1.2m(9n - 4)$

Complete the statement to illustrate the given property.

63. $3x + 6 =$ _____ Commutative property of addition

64. $8 + 0 =$ _ Additive identity property

65. $\dfrac{2}{3} + \left(-\dfrac{2}{3}\right) =$ _ Additive inverse property

66. $4(x + 3) =$ _____ Distributive property

67. $7 \cdot 1 =$ _ Multiplicative identity property

68. $0 \cdot (-5.4) =$ _ Multiplication property of zero

69. $10(2y) =$ _____ Associative property

70. $9y + (x + 3z) =$ _____ Associative property

71. To demonstrate the distributive property geometrically, represent the area of the larger rectangle in two ways: First as length a times width $b + c$, and second as the sum of the areas of the smaller rectangles.

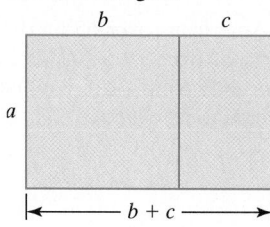

Write each of the following as an algebraic expression. See Examples 9 and 10.

72. Write an expression for the amount of money (in dollars) in n nickels.

73. Write an expression for the amount of money (in dollars) in d dimes.

74. Two numbers have a sum of 25. If one number is x, represent the other number as an expression in x.

75. Two numbers have a sum of 112. If one number is x, represent the other number as an expression in x.

76. Two angles are supplementary if the sum of their measures is $180°$. If the measure of one angle is x degrees, represent the measure of the other angle as an expression in x.

77. If the measure of an angle is $5x$ degrees, represent the measure of its complement as an expression in x.

78. The cost of x compact discs if each compact disc costs $6.49.

79. The cost of y books if each book costs $35.61.

80. If x is an odd integer, represent the next odd integer as an expression in x.

81. If $2x$ is an even integer, represent the next even integer as an expression in x.

MIXED PRACTICE

Simplify each expression. See Examples 8, 11, and 12.

82. $-9 + 4x + 18 - 10x$

83. $5y - 14 + 7y - 20y$

84. $5k - (3k - 10)$

85. $-11c - (4 - 2c)$

86. $(3x + 4) - (6x - 1)$

87. $(8 - 5y) - (4 + 3y)$

88. $3(xy - 2) + xy + 15 - x^2$

89. $-4(yz + 3) - 7yz + 1 + y^2$

90. $-(n + 5) + (5n - 3)$

91. $-(8 - t) + (2t - 6)$

92. $4(6n^2 - 3) - 3(8n^2 + 4)$

93. $5(2z^3 - 6) + 10(3 - z^3)$

94. $3x - 2(x - 5) + x$

95. $7n + 3(2n - 6) - 2$

96. $1.5x + 2.3 - 0.7x - 5.9$

97. $6.3y - 9.7 + 2.2y - 11.1$

98. $\frac{3}{4}b - \frac{1}{2} + \frac{1}{6}b - \frac{2}{3}$

99. $\frac{7}{8}a - \frac{11}{12} - \frac{1}{2}a + \frac{5}{6}$

100. $2(3x + 7)$

101. $4(5y + 12)$

102. $\frac{1}{4}(8x - 4) - \frac{1}{5}(20x - 6y)$

103. $\frac{1}{2}(10x - 2) - \frac{1}{6}(60x - 5y)$

104. $\frac{1}{6}(24a - 18b) - \frac{1}{7}(7a - 21b - 2) - \frac{1}{5}$

105. $\frac{1}{3}(6x - 33y) - \frac{1}{8}(24x - 40y + 1) - \frac{1}{3}$

Concept Extensions

Simplify each expression.

106. $-1.2(5.7x - 3.6) + 8.75x$

107. $5.8(-9.6 - 31.2y) - 18.65$

108. $8.1z + 7.3(z + 5.2) - 6.85$

109. $6.5y - 4.4(1.8x - 3.3) + 10.95$

△ **110.** Do figures with the same surface area always have the same volume? To see, take two $8\frac{1}{2}$-by-11-inch sheets of paper and construct two cylinders using the following figures as a guide. Working with a partner, measure the height and the radius of each resulting cylinder and use the expression $\pi r^2 h$ to approximate each volume to the nearest tenth of a cubic inch. Explain your results.

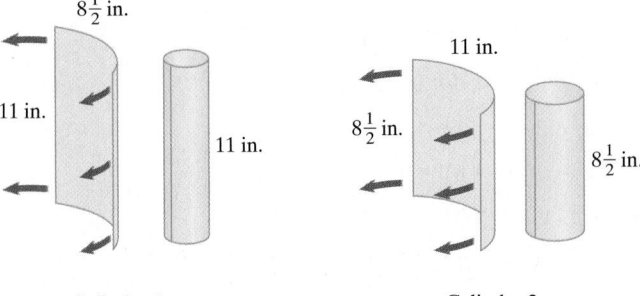

Cylinder 1   Cylinder 2

△ **111.** Use the same idea as in Exercise 110, work with a partner, and discover whether two rectangles with the same perimeter always have the same area. Explain your results.

The following graph is called a broken-line graph, or simply a line graph. This particular graph shows the past, present, and future predicted U.S. population over 65. Just as with a bar graph, to find the population over 65 for a particular year, read the height of the corresponding point. To read the height, follow the point horizontally to the left until you reach the vertical axis. Use this graph to answer Exercise 112 through 117.

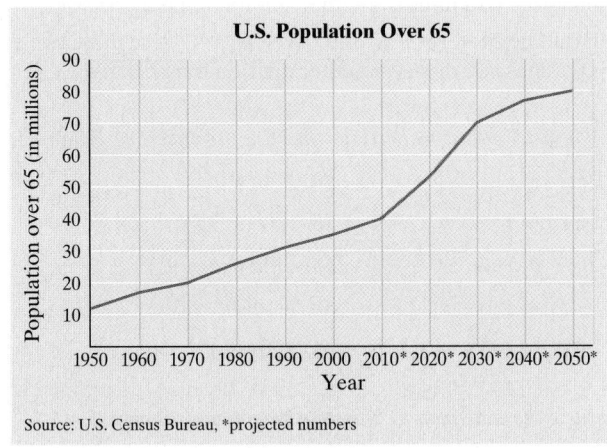

Source: U.S. Census Bureau, *projected numbers

112. Estimate the population over 65 in the year 1970.

113. Estimate the predicted population over 65 in the year 2050.

114. Estimate the predicted population over 65 in the year 2030.

115. Estimate the population over 65 in the year 2000.

116. Is the population over 65 increasing as time passes or decreasing? Explain how you arrived at your answer.

117. The percent of Americans over 65 in 1950 was 8.1%. The percent of Americans over 65 in 2050 is expected to be 2.5 times the percent over 65 in 1950. Estimate the percent of Americans expected to be over age 65 in 2050.

STUDY SKILLS REMINDER

Are You Preparing for a Test on Chapter 1?

Below I have listed some common trouble areas for students in Chapter 1. After studying for your test—but before taking your test—read these.

▶ Don't forget the order of operations and the distributive property.

$$7 - 3(2x - 6y) + 5 = 7 - 6x + 18y + 5$$ Use the distributive property.

Notice the sign.

$$= -6x + 18y + 12$$ Combine like terms.

▶ Don't forget the difference between $(-3)^2$ and -3^2.

$$(-3)^2 = (-3)(-3) = 9$$
$$-3^2 = -1 \cdot 3^2 = -1 \cdot (3 \cdot 3) = -9$$

▶ Remember that

$$\frac{0}{8} = 0 \text{ while } \frac{8}{0} \text{ is undefined.}$$

▶ Don't forget the difference between reciprocal and opposite.

The opposite of $-\frac{3}{5}$ is $\frac{3}{5}$.

The reciprocal of $-\frac{3}{5}$ is $-\frac{5}{3}$.

Remember: This is simply a checklist of common trouble areas. For a review of Chapter 1, see the Highlights and Chapter Review at the end of Chapter 1.

CHAPTER 1 PROJECT

Analyzing Newspaper Circulation

The number of daily newspapers in business in the United States has declined steadily recently, continuing a trend that started in the mid-1970s. In 1900, there were roughly 2300 daily newspapers in operation. However, by 1998, that number had dropped to only 1509 newspapers in existence. Average overall daily newspaper circulation also continues to decline, from 60.2 million in 1992 to 56.7 million in 1997.

The table on the next page gives data about daily newspaper circulation for New York City–based newspapers for the years 2000 and 2001. In this project, you will have the opportunity to

New York–based Newspaper	2000 Daily Circulation	2001 Daily Circulation	Daily Edition Newsstand Price
Wall Street Journal	1,762,751	1,780,605	$1.00
New York Times	1,097,180	1,109,371	$1.00
New York Daily News	704,463	734,473	$0.50
New York Post	443,951	533,860	$0.50

analyze this data. This project may be completed by working in groups or individually.

1. Find the change in circulation from 2000 to 2001 for each newspaper. Did any newspaper gain circulation? If so, which one(s) and by how much?

2. Construct a bar graph showing the change in circulation from 2000 to 2001 for each newspaper. Which newspaper experienced the largest change in circulation?

3. What was the total daily circulation of these New York City–based newspapers in 2000? In 2001? Did total circulation increase or decrease from 2000 to 2001? By how much?

4. Discuss factors that may have contributed to the overall change in daily newspaper circulation.

5. The population of New York City is approximately 7,381,000. Find the number of New York City–based newspapers sold per person in 2001 for New York City. (*Source:* U.S. Bureau of the Census)

6. The population of the New York City metropolitan area is approximately 16,332,000. Find the number of New York City–based newspapers sold per person in 2001 for the New York City metropolitan area. (*Source:* The United Nations)

7. Which of the figures found in Questions 5 and 6 do you think is more meaningful? Why? Why might neither of these figures be capable of describing the full circulation situation?

8. Assuming that each copy was sold from a newsstand in the New York City metropolitan area, use the daily edition newspaper prices given in the table to approximate the total amount spent each day on these New York City–based newspapers in 2001. Find the total amount spent annually on these daily newspapers in 2001.

9. How accurate do you think the figures you found in Question 8 are? Explain your reasoning.

CHAPTER VOCABULARY CHECK

Fill in each blank with one of the words or phrases listed below.

distributive   real   reciprocals   absolute value   opposite   associative
inequality   commutative   whole   algebraic expression   exponent   variable

1. A(n) _____ is formed by numbers and variables connected by the operations of addition, subtraction, multiplication, division, raising to powers, and/or taking roots.

2. The _____ of a number a is $-a$.

3. $3(x - 6) = 3x - 18$ by the _____ property.

4. The _____ of a number is the distance between that number and 0 on the number line.

5. A(n) _____ is a shorthand notation for repeated multiplication of the same factor.

6. A letter that represents a number is called a _____.

7. The symbols $<$ and $>$ are called _____ symbols.

8. If a is not 0, then a and $1/a$ are called _____

9. $A + B = B + A$ by the _____ property.

10. $(A + B) + C = A + (B + C)$ by the _____ property.

11. The numbers $0, 1, 2, 3, \ldots$ are called _____ numbers.

12. If a number corresponds to a point on the number line, we know that number is a ____ number.

CHAPTER 1 HIGHLIGHTS

Definitions and Concepts	**Examples**

Section 1.2   Algebraic Expressions and Sets of Numbers

Letters that represent numbers are called **variables.**

An **algebraic expression** is formed by numbers and variables connected by the operations of addition, subtraction, multiplication, division, raising to powers, and/or taking roots.

To **evaluate** an algebraic expression containing variables, substitute the given numbers for the variables and simplify. The result is called the **value** of the expression.

Natural numbers: $\{1, 2, 3, \dots\}$
Whole numbers: $\{0, 1, 2, 3, \dots\}$
Integers: $\{\dots, -3, -2, -1, 0, 1, 2, 3, \dots\}$
Each listing of three dots above is called an **ellipsis,** which means the pattern continues.
The members of a set are called its **elements.**
Set builder notation describes the elements of a set but does not list them.
Real numbers: $\{x \mid x$ corresponds to a point on the number line.$\}$
Rational numbers: $\{\frac{a}{b} \mid a$ and b are intergers and $b \neq 0\}$.
Irrational numbers: $\{x \mid x$ is a real number and x is not a rational number$\}$.
If 3 is an element of set A, we write $3 \in A$.
If all the elements of set A are also in set B, we say that set A is a **subset** of set B, and we write $A \subseteq B$.
Absolute value:
$$|a| = \begin{cases} a \text{ if } a \text{ is 0 or a positive number} \\ -a \text{ if } a \text{ is a negative number} \end{cases}$$
The opposite of a number a is the number $-a$.

Examples of variables are
$$x, a, m, y$$
Examples of algebraic expressions are
$$7y, -3, \frac{x^2 - 9}{-2} + 14x, \sqrt{3} + \sqrt{m}$$
Evaluate $2.7x$ if $x = 3$.
$$2.7x = 2.7(3)$$
$$= 8.1$$

Given the set $\{-9.6, -5, -\sqrt{2}, 0, \frac{2}{5}, 101\}$ list the elements that belong to the set of

Natural numbers 101

Whole numbers $0, 101$

Integers $-5, 0, 101$

Real numbers $-9.6, -5, -\sqrt{2}, 0, \frac{2}{5}, 101$

Rational numbers $-9.6, -5, 0, \frac{2}{5}, 101$

Irrational numbers $-\sqrt{2}$

List the elements in the set
$\{x \mid x$ is an integer between -2 and $5\}$.
$$\{-1, 0, 1, 2, 3, 4\}$$
$$\{1, 2, 4\} \subseteq \{1, 2, 3, 4\}.$$
$$|3| = 3, \quad |0| = 0, \quad |-7.2| = 7.2$$

The opposite of 5 is -5. The opposite of -11 is 11.

Section 1.3   Operations on Real Numbers

Adding real numbers:

1. To add two numbers with the same sign, add their absolute values and attach their common sign.
2. To add two numbers with different signs, subtract the smaller absolute value from the larger absolute value and attach the sign of the number with the larger absolute value.

Subtracting real numbers:
$$a - b = a + (-b)$$
Multiplying and dividing real numbers:

The product or quotient of two numbers with the same sign is positive.
The product or quotient of two numbers with different signs is negative.

$$\frac{2}{7} + \frac{1}{7} = \frac{3}{7}$$
$$-5 + (-2.6) = -7.6$$
$$-18 + 6 = -12$$
$$20.8 + (-10.2) = 10.6$$
$$18 - 21 = 18 + (-21) = -3$$
$$(-8)(-4) = 32 \qquad \frac{-8}{-4} = 2$$
$$8 \cdot 4 = 32 \qquad \frac{8}{4} = 2$$
$$-17 \cdot 2 = -34 \qquad \frac{-14}{2} = -7$$
$$4(-1.6) = -6.4 \qquad \frac{22}{-2} = -11 \quad \textit{(continued)}$$

Definitions and Concepts	**Examples**

Section 1.3   Operations on Real Numbers

A natural number **exponent** is a shorthand notation for repeated multiplication of the same factor.

$$3^4 = 3 \cdot 3 \cdot 3 \cdot 3 = 81$$

The notation $\sqrt{a}$ is used to denote the **positive**, or **principal, square root** of a nonnegative number a.

$$\sqrt{a} = b \text{ if } b^2 = a \text{ and } b \text{ is positive}.$$

Also,

$$\sqrt[3]{a} = b \text{ if } b^3 = a$$
$$\sqrt[4]{a} = b \text{ if } b^4 = a \text{ and } b \text{ is positive}$$

$$\sqrt{49} = 7$$
$$\sqrt[3]{64} = 4$$
$$\sqrt[4]{16} = 2$$

Order of Operations

Simplify expressions using the order that follows. If grouping symbols such as parentheses are present, simplify expressions within those first, starting with the innermost set. If fraction bars are present, simplify the numerator and denominator separately.

1. Raise to powers or take roots in order from left to right.

2. Multiply or divide in order from left to right.

3. Add or subtract in order from left to right.

Simplifly $\dfrac{42 - 2(3^2 - \sqrt{16})}{-8}$.

$$\frac{42 - 2(3^2 - \sqrt{16})}{-8} = \frac{42 - 2(9 - 4)}{-8}$$
$$= \frac{42 - 2(5)}{-8}$$
$$= \frac{42 - 10}{-8}$$
$$= \frac{32}{-8} = -4$$

Section 1.4   Properties of Real Numbers

Symbols: $=$ is equal to
$\neq$ is not equal to
$>$ is greater than
$<$ is less than
$\geq$ is greater than or equal to
$\leq$ is less than or equal to

$$-5 = -5$$
$$-5 \neq -3$$
$$1.7 < 1.2$$
$$-1.7 < -1.2$$
$$\frac{5}{3} \geq \frac{5}{3}$$
$$-\frac{1}{2} \leq \frac{1}{2}$$

Identity:

$$a + 0 = a \qquad 0 + a = a$$
$$a \cdot 1 = a \qquad 1 \cdot a = a$$

$$3 + 0 = 3 \qquad\qquad 0 + 3 = 3$$
$$-1.8 \cdot 1 = -1.8 \qquad 1 \cdot -1.8 = -1.8$$

Inverse:

$$a + (-a) = 0 \qquad -a + a = 0$$
$$a \cdot \frac{1}{a} = 1 \qquad \frac{1}{a} \cdot a = 1, a \neq 0$$

$$7 + (-7) = 0 \qquad -7 + 7 = 0$$
$$5 \cdot \frac{1}{5} = 1 \qquad \frac{1}{5} \cdot 5 = 1$$

Commutative:

$$a + b = b + a$$
$$a \cdot b = b \cdot a$$

$$x + 7 = 7 + x$$
$$9 \cdot y = y \cdot 9$$

Associative:

$$(a + b) + c = a + (b + c)$$
$$(a \cdot b) \cdot c = a \cdot (b \cdot c)$$

$$(3 + 1) + 10 = 3 + (1 + 10)$$
$$(3 \cdot 1) \cdot 10 = 3(1 \cdot 10)$$

Distributive:

$$a(b + c) = ab + ac$$

$$6(x + 5) = 6 \cdot x + 6 \cdot 5$$
$$= 6x + 30$$

CHAPTER REVIEW

(1.2) *Find the value of each algebraic expression at the given replacement values.*

1. $7x$ when $x = 3$

2. st when $s = 1.6$ and $t = 5$

3. The hummingbird has an average wing speed of 90 beats per second. The expression $90t$ gives the number of wing beats in t seconds. Calculate the number of wing beats in *1 hour* for the hummingbird.

List the elements in each set.

4. $\{x \mid x \text{ is an odd integer between } -2 \text{ and } 4\}$

5. $\{x \mid x \text{ is an even integer between } -3 \text{ and } 7\}$

6. $\{x \mid x \text{ is a negative whole number}\}$

7. $\{x \mid x \text{ is a natural number that is not a rational number}$

8. $\{x \mid x \text{ is a whole number greater than } 5\}$

9. $\{x \mid x \text{ is an integer less than } 3\}$

Determine whether each statement is true or false if $A = \{6, 10, 12\}$, $B = \{5, 9, 11\}$, $C = \{\ldots, -3, -2, -1, 0, 1, 2, 3, \ldots\}$, $D = \{2, 4, 6, \ldots, 16\}$ $E = \{x \mid x \text{ is a rational number}\}$, $F = \{\ \}$, $G = \{x \mid x \text{ is an irrational number}\}$, and $H = \{x \mid x \text{ is a real number}\}$.

10. $10 \in D$

11. $B \in 9$

12. $\sqrt{169} \notin G$

13. $0 \notin F$

14. $\pi \in E$

15. $\pi \in H$

16. $\sqrt{4} \in G$

17. $-9 \in E$

18. $A \subseteq D$

19. $C \not\subseteq B$

20. $C \not\subseteq E$

21. $F \subseteq H$

22. $B \subseteq B$

23. $D \subset C$

24. $C \subseteq H$

25. $G \subseteq H$

26. $\{5\} \in B$

27. $\{5\} \subseteq B$

List the elements of the set
$$\left\{5, -\frac{2}{3}, \frac{8}{2}, \sqrt{9}, 0.3, \sqrt{7}, 1\frac{5}{8}, -1, \pi\right\}$$ *that are also elements of each given set.*

28. Whole numbers

29. Natural numbers

30. Rational numbers

31. Irrational numbers

32. Real numbers

33. Integers

Find the opposite.

34. $-\dfrac{3}{4}$

35. 0.6

36. 0

37. 1

Find the reciprocal.

38. $-\dfrac{3}{4}$

39. 0.6

40. 0

41. 1

(1.3) *Simplify.*

42. $-7 + 3$

43. $-10 + (-25)$

44. $5(-0.4)$

45. $(-3.1)(-0.1)$

46. $-7 - (-15)$

47. $9 - (-4.3)$

48. $(-6)(-4)(0)(-3)$

49. $(-12)(0)(-1)(-5)$ 0

50. $(-24) \div 0$

51. $0 \div (-45)$

52. $(-36) \div (-9)$

53. $60 \div (-12)$

54. $\left(-\dfrac{4}{5}\right) - \left(-\dfrac{2}{3}\right)$

55. $\left(\dfrac{5}{4}\right) - \left(-2\dfrac{3}{4}\right)$

56. Determine the unknown fractional part.

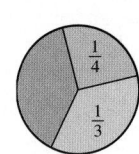

Simplify.

57. $-5 + 7 - 3 - (-10)$

58. $8 - (-3) + (-4) + 6$

59. $3(4 - 5)^4$

60. $6(7 - 10)^2$

61. $\left(-\dfrac{8}{15}\right) \cdot \left(-\dfrac{2}{3}\right)^2$

62. $\left(-\dfrac{3}{4}\right)^2 \cdot \left(-\dfrac{10}{21}\right)$

63. $\dfrac{-\dfrac{6}{15}}{\dfrac{8}{25}}$

64. $\dfrac{\dfrac{4}{9}}{-\dfrac{8}{45}}$

65. $-\dfrac{3}{8} + 3(2) \div 6$

66. $5(-2) - (-3) - \dfrac{1}{6} + \dfrac{2}{3}$

67. $|2^3 - 3^2| - |5 - 7|$

68. $|5^2 - 2^2| + |9 \div (-3)|$

69. $(2^3 - 3^2) - (5 - 7)$

70. $(5^2 - 2^4) + [9 \div (-3)]$

71. $\dfrac{(8 - 10)^3 - (-4)^2}{2 + 8(2) \div 4}$

72. $\dfrac{(2 + 4)^2 + (-1)^5}{12 \div 2 \cdot 3 - 3}$

73. $\dfrac{(4 - 9) + 4 - 9}{10 - 12 \div 4 \cdot 8}$

74. $\dfrac{3 - 7 - (7 - 3)}{15 + 30 \div 6 \cdot 2}$

75. $\dfrac{\sqrt{25}}{4 + 3 \cdot 7}$

76. $\dfrac{\sqrt{64}}{24 - 8 \cdot 2}$

Find the value of each expression when $x = 0$, $y = 3$, and $z = -2$.

77. $x^2 - y^2 + z^2$

78. $\dfrac{5x + z}{2y}$

79. $\dfrac{-7y - 3z}{-3}$

80. $(x - y + z)^2$

△ **81.** The algebraic expression $2\pi r$ represents the circumference of (distance around) a circle of radius r.

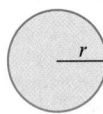

a. Complete the table below by evaluating the expression at given values of r. (Use 3.14 for π)

Radius	r	1	10	100
Circumference	$2\pi r$			

b. As the radius of a circle increases, does the circumference of the circle increase or decrease?

(1.4) Simplify each expression.

82. $5xy - 7xy + 3 - 2 + xy$

83. $4x + 10x - 19x + 10 - 19$

84. $6x^2 + 2 - 4(x^2 + 1)$

85. $-7(2x^2 - 1) - x^2 - 1$

86. $(3.2x - 1.5) - (4.3x - 1.2)$

87. $(7.6x + 4.7) - (1.9x + 3.6)$

Write each statement using mathematical symbols.

88. Twelve is the product of x and negative 4.

89. The sum of n and twice n is negative fifteen.

90. Four times the sum of y and three is -1.

91. The difference of t and five, multiplied by six is four.

92. Seven subtracted from z is six.

93. Ten less than the product of x and nine is five.

94. The difference of x and 5 is at least 12.

95. The opposite of four is less than the product of y and seven.

96. Two-thirds is not equal to twice the sum of n and one-fourth.

97. The sum of t and six is not more than negative twelve.

Name the property illustrated.

98. $(M + 5) + P = M + (5 + P)$

99. $5(3x - 4) = 15x - 20$

100. $(-4) + 4 = 0$

101. $(3 + x) + 7 = 7 + (3 + x)$

102. $(XY)Z = (YZ)X$

103. $\left(-\dfrac{3}{5}\right) \cdot \left(-\dfrac{5}{3}\right) = 1$

104. $T \cdot 0 = 0$

105. $(ab)c = a(bc)$

106. $A + 0 = A$

107. $8 \cdot 1 = 8$

Complete the equation using the given property.

108. $5x - 15z =$ _____ Distributive property

109. $(7 + y) + (3 + x) =$ _____ Commutative property

110. $0 =$ _____ Additive inverse property

111. $1 =$ _____ Multiplicative inverse property

112. $[(3.4)(0.7)]5 =$ _____ Associative property

113. $7 =$ _____ Additive identity property

Insert $<$, $>$, or $=$ to make each statement true.

114. -9 _____ -12

115. 0 _____ -6

116. -3 _____ -1

117. 7 _____ $|-7|$

118. -5 _____ $-(-5)$

119. $-(-2)$ _____ -2

CHAPTER 1 TEST

Remember to use your Chapter Test Prep Video CD to help you study and view solutions to the test questions you need help with.

Determine whether each statement is true or false.

1. $-2.3 > -2.33$

2. $-6^2 = (-6)^2$

3. $-5 - 8 = -(5 - 8)$

4. $(-2)(-3)(0) = \dfrac{-4}{0}$

5. All natural numbers are integers.

6. All rational numbers are integers.

Simplify.

7. $5 - 12 \div 3(2)$

8. $5^2 - 3^4$

9. $(4 - 9)^3 - |-4 - 6|^2$

10. $12 + \{6 - [5 - 2(-5)]\}$

11. $\dfrac{6(7 - 9)^3 + (-2)}{(-2)(-5)(-5)}$

12. $\dfrac{(4 - \sqrt{16}) - (-7 - 20)}{-2(1 - 4)^2}$

Evaluate each expression when $q = 4, r = -2,$ and $t = 1.$

13. $q^2 - r^2$

14. $\dfrac{5t - 3q}{3r - 1}$

15. The algebraic expression $5.75x$ represents the total cost for x adults to attend the theater.
  a. Complete the table that follows.
  b. As the number of adults increases does the total cost increase or decrease?

Adults	x	1	3	10	20
Total Cost	$5.75x$				

Write each statement using mathematical symbols.

16. Twice the sum of x and five is 30.

17. The square of the difference of six and y, divided by seven, is less than -2.

18. The product of nine and z, divided by the absolute value of -12, is not equal to 10.

19. Three times the quotient of n and five is the opposite of n.

20. Twenty is equal to 6 subtracted from twice x.

21. Negative two is equal to x divided by the sum of x and five.

Name each property illustrated.

22. $6(x - 4) = 6x - 24$

23. $(4 + x) + z = 4 + (x + z)$

24. $(-7) + 7 = 0$

25. $(-18)(0) = 0$

26. Write an expression for the total amount of money (in dollars) in n nickels and d dimes.

Simplify each expression.

27. $-2(3x + 7)$

28. $\dfrac{1}{3}a - \dfrac{3}{8} + \dfrac{1}{6}a - \dfrac{3}{4}$

29. $4y + 10 - 2(y + 10)$

30. $(8.3x - 2.9) - (9.6x - 4.8)$

2

Equations, Inequalities, and Problem Solving

Mathematics is a tool for solving problems in such diverse fields as transportation, engineering, economics, medicine, business, and biology. We solve problems using mathematics by modeling real-world phenomena with mathematical equations or inequalities. Our ability to solve problems using mathematics, then, depends in part on our ability to solve equations and inequalities. In this chapter, we solve linear equations and inequalities in one variable and graph their solutions on number lines.

Since the beginning of civilization, education has been necessary for humanity to survive. The first public schools in the United States were established in Massachusetts in 1647. These schools were open to all children and were supported by public funds. After the Revolutionary War, attempts to unify public education resulted in the establishment of state public school systems.

Today, a large team of educators, principals, counselors, librarians, school board members, and a school superintendent administer today's complex system of public schools. Administrators establish policy and procedure as well as manage the budget and other business aspects involved in the maintenance of a large organization. Most jobs in school administration require a master's or doctoral degree in an education-related field of study.

In the Spotlight on Decision Making feature on page 91, you will have the opportunity to make a decision about long-term planning related to school enrollment as a school superintendent.

Link: www.aasa.org *(American Association of School Administrators)*
Sources of text: www.bls.gov/oco/ocos007.htm *(Bureau of Labor Statistics), World Book Millennium 2000 (encyclopedia on CD) "Education"*

2.1 LINEAR EQUATIONS IN ONE VARIABLE

Objectives

1 Solve linear equations using properties of equality.

2 Solve linear equations that can be simplified by combining like terms.

3 Solve linear equations containing fractions.

4 Recognize when an equation is an identity and when it has no solution.

1　Linear equations model many real-life problems. For example, we can use a linear equation to calculate the increase in households (in millions) with digital cameras.

With the help of your computer, digital cameras allow you to see your pictures and make copies immediately, send them in e-mail or use them on a Web page. Current projected number of households with these cameras are shown in the graph below.

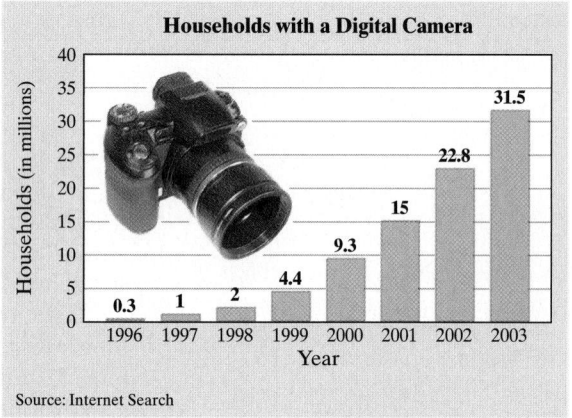

Households with a Digital Camera

Households (in millions)

| 1996 | 1997 | 1998 | 1999 | 2000 | 2001 | 2002 | 2003 |

0.3　1　2　4.4　9.3　15　22.8　31.5

Year

Source: Internet Search

To find the increase in households from 2002 to 2003, for example, we can use the equation below.

In words:

Increase in households	is	households in 2003	minus	households in 2002
x	=	31.5	−	22.8

Translate:

Since our variable x (increase in households) is by itself on one side of the equation, we can find the value of x by simplifying the right side.

$$x = 8.7$$

The increase in households with digital cameras from 2002 to 2003 is $8.7 million.

The **equation**, $x = 31.5 - 22.8$, like every other equation, is a statement that two expressions are equal. Oftentimes, the unknown variable is not by itself on one side of the equation. In these cases, we will use properties of equality to write equivalent equations so that a solution many be found. This is called **solving the equation**. In this section, we concentrate on solving equations such as this one, called **linear equations** in one variable. Linear equations are also called **first-degree equations** since the exponent on the variable is 1.

Linear Equations in One Variable

$$3x = -15 \qquad 7 - y = 3y \qquad 4n - 9n + 6 = 0 \qquad z = -2$$

Linear Equations in One Variable

A linear equation in one variable is an equation that can be written in the form

$$ax + b = c$$

where a, b, and c are real numbers and $a \neq 0$.

When a variable in an equation is replaced by a number and the resulting equation is true, then that number is called a **solution** of the equation. For example, 1 is a solution of the equation $3x + 4 = 7$, since $3(1) + 4 = 7$ is a true statement. But 2 is not a solution of this equation, since $3(2) + 4 = 7$ is not a true statement. The **solution set** of an equation is the set of solutions of the equation. For example, the solution set of $3x + 4 = 7$ is $\{1\}$.

To **solve an equation** is to find the solution set of an equation. Equations with the same solution set are called **equivalent equations**. For example,

$$3x + 4 = 7 \qquad 3x = 3 \qquad x = 1$$

are equivalent equations because they all have the same solution set, namely $\{1\}$. To solve an equation in x, we start with the given equation and write a series of simpler equivalent equations until we obtain an equation of the form

$$x = \textbf{number}$$

Two important properties are used to write equivalent equations.

The Addition and Multiplication Properties of Equality

If a, b, and c, are real numbers, then

$$a = b \quad \text{and} \quad a + c = b + c \text{ are equivalent equations.}$$

Also, $a = b$ and $ac = bc$ are equivalent equations as long as $c \neq 0$.

The **addition property of equality** guarantees that the same number may be added to both sides of an equation, and the result is an equivalent equation. The **multiplication property of equality** guarantees that both sides of an equation may be multiplied by the same nonzero number, and the result is an equivalent equation. Because we define subtraction in terms of addition $(a - b = a + (-b))$, and division in terms of multiplication $\left(\dfrac{a}{b} = a \cdot \dfrac{1}{b} \right)$, these properties also guarantee that we may *subtract* the same number from both sides of an equation, or *divide* both sides of an equation by the same nonzero number and the result is an equivalent equation.

For example, to solve $2x + 5 = 9$, use the addition and multiplication properties of equality to isolate x—that is, to write an equivalent equation of the form

$$x = \text{number}$$

EXAMPLE 1

Solve for x: $2x + 5 = 9$.

Solution First, use the addition property of equality and subtract 5 from both sides. We do this so that our only variable term, $2x$, is by itself on one side of the equation.

$$2x + 5 = 9$$
$$2x + 5 - 5 = 9 - 5 \qquad \text{Subtract 5 from both sides.}$$
$$2x = 4 \qquad \text{Simplify.}$$

Now that the variable term is isolated, we can finish solving for x by using the multiplication property of equality and dividing both sides by 2.

$$\frac{2x}{2} = \frac{4}{2} \qquad \text{Divide both sides by 2.}$$
$$x = 2 \qquad \text{Simplify.}$$

Check To see that 2 is the solution, replace x in the original equation with 2.

$$2x + 5 = 9 \qquad \text{Original equation.}$$
$$2(2) + 5 \stackrel{?}{=} 9 \qquad \text{Let } x = 2.$$
$$4 + 5 \stackrel{?}{=} 9$$
$$9 = 9 \qquad \text{True.}$$

Since we arrive at a true statement, 2 is the solution or the solution set is $\{2\}$.

EXAMPLE 2

Solve: $0.6 = 2 - 3.5c$.

Solution We use both the addition property and the multiplication property of equality.

> **Helpful Hint**
> Don't forget that
>
> $0.4 = c$ and $c = 0.4$ are equivalent equations.
>
> We may solve an equation so that the variable is alone on either side of the equation.

$$0.6 = 2 - 3.5c$$
$$0.6 - 2 = 2 - 3.5c - 2 \qquad \text{Subtract 2 from both sides.}$$
$$-1.4 = -3.5c \qquad \text{Simplify. The variable term is now isolated.}$$
$$\frac{-1.4}{-3.5} = \frac{-3.5c}{-3.5} \qquad \text{Divide both sides by } -3.5.$$
$$0.4 = c \qquad \text{Simplify } \frac{-1.4}{-3.5}.$$

Check

$$0.6 = 2 - 3.5c$$
$$0.6 \stackrel{?}{=} 2 - 3.5(0.4) \qquad \text{Replace } c \text{ with } 0.4.$$
$$0.6 \stackrel{?}{=} 2 - 1.4 \qquad \text{Multiply.}$$
$$0.6 = 0.6 \qquad \text{True.}$$

The solution is 0.4, or the solution set is $\{0.4\}$.

2 Often, an equation can be simplified by removing any grouping symbols and combining any like terms.

EXAMPLE 3

Solve: $-6x - 1 + 5x = 3$.

Solution   First, the left side of this equation can be simplified by combining like terms $-6x$ and $5x$. Then use the addition property of equality and add 1 to both sides of the equation.

$$-6x - 1 + 5x = 3$$
$$-x - 1 = 3 \qquad \text{Combine like terms.}$$
$$-x - 1 + 1 = 3 + 1 \qquad \text{Add 1 to both sides of the equation.}$$
$$-x = 4 \qquad \text{Simplify.}$$

Notice that this equation is not solved for x since we have $-x$ or $-1x$, not x. To solve for x, divide both sides by -1.

$$\frac{-x}{-1} = \frac{4}{-1} \qquad \text{Divide both sides by } -1.$$
$$x = -4 \qquad \text{Simplify.}$$

Check to see that the solution is -4.

If an equation contains parentheses, use the distributive property to remove them.

EXAMPLE 4

Solve: $2(x - 3) = 5x - 9$.

Solution   First, use the distributive property.

$$2(x - 3) = 5x - 9$$
$$2x - 6 = 5x - 9 \qquad \text{Use the distributive property.}$$

Next, get variable terms on the same side of the equation by subtracting $5x$ from both sides.

$$2x - 6 - 5x = 5x - 9 - 5x \qquad \text{Subtract } 5x \text{ from both sides.}$$
$$-3x - 6 = -9 \qquad \text{Simplify.}$$
$$-3x - 6 + 6 = -9 + 6 \qquad \text{Add 6 to both sides.}$$
$$-3x = -3 \qquad \text{Simplify.}$$
$$\frac{-3x}{-3} = \frac{-3}{-3} \qquad \text{Divide both sides by } -3.$$
$$x = 1$$

Let $x = 1$ in the original equation to see that 1 is the solution.

3   If an equation contains fractions, we first clear the equation of fractions by multiplying both sides of the equation by the *least common denominator* (LCD) of all fractions in the equation.

EXAMPLE 5

Solve for y: $\dfrac{y}{3} - \dfrac{y}{4} = \dfrac{1}{6}$.

Solution   First, clear the equation of fractions by multiplying both sides of the equation by 12, the LCD of denominators 3, 4, and 6.

$$\frac{y}{3} - \frac{y}{4} = \frac{1}{6}$$

$$12\left(\frac{y}{3} - \frac{y}{4}\right) = 12\left(\frac{1}{6}\right) \qquad \text{Multiply both sides by the LCD 12.}$$

$$12\left(\frac{y}{3}\right) - 12\left(\frac{y}{4}\right) = 2 \qquad \text{Apply the distributive property.}$$

$$4y - 3y = 2 \qquad \text{Simplify.}$$

$$y = 2 \qquad \text{Simplify.}$$

Check   To check, let $y = 2$ in the original equation.

$$\frac{y}{3} - \frac{y}{4} = \frac{1}{6} \qquad \text{Original equation.}$$

$$\frac{2}{3} - \frac{2}{4} \stackrel{?}{=} \frac{1}{6} \qquad \text{Let } y = 2.$$

$$\frac{8}{12} - \frac{6}{12} \stackrel{?}{=} \frac{1}{6} \qquad \text{Write fractions with the LCD.}$$

$$\frac{2}{12} \stackrel{?}{=} \frac{1}{6} \qquad \text{Subtract.}$$

$$\frac{1}{6} = \frac{1}{6} \qquad \text{Simplify.}$$

This is a true statement, so the solution is 2.

As a general guideline, the following steps may be used to solve a linear equation in one variable.

Solving A Linear Equation in One Variable

Step 1: Clear the equation of fractions by multiplying both sides of the equation by the least common denominator (LCD) of all denominators in the equation.

Step 2: Use the distributive property to remove grouping symbols such as parentheses.

Step 3: Combine like terms on each side of the equation.

Step 4: Use the addition property of equality to rewrite the equation as an equivalent equation with variable terms on one side and numbers on the other side.

Step 5: Use the multiplication property of equality to isolate the variable.

Step 6: Check the proposed solution in the original equation.

EXAMPLE 6

Solve for x: $\dfrac{x + 5}{2} + \dfrac{1}{2} = 2x - \dfrac{x - 3}{8}$.

Solution   Multiply both sides of the equation by 8, the LCD of 2 and 8.

Helpful Hint

When we multiply both sides of an equation by a number, the distributive property tells us that each term of the equation is multiplied by the number.

$$8\left(\dfrac{x + 5}{2} + \dfrac{1}{2}\right) = 8\left(2x - \dfrac{x - 3}{8}\right) \qquad \text{Multiply both sides by } 8.$$

$$8\left(\dfrac{x + 5}{2}\right) + 8 \cdot \dfrac{1}{2} = 8 \cdot 2x - 8\left(\dfrac{x - 3}{8}\right) \qquad \text{Apply the distributive property.}$$

$$4(x + 5) + 4 = 16x - (x - 3) \qquad \text{Simplify.}$$

$$4x + 20 + 4 = 16x - x + 3 \qquad \begin{array}{l}\text{Use the distributive property}\\\text{to remove parentheses.}\end{array}$$

$$4x + 24 = 15x + 3 \qquad \text{Combine like terms.}$$

$$-11x + 24 = 3 \qquad \text{Subtract } 15x \text{ from both sides.}$$

$$-11x = -21 \qquad \text{Subtract } 24 \text{ from both sides.}$$

$$\dfrac{-11x}{-11} = \dfrac{-21}{-11} \qquad \text{Divide both sides by } -11.$$

$$x = \dfrac{21}{11} \qquad \text{Simplify.}$$

Solution   To check, verify that replacing x with $\dfrac{21}{11}$ makes the original equation true. The solution is $\dfrac{21}{11}$.

If an equation contains decimals, you may want to first clear the equation of decimals.

EXAMPLE 7

Solve: $0.3x + 0.1 = 0.27x - 0.02$.

Solution   To clear this equation of decimals, we multiply both sides of the equation by 100. Recall that multiplying a number by 100 moves its decimal point two places to the right.

$$100(0.3x + 0.1) = 100(0.27x - 0.02)$$

$$100(0.3x) + 100(0.1) = 100(0.27x) - 100(0.02) \qquad \text{Use the distributive property.}$$

$$30x + 10 = 27x - 2 \qquad \text{Multiply.}$$

$$30x - 27x = -2 - 10 \qquad \begin{array}{l}\text{Subtract } 27x \text{ and } 10 \text{ from}\\\text{both sides.}\end{array}$$

$$3x = -12 \qquad \text{Simplify.}$$

$$\dfrac{3x}{3} = \dfrac{-12}{3} \qquad \text{Divide both sides by } 3.$$

$$x = -4 \qquad \text{Simplify.}$$

Check to see that the solution is -4.

✔ **CONCEPT CHECK**

Explain what is wrong with the following:

$$3x - 5 = 16$$
$$3x = 11$$
$$\frac{3x}{3} = \frac{11}{3}$$
$$x = \frac{11}{3}$$

4   So far, each linear equation that we have solved has had a single solution. A linear equation in one variable that has exactly one solution is called a **conditional equation**. We will now look at two other types of equations: contradictions and identities.

An equation in one variable that has no solution is called a **contradiction**, and an equation in one variable that has every number (for which the equation is defined) as a solution is called an **identity**. The next examples show how to recognize contradictions and identities.

EXAMPLE 8

Solve for x: $3x + 5 = 3(x + 2)$.

Solution   First, use the distributive property and remove parentheses.

$$3x + 5 = 3(x + 2)$$
$$3x + 5 = 3x + 6 \qquad \text{Apply the distributive property.}$$
$$3x + 5 - 3x = 3x + 6 - 3x \qquad \text{Subtract } 3x \text{ from both sides.}$$
$$5 = 6$$

> **Helpful Hint**
>
> A solution set of $\{0\}$ and a solution set of $\{\ \}$ are not the same. The solution set $\{0\}$ means 1 solution, 0. The solution set $\{\ \}$ means no solution.

The equation $5 = 6$ is a false statement no matter what value the variable x might have. Thus, the original equation has no solution. Its solution set is written either as $\{\ \}$ or $\varnothing$. This equation is a contradiction.

EXAMPLE 9

Solve for x: $6x - 4 = 2 + 6(x - 1)$.

Solution   First, use the distributive property and remove parentheses.

$$6x - 4 = 2 + 6(x - 1)$$
$$6x - 4 = 2 + 6x - 6 \qquad \text{Apply the distributive property.}$$
$$6x - 4 = 6x - 4 \qquad \text{Combine like terms.}$$

At this point we might notice that both sides of the equation are the same, so replacing x by any real number gives a true statement. Thus the solution set of this equation is the set of real numbers, and the equation is an identity. Continuing to "solve" $6x - 4 = 6x - 4$, we eventually arrive at the same conclusion.

$$6x - 4 + 4 = 6x - 4 + 4 \qquad \text{Add 4 to both sides.}$$
$$6x = 6x \qquad \text{Simplify.}$$
$$6x - 6x = 6x - 6x \qquad \text{Subtract } 6x \text{ from both sides.}$$
$$0 = 0 \qquad \text{Simplify.}$$

Concept Check Answer:

$$3x - 5 = 16$$
$$3x = 21$$
$$x = 7$$

Therefore the correct solution set is $\{7\}$.

Since $0 = 0$ is a true statement for every value of x, all real numbers are solutions. The solution set is the set of all real numbers or, $\mathbb{R}$, $\{x \mid x \text{ is a real number}\}$, and the equation is called an identity.

> ### Helpful Hint
>
> For linear equations, *any* false statement such as $5 = 6$, $0 = 1$, or $-2 = 2$ informs us that the original equation has no solution. Also, *any* true statement such as $0 = 0$, $2 = 2$, or $-5 = -5$ informs us that the original equation is an identity.

STUDY SKILLS REMINDER

This is a special reminder that will be repeated and expanded throughout this text. It is very important for you to be able to recognize and solve different types of equations and inequalities. To help you do this, we will begin an outline below and continually expand this outline as different equations and inequalities are introduced. Although suggestions will be given, this outline should be in your own words and you should include at least "how to recognize" and "how to begin to solve" under each letter heading.

For example:

Solving Equations and Inequalities

I. Equations

    A. **Linear equations**—Recognize: *power on variable is 1 when there are no variables in denominator*—Solve: simplify (if fractions, multiply by LCD) and move variable terms to one side of the equation, constants to the other side.

II. Inequalities

See Appendix A for exercises.

MENTAL MATH

Simplify each expression by combining like terms.

1. $3x + 5x + 6 + 15$

2. $8y + 3y + 7 + 11$

3. $5n + n + 3 - 10$

4. $m + 2m + 4 - 8$

5. $8x - 12x + 5 - 6$

6. $4x - 10x + 13 - 16$

Identify each as an equation or an expression.

7. $\dfrac{1}{3}x - 5$

8. $2(x - 3) = 7$

9. $\dfrac{5}{9}x + \dfrac{1}{3} = \dfrac{2}{9} - x$

10. $\dfrac{5}{9}x + \dfrac{1}{3} - \dfrac{2}{9} - x$

Decide which equations have no solution and which equations have all real numbers as solutions.

11. $2x + 3 = 2x + 3$

12. $2x + 1 = 2x + 3$

13. $5x - 2 = 5x - 7$

14. $5x - 3 = 5x - 3$

EXERCISE SET 2.1

Solve for the variable. See Examples 1 and 2.

1. $-3x = 36$

2. $8x = -40$

3. $x + 2.8 = 1.9$

4. $y - 8.6 = -6.3$

5. $5x - 4 = 26$

6. $2y - 3 = 11$

7. $-4 = 3x + 11$

8. $-9 = 5x + 11$

9. $-4.1 - 7z = 3.6$

10. $10.3 - 6x = -2.3$

11. $5y + 12 = 2y - 3$

12. $4x + 14 = 6x + 8$

Solve for the variable. See Examples 3 and 4.

13. $8x - 5x + 3 = x - 7 + 10$

14. $6 + 3x + x = -x + 2 - 26$

15. $5x + 12 = 2(2x + 7)$

16. $2(x + 3) = x + 5$

17. $3(x - 6) = 5x$

18. $6x = 4(5 + x)$

19. $-2(5y - 1) - y = -4(y - 3)$

20. $-3(2w - 7) - 10 = 9 - 2(5w + 4)$

21. a. Simplify the expression $4(x + 1) + 1$.

   b. Solve the equation $4(x + 1) + 1 = -7$.

   c. Explain the difference between solving an equation for a variable and simplifying an expression.

22. Explain why the multiplication property of equality does not include multiplying both sides of an equation by 0. (*Hint:* Write down a false statement and then multiply both sides by 0. Is the result true or false? What does this mean?)

Solve for the variable. See Examples 5 through 7.

23. $\dfrac{x}{2} + \dfrac{2}{3} = \dfrac{3}{4}$

24. $\dfrac{x}{2} + \dfrac{x}{3} = \dfrac{5}{2}$

25. $\dfrac{3t}{4} - \dfrac{t}{2} = 1$

26. $\dfrac{4r}{5} - 7 = \dfrac{r}{10}$

27. $\dfrac{n - 3}{4} + \dfrac{n + 5}{7} = \dfrac{5}{14}$

28. $\dfrac{2 + h}{9} + \dfrac{h - 1}{3} = \dfrac{1}{3}$

29. $0.6x - 10 = 1.4x - 14$

30. $0.3x + 2.4 = 0.1x + 4$

Solve the following. See Examples 8 and 9.

31. $4(n + 3) = 2(6 + 2n)$

32. $6(4n + 4) = 8(3 + 3n)$

33. $3(x - 1) + 5 = 3x + 7$

34. $5x - (x + 4) = 5 + 4(x - 2)$

35. In your own words, explain why the equation $x + 7 = x + 6$ has no solution while the solution set of the equation $x + 7 = x + 7$ contains all real numbers.

36. In your own words, explain why the equation $x = -x$ has one solution, namely 0, while the solution set of the equation $x = x$ is all real numbers.

MIXED PRACTICE

Solve the following.

37. $-9x = -72$

38. $-7x = 56$

39. $x - 1.7 = -7.6$

40. $y - 9.3 = -12.6$

41. $6x + 9 = 51$

42. $4x + 11 = 47$

43. $-5x + 1.5 = -19.5$

44. $-3x - 4.7 = 11.8$

45. $x - 10 = -6x + 4$

46. $4x - 7 = 2x - 7$

47. $3x - 4 - 5x = x + 4 + x$

48. $13x - 15x + 8 = 4x + 2 - 24$

49. $5(y + 4) = 4(y + 5)$

50. $6(y - 4) = 3(y - 8)$

51. $-1.2x + 20 = -2.8x + 28$

52. $-0.9x - 7.2 = -0.3x - 12$

53. $6x - 2(x - 3) = 4(x + 1) + 4$

54. $10x - 2(x + 4) = 8(x - 2) + 6$

55. $\dfrac{3}{8} + \dfrac{b}{3} = \dfrac{5}{12}$

56. $\dfrac{a}{2} + \dfrac{7}{4} = 5$

57. $z + 3(2 + 4z) = 6(z + 1) + 5z$

58. $4(m - 6) - m = 8(m - 3) - 5m$

59. $\dfrac{3t + 1}{8} = \dfrac{5 + 2t}{7} + 2$

60. $4 - \dfrac{2z + 7}{9} = \dfrac{7 - z}{12}$

61. $\dfrac{m - 4}{3} - \dfrac{3m - 1}{5} = 1$

62. $\dfrac{n + 1}{8} - \dfrac{2 - n}{3} = \dfrac{5}{6}$

63. $5(x - 2) + 2x = 7(x + 4) - 38$

64. $3x + 2(x + 4) = 5(x + 1) + 3$

65. $y + 0.2 = 0.6(y + 3)$

66. $-(w + 0.2) = 0.3(4 - w)$

67. $-(3x - 5) - (2x - 6) + 1 = -5(x - 1) - (3x + 2) + 3$

68. $-4(2x - 3) - (10x + 7) - 2 = -(12x - 5) - (4x + 9) - 1$

69. $2(x - 8) + x = 3(x - 6) + 2$

70. $4(x + 5) = 3(x - 4) + x$

71. $\dfrac{3x - 1}{9} + x = \dfrac{3x + 1}{3} + 4$

72. $\dfrac{2z + 7}{8} - 2 = z + \dfrac{z - 1}{2}$

2.4 LINEAR INEQUALITIES AND PROBLEM SOLVING

Objectives

1   Use interval notation.

2   Solve linear inequalities using the addition property of inequality.

3   Solve linear inequalities using the multiplication property of inequality.

4   Solve problems that can be modeled by linear inequalities.

1   Relationships among measureable quantities are not always described by equations. For example, suppose that a salesperson earns a base of $600 per month plus a commission of 20% of sales. Find the minimum amount of sales needed to receive a total income of *at least* $1500 per month. Here, the phrase "at least" implies that an income of $1500 *or more* is acceptable. In symbols, we can write

$$\text{income} \geq 1500$$

This is an example of an inequality, and we will solve this problem in Example 8.

A **linear inequality** is similar to a linear equation except that the equality symbol is replaced with an inequality symbol, such as $<$, $>$, $\leq$, or $\geq$.

Linear Inequalities in One Variable

$3x + 5 \geq 4$	$2y < 0$	$3(x - 4) > 5x$	$\dfrac{x}{3} \leq 5$
↑	↑	↑	↑
is greater than or equal to	is less than	is greater than	is less than or equal to

---

Linear Inequality in One Variable

A linear inequality in one variable is an inequality that can be written in the form

$$ax + b < c$$

where $a, b,$ and c are real numbers and $a \neq 0$.

In this section, when we make definitions, state properties, or list steps about an inequality containing the symbol $<$, we mean that the definition, property, or steps apply to inequalities containing the symbols $>$, $\leq$ and $\geq$ also.

A **solution** of an inequality is a value of the variable that makes the inequality a true statement. The **solution set** of an inequality is the set of all solutions. Notice that the solution set of the inequality $x > 2$, for example, contains all numbers greater than 2. Its graph is an interval on the number line since an infinite number of values satisfy the variable. If we use open/closed-circle notation, the graph of $\{x \mid x > 2\}$ looks like the following.

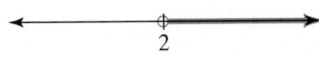

In this text **interval notation** will be used to write solution sets of inequalities. To help us understand this notation, a different graphing notation will be used. Instead of an open circle, we use a parenthesis. With this new notation, the graph of $\{x|x > 2\}$ now looks like

and can be represented in interval notation as $(2, \infty)$. The symbol ∞ is read "infinity" and indicates that the interval includes *all* numbers greater than 2. The left parenthesis indicates that 2 *is not* included in the interval.

In the case 2 *is* included in the interval, we use a bracket. The graph of $\{x|x \geq 2\}$ is below

and can be represented as $[2, \infty)$. The following table shows three equivalent ways to describe an interval: in set notation, as a graph, and in interval notation.

Set Notation	*Graph*	*Interval Notation*
$\{x|x < a\}$		$(-\infty, a)$
$\{x|x > a\}$		(a, ∞)
$\{x|x \leq a\}$		$(-\infty, a]$
$\{x|x \geq a\}$		$[a, \infty)$
$\{x|a < x < b\}$		(a, b)
$\{x|a \leq x \leq b\}$		$[a, b]$
$\{x|a < x \leq b\}$		$(a, b]$
$\{x|a \leq x < b\}$		$[a, b)$

> **Helpful Hint**
> Notice that a parenthesis is always used to enclose ∞ and $-\infty$.

 CONCEPT CHECK

Explain what is wrong with writing the interval $(5, \infty]$.

MIXED PRACTICE

Solve. Write the solution set using interval notation.

57. $-5x + 4 \leq -4(x - 1)$

58. $-6x + 2 < -3(x + 4)$

59. $\frac{1}{4}(x - 7) \geq x + 2$

60. $\frac{3}{5}(x + 1) \leq x + 1$

61. $\frac{2}{3}(x + 2) < \frac{1}{5}(2x + 7)$

62. $\frac{1}{6}(3x + 10) > \frac{5}{12}(x - 1)$

63. $4(x - 6) + 2x - 4 \geq 3(x - 7) + 10x$

64. $7(2x + 3) + 4x \leq 7 + 5(3x - 4)$

65. $\frac{5x + 1}{7} - \frac{2x - 6}{4} \geq -4$

66. $\frac{1 - 2x}{3} + \frac{3x + 7}{7} > 1$

67. $\frac{-x + 2}{2} - \frac{1 - 5x}{8} < -1$

68. $\frac{3 - 4x}{6} - \frac{1 - 2x}{12} \leq -2$

69. $0.8x + 0.6x \geq 4.2$

70. $0.7x - x > 0.45$

71. $\frac{x + 5}{5} - \frac{3 + x}{8} \geq -\frac{3}{10}$

72. $\frac{x - 4}{2} - \frac{x - 2}{3} > \frac{5}{6}$

73. $\frac{x + 3}{12} + \frac{x - 5}{15} < \frac{2}{3}$

74. $\frac{3x + 2}{18} - \frac{1 + 2x}{6} \leq -\frac{1}{2}$

Solve. See Examples 8 and 9.

75. Shureka has scores of 72, 67, 82, and 79 on her algebra tests. Use an inequality to find the minimum score she can make on the final exam to pass the course with an average of 60 or higher, given that the final exam counts as two tests.

76. In a Winter Olympics speed-skating event, Hans scored times of 3.52, 4.04, and 3.87 minutes on his first three trials. Use an inequality to find the maximum time he can score on his last trial so that his average time is under 4.0 minutes.

77. A small plane's maximum takeoff weight for passengers, luggage, and cargo is 2000 pounds. Six passengers weigh an average of 160 pounds each. Use an inequality to find the maximum weight of luggage and cargo the plane can carry.

78. A clerk must use the elevator to move boxes of paper. The elevator's weight limit is 1500 pounds. If each box of paper weighs 66 pounds and the clerk weighs 147 pounds, use an inequality to find the maximum number of boxes she can move on the elevator at one time.

79. To mail an envelope first class, the U.S. Post Office charges 37 cents for the first ounce and 23 cents per ounce for each additional ounce. Use an inequality to find the maximum number of whole ounces that can be mailed for $4.00

80. A shopping mall parking garage charges $2 for the first half hour and $1.20 for each additional half hour or a portion of a half hour. Use an inequality to find how long you can park if you have $8.00 in cash.

81. Northeast Telephone Company offers two billing plans for local calls. Plan 1 charges $25 per month for unlimited calls, and plan 2 charges $13 per month plus 6 cents per call. Use an inequality to find the number of monthly calls for which plan 1 is more economical than plan 2.

82. A car rental company offers two subcompact rental plans. Plan A charges $32 per day for unlimited mileage, and plan B charges $24 per day plus 15 cents per mile. Use an inequality to find the number of daily miles for which plan A is more economical than plan B.

83. At room temperature, glass used in windows actually has some properties of a liquid. It has a very slow, viscous flow. (Viscosity is the property of a fluid that resists internal flow. For example, lemonade flows more easily than fudge syrup. Fudge syrup has a higher viscosity than lemonade.) Glass does not become a true liquid until temperatures are greater than or equal to 500°C. Find the Fahrenheit temperatures for which glass is a liquid. (Use the formula $F = \frac{9}{5}C + 32$.)

84. Stibnite is a silvery white mineral with a metallic luster. It is one of the few minerals that melts easily in match flame or at temperatures of approximately 977°F or greater. Find the Celsius temperatures for which stibnite melts. (Use the formula $C = \frac{5}{9}[F - 32]$.)

85. Although beginning salaries vary greatly according to your field of study, the equation $s = 2806.6t + 32,558$ can be used to approximate and to predict average beginning salaries for candidates with bachelor's degrees. The variable s is the starting salary and t is the number of years after 1995.

  a. Approximate when beginning salaries for candidates will be greater than $60,000.

  b. Determine the year you plan to graduate from college. Use this year to find the corresponding value of t and approximate your beginning salary.

86. Use the formula in Example 9 to estimate the years that the consumption of cigarettes will be less than 50 billion per year.

The average consumption per person per year of whole milk w in gallons can be approximated by the equation

$$w = -0.13t + 8$$

where t is the number of years after 1997. The average consumption of skim milk s per person per year can be approximated by the equation

$$s = -0.16t + 4$$

where t is the number of years after 1997. The consumption of whole milk is shown on the graph in blue and the consumption of skim milk is shown on the graph in red. Use this information to answer Exercises 87–94.

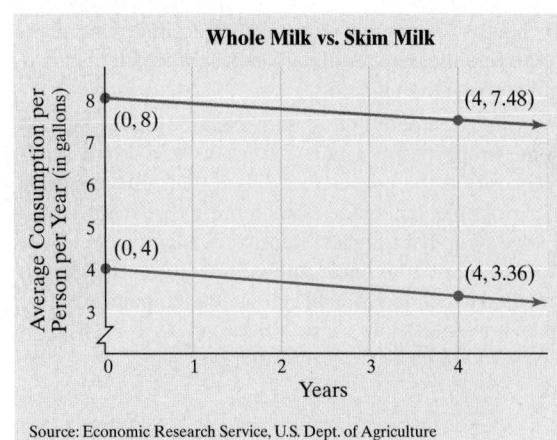

Whole Milk vs. Skim Milk

Source: Economic Research Service, U.S. Dept. of Agriculture

87. Is the consumption of whole milk increasing or decreasing over time? Explain how you arrived at your answer.

88. Is the consumption of skim milk increasing or decreasing over time? Explain how you arrived at your answer.

89. Predict the consumption of whole milk in the year 2008. (*Hint:* Find the value of t that corresponds to the year 2008.)

90. Predict the consumption of skim milk in the year 2008. (*Hint:* Find the value of t that corresponds to the year 2008.)

91. Determine when the consumption of whole milk will be less than 7 gallons per person per year.

92. Determine when the consumption of skim milk will be less than 2 gallons per person per year.

93. For 1997 through 2001 the consumption of whole milk was greater than the consumption of skim milk. Explain how this can be determined from the graph.

94. How will the two lines in the graph appear if the consumption of whole milk is the same as the consumption of skim milk?

REVIEW AND PREVIEW

List or describe the integers that make both inequalities true.

95. $x < 5$ and $x > 1$

96. $x \geq 0$ and $x \leq 7$

97. $x \geq -2$ and $x \geq 2$

98. $x < 6$ and $x < -5$

Graph each set on a number line and write it in interval notation. See Section 2.4.

99. $\{x \mid 0 \leq x \leq 5\}$

100. $\{x \mid -7 < x \leq 1\}$

101. $\left\{x \mid -\frac{1}{2} < x < \frac{3}{2}\right\}$

102. $\{x \mid -2.5 \leq x < 5.3\}$

Concept Extensions

Solve each inequality.

103. $4(x - 1) \geq 4x - 8$

104. $3x + 1 < 3(x - 2)$

105. $7x < 7(x - 2)$

106. $8(x + 3) \leq 7(x + 5) + x$

INTEGRATED REVIEW

Solve each equation or inequality. For inequalities, write the solution set in interval notation.

1. $-4x = 20$

2. $-4x < 20$

3. $\dfrac{3x}{4} \geq 2$

4. $5x + 3 \geq 2 + 4x$

5. $6(y - 4) = 3(y - 8)$

6. $-4x \leq \dfrac{2}{5}$

7. $-3x \geq \dfrac{1}{2}$

8. $5(y + 4) = 4(y + 5)$

9. $7x < 7(x - 2)$

10. $\dfrac{-5x + 11}{2} \leq 7$

11. $-5x + 1.5 = -19.5$

12. $-5x + 4 = -26$

13. $5 + 2x - x = -x + 3 - 14$

14. $12x + 14 < 11x - 2$

15. $\dfrac{x}{5} - \dfrac{x}{4} = \dfrac{x - 2}{2}$

16. $12x - 12 = 8(x - 1)$

17. $2(x - 3) > 70$

18. $-3x - 4.7 = 11.8$

19. $-2(b - 4) - (3b - 1) = 5b + 3$

20. $8(x + 3) < 7(x + 5) + x$

21. $\dfrac{3t + 1}{8} = \dfrac{5 + 2t}{7} + 2$

22. $4(x - 6) - x = 8(x - 3) - 5x$

23. $\dfrac{x + 3}{12} + \dfrac{x - 5}{15} < \dfrac{2}{3}$

24. $\dfrac{y}{3} + \dfrac{y}{5} = \dfrac{y + 3}{10}$

25. $5(x - 6) + 2x > 3(2x - 1) - 4$

26. $14(x - 1) - 7x \leq 2(3x - 6) + 4$

27. $\dfrac{1}{4}(3x + 2) - x \geq \dfrac{3}{8}(x - 5) + 2$

28. $\dfrac{1}{3}(x - 10) - 4x > \dfrac{5}{6}(2x + 1) - 1$

STUDY SKILLS REMINDER

Have You Decided to Successfully Complete This Course?

Ask yourself if one of your current goals is to successfully complete this course.

If it is not a goal of yours, ask yourself why? One common reason is fear of failure. Amazingly enough, fear of failure alone can be strong enough to keep many of us from doing our best in any endeavor. Another common reason is that you simply haven't taken the time to make successfully completing this course one of your goals.

If you are taking this mathematics course, then successfully completing this course probably should be one of your goals. To make it a goal, start by writing this goal in your mathematics notebook. Then read or reread Section 1.1 and make a commitment to try the suggestions in this section.

If successfully completing this course is already a goal of yours, also read or reread Section 1.1 and try some suggestions in this section so that you are actively working toward your goal.

Good luck and don't forget that a positive attitude will make a big difference!

2.5 COMPOUND INEQUALITIES

Objectives

1. Find the intersection of two sets.
2. Solve compound inequalities containing **and**.
3. Find the union of two sets.
4. Solve compound inequalities containing **or**.

Two inequalities joined by the words **and** or **or** are called **compound inequalities.**

Compound Inequalities

$$x + 3 < 8 \text{ and } x > 2$$

$$\frac{2x}{3} \geq 5 \text{ or } -x + 10 < 7$$

1 The solution set of a compound inequality formed by the word **and** is the **intersection** of the solution sets of the two inequalities. We use the symbol $\cap$ to represent "intersection."

Now we can graph each interval and find their union.

$\{x | x > -1\}$ 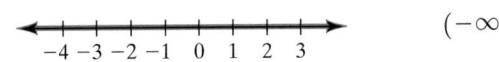 $(-1, \infty)$

$\{x | x < 0\}$ 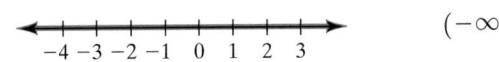 $(-\infty, 0)$

$\{x | x > -1 \text{ or } x < 0\}$ 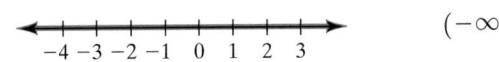 $(-\infty, \infty)$
= all real numbers

The solution set is $(-\infty, \infty)$.

STUDY SKILLS REMINDER

Continue your outline started in Section 2.1. Write how to recognize and how to solve compound inequalities in your own words. For example:

Solving Equations and Inequalities

I. Equations
   A. Linear equations—(Section 2.1)

II. Inequalities
   A. Linear inequalities—(Section 2.4)
   B. **Compound inequalities**—Recognize: *2 inequality signs or 2 inequalities separated by "and" or "or"*—Solve: if 2 inequality signs, then solve for *x* in the middle, remember that "and" means intersection and "or" means union.

See Appendix A for summary exercises.

EXERCISE SET 2.5

STUDY   CD/   PH MATH   MathXL®Tutorials   MathXL®   MyMathLab®
GUIDE/SSM   VIDEO   TUTOR CENTER   ON CD

If $A = \{x | x \text{ is an even integer}\}$, $B = \{x | x \text{ is an odd integer}\}$, $C = \{2, 3, 4, 5\}$, and $D = \{4, 5, 6, 7\}$, list the elements of each set. See Examples 1 and 6.

1. $C \cup D$

2. $C \cap D$

3. $A \cap D$

4. $A \cup D$

5. $A \cup B$

6. $A \cap B$

7. $B \cap D$

8. $B \cup D$

9. $B \cup C$

10. $B \cap C$

11. $A \cap C$

12. $A \cup C$

Solve each compound inequality. Graph the solution set and write it in interval notation. See Examples 2 and 3.

13. $x < 5$ and $x > -2$

14. $x \leq 7$ and $x \leq 1$

15. $x + 1 \geq 7$ and $3x - 1 \geq 5$

16. $-2x < -8$ and $x - 5 < 5$

17. $4x + 2 \leq -10$ and $2x \leq 0$

18. $x + 4 > 0$ and $4x > 0$

Solve each compound inequality. Graph the solution set and write it in interval notation. See Examples 4 and 5.

19. $5 < x - 6 < 11$

20. $-2 \le x + 3 \le 0$

21. $-2 \le 3x - 5 \le 7$

22. $1 < 4 + 2x < 7$

23. $1 \le \dfrac{2}{3}x + 3 \le 4$

24. $-2 < \dfrac{1}{2}x - 5 < 1$

25. $-5 \le \dfrac{x + 1}{4} \le -2$

26. $-4 \le \dfrac{2x + 5}{3} \le 1$

Solve each compound inequality. Graph the solution set and write it in interval notation. See Examples 7 and 8.

27. $x < -1$ or $x > 0$

28. $x \le 1$ or $x \le -3$

29. $-2x \le -4$ or $5x - 20 \ge 5$

30. $x + 4 < 0$ or $6x > -12$

31. $3(x - 1) < 12$ or $x + 7 > 10$

32. $5(x - 1) \ge -5$ or $5 - x \le 11$

33. Explain how solving an and–compound inequality is similar to finding the intersection of two sets.

34. Explain how solving an or–compound inequality is similar to finding the union of two sets.

MIXED PRACTICE

Solve each compound inequality. Graph the solution set and write it in interval notation.

35. $x < 2$ and $x > -1$

36. $x < 5$ and $x < 1$

37. $x < 2$ or $x > -1$

38. $x < 5$ or $x < 1$

39. $x \ge -5$ and $x \ge -1$

40. $x \le 0$ or $x \ge -3$

41. $x \ge -5$ or $x \ge -1$

42. $x \le 0$ and $x \ge -3$

43. $0 \le 2x - 3 \le 9$

44. $3 < 5x + 1 < 11$

45. $\dfrac{1}{2} < x - \dfrac{3}{4} < 2$

46. $\dfrac{2}{3} < x + \dfrac{1}{2} < 4$

47. $x + 3 \ge 3$ and $x + 3 \le 2$

48. $2x - 1 \ge 3$ and $-x > 2$

49. $3x \ge 5$ or $-x - 6 < 1$

50. $\dfrac{3}{8}x + 1 \le 0$ or $-2x < -4$

51. $0 < \dfrac{5 - 2x}{3} < 5$

52. $-2 < \dfrac{-2x - 1}{3} < 2$

53. $-6 < 3(x - 2) \le 8$

54. $-5 < 2(x + 4) < 8$

55. $-x + 5 > 6$ and $1 + 2x \le -5$

56. $5x \le 0$ and $-x + 5 < 8$

57. $3x + 2 \le 5$ or $7x > 29$

58. $-x < 7$ or $3x + 1 < -20$

59. $5 - x > 7$ and $2x + 3 \ge 13$

60. $-2x < -6$ or $1 - x > -2$

61. $-\dfrac{1}{2} \le \dfrac{4x - 1}{6} < \dfrac{5}{6}$

62. $-\dfrac{1}{2} \le \dfrac{3x - 1}{10} < \dfrac{1}{2}$

63. $\dfrac{1}{15} < \dfrac{8 - 3x}{15} < \dfrac{4}{5}$

64. $-\dfrac{1}{4} < \dfrac{6 - x}{12} < -\dfrac{1}{6}$

65. $0.3 < 0.2x - 0.9 < 1.5$

66. $-0.7 \le 0.4x + 0.8 < 0.5$

REVIEW AND PREVIEW

Evaluate the following. See Sections 1.2 and 1.3.

67. $|-7| - |19|$

68. $|-7 - 19|$

69. $-(-6) - |-10|$

70. $|-4| - (-4) + |-20|$

Find by inspection all values for x that make each equation true.

71. $|x| = 7$

72. $|x| = 5$

73. $|x| = 0$

74. $|x| = -2$

Concept Extensions

The formula for converting Fahrenheit temperatures to Celsius temperatures is $C = \frac{5}{9}(F - 32)$. Use this formula for Exercises 75 and 76.

75. During a recent year, the temperatures in Chicago ranged from $-29°$ to $35°$C. Use a compound inequality to convert these temperatures to Fahrenheit temperatures.

76. In Oslo, the average temperature ranges from $-10°$ to $18°$ Celsius. Use a compound inequality to convert these temperatures to the Fahrenheit scale.

Solve.

77. Christian D'Angelo has scores of 68, 65, 75, and 78 on his algebra tests. Use a compound inequality to find the scores he can make on his final exam to receive a C in the course. The final exam counts as two tests, and a C is received if the final course average is from 70 to 79.

78. Wendy Wood has scores of 80, 90, 82, and 75 on her chemistry tests. Use a compound inequality to find the range of scores she can make on her final exam to receive a B in the course. The final exam counts as two tests, and a B is received if the final course average is from 80 to 89.

Use the graph to answer Exercises 79 and 80.

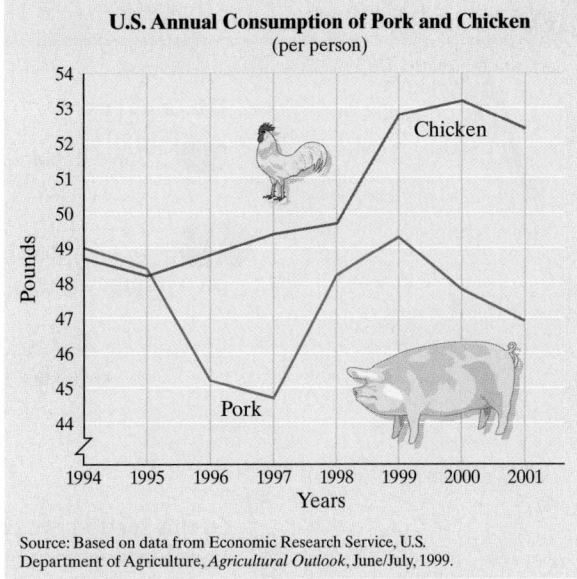

U.S. Annual Consumption of Pork and Chicken
(per person)

Source: Based on data from Economic Research Service, U.S. Department of Agriculture, *Agricultural Outlook*, June/July, 1999.

79. For what years was the consumption of pork greater than 48 pounds per person *and* the consumption of chicken greater than 48 pounds per person?

80. For what years was the consumption of pork less than 48 pounds per person *or* the consumption of chicken greater than 49 pounds per person?

Solve each compound inequality for x. See the example below.

*To solve $x - 6 < 3x < 2x + 5$, notice that this inequality contains a variable not only in the middle, but also on the left and the right. When this occurs, we solve by rewriting the inequality using the word **and**.*

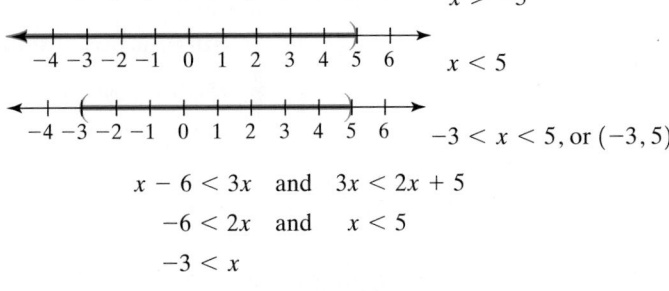

$x - 6 < 3x$ and $3x < 2x + 5$

$-6 < 2x$ and $x < 5$

$-3 < x$

$x > -3$ and $x < 5$

81. $2x - 3 < 3x + 1 < 4x - 5$

82. $x + 3 < 2x + 1 < 4x + 6$

83. $-3(x - 2) \le 3 - 2x \le 10 - 3x$

84. $7x - 1 \le 7 + 5x \le 3(1 + 2x)$

85. $5x - 8 < 2(2 + x) < -2(1 + 2x)$

86. $1 + 2x < 3(2 + x) < 1 + 4x$

2.6   ABSOLUTE VALUE EQUATIONS

Objective

1   Solve absolute value equations.

1   In Chapter 1, we defined the absolute value of a number as its distance from 0 on a number line.

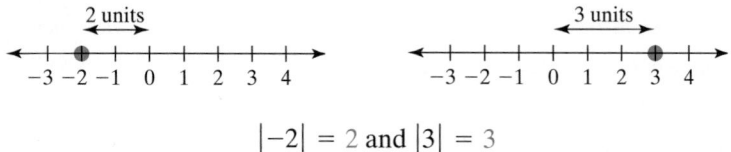

$$|-2| = 2 \text{ and } |3| = 3$$

In this section, we concentrate on solving equations containing the absolute value of a variable or a variable expression. Examples of absolute value equations are

$$|x| = 3 \qquad -5 = |2y + 7| \qquad |z - 6.7| = |3z + 1.2|$$

Since distance and absolute value are so closely related, absolute value equations and inequalities (see Section 2.7) are extremely useful in solving distance-type problems, such as calculating the possible error in a measurement. For the absolute value equation $|x| = 3$, its solution set will contain all numbers whose distance from 0 is 3 units. Two numbers are 3 units away from 0 on the number line: 3 and -3.

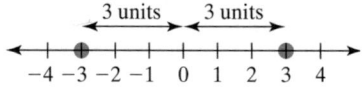

Thus, the solution set of the equation $|x| = 3$ is $\{3, -3\}$. This suggests the following:

Solving Equations of the Form $|X| = a$

If a is a positive number, then $|X| = a$ is equivalent to $X = a$ or $X = -a$.

EXAMPLE 1

Solve $|p| = 2$.

Solution   Since 2 is positive, $|p| = 2$ is equivalent to $p = 2$ or $p = -2$.

To check, let $p = 2$ and then $p = -2$ in the original equation.

$|p| = 2$ *Original equation.*	$|p| = 2$ *Original equation.*
$|2| = 2$ *Let $p = 2$.*	$|-2| = 2$ *Let $p = -2$.*
$2 = 2$ *True.*	$2 = 2$ *True.*

The solutions are 2 and -2 or the solution set is $\{2, -2\}$.

If the expression inside the absolute value bars is more complicated than a single variable x, we can still apply the absolute value property.

> ▶ **Helpful Hint**
> For the equation $|X| = a$ in the box on the previous page, X can be a single variable or a variable expression.

EXAMPLE 2

Solve $|5w + 3| = 7$.

Solution Here the expression inside the absolute value bars is $5w + 3$. If we think of the expression $5w + 3$ as x in the absolute value property, we see that $|x| = 7$ is equivalent to

$$x = 7 \quad \text{or} \quad x = -7$$

Then substitute $5w + 3$ for x, and we have

$$5w + 3 = 7 \quad \text{or} \quad 5w + 3 = -7$$

Solve these two equations for w.

$$
\begin{aligned}
5w + 3 &= 7 && \text{or} & 5w + 3 &= -7 \\
5w &= 4 && \text{or} & 5w &= -10 \\
w &= \frac{4}{5} && \text{or} & w &= -2
\end{aligned}
$$

Check To check, let $w = -2$ and then $w = \frac{4}{5}$ in the original equation.

Let $w = -2$	Let $w = \frac{4}{5}$
$|5(-2) + 3| = 7$	$\left|5\left(\frac{4}{5}\right) + 3\right| = 7$
$|-10 + 3| = 7$	$|4 + 3| = 7$
$|-7| = 7$	$|7| = 7$
$7 = 7$ True.	$7 = 7$ True.

Both solutions check, and the solutions are -2 and $\frac{4}{5}$ or the solution set is $\left\{-2, \frac{4}{5}\right\}$.

EXAMPLE 3

Solve $\left|\dfrac{x}{2} - 1\right| = 11$.

Solution $\left|\dfrac{x}{2} - 1\right| = 11$ is equivalent to

$$
\begin{aligned}
\frac{x}{2} - 1 &= 11 && \text{or} & \frac{x}{2} - 1 &= -11 \\
2\left(\frac{x}{2} - 1\right) &= 2(11) && \text{or} & 2\left(\frac{x}{2} - 1\right) &= 2(-11) && \text{Clear fractions.} \\
x - 2 &= 22 && \text{or} & x - 2 &= -22 && \text{Apply the distributive property.} \\
x &= 24 && \text{or} & x &= -20
\end{aligned}
$$

The solutions are 24 and -20.

To apply the absolute value rule, first make sure that the absolute value expression is isolated.

> ### Helpful Hint
> If the equation has a single absolute value expression containing variables, isolate the absolute value expression first.

EXAMPLE 4

Solve $|2x| + 5 = 7$.

Solution We want the absolute value expression alone on one side of the equation, so begin by subtracting 5 from both sides. Then apply the absolute value property.

$$|2x| + 5 = 7$$
$$|2x| = 2 \qquad \text{Subtract 5 from both sides.}$$
$$2x = 2 \quad \text{or} \quad 2x = -2$$
$$x = 1 \quad \text{or} \quad x = -1$$

The solutions are -1 and 1.

EXAMPLE 5

Solve $|y| = 0$.

Solution We are looking for all numbers whose distance from 0 is zero units. The only number is 0. The solution is 0.

The next two examples illustrate a special case for absolute value equations. This special case occurs when an isolated absolute value is equal to a negative number.

EXAMPLE 6

Solve $2|x| + 25 = 23$.

Solution First, isolate the absolute value.

$$2|x| + 25 = 23$$
$$2|x| = -2 \qquad \text{Subtract 25 from both sides.}$$
$$|x| = -1 \qquad \text{Divide both sides by 2.}$$

The absolute value of a number is never negative, so this equation has no solution. The solution set is $\{\ \}$ or $\emptyset$.

EXAMPLE 7

Solve $\left|\dfrac{3x + 1}{2}\right| = -2$.

Solution Again, the absolute value of any expression is never negative, so no solution exists. The solution set is $\{\ \}$ or $\emptyset$.

Given two absolute value expressions, we might ask, when are the absolute values of two expressions equal? To see the answer, notice that

$$|2| = |2|, \quad |-2| = |-2|, \quad |-2| = |2|, \quad \text{and} \quad |2| = |-2|$$

same   same   opposites   opposites

Two absolute value expressions are equal when the expressions inside the absolute value bars are equal to or are opposites of each other.

EXAMPLE 8

Solve $|3x + 2| = |5x - 8|$.

Solution This equation is true if the expressions inside the absolute value bars are equal to or are opposites of each other.

$$3x + 2 = 5x - 8 \quad \text{or} \quad 3x + 2 = -(5x - 8)$$

Next, solve each equation.

$$3x + 2 = 5x - 8 \quad \text{or} \quad 3x + 2 = -5x + 8$$
$$-2x + 2 = -8 \quad \text{or} \quad 8x + 2 = 8$$
$$-2x = -10 \quad \text{or} \quad 8x = 6$$
$$x = 5 \quad \text{or} \quad x = \frac{3}{4}$$

The solutions are $\frac{3}{4}$ and 5.

EXAMPLE 9

Solve $|x - 3| = |5 - x|$.

Solution
$$x - 3 = 5 - x \quad \text{or} \quad x - 3 = -(5 - x)$$
$$2x - 3 = 5 \quad \text{or} \quad x - 3 = -5 + x$$
$$2x = 8 \quad \text{or} \quad x - 3 - x = -5 + x - x$$
$$x = 4 \quad \text{or} \quad -3 = -5 \qquad \text{False.}$$

Recall from Section 2.1 that when an equation simplifies to a false statement, the equation has no solution. Thus, the only solution for the original absolute value equation is 4.

✔ **CONCEPT CHECK**

True or false? Absolute value equations always have two solutions. Explain your answer.

The following box summarizes the methods shown for solving absolute value equations.

Absolute Value Equations

$|X| = a$ { If a is positive, then solve $X = a$ or $X = -a$.
           If a is 0, solve $X = 0$.
           If a is negative, the equation $|X| = a$ has no solution.

$|X| = |Y|$ Solve $X = Y$ or $X = -Y$.

Concept Check Answer:
false; answers may vary

STUDY SKILLS REMINDER

Continue your outline started in Section 2.1. Write how to recognize and how to solve absolute value equations in your own words. For example:

Solving Equations and Inequalities

I. Equations
    A. Linear equations—(Section 2.1)
    B. **Absolute value equations**—Recognize: *linear equation with absolute value bars*—Solve: if possible, first isolate absolute value: if $|x| = a$ (positive), then solve $x = a$ or $x = -a$, if $|x| = 0$, then solve $x = 0$, if $|x| = -a$, then there is no solution, if $|x| = |y|$, then solve $x = y$ or $x = -y$.

II. Inequalities
    A. Linear inequalities—(Section 2.4)
    B. Compound inequalities—(Section 2.5)

See Appendix A for summary exercises.

MENTAL MATH

Simplify each expression.

1. $|-7|$

2. $|-8|$

3. $-|5|$

4. $-|10|$

5. $-|-6|$

6. $-|-3|$

7. $|-3| + |-2| + |-7|$

8. $|-1| + |-6| + |-8|$

EXERCISE SET 2.6

STUDY GUIDE/SSM   CD/VIDEO   PH MATH TUTOR CENTER   MathXL®Tutorials ON CD   MathXL®   MyMathLab®

Solve each absolute value equation. See Examples 1 through 7.

 1. $|x| = 7$

2. $|y| = 15$

3. $|3x| = 12.6$

4. $|6n| = 12.6$

5. $|2x - 5| = 9$

6. $|6 + 2n| = 4$

7. $\left|\dfrac{x}{2} - 3\right| = 1$

8. $\left|\dfrac{n}{3} + 2\right| = 4$

9. $|z| + 4 = 9$

10. $|x| + 1 = 3$

11. $|3x| + 5 = 14$

12. $|2x| - 6 = 4$

13. $|2x| = 0$

14. $|7z| = 0$

15. $|4n + 1| + 10 = 4$

16. $|3z - 2| + 8 = 1$

17. $|5x - 1| = 0$

18. $|3y + 2| = 0$

19. Write an absolute value equation representing all numbers x whose distance from 0 is 5 units.

20. Write an absolute value equation representing all numbers x whose distance from 0 is 2 units.

Solve. See Examples 8 and 9.

21. $|5x - 7| = |3x + 11|$

22. $|9y + 1| = |6y + 4|$

23. $|z + 8| = |z - 3|$

24. $|2x - 5| = |2x + 5|$

25. Describe how solving an absolute value equation such as $|2x - 1| = 3$ is similar to solving an absolute value equation such as $|2x - 1| = |x - 5|$.

26. Describe how solving an absolute value equation such as $|2x - 1| = 3$ is different from solving an absolute value equation such as $|2x - 1| = |x - 5|$.

73. Explain why some absolute value equations have two solutions.

74. Explain why some absolute value equations have one solution.

MIXED PRACTICE

Solve each absolute value equation.

27. $|x| = 4$

28. $|x| = 1$

29. $|y| = 0$

30. $|y| = 8$

31. $|z| = -2$

32. $|y| = -9$

33. $|7 - 3x| = 7$

34. $|4m + 5| = 5$

35. $|6x| - 1 = 11$

36. $|7z| + 1 = 22$

37. $|4p| = -8$

38. $|5m| = -10$

39. $|x - 3| + 3 = 7$

40. $|x + 4| - 4 = 1$

41. $\left|\dfrac{z}{4} + 5\right| = -7$

42. $\left|\dfrac{c}{5} - 1\right| = -2$

43. $|9v - 3| = -8$

44. $|1 - 3b| = -7$

45. $|8n + 1| = 0$

46. $|5x - 2| = 0$

47. $|1 + 6c| - 7 = -3$

48. $|2 + 3m| - 9 = -7$

49. $|5x + 1| = 11$

50. $|8 - 6c| = 1$

51. $|4x - 2| = |-10|$

52. $|3x + 5| = |-4|$

53. $|5x + 1| = |4x - 7|$

54. $|3 + 6n| = |4n + 11|$

55. $|6 + 2x| = -|-7|$

56. $|4 - 5y| = -|-3|$

57. $|2x - 6| = |10 - 2x|$

58. $|4n + 5| = |4n + 3|$

59. $\left|\dfrac{2x - 5}{3}\right| = 7$

60. $\left|\dfrac{1 + 3n}{4}\right| = 4$

61. $2 + |5n| = 17$

62. $8 + |4m| = 24$

63. $\left|\dfrac{2x - 1}{3}\right| = |-5|$

64. $\left|\dfrac{5x + 2}{2}\right| = |-6|$

65. $|2y - 3| = |9 - 4y|$

66. $|5z - 1| = |7 - z|$

67. $\left|\dfrac{3n + 2}{8}\right| = |-1|$

68. $\left|\dfrac{2r - 6}{5}\right| = |-2|$

69. $|x + 4| = |7 - x|$

70. $|8 - y| = |y + 2|$

71. $\left|\dfrac{8c - 7}{3}\right| = -|-5|$

72. $\left|\dfrac{5d + 1}{6}\right| = -|-9|$

REVIEW AND PREVIEW

The circle graph shows the U.S. Cheese consumption for 2001. Use this graph to answer Exercises 75–77. See Section 2.2.

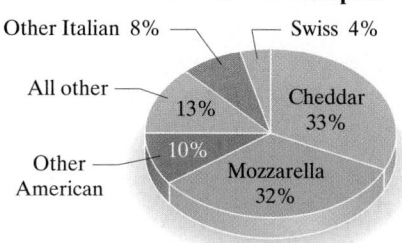

U.S. Cheese Consumption

Other Italian 8% — Swiss 4%
All other — 13% — Cheddar 33%
Other American — 10% — Mozzarella 32%

75. What percent of cheese consumption came from chedder cheese?

76. A circle contains 360°. Find the number of degrees in the 4% sector for swiss cheese.

77. If a family consumed 120 pounds of cheese in 2001, find the amount of mozzarella we might expect they consumed.

List five integer solutions of each inequality.

78. $|x| \leq 3$

79. $|x| \geq -2$

80. $|y| > -10$

81. $|y| < 0$

Concept Extensions

82. Write an absolute value equation representing all numbers x whose distance from 0 is 5 units.

83. Write an absolute value equation representing all numbers x whose distance from 0 is 2 units.

Write each as an equivalent absolute value.

84. $x = 6$ or $x = -6$

85. $2x - 1 = 4$ or $2x - 1 = -4$

86. $x - 2 = 3x - 4$ or $x - 2 = -(3x - 4)$

For what value(s) of c will an absolute value equation of the form $|ax + b| = c$ *have*

   a. one solution?

   b. no solution?

   c. two solutions?

2.7   *ABSOLUTE VALUE INEQUALITIES*

Objectives

1   Solve absolute value inequalities of the form $|x| < a$.

2   Solve absolute value inequalities of the form $|x| > a$.

1   The solution set of an absolute value inequality such as $|x| < 2$ contains all numbers whose distance from 0 is less than 2 units, as shown below.

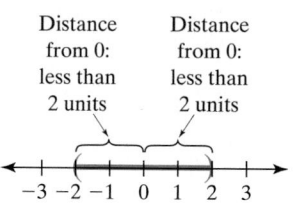

The solution set is $\{x | -2 < x < 2\}$, or $(-2, 2)$ in interval notation.

EXAMPLE 1

Solve $|x| \leq 3$.

Solution   The solution set of this inequality contains all numbers whose distance from 0 is less than or equal to 3. Thus 3, -3, and all numbers between 3 and -3 are in the solution set.

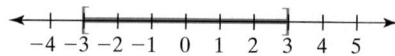

The solution set is $[-3, 3]$.

In general, we have the following.

Solving Absolute Value Inequalities of the Form $|X| < a$

If a is a positive number, then $|X| < a$ is equivalent to $-a < X < a$.

This property also holds true for the inequality symbol $\leq$.

EXAMPLE 2

Solve for m: $|m - 6| < 2$.

Solution   Replace X with $m - 6$ and a with 2 in the preceding property, and we see that

$$|m - 6| < 2 \quad \text{is equivalent to} \quad -2 < m - 6 < 2$$

Solve this compound inequality for m by adding 6 to all three parts.

$$-2 < m - 6 < 2$$
$$-2 + 6 < m - 6 + 6 < 2 + 6 \qquad \text{Add 6 to all three parts.}$$
$$4 < m < 8 \qquad \text{Simplify.}$$

The solution set is $(4, 8)$, and its graph is shown.

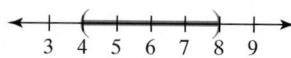

> **Helpful Hint**
>
> Before using an absolute value inequality property, isolate the absolute value expression on one side of the inequality.

EXAMPLE 3

Solve for x: $|5x + 1| + 1 \le 10$.

Solution First, isolate the absolute value expression by subtracting 1 from both sides.

$$|5x + 1| + 1 \le 10$$

$$|5x + 1| \le 10 - 1 \qquad \text{Subtract 1 from both sides.}$$

$$|5x + 1| \le 9 \qquad \text{Simplify.}$$

Since 9 is positive, we apply the absolute value property for $|X| \le a$.

$$-9 \le 5x + 1 \le 9$$

$$-9 - 1 \le 5x + 1 - 1 \le 9 - 1 \qquad \text{Subtract 1 from all three parts.}$$

$$-10 \le 5x \le 8 \qquad \text{Simplify.}$$

$$-2 \le x \le \frac{8}{5} \qquad \text{Divide all three parts by } 5.$$

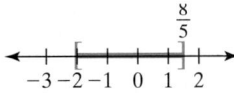

The solution set is $\left[-2, \dfrac{8}{5} \right]$, and the graph is shown above.

EXAMPLE 4

Solve for x: $\left| 2x - \dfrac{1}{10} \right| < -13$.

Solution The absolute value of a number is always nonnegative and can never be less than -13. Thus this absolute value inequality has no solution. The solution set is $\{ \ \}$ or $\varnothing$.

2 Let us now solve an absolute value inequality of the form $|X| > a$, such as $|x| \ge 3$. The solution set contains all numbers whose distance from 0 is 3 or more units. Thus the graph of the solution set contains 3 and all points to the right of 3 on the number line or -3 and all points to the left of -3 on the number line.

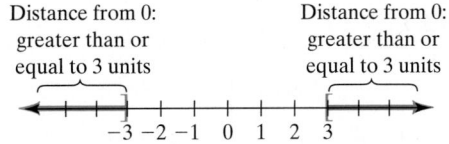

This solution set is written as $\{ x | x \le -3 \text{ or } x \ge 3 \}$. In interval notation, the solution is $(-\infty, -3] \cup [3, \infty)$, since "or" means "union." In general, we have the following.

Solving Absolute Value Inequalities of the Form $|X| > a$

If a is a positive number, then $|X| > a$ is equivalent to $X < -a$ or $X > a$.

This property also holds true for the inequality symbol $\ge$.

EXAMPLE 5

Solve for y: $|y - 3| > 7$.

Solution   Since 7 is positive, we apply the property for $|X| > a$.

$$|y - 3| > 7 \text{ is equivalent to } y - 3 < -7 \text{ or } y - 3 > 7$$

Next, solve the compound inequality.

$$
\begin{array}{ccc}
y - 3 < -7 & \text{or} & y - 3 > 7 \\
y - 3 + 3 < -7 + 3 & \text{or} & y - 3 + 3 > 7 + 3 \quad \text{Add 3 to both sides.}\\
y < -4 & \text{or} & y > 10 \quad\quad\quad \text{Simplify.}
\end{array}
$$

The solution set is $(-\infty, -4) \cup (10, \infty)$, and its graph is shown.

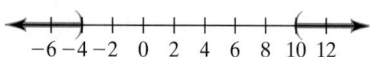

Examples 6 and 8 illustrate special cases of absolute value inequalities. These special cases occur when an isolated absolute value expression is less than, less than or equal to, greater than, or greater than or equal to a negative number or 0.

EXAMPLE 6

Solve $|2x + 9| + 5 > 3$.

Solution   First isolate the absolute value expression by subtracting 5 from both sides.

$$
\begin{array}{ll}
|2x + 9| + 5 > 3 & \\
|2x + 9| + 5 - 5 > 3 - 5 & \text{Subtract 5 from both sides.}\\
|2x + 9| > -2 & \text{Simplify.}
\end{array}
$$

The absolute value of any number is always nonnegative and thus is always greater than -2. This inequality and the original inequality are true for all values of x. The solution set is $\{x | x \text{ is a real number}\}$ or $(-\infty, \infty)$ and its graph is shown.

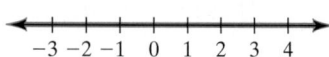

✔ **CONCEPT CHECK**

Without taking any solution steps, how do you know that the absolute value inequality $|3x - 2| > -9$ has a solution? What is its solution?

EXAMPLE 7

Solve $\left|\dfrac{x}{3} - 1\right| - 7 \geq -5$.

Solution   First, isolate the absolute value expression by adding 7 to both sides.

$$\left|\frac{x}{3} - 1\right| - 7 \geq -5$$

$$\left|\frac{x}{3} - 1\right| - 7 + 7 \geq -5 + 7 \quad \text{Add 7 to both sides.}$$

$$\left|\frac{x}{3} - 1\right| \geq 2 \quad\quad\quad\quad \text{Simplify.}$$

Concept Check Answer:
$(-\infty, \infty)$ since the absolute value is
always nonnegative

Next, write the absolute value inequality as an equivalent compound inequality and solve.

$$\frac{x}{3} - 1 \le -2 \qquad \text{or} \qquad \frac{x}{3} - 1 \ge 2$$

$$3\left(\frac{x}{3} - 1\right) \le 3(-2) \qquad \text{or} \qquad 3\left(\frac{x}{3} - 1\right) \ge 3(2) \qquad \text{Clear the inequalities of fractions.}$$

$$x - 3 \le -6 \qquad \text{or} \qquad x - 3 \ge 6 \qquad \text{Apply the distributive property.}$$

$$x \le -3 \qquad \text{or} \qquad x \ge 9 \qquad \text{Add 3 to both sides.}$$

The solution set is $(-\infty, -3] \cup [9, \infty)$, and its graph is shown.

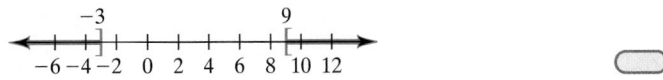

EXAMPLE 8

Solve for x: $\left|\dfrac{2(x + 1)}{3}\right| \le 0$.

Solution   Recall that "$\le$" means "less than or equal to." The absolute value of any expression will never be less than 0, but it may be equal to 0. Thus, to solve $\left|\dfrac{2(x + 1)}{3}\right| \le 0$ we solve $\left|\dfrac{2(x + 1)}{3}\right| = 0$

$$\frac{2(x + 1)}{3} = 0$$

$$3\left[\frac{2(x + 1)}{3}\right] = 3(0) \qquad \text{Clear the equation of fractions.}$$

$$2x + 2 = 0 \qquad \text{Apply the distributive property.}$$

$$2x = -2 \qquad \text{Subtract 2 from both sides.}$$

$$x = -1 \qquad \text{Divide both sides by 2.}$$

The solution set is $\{-1\}$.

The following box summarizes the types of absolute value equations and inequalities.

Solving Absolute Value Equations and Inequalities With $a > 0$

Algebraic Solution	Solution Graph
$\lvert X \rvert = a$ is equivalent to $X = a$ or $X = -a$.	
$\lvert X \rvert < a$ is equivalent to $-a < X < a$.	
$\lvert X \rvert > a$ is equivalent to $X < -a$ or $X > a$.	

STUDY SKILLS REMINDER

Continue your outline started in Section 2.1. Write how to recognize and how to solve absolute value inequalities in your own words. For example:

Solving Equations and Inequalities

I. Equations
   A. Linear equations (Section 2.1)
   B. Absolute value equations (Section 2.6)
II. Inequalities
   A. Linear inequalities (Section 2.4)
   B. Compound inequalities (Section 2.5)
   C. **Absolute value inequalities**—Recognize: *inequality with absolute value bars*—Solve: if possible, first isolate absolute value: if $|x| > a$ (positive), solve $x < -a$ or $x > a$, if $|x| < a$ (positive) then solve $-a < x < a$.

See Appendix A for summary exercises.

MENTAL MATH

Match each absolute value inequality with an equivalent statement.

1. $|2x + 1| = 3$ A. $2x + 1 > 3$ or $2x + 1 < -3$

2. $|2x + 1| \leq 3$ B. $2x + 1 \geq 3$ or $2x + 1 \leq -3$

3. $|2x + 1| < 3$ C. $-3 < 2x + 1 < 3$

4. $|2x + 1| \geq 3$ D. $2x + 1 = 3$ or $2x + 1 = -3$

5. $|2x + 1| > 3$ E. $-3 \leq 2x + 1 \leq 3$

EXERCISE SET 2.7

STUDY GUIDE/SSM   CD/VIDEO   PH MATH TUTOR CENTER   MathXL®Tutorials ON CD   MathXL®   MyMathLab®

Solve each inequality. Then graph the solution set. See Examples 1 through 4.

1. $|x| \leq 4$ **2.** $|x| < 6$

3. $|x - 3| < 2$ **4.** $|y| \leq 5$

5. $|x + 3| < 2$ **6.** $|x + 4| < 6$

7. $|2x + 7| \leq 13$ **8.** $|5x - 3| \leq 18$

9. $|x| + 7 \leq 12$ **10.** $|x| + 6 \leq 7$

11. $|3x - 1| < -5$ **12.** $|8x - 3| < -2$

13. $|x - 6| - 7 \leq -1$ **14.** $|z + 2| - 7 < -3$

Solve each inequality. Graph the solution set. See Examples 5 through 7.

15. $|x| > 3$ **16.** $|y| \geq 4$

17. $|x + 10| \geq 14$ **18.** $|x - 9| \geq 2$

19. $|x| + 2 > 6$ **20.** $|x| - 1 > 3$

21. $|5x| > -4$ **22.** $|4x - 11| > -1$

23. $|6x - 8| + 3 > 7$ **24.** $|10 + 3x| + 1 > 2$

Solve each inequality. Graph the solution set. See Example 8.

25. $|x| \leq 0$ **26.** $|x| \geq 0$

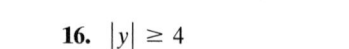

27. $|8x + 3| > 0$ **28.** $|5x - 6| < 0$

58. $|7x - 3| - 1 \le 10$

MIXED PRACTICE

Solve each inequality. Graph the solution set.

29. $|x| \le 2$ **30.** $|z| < 6$

31. $|y| > 1$ **32.** $|x| \ge 10$

33. $|x - 3| < 8$ **34.** $|-3 + x| \le 10$

35. $|0.6x - 3| > 0.6$ **36.** $|1 + 0.3x| \ge 0.1$

37. $5 + |x| \le 2$

38. $8 + |x| < 1$

39. $|x| > -4$

40. $|x| \le -7$

41. $|2x - 7| \le 11$

42. $|5x + 2| < 8$

43. $|x + 5| + 2 \ge 8$

44. $|-1 + x| - 6 > 2$

45. $|x| > 0$

46. $|x| < 0$

47. $9 + |x| > 7$

48. $5 + |x| \ge 4$

49. $6 + |4x - 1| \le 9$

50. $-3 + |5x - 2| \le 4$

51. $\left| \dfrac{2}{3}x + 1 \right| > 1$

52. $|5x - 1| \ge 2$

53. $|5x + 3| < -6$

54. $|4 + 9x| \ge -6$

55. $|8x + 3| \ge 0$

56. $|5x - 6| \le 0$

57. $|1 + 3x| + 4 < 5$

59. $\left| \dfrac{x + 6}{3} \right| > 2$

60. $\left| \dfrac{7 + x}{2} \right| \ge 4$

61. $-15 + |2x - 7| \le -6$

62. $-9 + |3 + 4x| < -4$

63. $\left| 2x + \dfrac{3}{4} \right| - 7 \le -2$

64. $\left| \dfrac{3}{5} + 4x \right| - 6 < -1$

Solve each equation or inequality for x.

65. $|2x - 3| < 7$ **66.** $|2x - 3| > 7$

67. $|2x - 3| = 7$ **68.** $|5 - 6x| = 29$

69. $|x - 5| \ge 12$ **70.** $|x + 4| \ge 20$

71. $|9 + 4x| = 0$ **72.** $|9 + 4x| \ge 0$

73. $|2x + 1| + 4 < 7$ **74.** $8 + |5x - 3| \ge 11$

75. $|3x - 5| + 4 = 5$ **76.** $|8x| = -5$

77. $|x + 11| = -1$ **78.** $|4x - 4| = -3$

79. $\left| \dfrac{2x - 1}{3} \right| = 6$ **80.** $\left| \dfrac{6 - x}{4} \right| = 5$

81. $\left| \dfrac{3x - 5}{6} \right| > 5$ **82.** $\left| \dfrac{4x - 7}{5} \right| < 2$

REVIEW AND PREVIEW

Recall the formula:

$$\text{Probability of an event} = \frac{\text{number of ways that the event can occur}}{\text{number of possible outcomes}}$$

Find the probability of rolling each number on a single toss of a die. (Recall that a die is a cube with each of its six sides containing 1, 2, 3, 4, 5, and 6 black dots, respectively.) See Section 2.3.

83. $P(\text{rolling a 2})$ **84.** $P(\text{rolling a 5})$

85. $P(\text{rolling a 7})$ **86.** $P(\text{rolling a 0})$

87. $P(\text{rolling a 1 or 3})$ **88.** $P(\text{rolling a } 1, 2, 3, 4, 5, \text{ or } 6)$

Consider the equation $3x - 4y = 12$. For each value of x or y given, find the corresponding value of the other variable that makes the statement true. See Section 2.3.

89. If $x = 2$, find y

90. If $y = -1$, find x

91. If $y = -3$, find x

92. If $x = 4$, find y

Concept Extensions

93. Write an absolute value inequality representing all numbers x whose distance from 0 is less than 7 units.

94. Write an absolute value inequality representing all numbers x whose distance from 0 is greater than 4 units.

95. Write $-5 \leq x \leq 5$ as an equivalent inequality containing an absolute value.

96. Write $x > 1$ or $x < -1$ as an equivalent inequality containing an absolute value.

97. Describe how solving $|x - 3| = 5$ is different from solving $|x - 3| < 5$.

98. Describe how solving $|x + 4| = 0$ is similar to solving $|x + 4| \leq 0$.

The expression $|x_T - x|$ is defined to be the absolute error in x, where x_T is the true value of a quantity and x is the measured value or value as stored in a computer.

99. If the true value of a quantity is 3.5 and the absolute error must be less than 0.05, find the acceptable measured values.

100. If the true value of a quantity is 0.2 and the approximate value stored in a computer is $\dfrac{51}{256}$, find the absolute error.

CHAPTER 2 PROJECT

Analyzing Municipal Budgets

Nearly all cities, towns, and villages operate with an annual budget. Budget items might include expenses for fire and police protection as well as for street maintenance and parks. No matter how big or small the budget, city officials need to know if municipal spending is over or under budget. In this project, you will have the opportunity to analyze a municipal budget and make budgetary recommendations. This project may be completed by working in groups or individually.

Suppose that each year your town creates a municipal budget. The next year's annual municipal budget is submitted for approval by the town's citizens at the annual town meeting. This year's budget was printed in the town newspaper earlier in the year.

You have joined a group of citizens who are concerned about your town's budgeting and spending processes. Your group plans to analyze this year's budget along with what was actually spent by the town this year. You hope to present your findings at the annual town meeting and make some budgetary recommendations for next year's budget. The municipal budget contains many different areas of spending. To help focus your group's analysis, you have decided to research spending habits only for categories in which the actual expenses differ from the budgeted amount by more than 12% of the budgeted amount.

1. For each category in the budget, write a specific absolute value inequality that describes the condition that must be met before your group will research spending habits for that category. In each case, let the variable x represent the actual expense for a budget category.

2. For each category in the budget, write an equivalent compound inequality for the condition described in Question 1. Again, let the variable x represent the actual expense for a budget category.

3. On the next page is a listing of the actual expenditures made this year for each budget category. Use the inequalities from either Question 1 or Question 2 to complete the Budget Worksheet given at the end of this project. (The first category has been filled in.) From the Budget Worksheet, decide which categories must be researched.

4. Can you think of possible reasons why spending in the categories that must be researched were over or under budget?

5. Based on this year's municipal budget and actual expenses, what recommendations would you make for next year's budget? Explain your reasoning.

6. (Optional) Research the annual budget used by your own town or your college or university. Conduct a similar analysis of the budget with respect to actual expenses. What can you conclude?

	Department/Program	Actual Expenditure
I.	**Board of Health**	
	Immunization Programs	$14,800
	Inspections	$41,900
II.	**Fire Department**	
	Equipment	$375,000
	Salaries	$268,500
III.	**Libraries**	
	Book/Periodical Purchases	$107,300
	Equipment	$29,000
	Salaries	$118,400
IV.	**Parks and Recreation**	
	Maintenance	$82,500
	Playground Equipment	$45,000
	Salaries	$118,000
	Summer Programs	$96,200
V.	**Police Department**	
	Equipment	$328,000
	Salaries	$405,000
VI.	**Public Works**	
	Recycling	$48,100
	Sewage	$92,500
	Snow Removal & Road Salt	$268,300
	Street Maintenance	$284,000
	Water Treatment	$94,100
	TOTAL	$2,816,600

THE TOWN CRIER
Annual Budget Set at Town Meeting
ANYTOWN, USA (MG)—This year's annual budget is as follows:

	Amount Budgeted
BOARD OF HEALTH	
Immunization Programs	$15,000
Inspections	$50,000
FIRE DEPARTMENT	
Equipment	$450,000
Salaries	$275,000
LIBRARIES	
Book/Periodical Purchases	$90,000
Equipment	$30,000
Salaries	$120,000
PARKS AND RECREATION	
Maintenance	$70,000
Playground Equipment	$50,000
Salaries	$140,000
Summer Programs	$80,000
POLICE DEPARTMENT	
Equipment	$300,000
Salaries	$400,000
PUBLIC WORKS	
Recycling	$50,000
Sewage	$100,000
Snow Removal & Road Salt	$200,000
Street Maintenance	$250,000
Water Treatment	$100,000
TOTAL	**$2,770,000**

BUDGET WORKSHEET

Budget category	Budgeted amount	Minimum allowed	Actual expense	Maximum allowed	Within budget?	Amt over/ under budget
Immunization Programs	$15,000	$13,200	$14,800	$16,800	Yes	Under $200

STUDY SKILLS REMINDER

Are You Preparing for a Test on Chapter 2?

Below I have listed some common trouble areas for students in Chapter 2. After studying for your test—but before taking your test—read these.

▶ Remember to reverse the direction of the inequality symbol when multiplying or dividing both sides of an inequality by a negative number.

$$-11x < 33 \qquad \text{Direction of arrow is reversed.}$$
$$\frac{-11x}{-11} > \frac{33}{-11}$$
$$x > -3$$

▶ Remember the differences when solving absolute value equations and inequalities.

$$|x + 1| = 3$$
$$x + 1 = 3 \quad \text{or} \quad x + 1 = -3$$
$$x = 2 \quad \text{or} \quad x = -4$$
$$\{2, -4\}$$

$$|x + 1| < 3$$
$$-3 < x + 1 < 3$$
$$-3 - 1 < x < 3 - 1$$
$$-4 < x < 2$$
$$(-4, 2)$$

$$|x + 1| > 3$$
$$x + 1 < -3 \quad \text{or} \quad x + 1 > 3$$
$$x < -4 \quad \text{or} \quad x > 2$$
$$(-\infty, -4) \cup (2, \infty)$$

▶ Remember that an equation is not solved for a specified variable unless the variable is alone on one side of an equation *and* the other side contains *no* specified variables.

$$y = 10x + 6 - y \qquad \text{Equation is not solved for } y.$$
$$2y = 10x + 6 \qquad \text{Add } y \text{ to both sides.}$$
$$y = 5x + 3 \qquad \text{Divide both sides by 2.}$$

Remember: This is simply a checklist of common trouble areas. For a review of Chapter 2, see the Highlights and Chapter Review at the end of this chapter.

CHAPTER VOCABULARY CHECK

Fill in each blank with one of the words or phrases listed below.

contradiction
absolute value
formula

linear inequality in one variable
consecutive integers
linear equation in one variable

compound inequality
identity
intersection

solution
union

1. The statement "$x < 5$ or $x > 7$" *is called a(n)* _____.

2. An equation in one variable that has no solution is called a(n) _____.

3. The _____ of two sets is the set of all elements common to both sets.

4. The _____ of two sets is the set of all elements that belong to either of the sets.

5. An equation in one variable that has every number (for which the equation is defined) as a solution is called a(n) _____.

6. The equation $d = rt$ is also called a(n) _____.

7. A number's distance from 0 is called its _____.

8. When a variable in an equation is replaced by a number and the resulting equation is true, then that number is called a(n) _____ of the equation.

9. The integers 17, 18, 19 are examples of _____.

10. The statement $5x - 0.2 < 7$ is an example of a(n) _____.

11. The statement $5x - 0.2 = 7$ is an example of a(n) _____.

CHAPTER 2   HIGHLIGHTS

Definitions and Concepts	**Examples**

Section 2.1   Linear Equations in One Variable

An **equation** is a statement that two expressions are equal.

A **linear equation in one variable** is an equation that can be written in the form $ax + b = c$, where a, b, and c are real numbers and a is not 0.

A **solution** of an equation is a value for the variable that makes the equation a true statement.

Equations:
$$5 = 5 \qquad 7x + 2 = -14 \qquad 3(x - 1)^2 = 9x^2 - 6$$

Linear equations:
$$7x + 2 = -14 \qquad x = -3$$
$$5(2y - 7) = -2(8y - 1)$$

Check to see that -1 is a solution of
$$3(x - 1) = 4x - 2.$$

$$3(-1 - 1) = 4(-1) - 2$$
$$3(-2) = -4 - 2$$
$$-6 = -6 \qquad \text{True.}$$

Thus, -1 is a solution.

Equivalent equations have the same solution.

The **addition property of equality** guarantees that the same number may be added to (or subtracted from) both sides of an equation, and the result is an equivalent equation.

The **multiplication property of equality** guarantees that both sides of an equation may be multiplied by (or divided by) the same nonzero number, and the result is an equivalent equation.

$x - 12 = 14$ and $x = 26$ are equivalent equations.

Solve for x: $-3x - 2 = 10$.

$$-3x - 2 + 2 = 10 + 2 \qquad \text{Add 2 to both sides.}$$
$$-3x = 12$$
$$\frac{-3x}{-3} = \frac{12}{-3} \qquad \text{Divide both sides by } -3.$$
$$x = -4$$

To solve linear equations in one variable:

Solve for x:
$$x - \frac{x - 2}{6} = \frac{x - 7}{3} + \frac{2}{3}$$

1. Clear the equation of fractions.

1. $6\left(x - \dfrac{x - 2}{6}\right) = 6\left(\dfrac{x - 7}{3} + \dfrac{2}{3}\right)$ Multiply both sides by 6.

$$6x - (x - 2) = 2(x - 7) + 2(2)$$

2. Remove grouping symbols such as parentheses.

2. $\quad 6x - x + 2 = 2x - 14 + 4$ Remove grouping symbols.

3. Simplify by combining like terms.

3. $\quad\quad 5x + 2 = 2x - 10$

4. Write variable terms on one side and numbers on the other side using the addition property of equality.

4. $\quad 5x + 2 - 2 = 2x - 10 - 2$ Subtract 2.
$$5x = 2x - 12$$
$$5x - 2x = 2x - 12 - 2x \qquad \text{Subtract } 2x.$$
$$3x = -12$$

5. Isolate the variable using the multiplication property of equality.

5. $\quad\quad \dfrac{3x}{3} = \dfrac{-12}{3}$ Divide by 3.
$$x = -4$$

6. Check the proposed solution in the original equation.

6. $\quad -4 - \dfrac{-4 - 2}{6} \stackrel{?}{=} \dfrac{-4 - 7}{3} + \dfrac{2}{3}$ Replace x with -4 in the original equation.

$$-4 - \frac{-6}{6} \stackrel{?}{=} \frac{-11}{3} + \frac{2}{3}$$
$$-4 - (-1) \stackrel{?}{=} \frac{-9}{3}$$
$$-3 = -3 \qquad \text{True.}$$

Definitions and Concepts	**Examples**

Section 2.2 An Introduction to Problem Solving

Problem-Solving Strategy	Colorado is shaped like a rectangle whose length is about 1.3 times its width. If the perimeter of Colorado is 2070 kilometers, find its dimensions.
1. UNDERSTAND the problem.	**1.** Read and reread the problem. Guess a solution and check your guess. Let x = width of Colorado in kilometers. Then $1.3x$ = length of Colorado in kilometers 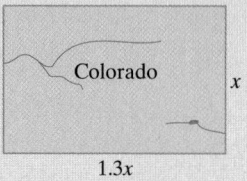 1.3x
2. TRANSLATE the problem.	**2.** In words: twice the length $+$ twice the width $=$ perimeter Translate: $2(1.3x) + 2x = 2070$
3. SOLVE the equation.	**3.** $2.6x + 2x = 2070$ $4.6x = 2070$ $x = 450$
4. INTERPRET the results.	**4.** If $x = 450$ kilometers, then $1.3x = 1.3(450) = 585$ kilometers. *Check*: The perimeter of a rectangle whose width is 450 kilometers and length is 585 kilometers is $2(450) + 2(585) = 2070$ kilometers, the required perimeter. *State*: The dimensions of Colorado are 450 kilometers by 585 kilometers

Section 2.3 Formulas and Problem Solving

An equation that describes a known relationship among quantities is called a **formula.**	*Formulas:* $A = \pi r^2$ (area of a circle) $I = PRT$ (interest = principal · rate · time)
To solve a formula for a specified variable, use the steps for solving an equation. Treat the specified variable as the only variable of the equation.	Solve $A = 2HW + 2LW + 2LH$ for H $A - 2LW = 2HW + 2LH$ Subtract $2LW$. $A - 2LW = H(2W + 2L)$ Factor out H. $\dfrac{A - 2LW}{2W + 2L} = \dfrac{H(2W + 2L)}{2W + 2L}$ Divide by $2W + 2L$. $\dfrac{A - 2LW}{2W + 2L} = H$ Simplify.

Definitions and Concepts	**Examples**

Section 2.4   Linear Inequalities and Problem Solving

A **linear inequality in one variable** is an inequality that can be written in the form $ax + b < c$, where a, b, and c are real numbers and $a \neq 0$. (The inequality symbols $\leq, >,$ and $\geq$ also apply here.)	Linear inequalities: $5x - 2 \leq -7 \qquad 3y > 1 \qquad \dfrac{z}{7} < -9(z - 3)$ $$x - 9 \leq -16$$ $$x - 9 + 9 \leq -16 + 9 \qquad \text{Add 9.}$$ $$x \leq -7$$
The **addition property of inequality** guarantees that the same number may be added to (or subtracted from) both sides of an inequality, and the resulting inequality will have the same solution set.	Solve. $$6x < -66$$ $$\dfrac{6x}{6} < \dfrac{-66}{6} \qquad \text{\small Divide by 6. Do not reverse direction of inequality symbol.}$$ $$x < -11$$
The **multiplication property of inequality** guarantees that both sides of an inequality may be multiplied by (or divided by) the same **positive** number, and the resulting inequality will have the same solution set. We may also multiply (or divide) both sides of an inequality by the same **negative** number and **reverse the direction of the inequality symbol**, and the result is an inequality with the same solution set.	Solve. $$-6x < -66$$ $$\dfrac{-6x}{-6} > \dfrac{-66}{-6} \qquad \text{\small Divide by -6. Reverse direction of inequality symbol.}$$ $$x > 11$$
To solve a linear inequality in one variable:	Solve for x: $$\dfrac{3}{7}(x - 4) \geq x + 2$$
1. Clear the equation of fractions.	**1.** $7\left[\dfrac{3}{7}(x - 4)\right] \geq 7(x + 2) \qquad \text{\small Multiply by 7.}$ $\qquad 3(x - 4) \geq 7(x + 2)$
2. Remove grouping symbols such as parentheses. **3.** Simplify by combining like terms.	**2.** $\qquad 3x - 12 \geq 7x + 14 \qquad \text{\small Apply the distributive property.}$
4. Write variable terms on one side and numbers on the other side using the addition property of inequality.	**4.** $\qquad -4x - 12 \geq 14 \qquad \text{\small Subtract } 7x.$ $\qquad\qquad -4x \geq 26 \qquad \text{\small Add 12.}$ $\qquad\qquad \dfrac{-4x}{-4} \leq \dfrac{26}{-4} \qquad \text{\small Divide by -4. Reverse direction of inequality symbol.}$
5. Isolate the variable using the multiplication property of inequality.	$$x \leq -\dfrac{13}{2}$$

Section 2.5   Compound Inequalities

Two inequalities joined by the words **and** or **or** are called **compound inequalities**.	Compound inequalities: $x - 7 \leq 4 \qquad \text{and} \qquad x \geq -21$ $2x + 7 > x - 3 \qquad \text{or} \qquad 5x + 2 > -3$

(continued)

Definitions and Concepts	**Examples**

Section 2.5 Compound Inequalities

The solution set of a compound inequality formed by the word **and** is the **intersection** $\cap$ of the solution sets of the two inequalities.

Solve for x:

$$x < 5 \text{ and } x < 3$$

$\{x|x < 5\}$ $(-\infty, 5)$

$\{x|x < 3\}$ $(-\infty, 3)$

$\{x|x < 3$ and $x < 5\}$ $(-\infty, 3)$

The solution set of a compound inequality formed by the word **or** is the **union**, $\cup$, of the solution sets of the two inequalities.

Solve for x:

$$x - 2 \geq -3 \quad \text{or} \quad 2x \leq -4$$
$$x \geq -1 \quad \text{or} \quad x \leq -2$$

$\{x|x \geq -1\}$ $[-1, \infty)$

$\{x|x \leq -2\}$ $(-\infty, -2]$

$\{x|x \leq -2$ or $x \geq -1\}$ $(-\infty, -2]$ $\cup[-1, \infty)$

Section 2.6 Absolute Value Equations

If a is a positive number, then $|x| = a$ is equivalent to $x = a$ or $x = -a$.

Solve for y:

$$|5y - 1| - 7 = 4$$

$$|5y - 1| = 11$$

$5y - 1 = 11$ or $5y - 1 = -11$ Add 7.

$5y = 12$ or $5y = -10$ Add 1.

$y = \dfrac{12}{5}$ or $y = -2$ Divide by 5.

The solutions are -2 and $\frac{12}{5}$.

If a is negative, then $|x| = a$ has no solution.

Solve for x:

$$\left|\frac{x}{2} - 7\right| = -1$$

The solution set is $\{\ \}$ or $\varnothing$.

If an absolute value equation is of the form $|x| = |y|$, solve $x = y$ or $x = -y$.

Solve for x:

$$|x - 7| = |2x + 1|$$

$x - 7 = 2x + 1$ or $x - 7 = -(2x + 1)$

$x = 2x + 8$ $x - 7 = -2x - 1$

$-x = 8$ $x = -2x + 6$

$x = -8$ or $3x = 6$

                         $x = 2$

The solutions are -8 and 2.

Definitions and Concepts	**Examples**

Section 2.7 Absolute Value Inequalities

If a is a positive number, then $\lvert x \rvert < a$ is equivalent to $-a < x < a$.	Solve for y: $$\lvert y - 5 \rvert \le 3$$ $$-3 \le y - 5 \le 3$$ $$-3 + 5 \le y - 5 + 5 \le 3 + 5 \quad \text{Add 5.}$$ $$2 \le y \le 8$$ The solution set is $[2, 8]$.
If a is a positive number, then $\lvert x \rvert > a$ is equivalent to $x < -a$ or $x > a$.	Solve for x: $$\left\lvert \frac{x}{2} - 3 \right\rvert > 7$$ $$\frac{x}{2} - 3 < -7 \quad \text{or} \quad \frac{x}{2} - 3 > 7$$ $$x - 6 < -14 \quad \text{or} \quad x - 6 > 14 \qquad \text{Multiply by 2.}$$ $$x < -8 \quad \text{or} \quad x > 20 \qquad \text{Add 6.}$$ The solution set is $(-\infty, -8) \cup (20, \infty)$.

CHAPTER REVIEW

(2.1) Solve each linear equation.

1. $4(x - 5) = 2x - 14$

2. $x + 7 = -2(x + 8)$

3. $3(2y - 1) = -8(6 + y)$

4. $-(z + 12) = 5(2z - 1)$

5. $n - (8 + 4n) = 2(3n - 4)$

6. $4(9v + 2) = 6(1 + 6v) - 10$

7. $0.3(x - 2) = 1.2$

8. $1.5 = 0.2(c - 0.3)$

9. $-4(2 - 3h) = 2(3h - 4) + 6h$

10. $6(m - 1) + 3(2 - m) = 0$

11. $6 - 3(2g + 4) - 4g = 5(1 - 2g)$

12. $20 - 5(p + 1) + 3p = -(2p - 15)$

13. $\dfrac{x}{3} - 4 = x - 2$

14. $\dfrac{9}{4}y = \dfrac{2}{3}y$

15. $\dfrac{3n}{8} - 1 = 3 + \dfrac{n}{6}$

16. $\dfrac{z}{6} + 1 = \dfrac{z}{2} + 2$

17. $\dfrac{y}{4} - \dfrac{y}{2} = -8$

18. $\dfrac{2x}{3} - \dfrac{8}{3} = x$

19. $\dfrac{b - 2}{3} = \dfrac{b + 2}{5}$

20. $\dfrac{2t - 1}{3} = \dfrac{3t + 2}{15}$

21. $\dfrac{2(t + 1)}{3} = \dfrac{2(t - 1)}{3}$

22. $\dfrac{3a - 3}{6} = \dfrac{4a + 1}{15} + 2$

23. $\dfrac{x - 2}{5} + \dfrac{x + 2}{2} = \dfrac{x + 4}{3}$

24. $\dfrac{2z - 3}{4} - \dfrac{4 - z}{2} = \dfrac{z + 1}{3}$

(2.2) Solve.

25. Twice the difference of a number and 3 is the same as 1 added to three times the number. Find the number.

26. One number is 5 more than another number. If the sum of the numbers is 285, find the numbers.

27. Find 40% of 130.

28. Find 1.5% of 8.

29. In 1995, the Academy Awards (Oscars) had a peak in television viewership. By 2003, the number of Oscar viewers had decreased to 33 million. If this represented a decrease of 40%, find the number of Oscar viewers in 1995. (*Source:* Nielsen Media Research).

30. Find four consecutive integers such that twice the first subtracted from the sum of the other three integers is sixteen.

31. Determine whether there are two consecutive odd integers such that 5 times the first exceeds 3 times the second by 54.

△ **32.** The length of a rectangular playing field is 5 meters less than twice its width. If 230 meters of fencing goes around the field, find the dimensions of the field.

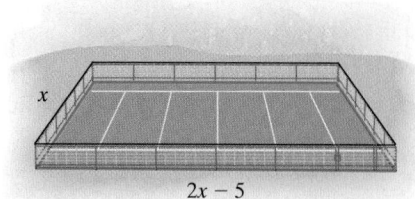

$2x - 5$

33. A car rental company charges $39.95 per day for a compact car plus 15 cents per mile for every mile over 100 miles driven per day. If a customer's bill for 2 days' use is $103.60 before taxes, find how many miles to the nearest whole mile were driven.

34. The cost C of producing x number of scientific calculators is given by $C = 4.50x + 3000$, and the revenue R from selling them is given by $R = 16.50x$. Find the number of calculators that must be sold to break even. (To break even, revenue = cost.)

35. An entrepreneur can sell her musically vibrating plants for $40 each, while her cost C to produce x number of plants is given by $C = 20x + 100$. Find her break-even point. Find her revenue if she sells exactly that number of plants.

(2.3) Solve each equation for the specified variable.

△ **36.** $V = lwh; w$

△ **37.** $C = 2\pi r; r$

38. $5x - 4y = -12; y$

39. $5x - 4y = -12; x$

40. $y - y_1 = m(x - x_1); m$

41. $y - y_1 = m(x - x_1); x$

42. $E = I(R + r); r$

43. $S = vt + gt^2; g$

44. $T = gr + gvt; g$

45. $I = Prt + P; P$

△ **46.** $A = \dfrac{h}{2}(B + b); B$

△ **47.** $V = \dfrac{1}{3}\pi r^2 h; h$

48. $R = \dfrac{r_1 + r_2}{2}; r_1$

49. $\dfrac{V_1}{T_1} = \dfrac{V_2}{T_2}; T_2$

Solve.

50. A principal of $3000 is invested in an account paying an annual percentage rate of 3%. Find the amount in the account after 7 years if the amount is compounded
   a. semiannually
   b. weekly
   (Approximate to the nearest cent.)

51. The high temperature in Slidell, Louisiana, one day was 90° Fahrenheit. Convert this temperature to degrees Celsius.

△ **52.** Angie Applegate has a photograph in which the length is 2 inches longer than the width. If she increases each dimension by 4 inches, the area is increased by 88 square inches. Find the original dimensions.

△ **53.** One-square-foot floor tiles come 24 to a package. Find how many packages are needed to cover a rectangular floor 18 feet by 21 feet.

△ **54.** Determine which container holds more ice cream, an 8 inch by 5 inch by 3 inch box or a cylinder with radius of 3 inches and height of 6 inches.

55. Ignacio Gonzales left Los Angeles at 11 A.M. and drove nonstop to San Diego, 130 miles away. If he arrived at 1:15 P.M., find his average speed, rounded to the nearest mile per hour.

(2.4) Solve each linear inequality.

56. $3(x - 5) > -(x + 3)$

57. $-2(x + 7) \geq 3(x + 2)$

58. $4x - (5 + 2x) < 3x - 1$

59. $3(x - 8) < 7x + 2(5 - x)$

60. $24 \geq 6x - 2(3x - 5) + 2x$

61. $48 + x \geq 5(2x + 4) - 2x$

62. $\dfrac{x}{3} + \dfrac{1}{2} > \dfrac{2}{3}$

63. $x + \dfrac{3}{4} < -\dfrac{x}{2} + \dfrac{9}{4}$

64. $\dfrac{x - 5}{2} \leq \dfrac{3}{8}(2x + 6)$

65. $\dfrac{3(x - 2)}{5} > \dfrac{-5(x - 2)}{3}$

Solve.

66. George Boros can pay his housekeeper $25 per week to do his laundry, or he can have the laundromat do it at a cost of 90 cents per pound for the first 10 pounds and 80 cents for each additional pound. Use an inequality to find the weight at which it is more economical to use the housekeeper than the laundromat.

67. Ceramic firing temperatures usually range from 500° to 1000° Fahrenheit. Use a compound inequality to convert this range to the Celsius scale. Round to the nearest degree.

68. In the Olympic gymnastics competition, Nana must average a score of 9.65 to win the silver medal. Seven of the eight judges have reported scores of $9.5, 9.7, 9.9, 9.7, 9.7, 9.6$, and 9.5. Use an inequality to find the minimum score that the last judge can give so that Nana wins the silver medal.

69. Carol would like to pay cash for a car when she graduates from college and estimates that she can afford a used car that costs between $4000 and $8000. She has saved $500 so far and plans to earn the rest of the money by working the next two summers. If Carol plans to save the same amount each summer, use a compound inequality to find the range of money she must save each summer to buy the car.

(2.5) Solve each inequality.

70. $1 \le 4x - 7 \le 3$

71. $-2 \le 8 + 5x < -1$

72. $-3 < 4(2x - 1) < 12$

73. $-6 < x - (3 - 4x) < -3$

74. $\dfrac{1}{6} < \dfrac{4x - 3}{3} \le \dfrac{4}{5}$

75. $0 \le \dfrac{2(3x + 4)}{5} \le 3$

76. $x \le 2$ and $x > -5$

77. $x \le 2$ or $x > -5$

78. $3x - 5 > 6$ or $-x < -5$

79. $-2x \le 6$ and $-2x + 3 < -7$

(2.6) Solve each absolute value equation.

80. $|x - 7| = 9$

81. $|8 - x| = 3$

82. $|2x + 9| = 9$

83. $|-3x + 4| = 7$

84. $|3x - 2| + 6 = 10$

85. $5 + |6x + 1| = 5$

86. $-5 = |4x - 3|$

87. $|5 - 6x| + 8 = 3$

88. $|7x| - 26 = -5$

89. $-8 = |x - 3| - 10$

90. $\left|\dfrac{3x - 7}{4}\right| = 2$

91. $\left|\dfrac{9 - 2x}{5}\right| = -3$

92. $|6x + 1| = |15 + 4x|$

93. $|x - 3| = |7 + 2x|$

(2.7) Solve each absolute value inequality. Graph the solution set and write in interval notation.

94. $|5x - 1| < 9$

95. $|6 + 4x| \ge 10$

96. $|3x| - 8 > 1$

97. $9 + |5x| < 24$

98. $|6x - 5| \le -1$

99. $|6x - 5| \ge -1$

100. $\left|3x + \dfrac{2}{5}\right| \ge 4$

101. $\left|\dfrac{4x - 3}{5}\right| < 1$

102. $\left|\dfrac{x}{3} + 6\right| - 8 > -5$

103. $\left|\dfrac{4(x - 1)}{7}\right| + 10 < 2$

CHAPTER 2 TEST

Remember to use your Chapter Test Prep Video CD to help you study and view solutions to the test questions you need help with.

Solve each equation.

1. $8x + 14 = 5x + 44$

2. $3(x + 2) = 11 - 2(2 - x)$

3. $3(y - 4) + y = 2(6 + 2y)$

4. $7n - 6 + n = 2(4n - 3)$

5. $\dfrac{7w}{4} + 5 = \dfrac{3w}{10} + 1$

6. $|6x - 5| - 3 = -2$

7. $|8 - 2t| = -6$

8. $|x - 5| = |x + 2|$

Solve each equation for the specified variable.

9. $3x - 4y = 8; y$

10. $S = gt^2 + gvt; g$

11. $F = \dfrac{9}{5}C + 32; C$

Solve each inequality.

12. $3(2x - 7) - 4x > -(x + 6)$

13. $8 - \dfrac{x}{2} \geq 7$

14. $-3 < 2(x - 3) \leq 4$

15. $|3x + 1| > 5$

16. $|x - 5| - 4 < -2$

17. $-x > 1$ and $3x + 3 \geq x - 3$

18. $6x + 1 > 5x + 4$ or $1 - x > -4$

19. Find 12% of 80.

Solve.

20. In 2006, the number of people employed as database administrators, computer support specialists, and all other computer scientists is expected to be 461,000 in the United States. This represents a 118% increase over the number of people employed in these occupations in 1996. Find the number of database administrators, computer support specialists, and all other computer scientists employed in 1996. (*Source:* U.S. Bureau of Labor Statistics)

△ **21.** A circular dog pen has a circumference of 78.5 feet. Approximate π by 3.14 and estimate how many hunting dogs could be safely kept in the pen if each dog needs at least 60 square feet of room.

22. The company that makes Photoray sunglasses figures that the cost C to make x number of sunglasses weekly is given by $C = 3910 + 2.8x$, and the weekly revenue R is given by $R = 7.4x$. Use an inequality to find the number of sunglasses that must be made and sold to make a profit. (Revenue must exceed cost in order to make a profit.)

23. Find the amount of money in an account after 10 years if a principal of $2500 is invested at 3.5% interest compounded quarterly. (Round to the nearest cent.)

24. The most populous city in the United States is New York, although it is only the fifth most populous city in the world. Tokyo is the most populous city in the world followed by Mexico City. Mexico City's population is 13.2 million more than New York's and Tokyo's population is twice New York's, increased by 0.7 million. If the sum of the populations of these three cities is 72.3 million, find the population of each city. Let x be the population of New York (in millions). (*Source:* Planet101.com)

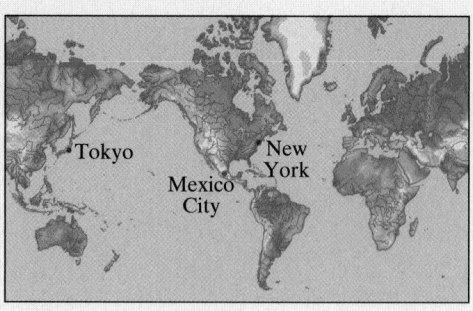

2 CHAPTER CUMULATIVE REVIEW

List the elements in each set.

1. **a.** $\{x \mid x$ is a whole number between 1 and 6$\}$
   b. $\{x \mid x$ is a natural number greater than 100$\}$

2. **a.** $\{x \mid x$ is an integer between -3 and 5$\}$
   b. $\{x \mid x$ is a whole number between 3 and 5$\}$

3. Find each value.
   a. $|3|$
   b. $|-5|$
   c. $-|2|$
   d. $-|-8|$
   e. $|0|$

4. Find the opposite of each number.
   a. $\frac{2}{3}$
   b. -9
   c. 1.5

5. Add.
   a. $-3 + (-11)$
   b. $3 + (-7)$
   c. $-10 + 15$
   d. $-8.3 + (-1.9)$
   e. $-\frac{2}{3} + \frac{3}{7}$

6. Subtract.
   a. $-2 - (-10)$
   b. $1.7 - 8.9$
   c. $-\frac{1}{2} - \frac{1}{4}$

7. Find the square roots.
   a. $\sqrt{9}$ **b.** $\sqrt{25}$
   c. $\sqrt{\frac{1}{4}}$ **d.** $-\sqrt{36}$
   e. $\sqrt{-36}$

8. Multiply or divide.
   a. $-3(-2)$
   b. $-\frac{3}{4}\left(-\frac{4}{7}\right)$
   c. $\frac{0}{-2}$
   d. $\frac{-20}{-2}$

9. Evaluate each algebraic expression when $x = 2$, $y = -1$, and $z = -3$.
   a. $z - y$
   b. z^2
   c. $\frac{2x + y}{z}$

10. Find the roots.
    a. $\sqrt[4]{1}$
    b. $\sqrt[3]{8}$
    c. $\sqrt[4]{81}$

11. Write each sentence using mathematical symbols.
    a. The sum of x and 5 is 20.
    b. Two times the sum of 3 and y amounts to 4.
    c. Subtract 8 from x, and the difference is the same as the product of 2 and x.
    d. The quotient of z and 9 is 3 times the difference of z and 5.

12. Insert $<, >$, or $=$ between each pair of numbers to form a true statement.
    a. $-3 \quad -5$
    b. $\frac{-12}{-4} \quad 3$
    c. $0 \quad -2$

13. Use the commutative property of addition to write an expression equivalent to $7x + 5$.

14. Use the associative property of multiplication to write an expression equivalent to $5 \cdot (7x)$. Then simplify the expression.

Solve for x.

15. $2x + 5 = 9$

16. $11.2 = 1.2 - 5x$

17. $6x - 4 = 2 + 6(x - 1)$

18. $2x + 1.5 = -0.2 + 1.6x$

19. Write the following as algebraic expressions. Then simplify.
    a. The sum of three consecutive integers, if x is the first consecutive integer.
    b. The perimeter of the triangle with sides of length x, $5x$, and $6x - 3$.

20. Write the following as algebraic expressions. Then simplify.

   a. The sum of three consecutive integers if x is the first consecutive integers.

   b. The perimeter of a square with side length $3x + 1$.

21. Find two numbers such that the second number is 3 more than twice the first number and the sum of the two numbers is 72.

22. Find two numbers such that the second number is 2 more than three times the first number and the difference of the two numbers is 24.

23. Solve $3y - 2x = 7$ for y.

24. Solve $7x - 4y = 10$ for x.

25. Solve $A = \dfrac{1}{2}(B + b)h$ for b.

26. Solve $P = 2l + 2w$ for l.

27. Graph each set on a number line and then write in interval notation.

   a. $\{x \mid x \geq 2\}$

   b. $\{x \mid x < -1\}$

   c. $\{x \mid 0.5 < x \leq 3\}$

28. Graph each set on a number line and then write in interval notation.

   a. $\{x \mid x \leq -3\}$

   b. $\{x \mid -2 \leq x < 0.1\}$

Solve.

29. $-(x - 3) + 2 \leq 3(2x - 5) + x$

30. $2(7x - 1) - 5x > -(-7x) + 4$

31. $2(x + 3) > 2x + 1$

32. $4(x + 1) - 3 < 4x + 1$

33. Find the intersection: $\{2, 4, 6, 8\} \cap \{3, 4, 5, 6\}$

34. Find the union: $\{-2, 0, 2, 4\} \cup \{-1, 1, 3, 5\}$

35. Solve: $x - 7 < 2$ and $2x + 1 < 9$

36. Solve: $x + 3 \leq 1$ or $3x - 1 < 8$

37. Find the union: $\{2, 4, 6, 8\} \cup \{3, 4, 5, 6\}$

38. Find the intersection: $\{-2, 0, 2, 4\} \cap \{-1, 1, 3, 5\}$

39. Solve: $-2x - 5 < -3$ or $6x < 0$

40. Solve: $-2x - 5 < -3$ and $6x < 0$

Solve.

41. $|p| = 2$

42. $|x| = 5$

43. $\left| \dfrac{x}{2} - 1 \right| = 11$

44. $\left| \dfrac{y}{3} + 2 \right| = 10$

45. $|x - 3| = |5 - x|$

46. $|x + 3| = |7 - x|$

47. $|x| \leq 3$

48. $|x| > 1$

49. $|2x + 9| + 5 > 3$

50. $|3x + 1| + 9 < 1$

Graphs and Functions

The linear equations and inequalities we explored in Chapter 2 are statements about a single variable. This chapter examines statements about two variables: linear equations and inequalities in two variables. We focus particularly on graphs of those equations and inequalities which lead to the notion of relation and to the notion of function, perhaps the single most important and useful concept in all of mathematics.

The Centers for Disease Control and Prevention (CDC), located in Atlanta, Georgia, was founded by the United States government as the primary federal agency devoted to public health. Public health officials there work constantly to provide information about current health issues. Prevention of diseases, injury, and disability is another focus of the public health specialists at the CDC.

The CDC employs approximately 8500 people in Atlanta, Washington, D.C., and at its many field sites nationwide. Positions at the CDC include medical officers, public health advisors, epidemiologists, behavioral scientists, statisticians, and information and technology specialists.

In the Spotlight on Decision Making feature on page 188, you will have the opportunity as a public health official to make a decision about a public awareness campaign concerning the eradication of mumps in the United States.

Link: www.cdc.gov *(Centers for Disease Control and Prevention)*
Source of text: (same)

3.1 GRAPHING EQUATIONS

Objectives

1 Plot ordered pairs.

2 Determine whether an ordered pair of numbers is a solution to an equation in two variables.

3 Graph linear equations.

4 Graph nonlinear equations.

1 Graphs are widely used today in newspapers, magazines, and all forms of newsletters. A few examples of graphs are shown here.

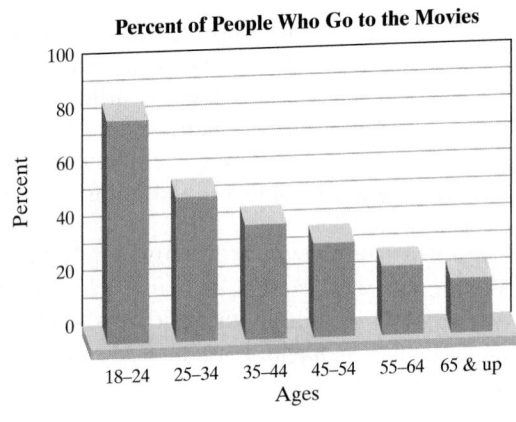

Percent of People Who Go to the Movies

Source: TELENATION/Market Facts, Inc.

Percent of Sales Completed Using Cards*

Source: The Nilson Report

* These include credit or debit cards, prepaid cards and EBT (electronic benefits transfer) cards.

To review how to read these graphs, we review their origin—the rectangular coordinate system. One way to locate points on a plane is by using a **rectangular coordinate system**, which is also called a **Cartesian coordinate system** after its inventor, René Descartes (1596–1650).

A rectangular coordinate system consists of two number lines that intersect at right angles at their 0 coordinates. We position these axes on paper such that one number line is horizontal and the other number line is then vertical. The horizontal number line is called the **x-axis** (or the axis of the **abscissa**), and the vertical number line is called the **y-axis** (or the axis of the **ordinate**). The point of intersection of these axes is named the **origin.**

Notice in the left figure on the next page that the axes divide the plane into four regions. These regions are called **quadrants.** The top-right region is quadrant I. Quadrants II, III, and IV are numbered counterclockwise from the first quadrant as shown. The x-axis and the y-axis are not in any quadrant.

Each point in the plane can be located, or **plotted**, or graphed by describing its position in terms of distances along each axis from the origin. An **ordered pair**, represented by the notation (x, y), records these distances.

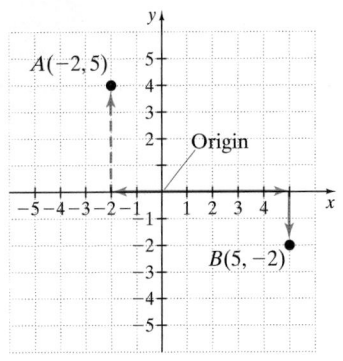

For example, the location of point A in the figure on the right above is described as 2 units to the left of the origin along the x-axis and 5 units upward parallel to the y-axis. Thus, we identify point A with the ordered pair $(-2, 5)$. Notice that the order of these numbers is critical. The x-value -2 is called the **x-coordinate** and is associated with the x-axis. The y-value 5 is called the **y-coordinate** and is associated with the y-axis. Compare the location of point A with the location of point B, which corresponds to the ordered pair $(5, -2)$.

Keep in mind that **each ordered pair corresponds to exactly one point in the real plane and that each point in the plane corresponds to exactly one ordered pair.** Thus, we may refer to the ordered pair (x, y) as the point (x, y).

EXAMPLE 1

Plot each ordered pair on a Cartesian coordinate system and name the quadrant in which the point is located.

a. $(2, -1)$ **b.** $(0, 5)$ **c.** $(-3, 5)$ **d.** $(-2, 0)$ **e.** $\left(-\frac{1}{2}, -4\right)$ **f.** $(1.5, \ 1.5)$

Solution   The six points are graphed as shown.

a. $(2, -1)$ lies in quadrant IV.

b. $(0, 5)$ is not in any quadrant.

c. $(-3, 5)$ lies in quadrant II.

d. $(-2, 0)$ is not in any quadrant.

e. $\left(-\dfrac{1}{2}, -4\right)$ is in quadrant III.

f. $(1.5, 1.5)$ is in quadrant I.

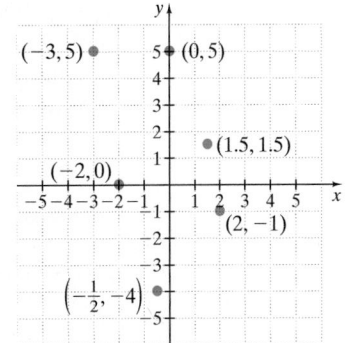

Notice that the y-coordinate of any point on the x-axis is 0. For example, the point with coordinates $(-2, 0)$ lies on the x-axis. Also, the x-coordinate of any point on the y-axis is 0. For example, the point with coordinates $(0, 5)$ lies on the y-axis. These points that lie on the axes do not lie in any quadrants.

✔ **CONCEPT CHECK**

Which of the following best describes the location of the point $(3, -6)$ in a rectangular coordinate system?

a. 3 units to the left of the y-axis and 6 units above the x-axis

b. 3 units above the x-axis and 6 units to the left of the y-axis

c. 3 units to the right of the y-axis and 6 units below the x-axis

d. 3 units below the x-axis and 6 units to the right of the y-axis

Concept Check Answer:

c

2   **Solutions** of equations in two variables consist of two numbers that form a true statement when substituted into the equation. A convenient notation for writing these numbers is as ordered pairs. A solution of an equation containing the variables x and y is written as a pair of numbers in the order (x, y). If the equation contains other variables, we will write ordered pair solutions in alphabetical order.

EXAMPLE 2

Determine whether $(0, -12)$, $(1, 9)$, and $(2, -6)$ are solutions of the equation $3x - y = 12$.

Solution   To check each ordered pair, replace x with the x-coordinate and y with the y-coordinate and see whether a true statement results.

Let $x = 0$ and $y = -12$.

$$3x - y = 12$$
$$3(0) - (-12) \stackrel{?}{=} 12$$
$$0 + 12 \stackrel{?}{=} 12$$
$$12 = 12 \quad \text{True.}$$

Let $x = 1$ and $y = 9$.

$$3x - y = 12$$
$$3(1) - 9 \stackrel{?}{=} 12$$
$$3 - 9 \stackrel{?}{=} 12$$
$$-6 = 12 \quad \text{False.}$$

Let $x = 2$ and $y = -6$.

$$3x - y = 12$$
$$3(2) - (-6) \stackrel{?}{=} 12$$
$$6 + 6 \stackrel{?}{=} 12$$
$$12 = 12 \quad \text{True.}$$

Thus, $(1, 9)$ is not a solution of $3x - y = 12$, but both $(0, -12)$ and $(2, -6)$ are solutions.

3   In fact, the equation $3x - y = 12$ has an infinite number of ordered pair solutions. Since it is impossible to list all solutions, we visualize them by graphing them.

A few more ordered pairs that satisfy $3x - y = 12$ are $(4, 0)$, $(3, -3)$, $(5, 3)$, and $(1, -9)$. These ordered pair solutions along with the ordered pair solutions from Example 2 are plotted on the following graph. The graph of $3x - y = 12$ is the single line containing these points. Every ordered pair solution of the equation corresponds to a point on this line, and every point on this line corresponds to an ordered pair solution.

x	y	$3x - y = 12$
5	3	$3 \cdot 5 - 3 = 12$
4	0	$3 \cdot 4 - 0 = 12$
3	-3	$3 \cdot 3 - (-3) = 12$
2	-6	$3 \cdot 2 - (-6) = 12$
1	-9	$3 \cdot 1 - (-9) = 12$
0	-12	$3 \cdot 0 - (-12) = 12$

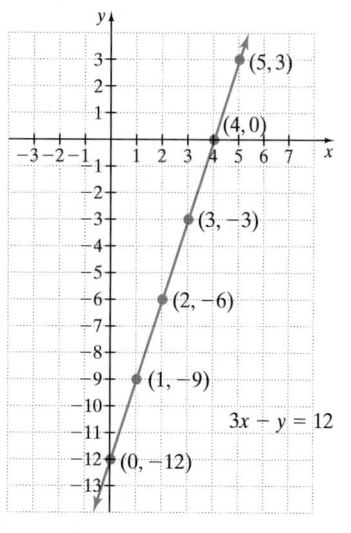

Spotlight on
DECISION
✐MAKING

Suppose you are a meteorologist. You are tracking Hurricane Felix. Hurricane position information is issued every 6 hours. The table lists Felix's most recent positions, given in latitude (vertical scale on the hurricane tracking chart) and longitude (horizontal scale on the hurricane tracking chart). Plot the position of the hurricane on the tracking chart and decide whether Felix is a threat to the United States. If so, what part?

National Hurricane Center Reconnaissance Report

Felix Coordinates

Date	Time	Latitude	Longitude
9/7	4 PM	23.2	88.0
9/7	10 PM	23.7	88.6
9/8	4 AM	23.4	89.1
9/8	10 AM	22.8	89.9
9/8	4 PM	22.2	91.2
9/8	10 PM	21.7	91.8
9/9	4 AM	21.5	92.4
9/9	10 AM	21.2	93.1

Hurricane Tracking Chart

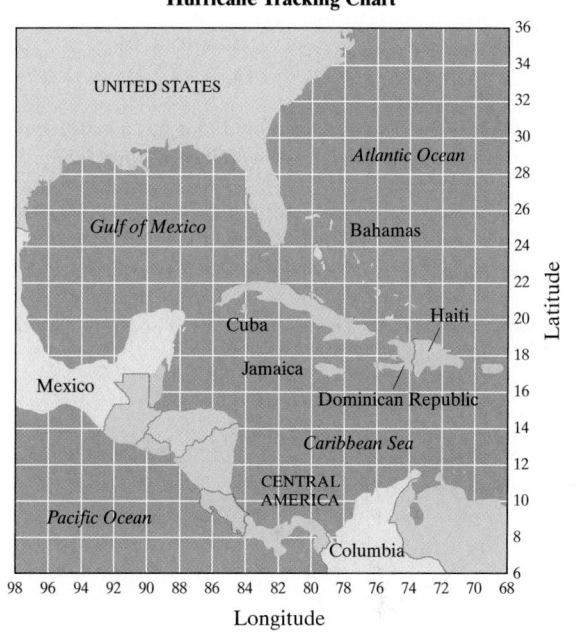

MENTAL MATH

Determine the coordinates of each point on the graph.

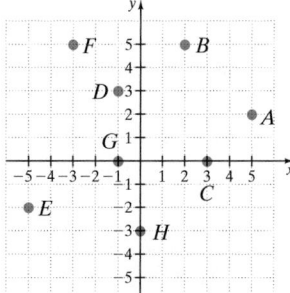

1. Point A **2.** Point B

3. Point C **4.** Point D

5. Point E **6.** Point F

7. Point G **8.** Point H

Without graphing, visualize the location of each point. Then give its location by quadrant or x- or y-axis.

9. $(2, 3)$ **10.** $(0, 5)$ **11.** $(-2, 7)$

12. $(-3, 0)$ **13.** $(-1, -4)$ **14.** $(4, -2)$

15. $(0, -100)$ **16.** $(10, 30)$ **17.** $(-10, -30)$

18. $(0, 0)$ **19.** $(-87, 0)$ **20.** $(-42, 17)$

EXERCISE SET 3.1

   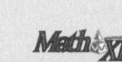

STUDY GUIDE/SSM   CD/ VIDEO   PH MATH TUTOR CENTER   MathXL®Tutorials ON CD   MathXL®   MyMathLab®

Plot each point and name the quadrant or axis in which the point lies. See Example 1.

1. $(3, 2)$

2. $(2, -1)$

3. $(-5, 3)$

4. $(-3, -1)$

5. $\left(5\frac{1}{2}, -4\right)$

6. $\left(-2, 6\frac{1}{3}\right)$

7. $(0, 3.5)$

8. $(-5.2, 0)$

9. $(-2, -4)$

10. $(-4.2, 0)$

Given that x is a positive number and that y is a positive number, determine the quadrant or axis in which each point lies.

11. $(x, -y)$

12. $(-x, y)$

13. $(x, 0)$

14. $(0, -y)$

15. $(-x, -y)$

16. $(0, 0)$

Determine whether each ordered pair is a solution of the given equation. See Example 2.

17. $y = 3x - 5; (0, 5), (-1, -8)$

18. $y = -2x + 7; (1, 5), (-2, 3)$

19. $-6x + 5y = -6; (1, 0), \left(2, \frac{6}{5}\right)$

20. $5x - 3y = 9; (0, 3), \left(\frac{12}{5}, -1\right)$

21. $y = 2x^2; (1, 2), (3, 18)$

22. $y = 2|x|; (-1, 2), (0, 2)$

23. $y = x^3; (2, 8), (3, 9)$

24. $y = x^4; (-1, 1), (2, 16)$

25. $y = \sqrt{x} + 2; (1, 3), (4, 4)$

26. $y = \sqrt[3]{x} - 4; (1, -3), (8, 6)$

MIXED PRACTICE

Determine whether each equation is linear or not. Then graph the equation. See Examples 3 through 7.

27. $x + y = 3$

28. $y - x = 8$

29. $y = 4x$

30. $y = 6x$

31. $y = 4x - 2$

32. $y = 6x - 5$

33. $y = |x| + 3$

34. $y = |x| + 2$

35. $2x - y = 5$

36. $4x - y = 7$

37. $y = 2x^2$

38. $y = 3x^2$

39. $y = x^2 - 3$

40. $y = x^2 + 3$

41. $y = -2x$

42. $y = -3x$

43. $y = -2x + 3$

44. $y = -3x + 2$

45. $y = |x + 2|$

46. $y = |x - 1|$

47. $y = x^3$

    Hint: Let $x = -3, -2, -1, 0, 1, 2$.

48. $y = x^3 - 2$

    Hint: Let $x = -3, -2, -1, 0, 1, 2$.

49. $y = -|x|$

50. $y = -x^2$

51. $y = \frac{1}{3}x - 1$

52. $y = \frac{1}{2}x - 3$

53. $y = -\frac{3}{2}x + 1$

54. $y = -\frac{2}{3}x + 1$

REVIEW AND PREVIEW

Solve the following equations. See Section 2.1.

55. $3(x - 2) + 5x = 6x - 16$

56. $5 + 7(x + 1) = 12 + 10x$

57. $3x + \frac{2}{5} = \frac{1}{10}$

58. $\frac{1}{6} + 2x = \frac{2}{3}$

Solve the following inequalities. See Section 2.4.

59. $3x \leq -15$

60. $-3x > 18$

61. $2x - 5 > 4x + 3$

62. $9x + 8 \leq 6x - 4$

Concept Extensions

For Exercises 63 through 66, match each description with the graph that best illustrates it.

63. Moe worked 40 hours per week until the fall semester started. He quit and didn't work again until he worked 60 hours a week during the holiday season starting mid-December break.

64. Kawana worked 40 hours a week for her father during the summer. She slowly cut back her hours to not working at all during the fall semester. During the holiday season in December, she started working again and increased her hours to 60 hours per week.

65. Wendy worked from July through February, never quitting. She worked between 10 and 30 hours per week.

66. Bartholomew worked from July through February. The rest of the time, he worked between 10 and 40 hours per week. During the holiday season between mid-November and the beginning of January, he worked 40 hours per week.

a.

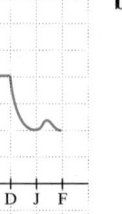

b.

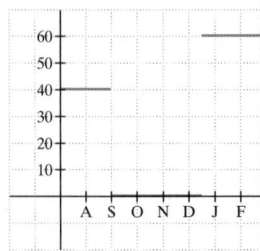

c.

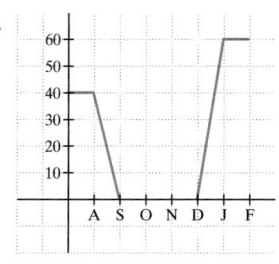

d.

74. The distance y traveled in a train moving at a constant speed of 50 miles per hour is given by the equation

$$y = 50x$$

where x is the time in hours traveled.
a. Draw a graph of this equation.
b. Read from the graph the distance y traveled after 6 hours.

For income tax purposes, Jason Verges, owner of Copy Services, uses a method called **straight-line depreciation** *to show the loss in value of a copy machine he recently purchased. Jason assumes that he can use the machine for 7 years. The following graph shows the value of the machine over the years. Use this graph to answer the following questions.*

This graph shows hourly minimum wages and the years it increased. Use this graph for Exercises 67 through 70.

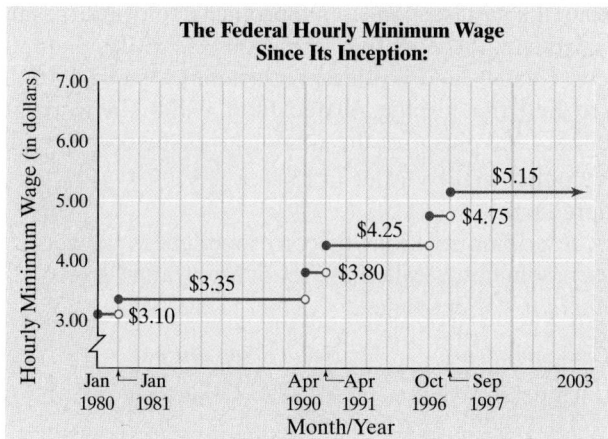

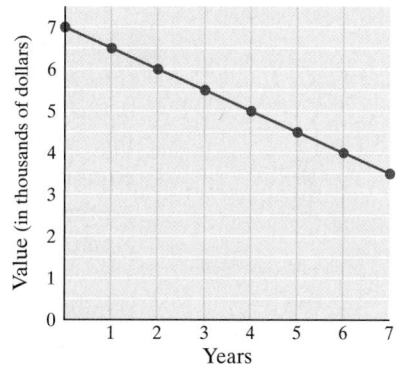

75. What was the purchase price of the copy machine?

76. What is the depreciated value of the machine in 7 years?

77. What loss in value occurred during the first year?

78. What loss in value occurred during the second year?

79. Why do you think that this method of depreciating is called straight-line depreciation?

80. Why is the line tilted downward?

81. On the same set of axes, graph $y = 2x$, $y = 2x - 5$, and $y = 2x + 5$. What patterns do you see in these graphs?

82. On the same set of axes, graph $y = 2x$, $y = x$, and $y = -2x$. Describe the differences and similarities in these graphs.

83. Explain why we generally use three points to graph a line, when only two points are needed.

Write each statement as an equation in two variables. Then graph each equation.

84. The y-value is 5 more than three times the x-value.

85. The y-value is -3 decreased by twice the x-value.

86. The y-value is 2 more than the square of the x-value.

87. The y-value is 5 decreased by the square of the x-value.

Use a graphing calculator to verify the graphs of the following exercises.

88. Exercise 39

89. Exercise 40

90. Exercise 47

91. Exercise 48

67. What was the first year that the minimum hourly wage rose above $4.00?

68. What was the first year that the minimum hourly wage rose above $5.00?

69. Why do you think that this graph is shaped the way it is?

70. The federal hourly minimum wage started in 1938 at $0.25. How much has it increased by in 2003?

71. Graph $y = x^2 - 4x + 7$. Let $x = 0, 1, 2, 3, 4$ to generate ordered pair solutions.

72. Graph $y = x^2 + 2x + 3$. Let $x = -3, -2, -1, 0, 1$ to generate ordered pair solutions.

73. The perimeter y of a rectangle whose width is a constant 3 inches and whose length is x inches is given by the equation

$$y = 2x + 6$$

a. Draw a graph of this equation.
b. Read from the graph the perimeter y of a rectangle whose length x is 4 inches.

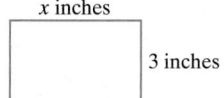

x inches

3 inches

3.2 INTRODUCTION TO FUNCTIONS

Objectives

1. Define relation, domain, and range.
2. Identify functions.
3. Use the vertical line test for functions.
4. Find the domain and range of a function.
5. Use function notation.

1 Recall our example from the last section about products sold and monthly salary. We modeled the data given by the equation $y = 1500 + \frac{1}{10}x$. This equation describes a relationship between x-values and y-values. For example, if $x = 100$, then this equation describes how to find the y-value related to $x = 100$. In words, the equation $y = 1500 + \frac{1}{10}x$ says that 1500 plus $\frac{1}{10}$ of the x-value gives the corresponding y-value. The x-value of 100 corresponds to the y-value of $1500 + \frac{1}{10} \cdot 100 = 1510$ for this equation, and we have the ordered pair $(100, 1510)$.

There are other ways of describing relations or correspondences between two numbers or, in general, a first set (sometimes called the set of *inputs*) and a second set (sometimes called the set of *outputs*). For example,

First Set: Input	***Correspondence***	***Second Set: Output***
People in a certain city	Each person's age	The set of nonnegative integers

A few examples of ordered pairs from this relation might be (Ana, 4); (Bob, 36); (Trey, 21); and so on.

Below are just a few other ways of describing relations between two sets and the ordered pairs that they generate.

Correspondence

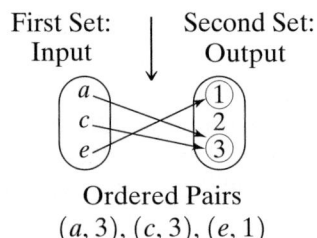

First Set:
Input

Second Set:
Output

Ordered Pairs
$(a, 3), (c, 3), (e, 1)$

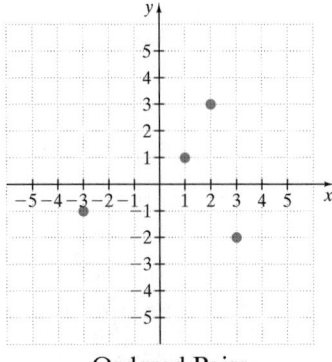

Ordered Pairs
$(-3, -1), (1, 1), (2, 3), (3, -2)$

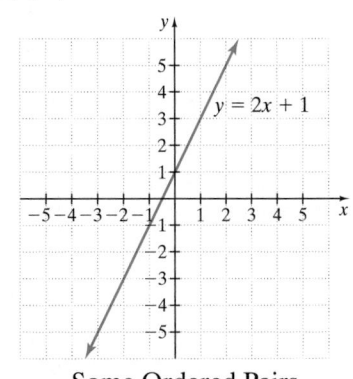

Some Ordered Pairs
$(1, 3), (0, 1)$, and so on

Relation, Domain, and Range

A **relation** is a set of ordered pairs.
The **domain** of the relation is the set of all first components of the ordered pairs.
The **range** of the relation is the set of all second components of the ordered pairs.

For example, the domain for our relation in the middle of the previous page is $\{a, c, e\}$ and the range is $\{1, 3\}$. Notice that the range does not include the element 2 of the second set. This is because no element of the first set is assigned to this element. If a relation is defined in terms of x- and y-values, we will agree that the domain corresponds to x-values and that the range corresponds to y-values that have x-values assigned to them.

EXAMPLE 1

Determine the domain and range of each relation.

a. $\{(2, 3), (2, 4), (0, -1), (3, -1)\}$

b.

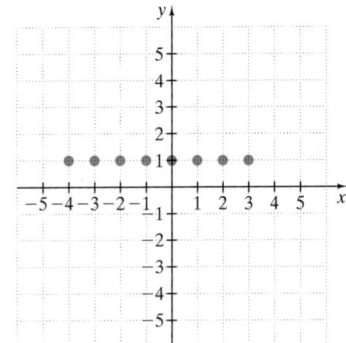

c.

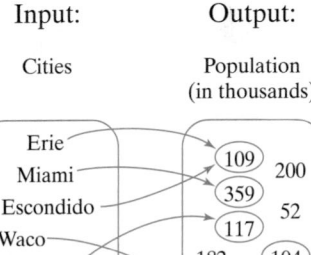

Solution   **a.** The domain is the set of all first coordinates of the ordered pairs, $\{2, 0, 3\}$. The range is the set of all second coordinates, $\{3, 4, -1\}$.

b. Ordered pairs are not listed here, but are given in graph form. The relation is $\{(-4, 1), (-3, 1), (-2, 1), (-1, 1), (0, 1), (1, 1), (2, 1), (3, 1)\}$. The domain is $\{-4, -3, -2, -1, 0, 1, 2, 3\}$. The range is $\{1\}$.

c. The domain is the first set, $\{Erie, Escondido, Gary, Miami, Waco\}$. The range is the numbers in the second set that correspond to elements in the first set $\{104, 109, 117, 359\}$.

   Now we consider a special kind of relation called a function.

Function

A **function** is a relation in which each first component in the ordered pairs corresponds to *exactly* one second component.

► Helpful Hint

A function is a special type of relation, so all functions are relations, but not all relations are functions.

EXAMPLE 2

Which of the following relations are also functions?

a. $\{(-2, 5), (2, 7), (-3, 5), (9, 9)\}$

b.

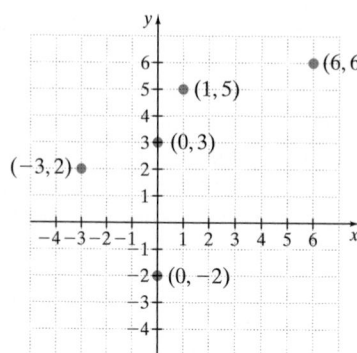

c.

Input	Correspondence	Output
People in a certain city	Each person's age	The set of nonnegative integers

Solution

a. Although the ordered pairs $(-2, 5)$ and $(-3, 5)$ have the same y-value, each x-value is assigned to only one y-value, so this set of ordered pairs is a function.

b. The x-value 0 is assigned to two y-values, -2 and 3, in this graph so this relation does not define a function.

c. This relation is a function because although two different people may have the same age, each person has only one age. This means that each element in the first set is assigned to only one element in the second set.

✔ **CONCEPT CHECK**

Explain why a function can contain both the ordered pairs $(1, 3)$ and $(2, 3)$ but not both $(3, 1)$ and $(3, 2)$.

We will call an equation such as $y = 2x + 1$ a **relation** since this equation defines a set of ordered pair solutions.

EXAMPLE 3

Is the relation $y = 2x + 1$ also a function?

Solution

The relation $y = 2x + 1$ is a function if each x-value corresponds to just one y-value. For each x-value substituted in the equation $y = 2x + 1$, the multiplication and addition performed on each gives a single result, so only one y-value will be associated with each x-value. Thus, $y = 2x + 1$ is a function.

 EXAMPLE 4

Is the relation $x = y^2$ also a function?

Solution

In $x = y^2$, if $y = 3$, then $x = 9$. Also, if $y = -3$, then $x = 9$. In other words, the x-value 9 corresponds to two y-values, 3 and -3. Thus, $x = y^2$ is not a function.

Concept Check Answer:
Two different ordered pairs can have the same y-value, but not the same x-value in a function.

3 As we have seen so far, not all relations are functions. Consider the graphs of $y = 2x + 1$ and $x = y^2$ shown next. For the graph of $y = 2x + 1$, notice that each *x*-value corresponds to only one *y*-value. Recall from Example 3 that $y = 2x + 1$ is a function.

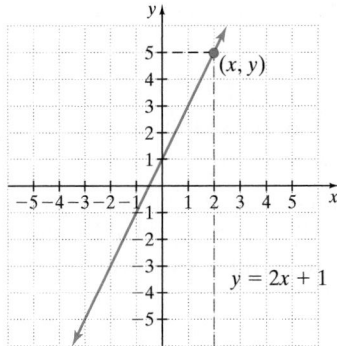
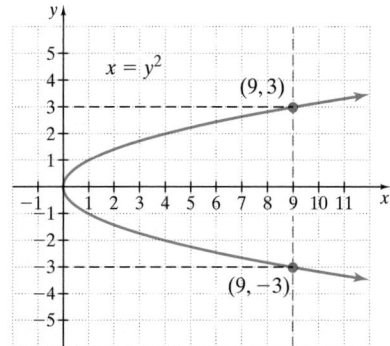

For the graph of $x = y^2$ the *x*-value 9, for example, corresponds to two *y*-values, 3 and -3, as shown by the vertical line. Recall from Example 4 that $x = y^2$ is not a function.

Graphs can be used to help determine whether a relation is also a function by the following vertical line test.

Vertical Line Test

If no vertical line can be drawn so that it intersects a graph more than once, the graph is the graph of a function.

EXAMPLE 5

Which of the following graphs are graphs of functions?

a.

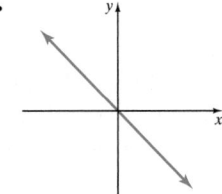

b.

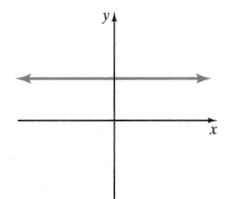

c.

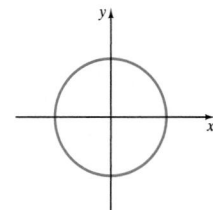

d.

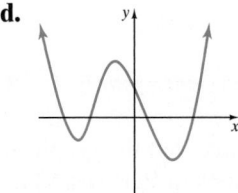

e.

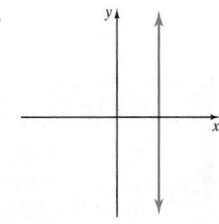

Solution
a. This graph is the graph of a function since no vertical line will intersect this graph more than once.

b. This graph is also the graph of a function.

c. This graph is not the graph of a function. Note that vertical lines can be drawn that intersect the graph in two points.

d. This graph is the graph of a function.

e. This graph is not the graph of a function. A vertical line can be drawn that intersects this line at every point.

Recall that the graph of a linear equation in two variables is a line, and a line that is not vertical will pass the vertical line test. Thus, **all linear equations are functions except those whose graph is a vertical line.**

 CONCEPT CHECK

Determine which equations represent functions. Explain your answer.

a. $y = 14$ **b.** $x = -5$ **c.** $x + y = 6$

 Next, we practice finding the domain and range of a relation from its graph

EXAMPLE 6

Find the domain and range of each relation. Determine whether the relation is also a function.

a.

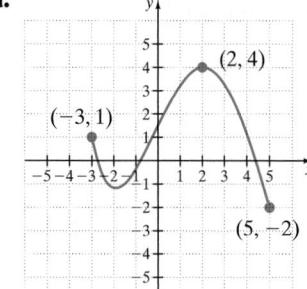

b.

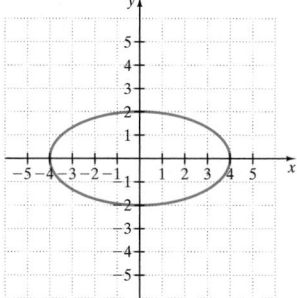

c.

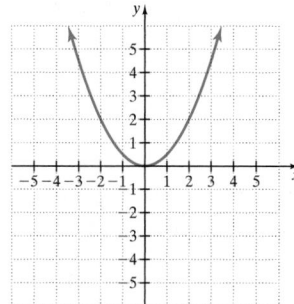

d.

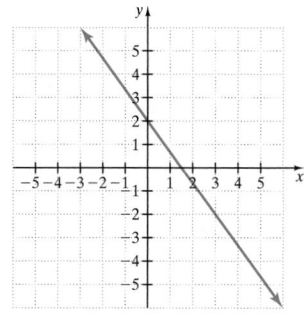

Helpful Hint

In Example 6, Part **a**, notice that the graph contains the endpoints $(-3, 1)$ and $(5, -2)$ whereas the graphs in Parts **c** and **d** contain arrows that indicate that they continue forever.

Concept Check Answer:
a, c

Solution   By the vertical line test, graphs **a**, **c**, and **d** are graphs of functions. The domain is the set of values of x and the range is the set of values of y. We read these values from each graph.

a.
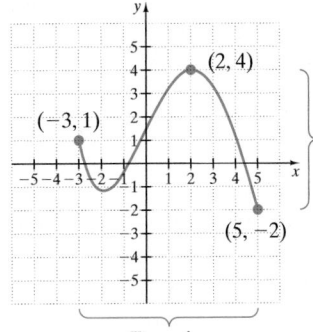

Range: The y-values graphed are from -2 to 4, or $[-2, 4]$.

Domain:
The x-values graphed are from -3 to 5, or $[-3, 5]$.

b.
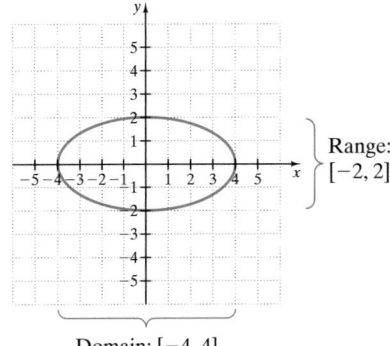

Range: $[-2, 2]$

Domain: $[-4, 4]$

c.
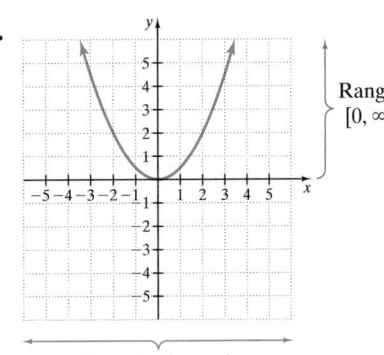

Range: $[0, \infty)$

Domain: $(-\infty, \infty)$

d.
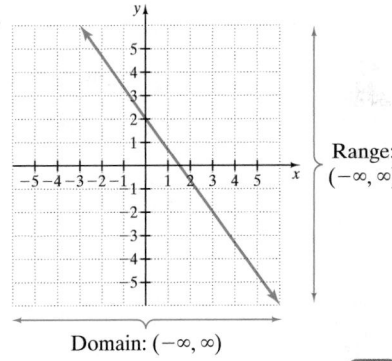

Range: $(-\infty, \infty)$

Domain: $(-\infty, \infty)$

5   Many times letters such as f, g, and h are used to name functions. To denote that y is a function of x, we can write

$$y = f(x)$$

This means that **y is a function of x** or that y *depends on x*. For this reason, y is called the **dependent variable** and x the **independent variable**. The notation $f(x)$ is read "f of x" and is called **function notation**.

For example, to use function notation with the function $y = 4x + 3$, we write $f(x) = 4x + 3$. The notation $f(1)$ means to replace x with 1 and find the resulting y or function value. Since

$$f(x) = 4x + 3$$

then

$$f(1) = 4(1) + 3 = 7$$

This means that when $x = 1$, y or $f(x) = 7$. The corresponding ordered pair is $(1, 7)$. Here, the input is 1 and the output is $f(1)$ or 7. Now let's find $f(2), f(0)$, and $f(-1)$.

$f(x) = 4x + 3$	$f(x) = 4x + 3$	$f(x)\ \ = 4(x) + 3$
$f(2) = 4(2) + 3$	$f(0) = 4(0) + 3$	$f(-1) = 4(-1) + 3$
$= 8 + 3$	$= 0 + 3$	$= -4 + 3$
$= 11$	$= 3$	$= -1$

Helpful Hint

Make sure you remember that $f(2) = 11$ corresponds to the ordered pair $(2, 11)$.

Ordered Pairs:

$(2, 11)$ $(0, 3)$ $(-1, -1)$

> ### Helpful Hint
> Note that $f(x)$ is a special symbol in mathematics used to denote a function. The symbol $f(x)$ is read "f of x." It does *not* mean $f \cdot x$ (f times x).

EXAMPLE 7

If $f(x) = 7x^2 - 3x + 1$ and $g(x) = 3x - 2$, find the following.

a. $f(1)$ **b.** $g(1)$ **c.** $f(-2)$ **d.** $g(0)$

Solution

a. Substitute 1 for x in $f(x) = 7x^2 - 3x + 1$ and simplify.

$$f(x) = 7x^2 - 3x + 1$$
$$f(1) = 7(1)^2 - 3(1) + 1 = 5$$

b. $g(x) = 3x - 2$

$$g(1) = 3(1) - 2 = 1$$

c. $f(x) = 7x^2 - 3x + 1$

$$f(-2) = 7(-2)^2 - 3(-2) + 1 = 35$$

d. $g(x) = 3x - 2$

$$g(0) = 3(0) - 2 = -2$$

✔ **CONCEPT CHECK**

Suppose $y = f(x)$ and we are told that $f(3) = 9$. Which is not true?

a. When $x = 3$, $y = 9$.
b. A possible function is $f(x) = x^2$.
c. A point on the graph of the function is $(3, 9)$.
d. A possible function is $f(x) = 2x + 4$.

If it helps, think of a function, f, as a machine that has been programmed with a certain correspondence or rule. An input value (a member of the domain) is then fed into the machine, the machine does the correspondence or rule and the result is the output (a member of the range).

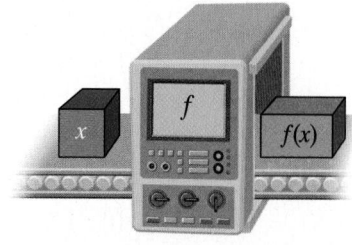
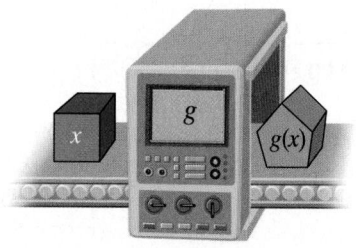

Concept Check Answer:
d

EXAMPLE 8

Given the graphs of the functions f and g, find each function value by inspecting the graphs.

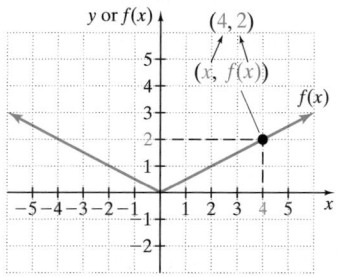
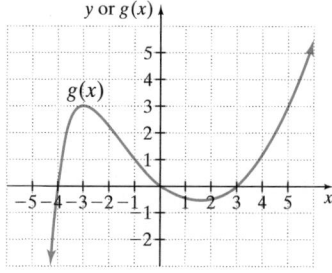

a. $f(4)$ **b.** $f(-2)$ **c.** $g(5)$ **d.** $g(0)$

e. Find all x-values such that $f(x) = 1$.

f. Find all x-values such that $g(x) = 0$.

Solution   **a.** To find $f(4)$, find the y-value when $x = 4$. We see from the graph that when $x = 4$, y or $f(x) = 2$. Thus, $f(4) = 2$.

b. $f(-2) = 1$ from the ordered pair $(-2, 1)$.

c. $g(5) = 3$ from the ordered pair $(5, 3)$.

d. $g(0) = 0$ from the ordered pair $(0, 0)$.

e. To find x-values such that $f(x) = 1$, I'm looking for any ordered pairs on the graph of f whose $f(x)$ or y-value is 1. They are $(2, 1)$ and $(-2, 1)$. Thus $f(2) = 1$ and $f(-2) = 1$. The x-values are 2 and -2.

f. Find ordered pairs on the graph of g whose $g(x)$ or y-value is 0. They are $(3, 0)$ $(0, 0)$ and $(-4, 0)$. Thus $g(3) = 0$, $g(0) = 0$, and $g(-4) = 0$. The x-values are 3, 0, and -4.

Many types of real-world paired data form functions. The broken-line graph below shows the research and development spending by the Pharmaceutical Manufacturers Association.

EXAMPLE 9

The following graph shows the research and development expenditures by the Pharmaceutical Manufacturers Association as a function of time.

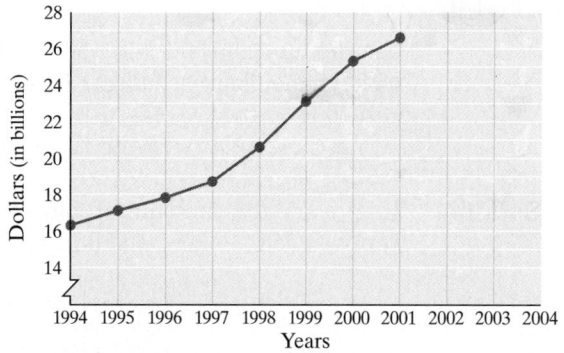

Source: Pharmaceutical Manufacturers Association

a. Approximate the money spent on research and development in 2000.

b. In 1958, research and development expenditures were $200 million. Find the increase in expenditures from 1958 to 2001.

Solution **a.** Find the year 2000 and move upward until you reach the graph. From the point on the graph move horizontally to the left until the other axis is reached. In 2000, approximately $25.3 billion was spent.

b. In 2001, approximately $26.6 billion, or $26,600 million, was spent. The increase in spending from 1958 to 2001 is $26,600 − $200 = $26,400 million or $26.4 billion.

Notice that the graph in Example 9 is the graph of a function since for each year there is only one total amount of money spent by the Pharmaceutical Manufacturers Association on research and development. Also notice that the graph resembles the graph of a line. Often, businesses depend on equations that "closely fit" data-defined functions like this one in order to model the data and predict future trends. For example, by a method called **least squares**, the function $f(x) = 1.558x - 3092$ approximates the data shown. For this function, x is the year and $f(x)$ is total money spent. Its graph and the actual data function are shown next.

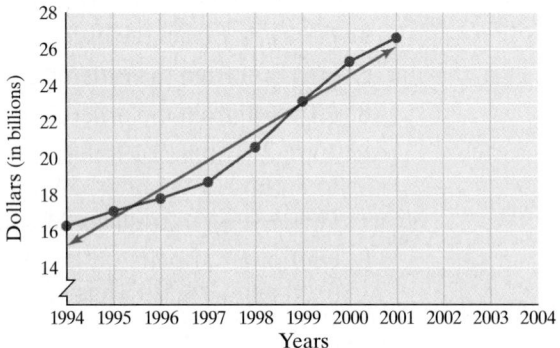

EXAMPLE 10

Use the function $f(x) = 1.558x - 3092$ to predict the amount of money that will be spent by the Pharmaceutical Manufacturers Association on research and development in 2010.

Solution To predict the amount of money that will be spent in the year 2010 we use $f(x) = 1.558x - 3092$ and find $f(2010)$.

$$f(x) = 1.558x - 3092$$

$$f(2010) = 1.558(2010) - 3092$$

$$= 39.58$$

We predict that in the year 2010, $39.58 billion dollars will be spent on research and development by the Pharmaceutical Manufacturers Association.

Graphing Calculator Explorations

It is possible to use a graphing calculator to sketch the graph of more than one equation on the same set of axes. For example, graph the functions $f(x) = x^2$ and $g(x) = x^2 + 4$ on the same set of axes.

To graph on the same set of axes, press the $\boxed{Y =}$ key and enter the equations on the first two lines.

$$Y_1 = x^2$$
$$Y_2 = x^2 + 4$$

Then press the $\boxed{\text{GRAPH}}$ key as usual. The screen should look like this.

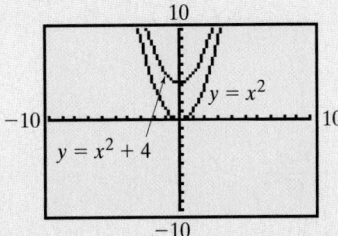

Notice that the graph of y or $g(x) = x^2 + 4$ is the graph of $y = x^2$ moved 4 units upward.

Graph each pair of functions on the same set of axes. Describe the similarities and differences in their graphs.

1. $f(x) = |x|$
   $g(x) = |x| + 1$

2. $f(x) = x^2$
   $h(x) = x^2 - 5$

3. $f(x) = x$
   $H(x) = x - 6$

4. $f(x) = |x|$
   $G(x) = |x| + 3$

5. $f(x) = -x^2$
   $F(x) = -x^2 + 7$

6. $f(x) = x$
   $F(x) = x + 2$

EXERCISE SET 3.2

STUDY GUIDE/SSM   CD/VIDEO   PH MATH TUTOR CENTER   MathXL®Tutorials ON CD   MathXL®   MyMathLab®

Find the domain and the range of each relation. Also determine whether the relation is a function. See Examples 1 and 2.

1. $\{(-1, 7), (0, 6), (-2, 2), (5, 6)\}$

2. $\{(4, 9), (-4, 9), (2, 3), (10, -5)\}$

3. $\{(-2, 4), (6, 4), (-2, -3), (-7, -8)\}$

4. $\{(6, 6), (5, 6), (5, -2), (7, 6)\}$

5. $\{(1, 1), (1, 2), (1, 3), (1, 4)\}$

6. $\{(1, 1), (2, 1), (3, 1), (4, 1)\}$

7. $\left\{\left(\frac{3}{2}, \frac{1}{2}\right), \left(1\frac{1}{2}, -7\right), \left(0, \frac{4}{5}\right)\right\}$

8. $\{(\pi, 0), (0, \pi), (-2, 4), (4, -2)\}$

9. $\{(-3, -3), (0, 0), (3, 3)\}$

10. $\left\{\left(\frac{1}{2}, \frac{1}{4}\right), \left(0, \frac{7}{8}\right), (0.5, \pi)\right\}$

11.

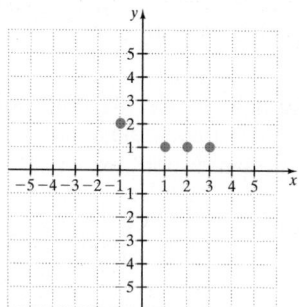

12.

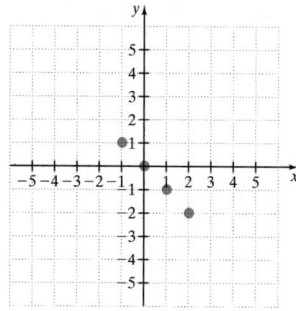

13. Input: Output:

State   Number of Congressional Representatives

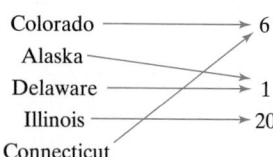

14. Input: Output:

Animal   Average Life Span (in years)

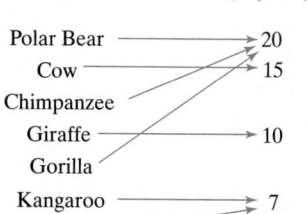

15. Input: Output:

Degrees Fahrenheit   Degrees Celsius

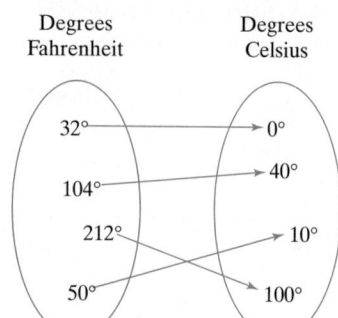

16. Input: Output:

Words   Number of Letters

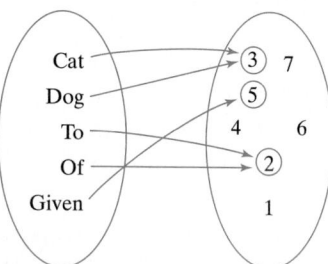

17 Input: Output:

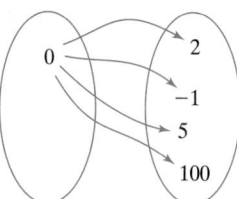

18. Input: Output:

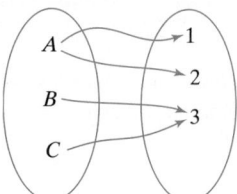

In Exercises 19 through 22, determine whether the relation is a function.

First Set: Input	Correspondence	Second Set: Output
19. Class of algebra students	Final grade average	non negative numbers
20. People who live in Cincinnati, Ohio	Birth date	days of the year
21. blue, green, brown	Eye color	People who live in Cincinnati, Ohio
22. Whole numbers from 0 to 4	Number of children	50 Women in a water aerobics class

Use the vertical line test to determine whether each graph is the graph of a function. See Example 5.

23.
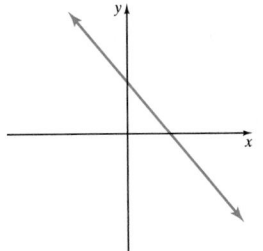

24.
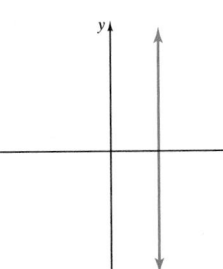

25.
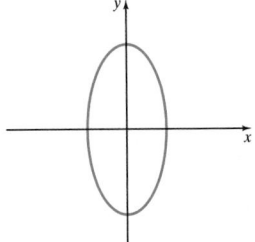

26.
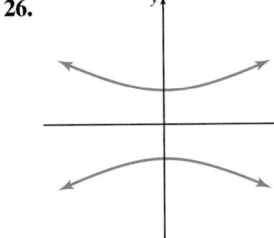

27.
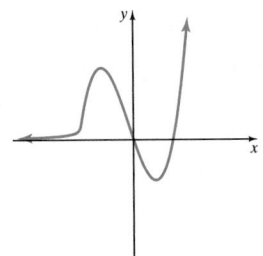

28.
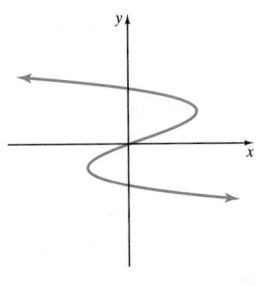

Find the domain and the range of each relation. Use the vertical line test to determine whether each graph is the graph of a function. See Example 6.

29.
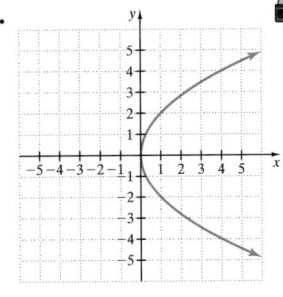

30.
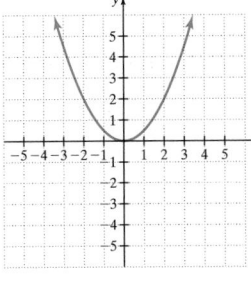

31.
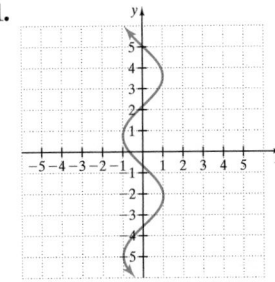

32.
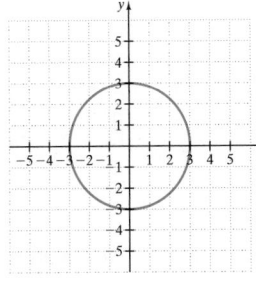

33.
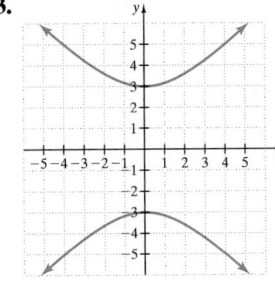

34.
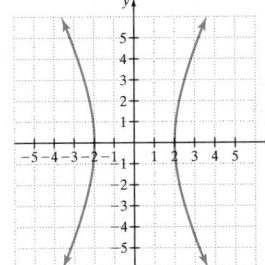

35.
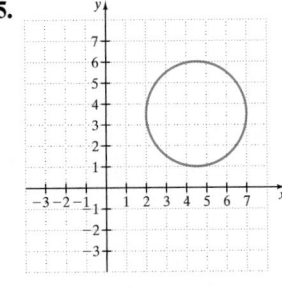

36.
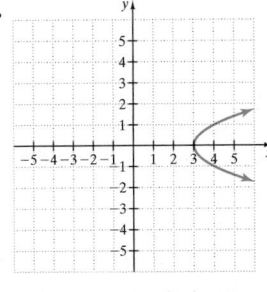

37.

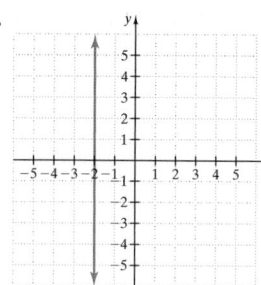

38.

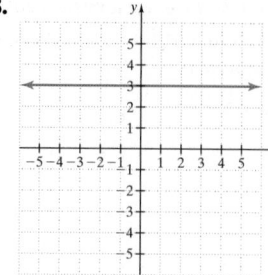

39.

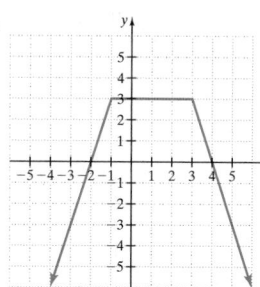

40.

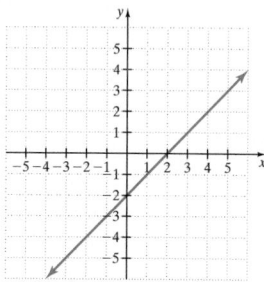

✎ **41.** In your own words define **(a)** function; **(b)** domain; **(c)** range.

✎ **42.** Explain the vertical line test and how it is used.

Decide whether each is a function. See Examples 3 and 4.

🔒 **43.** $y = x + 1$

44. $y = x - 1$

45. $x = 2y^2$

46. $y = x^2$

47. $y - x = 7$

48. $2x - 3y = 9$

49. $y = \dfrac{1}{x}$

50. $y = \dfrac{1}{x - 3}$

51. $y = 5x - 12$

52. $y = \dfrac{1}{2}x + 4$

53. $x = y^2$

54. $x = |y|$

If $f(x) = 3x + 3$, $g(x) = 4x^2 - 6x + 3$, and $h(x) = 5x^2 - 7$, find the following. See Example 7.

55. $f(4)$

56. $f(-1)$

🔒 **57.** $h(-3)$

58. $h(0)$

59. $g(2)$

60. $g(1)$

🔒 **61.** $g(0)$

62. $h(-2)$

Given the following functions, find the indicated values. See Example 7.

63. $f(x) = \dfrac{1}{2}x;$ **a.** $f(0)$

　　b. $f(2)$ **c.** $f(-2)$

64. $g(x) = -\dfrac{1}{3}x;$ **a.** $g(0)$

　　b. $g(-1)$ **c.** $g(3)$

65. $g(x) = 2x^2 + 4;$ **a.** $g(-11)$

b. $g(-1)$ **c.** $g\left(\dfrac{1}{2}\right)$

66. $h(x) = -x^2;$ **a.** $h(-5)$

b. $h\left(-\dfrac{1}{3}\right)$ **c.** $h\left(\dfrac{1}{3}\right)$

67. $f(x) = -5;$ **a.** $f(2)$

b. $f(0)$ **c.** $f(606)$

68. $h(x) = 7;$ **a.** $h(7)$

b. $h(542)$ **c.** $h\left(-\dfrac{3}{4}\right)$

69. $f(x) = 1.3x^2 - 2.6x + 5.1$ **a.** $f(2)$

b. $f(-2)$ **c.** $f(3.1)$

70. $g(x) = 2.7x^2 + 6.8x - 10.2$ **a.** $g(1)$

b. $g(-5)$ **c.** $g(7.2)$

Use the graph of the functions below to answer Exercises 71 through 82. See Example 8.

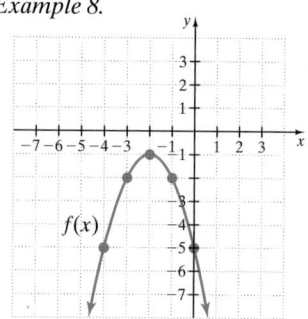

71. If $f(1) = -10$ write the corresponding ordered pair.

72. If $f(-5) = -10$, write the corresponding ordered pair.

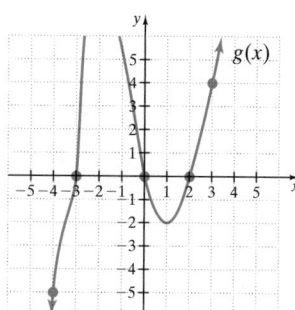

73. If $g(4) = 56$, write the corresponding ordered pair.

74. If $g(-2) = 8$, write the corresponding ordered pair.

75. Find $f(-1)$.

76. Find $f(-2)$.

77. Find $g(2)$.

78. Find $g(-4)$.

79. Find all values of x such that $f(x) = -5$.

80. Find all values of x such that $f(x) = -2$.

81. Find all positive values of x such that $g(x) = 4$.

82. Find all values of x such that $g(x) = 0$.

83. What is the greatest number of x-intercepts that a function may have? Explain your answer.

84. What is the greatest number of y-intercepts that a function may have? Explain your answer.

Use the graph in Example 9 to answer the following. Also see Example 10.

85. a. Use the graph to approximate the money spent on research and development in 1995.

   b. Recall that the function $f(x) = 1.558x - 3092$ approximates the graph of Example 9. Use this equation to approximate the money spent on research and development in 1995.

86. a. Use the graph to approximate the money spent on research and development in 1999.

   b. Use the function $f(x) = 1.558x - 3092$ to approximate the money spent on research and development in 1999.

87. Use the function $f(x) = 1.558x - 3092$ to predict the money that will be spent on research and development in 2008.

88. Use the function $f(x) = 1.558x - 3092$ to predict the money that will be spent on research and development in 2011.

89. Since $y = x + 7$ describes a function, rewrite the equation using function notation.

90. In your own words, explain how to find the domain of a function given its graph.

The function $A(r) = \pi r^2$ may be used to find the area of a circle if we are given its radius.

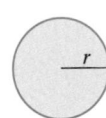

91. Find the area of a circle whose radius is 5 centimeters. (Do not approximate π.)

92. Find the area of a circular garden whose radius is 8 feet. (Do not approximate π.)

The function $V(x) = x^3$ may be used to find the volume of a cube if we are given the length x of a side.

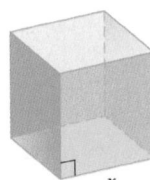

93. Find the volume of a cube whose side is 14 inches.

94. Find the volume of a die whose side is 1.7 centimeters.

Forensic scientists use the following functions to find the height of a woman if they are given the height of her femur bone f or her tibia bone t in centimeters.

$$H(f) = 2.59f + 47.24$$
$$H(t) = 2.72t + 61.28$$

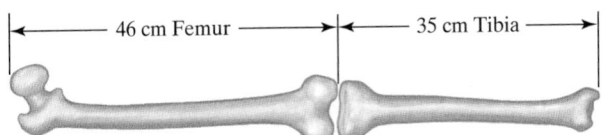

95. Find the height of a woman whose femur measures 46 centimeters.

96. Find the height of a woman whose tibia measures 35 centimeters.

The dosage in milligrams D of Ivermectin, a heartworm preventive, for a dog who weighs x pounds is given by

$$D(x) = \frac{136}{25}x;$$

97. Find the proper dosage for a dog that weighs 30 pounds.

98. Find the proper dosage for a dog that weighs 50 pounds.

99. The per capita consumption (in pounds) of all poultry in the United States is approximated by the function $C(x) = 1.69x + 87.54$, where x is the number of years since 1995. (*Source*: Based on actual and estimated data from the Economic Research Service, U.S. Department of Agriculture, 1995–2002)

   a. Find and interpret $C(5)$.

   b. Estimate the per capita consumption of all poultry in the United States in 2002.

100. The average length of U.S. hospital stays has been decreasing, following the equation $y = -0.09x + 8.02$ where x is the number of years since 1970. (*Source:* National Center for Health Statistics)

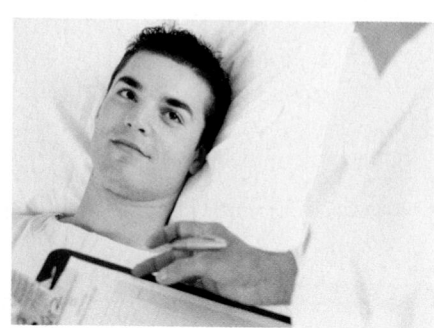

a. What was the length of the average hospital stay in 1995?

b. If this trend continues, what will the average length be in 2007?

REVIEW AND PREVIEW

Complete the given table and use the table to graph the linear equation. See Section 3.1.

101. $x - y = -5$

x	0		1
y		0	

102. $2x + 3y = 10$

x	0		
y		0	2

103. $7x + 4y = 8$

x	0		
y		0	-1

104. $5y - x = -15$

x	0		-2
y		0	

105. $y = 6x$

x	0		-1
y		0	

106. $y = -2x$

x	0		-2
y		0	

△ **107.** Is it possible to find the perimeter of the following geometric figure? If so, find the perimeter.

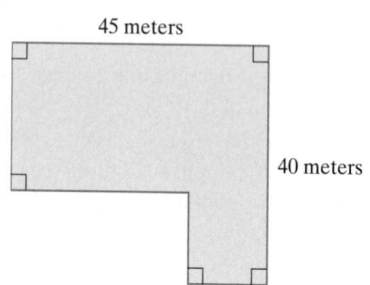

45 meters

40 meters

Concept Extensions

Given the following functions, find the indicated values.

108. $f(x) = 2x + 7$;

a. $f(2)$ **b.** $f(a)$

109. $g(x) = -3x + 12$;

a. $g(s)$ **b.** $g(r)$

110. $h(x) = x^2 + 7$;

a. $h(3)$ **b.** $h(a)$

111. $f(x) = x^2 - 12$;

a. $f(12)$ **b.** $f(a)$

112. Describe a function whose domain is the set of people in your hometown.

113. Describe a function whose domain is the set of people in your algebra class.

GRAPHING LINEAR FUNCTIONS

Objectives

1   Graph linear functions.

2   Graph linear functions by finding intercepts.

3   Graph vertical and horizontal lines.

1   In this section, we identify and graph linear functions. By the vertical line test, we know that all linear equations except those whose graphs are vertical lines are functions. For example, we know from Section 3.1 that $y = 2x$ is a linear equation in two variables. Its graph is shown.

x	$y = 2x$
1	2
0	0
-1	-2

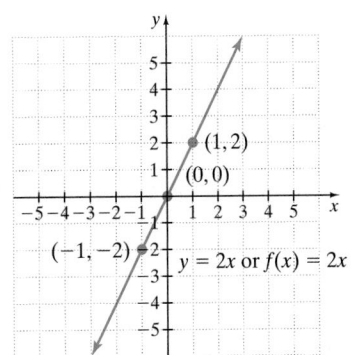

Because this graph passes the vertical line test, we know that $y = 2x$ is a function. If we want to emphasize that this equation describes a function, we may write $y = 2x$ as $f(x) = 2x$.

EXAMPLE 1

Graph $g(x) = 2x + 1$. Compare this graph with the graph of $f(x) = 2x$.

Solution   To graph $g(x) = 2x + 1$, find three ordered pair solutions.

x	$f(x) = 2x$	$g(x) = 2x + 1$
0	0	1
-1	-2	-1
1	2	3

add 1

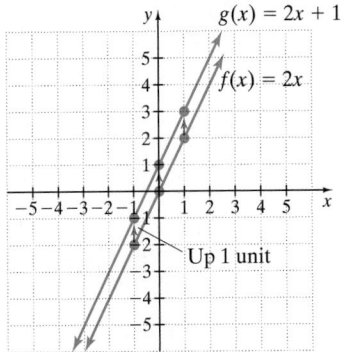

Notice that y-values for the graph of $g(x) = 2x + 1$ are obtained by adding 1 to each y-value of each corresponding point of the graph of $f(x) = 2x$. The graph of $g(x) = 2x + 1$ is the same as the graph of $f(x) = 2x$ shifted upward 1 unit.

In general, a **linear function** is a function that can be written in the form $f(x) = mx + b$. For example, $g(x) = 2x + 1$ is in this form, with $m = 2$ and $b = 1$.

EXAMPLE 2

Graph the linear functions $f(x) = -3x$ and $g(x) = -3x - 6$ on the same set of axes.

Solution To graph $f(x)$ and $g(x)$, find ordered pair solutions.

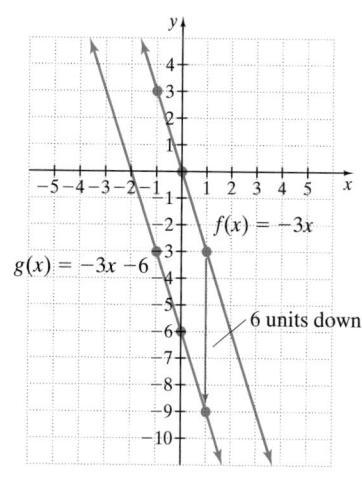

x	$f(x) = -3x$	$g(x) = -3x - 6$
0	0	−6
1	−3	−9
−1	3	−3
−2	6	0

subtract 6

subtract 6

Each y-value for the graph of $g(x) = -3x - 6$ is obtained by subtracting 6 from the y-value of the corresponding point of the graph of $f(x) = -3x$. The graph of $g(x) = -3x - 6$ is the same as the graph of $f(x) = -3x$ shifted down 6 units.

2   Notice that the y-intercept of the graph of $g(x) = -3x - 6$ in the preceding figure is $(0, -6)$. In general, if *a linear function is written in the form* $f(x) = mx + b$ *or* $y = mx + b$, *the y-intercept is* $(0, b)$. This is because if x is 0, then $f(x) = mx + b$ becomes $f(0) = m \cdot 0 + b = b$, and we have the ordered pair solution $(0, b)$. We will study this form more in the next section.

EXAMPLE 3

Find the y-intercept of the graph of each equation.

a. $f(x) = \dfrac{1}{2}x + \dfrac{3}{7}$ **b.** $y = -2.5x - 3.2$

Solution   **a.** The y-intercept of $f(x) = \dfrac{1}{2}x + \dfrac{3}{7}$ is $\left(0, \dfrac{3}{7}\right)$.

b. The y-intercept of $y = -2.5x - 3.2$ is $(0, -3.2)$.

In general, to find the y-intercept of the graph of an equation not in the form $y = mx + b$, let $x = 0$ since any point on the y-axis has an x-coordinate of 0. To find the x-intercept of a line, let $y = 0$ or $f(x) = 0$ since any point on the x-axis has a y-coordinate of 0.

> ### Finding x-and y-Intercepts
>
> To find an x-intercept, let $y = 0$ or $f(x) = 0$ and solve for x.
> To find a y-intercept, let $x = 0$ and solve for y.

Intercepts are usually easy to find and plot since one coordinate is 0.

EXAMPLE 4

Graph $x - 3y = 6$ by plotting intercepts.

Solution   Let $y = 0$ to find the x-intercept and $x = 0$ to find the y-intercept.

$$\text{If } y = 0 \qquad \text{then} \qquad \text{If } x = 0 \qquad \text{then}$$

$$x - 3(0) = 6 \qquad\qquad 0 - 3y = 6$$

$$x - 0 = 6 \qquad\qquad -3y = 6$$

$$x = 6 \qquad\qquad y = -2$$

The x-intercept is $(6, 0)$ and the y-intercept is $(0, -2)$. We find a third ordered pair solution to check our work. If we let $y = -1$, then $x = 3$. Plot the points $(6, 0)$, $(0, -2)$, and $(3, -1)$. The graph of $x - 3y = 6$ is the line drawn through these points, as shown.

x	y
6	0
0	-2
3	-1

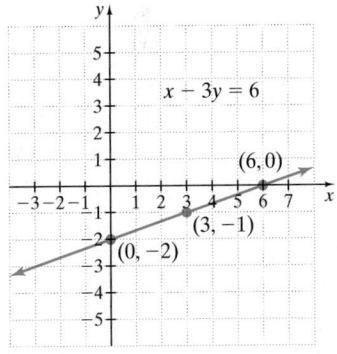

Notice that the equation $x - 3y = 6$ describes a linear function—"linear" because its graph is a line and "function" because the graph passes the vertical line test.

If we want to emphasize that the equation $x - 3y = 6$ from Example 4 describes a function, first solve the equation for y.

$$x - 3y = 6$$

$$-3y = -x + 6 \qquad \textit{Subtract } x \textit{ from both sides.}$$

$$\frac{-3y}{-3} = \frac{-x}{-3} + \frac{6}{-3} \qquad \textit{Divide both sides by } -3.$$

$$y = \frac{1}{3}x - 2 \qquad \textit{Simplify.}$$

Next, let $\qquad$ $y = f(x).$

$$f(x) = \frac{1}{3}x - 2$$

> **Helpful Hint**
>
> Any linear equation that describes a function can be written using function notation. To do so,
>
> 1. solve the equation for y and then
> 2. replace y with $f(x)$, as we did above.

EXAMPLE 5

Graph $x = -2y$ by plotting intercepts.

Solution Let $y = 0$ to find the x-intercept and $x = 0$ to find the y-intercept.

If $y = 0$	then	If $x = 0$	then
$x = -2(0)$	or	$0 = -2y$	or
$x = 0$		$0 = y$	
$(0, 0)$		$(0, 0)$	

Ordered pairs

Both the x-intercept and y-intercept are $(0, 0)$. This happens when the graph passes through the origin. Since two points are needed to determine a line, we must find at least one more ordered pair that satisfies $x = -2y$. Let $y = -1$ to find a second ordered pair solution and let $y = 1$ as a check point.

If $y = -1$	then	If $y = 1$	then
$x = -2(-1)$	or	$x = -2(1)$	or
$x = 2$		$x = -2$	

The ordered pairs are $(0, 0), (2, -1)$, and $(-2, 1)$. Plot these points to graph $x = -2y$.

x	y
0	0
2	-1
-2	1

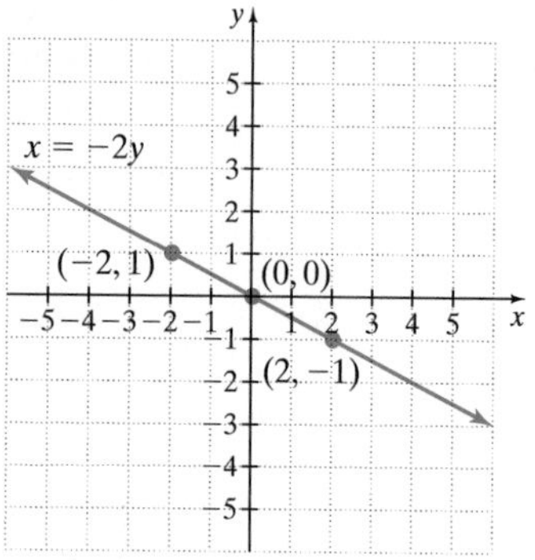

3   The equations $x = c$ and $y = c$, where c is a real number constant, are both linear equations in two variables. Why? Because $x = c$ can be written as $x + 0y = c$ and $y = c$ can be written as $0x + y = c$. We graph these two special linear equations below.

EXAMPLE 6

Graph $x = 2$.

Solution   The equation $x = 2$ can be written as $x + 0y = 2$. For any y-value chosen, notice that x is 2. No other value for x satisfies $x + 0y = 2$. Any ordered pair whose x-coordinate is 2 is a solution to $x + 0y = 2$ because 2 added to 0 times any value of y is $2 + 0$, or 2. We will use the ordered pairs $(2, 3), (2, 0)$ and $(2, -3)$ to graph $x = 2$.

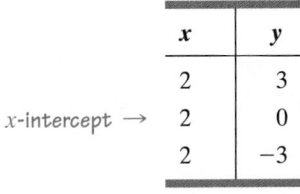

x	y
2	3
2	0
2	-3

x-intercept $\rightarrow$

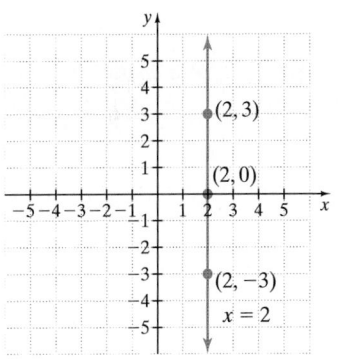

The graph is a vertical line with x-intercept $(2, 0)$. Notice that this graph is not the graph of a function, and it has no y-intercept because x is never 0.

EXAMPLE 7

Graph $y = -3$.

Solution   The equation $y = -3$ can be written as $0x + y = -3$. For any x-value chosen, y is -3. If we choose 4, 0, and -2 as x-values, the ordered pair solutions are $(4, -3), (0, -3)$, and $(-2, -3)$. We will use these ordered pairs to graph $y = -3$.

x	y
4	-3
0	-3
-2	-3

$\leftarrow$ y-intercept

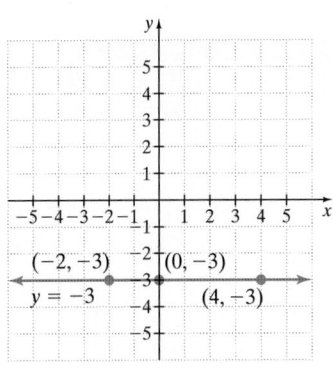

The graph is a horizontal line with y-intercept $(0, -3)$ and no x-intercept. Notice that this graph is the graph of a function.

From Examples 6 and 7, we have the following generalization.

Graphing Vertical and Horizontal Lines

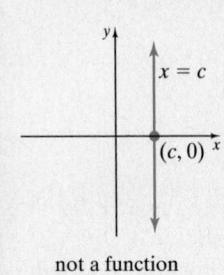

The graph of $x = c$, where c is a real number, is a vertical line with x-intercept $(c, 0)$.

The graph of $y = c$, where c is a real number, is a horizontal line with y-intercept $(0, c)$.

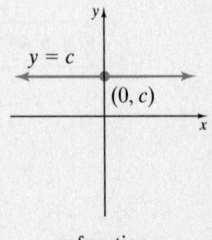

not a function   a function

Graphing Calculator Explorations

You may have noticed by now that to use the $\boxed{Y =}$ key on a graphing calculator to graph an equation, the equation must be solved for y.

Graph each function by first solving the function for y.

1. $x = 3.5y$

2. $-2.7y = x$

3. $5.78x + 2.31y = 10.98$

4. $-7.22x + 3.89y = 12.57$

5. $y - |x| = 3.78$

6. $3y - 5x^2 = 6x - 4$

7. $y - 5.6x^2 = 7.7x + 1.5$

8. $y + 2.6|x| = -3.2$

EXERCISE SET 3.3

STUDY GUIDE/SSM   CD/VIDEO   PH MATH TUTOR CENTER   MathXL®Tutorials ON CD   MathXL®   MyMathLab®

Graph each linear function. See Examples 1 and 2.

1. $f(x) = -2x$

2. $f(x) = 2x$

3. $f(x) = -2x + 3$

 4. $f(x) = 2x + 6$

5. $f(x) = \dfrac{1}{2}x$

6. $f(x) = \dfrac{1}{3}x$

7. $f(x) = \dfrac{1}{2}x - 4$

8. $f(x) = \dfrac{1}{3}x - 2$

The graph of $f(x) = 5x$ follows. Use this graph to match each linear function with its graph. See Examples 1 through 3.

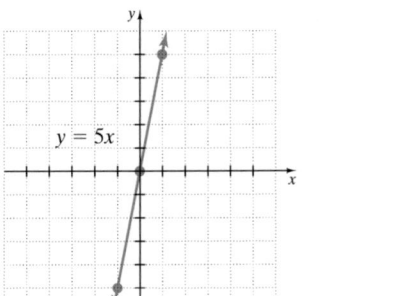

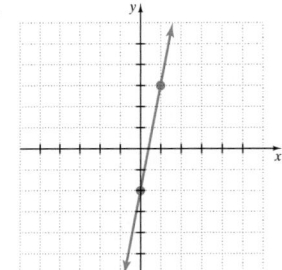

A

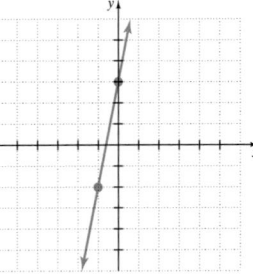

B

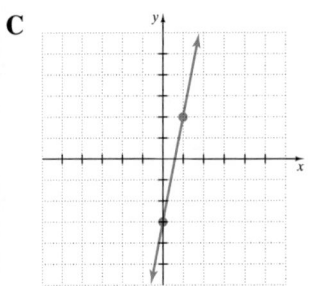

C

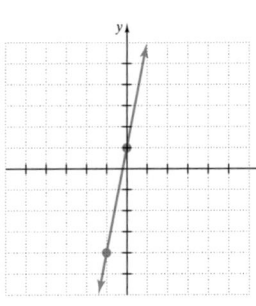

D

9. $f(x) = 5x - 3$ **10.** $f(x) = 5x - 2$

11. $f(x) = 5x + 1$ **12.** $f(x) = 5x + 3$

Graph each linear function by finding x-and y-intercepts. Then write each equation using function notation. See Examples 4 and 5.

13. $x - y = 3$

14. $x - y = -4$

15. $x = 5y$

16. $2x = y$

17. $-x + 2y = 6$

18. $x - 2y = -8$

19. $2x - 4y = 8$

20. $2x + 3y = 6$

21. In your own words, explain how to find x- and y-intercepts.

22. Explain why it is a good idea to use three points to graph a linear equation.

Graph each linear equation. See Examples 6 and 7.

 23. $x = -1$ **24.** $y = 5$

25. $y = 0$ **26.** $x = 0$

27. $y + 7 = 0$ **28.** $x - 3 = 0$

Match each equation below with its graph.

A

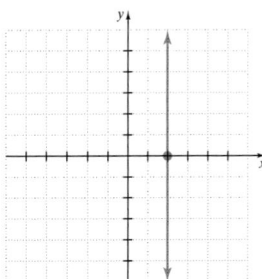

B

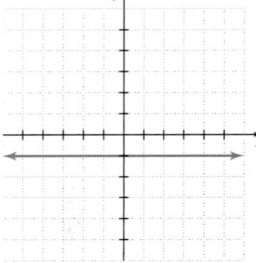

C

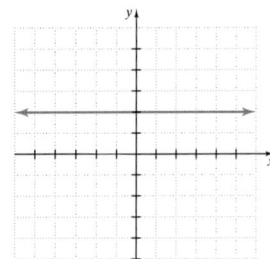

D

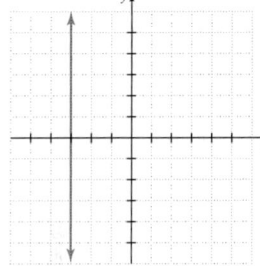

29. $y = 2$ **30.** $x = -3$

31. $x - 2 = 0$ **32.** $y + 1 = 0$

33. Discuss whether a vertical line ever has a y-intercept.

34. Discuss whether a horizontal line ever has an x-intercept.

MIXED PRACTICE

Graph each linear equation.

35. $x + 2y = 8$ **36.** $x - 3y = 3$

37. $3x + 5y = 7$ **38.** $3x - 2y = 5$

39. $x + 8y = 8$ **40.** $x - 3y = 9$

41. $5 = 6x - y$ **42.** $4 = x - 3y$

43. $-x + 10y = 11$ **44.** $-x + 9 = -y$

45. $y = \frac{3}{2}$ **46.** $x = \frac{3}{2}$

47. $2x + 3y = 6$ **48.** $4x + y = 5$

49. $x + 3 = 0$ **50.** $y - 6 = 0$

51. $f(x) = \frac{3}{4}x + 2$ **52.** $f(x) = \frac{4}{3}x + 2$

53. $f(x) = x$ **54.** $f(x) = -x$

55. $f(x) = \dfrac{1}{2}x$

56. $f(x) = -2x$

57. $f(x) = 4x - \dfrac{1}{3}$

58. $f(x) = -3x + \dfrac{3}{4}$

59. $x = -3$

60. $f(x) = 3$

REVIEW AND PREVIEW

Solve the following. See Sections 2.6 and 2.7.

61. $|x - 3| = 6$

62. $|x + 2| < 4$

63. $|2x + 5| > 3$

64. $|5x| = 10$

65. $|3x - 4| \le 2$

66. $|7x - 2| \ge 5$

Simplify. See Section 1.3.

67. $\dfrac{-6 - 3}{2 - 8}$

68. $\dfrac{4 - 5}{-1 - 0}$

69. $\dfrac{-8 - (-2)}{-3 - (-2)}$

70. $\dfrac{12 - 3}{10 - 9}$

71. $\dfrac{0 - 6}{5 - 0}$

72. $\dfrac{2 - 2}{3 - 5}$

Concept Extensions

Solve.

73. Broyhill Furniture found that it takes 2 hours to manufacture each table for one of its special dining room sets. Each chair takes 3 hours to manufacture. A total of 1500 hours is available to produce tables and chairs of this style. The linear equation that models this situation is $2x + 3y = 1500$, where x represents the number of tables produced and y the number of chairs produced.

   a. Complete the ordered pair solution $(0, \quad)$ of this equation. Describe the manufacturing situation this solution corresponds to.

   b. Complete the ordered pair solution $(\quad , 0)$ for this equation. Describe the manufacturing situation this solution corresponds to.

   c. If 50 tables are produced, find the greatest number of chairs the company can make.

74. While manufacturing two different camera models, Kodak found that the basic model costs $55 to produce, whereas the deluxe model costs $75. The weekly budget for these two models is limited to $33,000 in production costs. The linear equation that models this situation is $55x + 75y = 33,000$, where x represents the number of basic models and y the number of deluxe models.

   a. Complete the ordered pair solution $(0, \quad)$ of this equation. Describe the manufacturing situation this solution corresponds to.

   b. Complete the ordered pair solution $(\quad , 0)$ of this equation. Describe the manufacturing situation this solution corresponds to.

   c. If 350 deluxe models are produced, find the greatest number of basic models that can be made in one week.

75. The cost of renting a car for a day is given by the linear function $C(x) = 0.2x + 24$, where $C(x)$ is in dollars and x is the number of miles driven.

   a. Find the cost of driving the car 200 miles.

   b. Graph $C(x) = 0.2x + 24$.

   c. How can you tell from the graph of $C(x)$ that as the number of miles driven increases, the total cost increases also?

76. The cost of renting a piece of machinery is given by the linear function $C(x) = 4x + 10$, where $C(x)$ is in dollars and x is given in hours.

   a. Find the cost of renting the piece of machinery for 8 hours.

   b. Graph $C(x) = 4x + 10$.

   c. How can you tell from the graph of $C(x)$ that as the number of hours increases, the total cost increases also?

77. The yearly cost of tuition (in state) and required fees for attending a public two-year college full time can be estimated by the linear function $f(x) = 53.6x + 849.88$, where x is the number of years after 1990 and $f(x)$ is the total cost. (*Source:* U.S. National Center for Education Statistics)

   a. Use this function to approximate the yearly cost of attending a two-year college in the year 2010. [*Hint:* Find $f(20)$.]

   b. Use the given function to predict in what year the yearly cost of tuition and required fees will exceed $2000. [*Hint:* Let $f(x) = 2000$ and solve for x.]

   c. Use this function to approximate the yearly cost of attending a two-year college in the present year. If you attend a two-year college, is this amount greater than or less than the amount that is currently charged by the college that you attend?

78. The yearly cost of tuition (in state) and required fees for attending a public four-year college can be estimated by the linear function $f(x) = 174.4x + 2074.38$, where x is the number of years after 1990 and $f(x)$ is the total cost in dollars. (*Source:* U.S. National Center for Education Statistics)

   a. Use this function to approximate the yearly cost of attending a four-year college in the year 2010. [*Hint:* Find $f(20)$.]

   b. Use the given function to predict in what year the yearly cost of tuition and required fees will exceed $5000. [*Hint:* Let $f(x) = 5000$ and solve for x.]

   c. Use this function to approximate the yearly cost of attending a four-year college in the present year. If you attend a four-year college, is this amount greater than or less than the amount that is currently charged by the college that you attend?

Use a graphing calculator to verify the results of each exercise.

79. Exercise 9   **80.** Exercise 10

81. Exercise 17   **82.** Exercise 18

83. The graph of $f(x)$ or $y = -4x$ is given below.

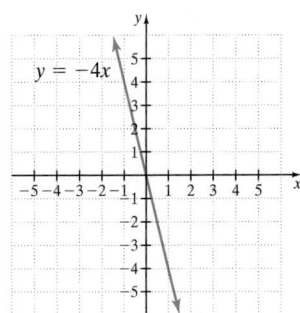

Without actually graphing, describe the shape and location of

   a. $y = -4x + 2$ **b.** $y = -4x - 5$

It is true that for any function $f(x)$, the graph of $f(x) + K$ is the same as the graph of $f(x)$ shifted K units up if K is positive and $|K|$ units down if K is negative.

The graph of $y = |x|$ is

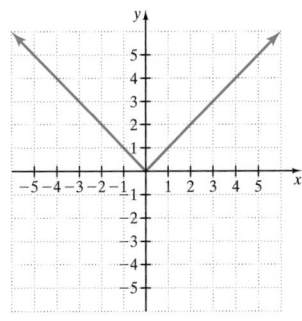

Without actually graphing, match each equation with its graph.

  a. $y = |x| - 1$ **b.** $y = |x| + 1$

  c. $y = |x| - 3$ **d.** $y = |x| + 3$

84.

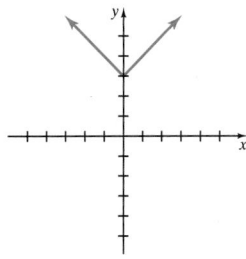

85.

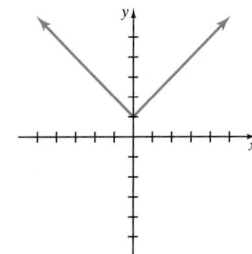

86.

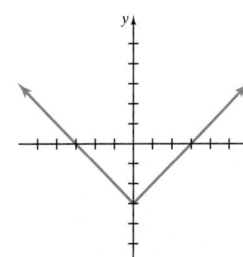

87.

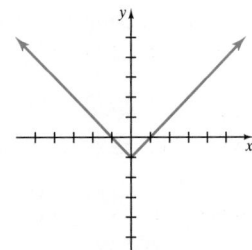

STUDY SKILLS REMINDER

Tips for Studying for an Exam

To prepare for an exam, try the following study techniques.

▶ Start the study process days before your exam.

▶ Make sure that you are current and up-to-date on your assignments.

▶ If there is a topic that you are unsure of, use one of the many resources that are available to you. For example,
See your instructor.
Visit a learning resource center on campus where math tutors are available.
Read the textbook material and examples on the topic.
View a videotape on the topic.

▶ Reread your notes and carefully review the Chapter Highlights at the end of the chapter.

▶ Work the review exercises at the end of the chapter and check your answers. Make sure that you correct any missed exercises. If you have trouble on a topic, use a resource.

▶ Find a quiet place to take the Chapter Test found at the end of the chapter. Do not use any resources when taking this sample test. This way you will have a clear indication of how prepared you are for your exam. Check your answers and use the Chapter Test Prep Video CD to correct any missed exercises.

▶ Get lots of rest the night before the exam. It's hard to show how well you know the material if your brain is foggy from lack of sleep.

Good luck and keep a positive attitude.

3.4 THE SLOPE OF A LINE

Objectives

1 Find the slope of a line given two points on the line.

2 Find the slope of a line given the equation of a line.

3 Interpret the slope–intercept form in an application.

4 Find the slopes of horizontal and vertical lines.

5 Compare the slopes of parallel and perpendicular lines.

1 You may have noticed by now that different lines often tilt differently. It is very important in many fields to be able to measure and compare the tilt, or **slope**, of lines. For example, a wheelchair ramp with a slope of $\frac{1}{12}$ means that the ramp rises 1 foot for every 12 horizontal feet. A road with a slope or grade of 11% (or $\frac{11}{100}$) means that the road rises 11 feet for every 100 horizontal feet.

We measure the slope of a line as a ratio of **vertical change** to **horizontal change**. Slope is usually designated by the letter m.

Suppose that we want to measure the slope of the following line.

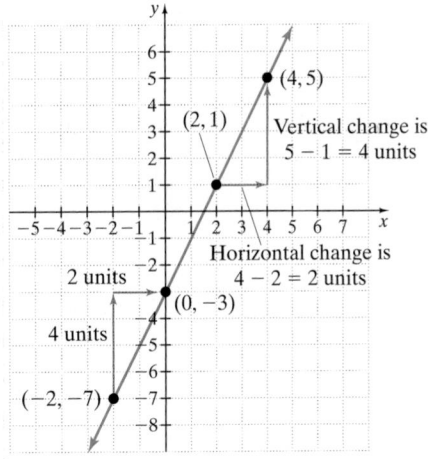

The vertical change between *both* pairs of points on the line is 4 units per horizontal change of 2 units. Then

$$\text{slope } m = \frac{\text{change in } y \text{ (vertical change)}}{\text{change in } x \text{ (horizontal change)}} = \frac{4}{2} = 2$$

We can also think of slope as a *rate of change* between points. A slope of 2 or $\frac{2}{1}$ means that between pairs of points on the line, the rate of change is a vertical change of 2 units per horizontal change of 1 unit.

Consider the line in the box on the next page, which passes through the points (x_1, y_1) and (x_2, y_2). (The notation x_1 is read "x-sub-one.") The vertical change, or *rise*, between these points is the difference of the y-coordinates: $y_2 - y_1$. The horizontal change, or *run*, between the points is the difference of the x-coordinates: $x_2 - x_1$.

Slope of a Line

Given a line passing through points (x_1, y_1) and (x_2, y_2) the **slope** m of the line is

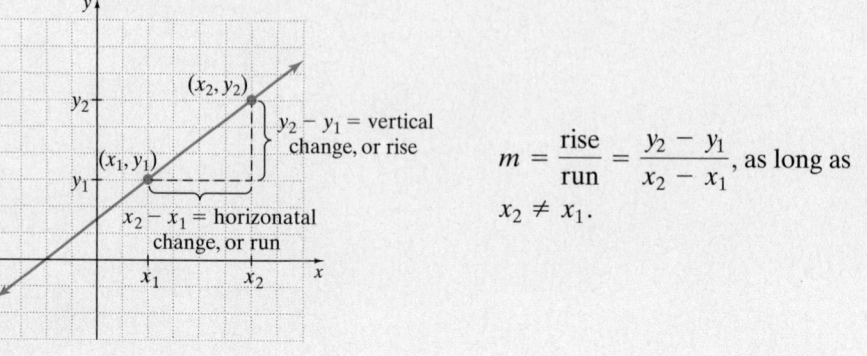

$y_2 - y_1 =$ vertical change, or rise

$x_2 - x_1 =$ horizonatal change, or run

$$m = \frac{\text{rise}}{\text{run}} = \frac{y_2 - y_1}{x_2 - x_1}, \text{ as long as}$$

$x_2 \neq x_1.$

✔ **CONCEPT CHECK**

In the definition of slope, we state that $x_2 \neq x_1$. Explain why.

EXAMPLE 1

Find the slope of the line containing the points $(0, 3)$ and $(2, 5)$. Graph the line.

Solution We use the slope formula. It does not matter which point we call (x_1, y_1) and which point we call (x_2, y_2). We'll let $(x_1, y_1) = (0, 3)$ and $(x_2, y_2) = (2, 5)$.

$$m = \frac{y_2 - y_1}{x_2 - x_1}$$

$$= \frac{5 - 3}{2 - 0} = \frac{2}{2} = 1$$

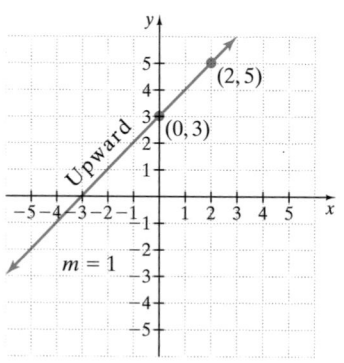

Notice in this example that the slope is positive and that the graph of the line containing $(0, 3)$ and $(2, 5)$ moves upward, or increases, as we go from left to right.

> **Helpful Hint**
>
> The slope of a line is the same no matter which 2 points of a line you choose to calculate slope. The line in Example 1 also contains the point $(-3, 0)$. Below, we calculate the slope of the line using $(0, 3)$ as (x_1, y_1) and $(-3, 0)$ as (x_2, y_2).
>
> $$m = \frac{y_2 - y_1}{x_2 - x_1} = \frac{0 - 3}{-3 - 0} = \frac{-3}{-3} = 1 \quad \text{Same slope as found in Example 1.}$$

Concept Check Answer:
So that the denominator is not 0

EXAMPLE 2

Find the slope of the line containing the points $(5, -4)$ and $(-3, 3)$. Graph the line.

Solution   We use the slope formula, and let $(x_1, y_1) = (5, -4)$ and $(x_2, y_2) = (-3, 3)$.

$$m = \frac{y_2 - y_1}{x_2 - x_1}$$

$$= \frac{3 - (-4)}{-3 - 5} = \frac{7}{-8} = -\frac{7}{8}$$

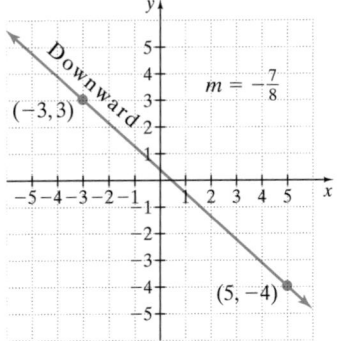

Notice in this example that the slope is negative and that the graph of the line through $(5, -4)$ and $(-3, 3)$ moves downward, or decreases, as we go from left to right.

> **Helpful Hint**
> When we are trying to find the slope of a line through two given points, it makes no difference which given point is called (x_1, y_1) and which is called (x_2, y_2). Once an x-coordinate is called x_1, however, make sure its corresponding y-coordinate is called y_1.

✔ **CONCEPT CHECK**

Find and correct the error in the following calculation of slope of the line containing the points $(12, 2)$ and $(4, 7)$.

$$m = \frac{12 - 4}{2 - 7} = \frac{8}{-5} = -\frac{8}{5}$$

2   As we have seen, the slope of a line is defined by two points on the line. Thus, if we know the equation of a line, we can find its slope.

EXAMPLE 3

Find the slope of the line whose equation is $f(x) = \frac{2}{3}x + 4$.

Solution   Two points are needed on the line defined by $f(x) = \frac{2}{3}x + 4$ or $y = \frac{2}{3}x + 4$ to find its slope. We will use intercepts as our two points.

$$\text{If } x = 0, \text{ then} \quad \text{If } y = 0, \text{ then}$$

$$y = \frac{2}{3} \cdot 0 + 4 \qquad 0 = \frac{2}{3}x + 4$$

$$y = 4 \qquad\qquad -4 = \frac{2}{3}x \qquad \text{Subtract 4.}$$

$$\frac{3}{2}(-4) = \frac{3}{2} \cdot \frac{2}{3}x \qquad \text{Multiply by } \frac{3}{2}.$$

$$-6 = x$$

Use the points $(0, 4)$ and $(-6, 0)$ to find the slope. Let (x_1, y_1) be $(0, 4)$ and (x_2, y_2) be $(-6, 0)$. Then

$$m = \frac{y_2 - y_1}{x_2 - x_1} = \frac{0 - 4}{-6 - 0} = \frac{-4}{-6} = \frac{2}{3}$$

Analyzing the results of Example 3, you may notice a striking pattern:

The slope of $y = \frac{2}{3}x + 4$ is $\frac{2}{3}$, the same as the coefficient of x.

Also, the y-intercept is $(0, 4)$, as expected.

When a linear equation is written in the form $f(x) = mx + b$ or $y = mx + b$, m is the slope of the line and $(0, b)$ is its y-intercept. The form $y = mx + b$ is appropriately called the **slope–intercept form**.

Slope–Intercept Form

When a linear equation in two variables is written in slope–intercept form,

slope y-intercept is $(0, b)$
↓   ↓

$$y = mx + b$$

then m is the slope of the line and $(0, b)$ is the y-intercept of the line.

EXAMPLE 4

Find the slope and the y-intercept of the line $3x - 4y = 4$.

Solution   We write the equation in slope–intercept form by solving for y.

$$3x - 4y = 4$$
$$-4y = -3x + 4 \qquad \text{Subtract } 3x \text{ from both sides.}$$
$$\frac{-4y}{-4} = \frac{-3x}{-4} + \frac{4}{-4} \qquad \text{Divide both sides by } -4.$$
$$y = \frac{3}{4}x - 1 \qquad \text{Simplify.}$$

The coefficient of x, $\frac{3}{4}$, is the slope, and the y-intercept is $(0, -1)$.

3   On the following page is the graph of one-day ticket prices at Disney World for the years shown.

Notice that the graph resembles the graph of a line. Recall that businesses often depend on equations that "closely fit" graphs like this one to model the data and to predict future trends. By the **least squares** method, the linear function $f(x) = 1.618x + 32.17$

approximates the data shown, where x is the number of years since 1990 and y is the ticket price for that year.

Helpful Hint

The notation $0 \leftrightarrow 1990$ means that the number 0 corresponds to the year 1990, 1 corresponds to the year 1991, and so on.

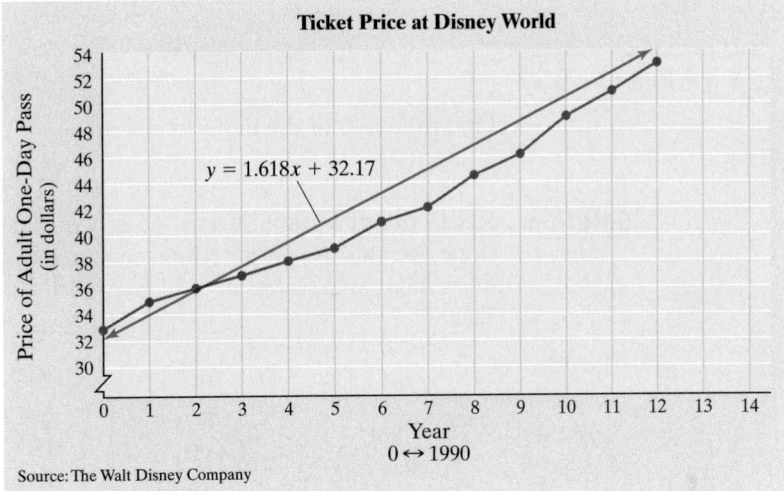

Ticket Price at Disney World

Price of Adult One-Day Pass (in dollars)

$y = 1.618x + 32.17$

Year
$0 \leftrightarrow 1990$

Source: The Walt Disney Company

EXAMPLE 5

PREDICTING FUTURE PRICES

The adult one-day pass price $f(x)$ for Disney World is given by

$$f(x) = 1.618x + 32.17$$

where x is the number of years since 1990

a. Use this equation to predict the ticket price for the year 2008.
b. What does the slope of this equation mean?
c. What does the y-intercept of this equation mean?

Solution   **a.** To predict the price of a pass in 2008, we need to find $f(18)$. (Since year 1990 corresponds to $x = 0$, year 2008 corresponds to $x = 18$.)

$$f(x) = 1.618x + 32.17$$
$$f(18) = 1.618(18) + 32.17 \quad \text{Let } x = 18.$$
$$= 61.294$$

We predict that in the year 2008 the price of an adult one-day pass to Disney World will be about $61.29.

b. The slope of $f(x) = 1.618x + 32.17$ is 1.618. We can think of this number as $\dfrac{\text{rise}}{\text{run}}$ or $\dfrac{1.618}{1}$. This means that the ticket price increases on the average by $1.618 every 1 year.

c. The y-intercept of $y = 1.618x + 32.17$ is $(0, 32.17)$.

↑　　↖
year　price

This means that at year $x = 0$ or 1990, the ticket price was about $32.17.

4   Next we find the slopes of two special types of lines: vertical lines an
horizontal lines.

EXAMPLE 6

Find the slope of the line $x = -5$.

Solution   Recall that the graph of $x = -5$ is a vertical line with x-intercept $(-5, 0)$. To find th
slope, we find two ordered pair solutions of $x = -5$. Of course, solutions of $x = -$
must have an x-value of -5. We will let $(x_1, y_1) = (-5, 0)$ and $(x_2, y_2) = (-5, 4)$
Then

$$m = \frac{y_2 - y_1}{x_2 - x_1}$$

$$= \frac{4 - 0}{-5 - (-5)}$$

$$= \frac{4}{0}$$

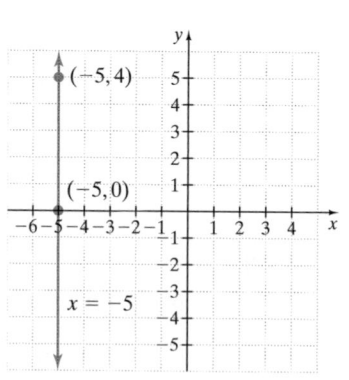

Since $\frac{4}{0}$ is undefined, we say that the slope of the vertical line $x = -5$ is undefined.

EXAMPLE 7

Find the slope of the line $y = 2$.

Solution   Recall that the graph of $y = 2$ is a horizontal line with y-intercept $(0, 2)$. To find th
slope, we find two points on the line, such as $(0, 2)$ and $(1, 2)$, and use these points to
find the slope.

$$m = \frac{2 - 2}{1 - 0}$$

$$= \frac{0}{1}$$

$$= 0$$

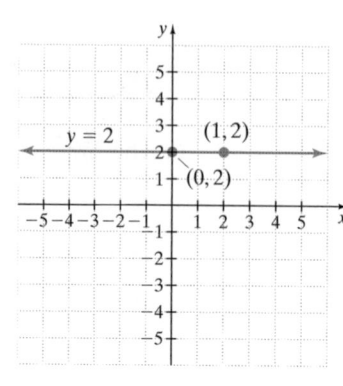

The slope of the horizontal line $y = 2$ is 0.

From the previous two examples, we have the following generalization.

The slope of any vertical line is undefined.
The slope of any horizontal line is 0.

> **Helpful Hint**
> Slope of 0 and undefined slope are not the same. Vertical lines have undefined slope, whereas horizontal lines have slope of 0.

The following four graphs summarize the overall appearance of lines with positive, negative, zero, or undefined slopes.

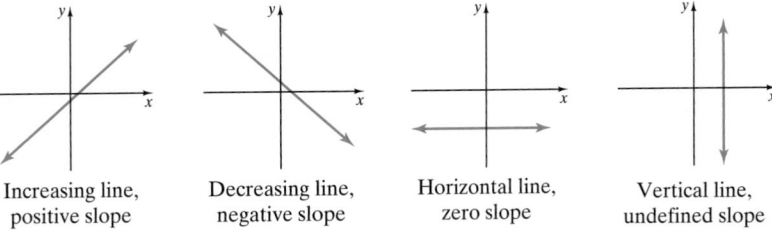

Increasing line,   Decreasing line,   Horizontal line,   Vertical line,
positive slope   negative slope   zero slope   undefined slope

The appearance of a line can give us further information about its slope.

The graphs of $y = \frac{1}{2}x + 1$ and $y = 5x + 1$ are shown to the right. Recall that the graph of $y = \frac{1}{2}x + 1$ has a slope of $\frac{1}{2}$ and that the graph of $y = 5x + 1$ has a slope of 5.

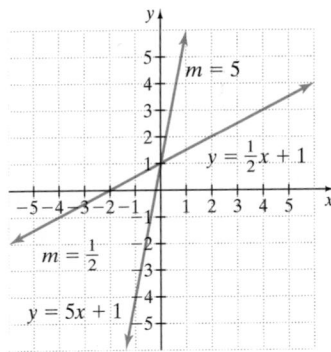

Notice that the line with the slope of 5 is steeper than the line with the slope of $\frac{1}{2}$. This is true in general for positive slopes.

For a line with positive slope m, as m increases, the line becomes steeper.

To see why this is so, compare the slopes from above.

$\frac{1}{2}$ means a vertical change of 1 unit per horizontal change of 2 units

5 or $\frac{10}{2}$ means a vertical change of 10 units per horizontal change of 2 units

For larger positive slopes, the vertical change is greater for the same horizontal change. Thus, larger positive slopes mean steeper lines.

5 Slopes of lines can help us determine whether lines are parallel. Parallel line are distinct lines with the same steepness, so it follows that they have the same slope

Parallel Lines

Two nonvertical lines are parallel if they have the same slope and different y-intercepts.

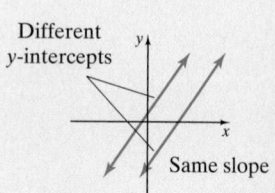

How do the slopes of perpendicular lines compare? (Two lines intersecting a right angles are called **perpendicular lines**.) Suppose that a line has a slope of $\frac{a}{b}$. If the line is rotated 90°, the rise and run are now switched, except that the run is now negative. This means that the new slope is $-\frac{b}{a}$. Notice that

$$\left(\frac{a}{b}\right) \cdot \left(-\frac{b}{a}\right) = -1$$

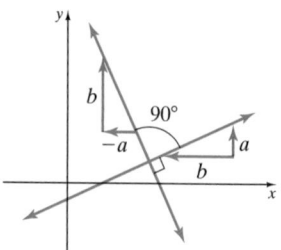

This is how we tell whether two lines are perpendicular.

Perpendicular Lines

Two nonvertical lines are perpendicular if the product of their slopes is −1.

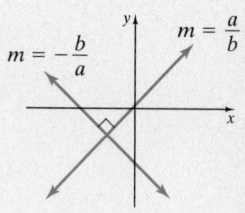

In other words, two nonvertical lines are perpendicular if the slope of one is the negative reciprocal of the slope of the other.

EXAMPLE 8

Are the following pairs of lines parallel, perpendicular, or neither?

a. $3x + 7y = 4$

$6x + 14y = 7$

b. $-x + 3y = 2$

$2x + 6y = 5$

Solution   Find the slope of each line by solving each equation for y.

a.

$$3x + 7y = 4 \qquad\qquad 6x + 14y = 7$$

$$7y = -3x + 4 \qquad\qquad 14y = -6x + 7$$

$$\frac{7y}{7} = \frac{-3x}{7} + \frac{4}{7} \qquad\qquad \frac{14y}{14} = \frac{-6x}{14} + \frac{7}{14}$$

$$y = -\frac{3}{7}x + \frac{4}{7} \qquad\qquad y = -\frac{3}{7}x + \frac{1}{2}$$

slope y-intercept   slope y-intercept

$\left(0, \dfrac{4}{7}\right)$ $\left(0, \dfrac{1}{2}\right)$

The slopes of both lines are $-\dfrac{3}{7}$.

The y-intercepts are different, so the lines are not the same. Therefore, the lines are parallel.

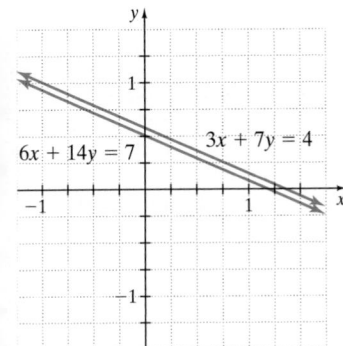

b.

$$-x + 3y = 2 \qquad\qquad 2x + 6y = 5$$

$$3y = x + 2 \qquad\qquad 6y = -2x + 5$$

$$\frac{3y}{3} = \frac{x}{3} + \frac{2}{3} \qquad\qquad \frac{6y}{6} = \frac{-2x}{6} + \frac{5}{6}$$

$$y = \frac{1}{3}x + \frac{2}{3} \qquad\qquad y = -\frac{1}{3}x + \frac{5}{6}$$

slope y-intercept   slope y-intercept

$\left(0, \dfrac{2}{3}\right)$ $\left(0, \dfrac{5}{6}\right)$

The slopes are not the same and their product is not -1. $\left[\left(\dfrac{1}{3}\right)\cdot\left(-\dfrac{1}{3}\right) = -\dfrac{1}{9}\right]$

Therefore, the lines are neither parallel nor perpendicular.

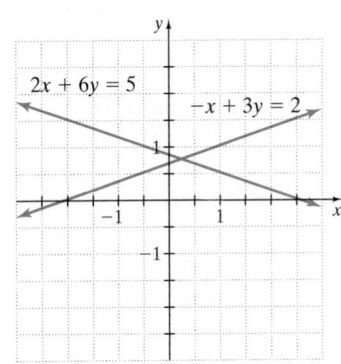

✔ **CONCEPT CHECK**

What is *different* about the equations of two parallel lines?

Graphing Calculator Explorations

Many graphing calculators have a TRACE feature. This feature allows you to trace along a graph and see the corresponding x- and y-coordinates appear on the screen. Use this feature for the following exercises.

Graph each function and then use the TRACE feature to complete each ordered pair solution. (Many times the tracer will not show an exact x- or y-value asked for. In each case, trace as closely as you can to the given x- or y-coordinate and approximate the other, unknown coordinate to one decimal place.)

1. $y = 2.3x + 6.7$
   $x = 5.1, y = ?$

2. $y = -4.8x + 2.9$
   $x = -1.8, y = ?$

3. $y = -5.9x - 1.6$
   $x = ?, y = 7.2$

4. $y = 0.4x - 8.6$
   $x = ?, y = -4.4$

5. $y = x^2 + 5.2x - 3.3$
   $x = 2.3, y = ?$
   $x = ?, y = 36$
   (There will be two answers here.)

6. $y = 5x^2 - 6.2x - 8.3$
   $x = 3.2, y = ?$
   $x = ?, y = 12$
   (There will be two answers here.)

Spotlight on

DECISION
✄MAKING

Suppose you are the manager of an apartment complex. You have just notified residents of a rent increase. Some residents think that the increase may be unjustified and out of line with recent increases. A group of concerned residents asks you to hold an open meeting to answer questions about the increase. You are preparing a set of overheads to use during the meeting to show the history of rent increases at the apartment complex. Which overhead would you use and why?

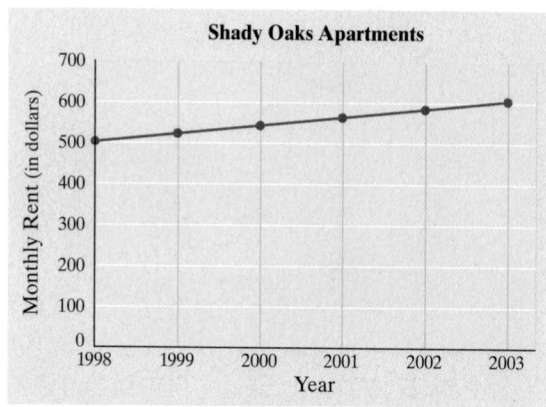

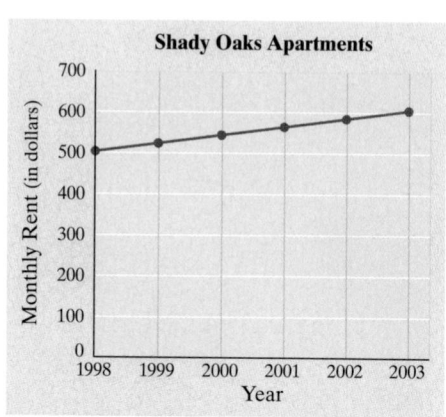

MENTAL MATH

Decide whether a line with the given slope s _____ *t to right.*

1. $m = \dfrac{7}{6}$ **2.** $m = -3$ _____ efined

EXERCISE SET 3.4

Find the slope of the line that goes thro _____
Examples 1 and 2.

1. $(3, 2), (8, 11)$ **2.**

3. $(3, 1), (1, 8)$ **4**

5. $(-2, 8), (4, 3)$ **6**

7. $(-2, -6), (4, -4)$

9. $(-3, -1), (-12, 11)$ **1**

11. $(-2, 5), (3, 5)$

13. $(-1, 1), (-1, -5)$

15. $(0, 6), (-3, 0)$

17. $(-1, 2), (-3, 4)$

Two lines are graphed on each se _____
has the greater slope.

19.

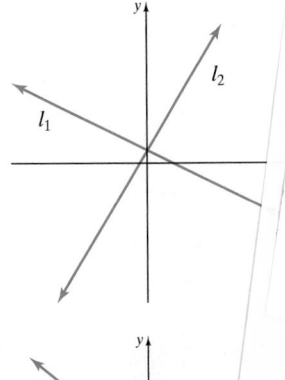

21.

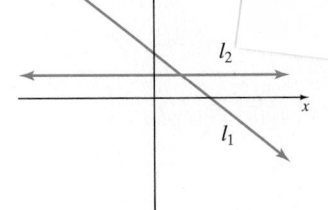

d the y-intercept of each line. See Examples 3

_____ 2

_____ + 6

_____ 10

_____ 10

_____ = 6

31. $f(x) = \dfrac{1}{2}x$

32. $f(x) = -\dfrac{1}{4}x$

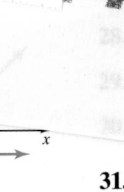

Match each graph with its equation.

A

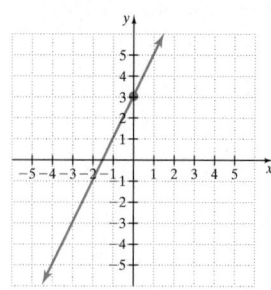

B

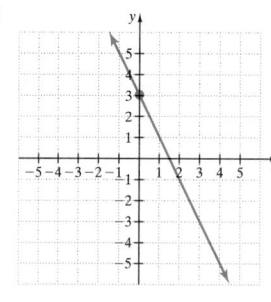

C

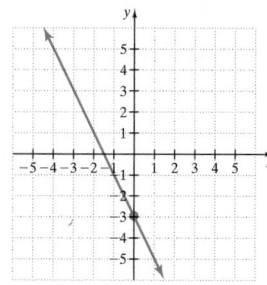

D

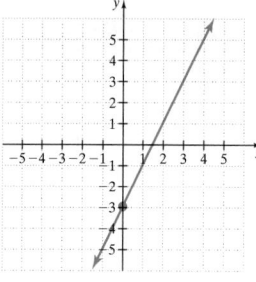

33. $f(x) = 2x + 3$

34. $f(x) = 2x - 3$

35. $f(x) = -2x + 3$

36. $f(x) = -2x - 3$

Find the slope of each line. See Examples 6 and 7.

37. $x = 1$

38. $y = -2$

39. $y = -3$

40. $x = 4$

41. $x + 2 = 0$

42. $y - 7 = 0$

43. Explain how merely looking at a line can tell us whether its slope is negative, positive, undefined, or zero.

44. Explain why the graph of $y = b$ is a horizontal line.

Find the slope and the y-intercept of each line.

45. $f(x) = -x + 5$

46. $f(x) = x + 2$

47. $-6x + 5y = 30$

48. $4x - 7y = 28$

49. $3x + 9 = y$

50. $2y - 7 = x$

51. $y = 4$

52. $x = 7$

53. $f(x) = 7x$

54. $f(x) = \frac{1}{7}x$

55. $6 + y = 0$

56. $x - 7 = 0$

57. $2 - x = 3$

58. $2y + 4 = -7$

Determine whether the lines are parallel, perpendicular, or neither. See Example 8.

59. $f(x) = -3x + 6$
$g(x) = 3x + 5$

60. $f(x) = 5x - 6$
$g(x) = 5x + 2$

61. $-4x + 2y = 5$
$2x - y = 7$

62. $2x - y = -10$
$2x + 4y = 2$

63. $-2x + 3y = 1$
$3x + 2y = 12$

64. $x + 4y = 7$
$2x - 5y = 0$

65. Explain whether two lines, both with positive slopes, can be perpendicular.

66. Explain why it is reasonable that nonvertical parallel lines have the same slope.

Determine the slope of each line.

67.

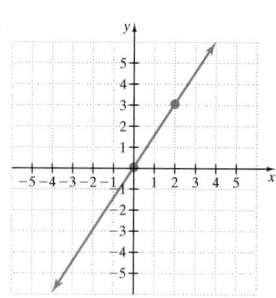

68.

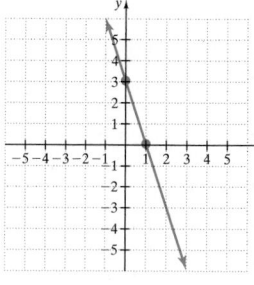

69.

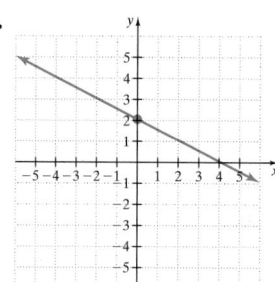

70.

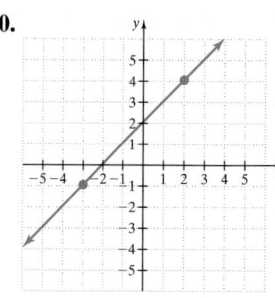

Find each slope.

71. Find the pitch, or slope, of the roof shown.

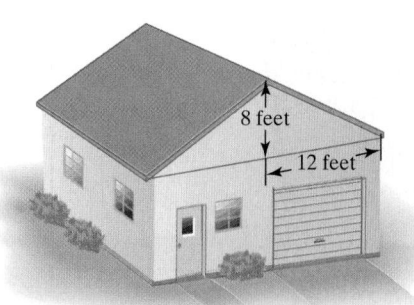

72. Upon takeoff, a Delta Airlines jet climbs to 3 miles as it passes over 25 miles of land below it. Find the slope of its climb.

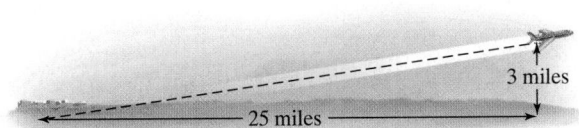

73. Driving down Bald Mountain in Wyoming, Bob Dean finds that he descends 1600 feet in elevation by the time he is 2.5 miles (horizontally) away from the high point on the mountain road. Find the slope of his descent rounded to two decimal places (1 mile = 5280 feet).

74. Find the grade, or slope, of the road shown.

Solve. See Example 5.

75. The annual average income y of an American man over 25 with an associate's degree is approximated by the linear equation $y = 1545.4x + 33,858.4$, where x is the number of years after 1997. (*Source:* Based on data from the U.S. Bureau of the Census).

   a. Predict the average income of an American man with an associate's degree in 2005.

   b. Find and interpret the slope of the equation.

   c. Find and interpret the y-intercept of the equation.

76. The annual average income of an American woman over 25 with a bachelor's degree is given by the linear equation $y = 1280.3x + 28,421.6$, where x is the number of years after 1997. (*Source:* Based on data from the U.S. Bureau of the Census).

   a. Find the average income of an American woman with a bachelor's degree in 2005.

   b. Find and interpret the slope of the equation.

   c. Find and interpret the y-intercept of the equation.

77. With wireless Internet (WiFi) gaining popularity, the number of public wireless Internet access points (in thousands) is projected to grow from 2002 to 2006 according to the equation

$$-245x + 10y = 59$$

where x is the number of years after 2002.

   a. Find the slope and y-intercept of the linear equation.

   b. What does the slope mean in this context?

   c. What does the y-intercept mean in this context?

78. One of the faster growing occupations over the next few years is expected to be paralegal. The number of people y in thousands employed as paralegals in the United States can be estimated by the linear equation $-63x + 10y = 1880$, where x is the number of years after 1996. (*Source:* Based on projections from the U.S. Bureau of Labor Statistics, 2000–2010)

   a. Find the slope and y-intercept of the linear equation.

   b. What does the slope mean in this context?

   c. What does the y-intercept mean in this context?

79. In an earlier section, it was given that the yearly cost of tuition and required fees for attending a public four-year college full-time can be estimated by the linear function

$$f(x) = 174.4x + 2074.38$$

where x is the number of years after 1990 and $f(x)$ is the total cost. (*Source:* U.S. National Center for Education Statistics)

   a. Find and interpret the slope of this equation.

   b. Find and interpret the y-intercept of this equation.

80. If an earlier section, it was given that the yearly cost of tuition and required fees for attending a public two-year college full-time can be estimated by the linear function

$$f(x) = 53.6x + 849.88$$

where x is the number of years after 1990 and $f(x)$ is the total cost. (*Source:* U.S. National Center for Education Statistics)

   a. Find and interpret the slope of this equation.

   b. Find and interpret the y-intercept of this equation.

Solve.

81. Find the slope of a line parallel to the line

$$f(x) = -\frac{7}{2}x - 6.$$

△ **82.** Find the slope of a line parallel to the line $f(x) = x$.

△ **83.** Find the slope of a line perpendicular to the line

$$f(x) = -\frac{7}{2}x - 6.$$

△ **84.** Find the slope of a line perpendicular to the line $f(x) = x$.

△ **85.** Find the slope of a line parallel to the line $5x - 2y = 6$.

△ **86.** Find the slope of a line parallel to the line $-3x + 4y = 10$.

△ **87.** Find the slope of a line perpendicular to the line $5x - 2y = 6$.

REVIEW AND PREVIEW

Recall the formula

$$Probability\ of\ an\ event = \frac{\begin{array}{c} number\ of\ ways\ that \\ the\ event\ can\ occur \end{array}}{\begin{array}{c} number\ of\ possible \\ outcomes \end{array}}$$

Suppose these cards are shuffled and one card is turned up. Find the possibility of selecting each letter.

88. $P(\text{R})$ **89.** $P(\text{B})$

90. $P(\text{E})$ **91.** $P(\text{I or T})$

92. $P(\text{selecting a letter of the alphabet})$

93. $P(\text{vowel})$

Simplify and solve for y. See Section 2.3.

94. $y - 2 = 5(x + 6)$

95. $y - 0 = -3[x - (-10)]$

96. $y - (-1) = 2(x - 0)$

97. $y - 9 = -8[x - (-4)]$

Concept Extensions

98. Each line below has negative slope.

    a. Find the slope of each line.

    b. Use the result of Part **a** to fill in the blank. For lines with negative slopes, the steeper line has the _____ (greater/lesser) slope.

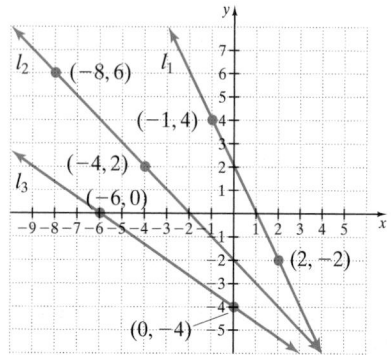

99. The following graph shows the altitude of a seagull in flight over a time period of 30 seconds.

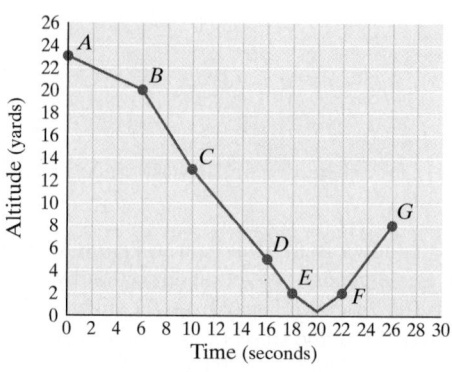

    a. Find the coordinates of point B.

    b. Find the coordinates of point C.

    c. Find the rate of change of altitude between points B and C. (Recall that the rate of change between points is the slope between points. This rate of change will be in yards per second.)

    d. Find the rate of change of altitude (in yards per second) between points F and G.

100. Professional plumbers suggest that a sewer pipe should be sloped 0.25 inch for every foot. Find the recommended slope for a sewer pipe. (*Source: Rules of Thumb* by Tom Parker, 1983, Houghton Mifflin Company)

101. Support the result of Exercise 61 by graphing the pair of equations on a graphing calculator.

102. Support the result of Exercise 62 by graphing the pair of equations on a graphing calculator. (*Hint:* Use the window showing $[-15, 15]$ on the x-axis and $[-10, 10]$ on the y-axis.)

103. **a.** On a single screen, graph $y = \frac{1}{2}x + 1$, $y = x + 1$ and $y = 2x + 1$. Notice the change in slope for each graph.

    b. On a single screen, graph $y = -\frac{1}{2}x + 1$, $y = -x + 1$ and $y = -2x + 1$. Notice the change in slope for each graph.

    c. Determine whether the following statement is true or false for slope m of a given line. As $|m|$ becomes greater, the line becomes steeper.

3.5   *EQUATIONS OF LINES*

Objectives

1 Use the slope–intercept form to write the equation of a line.

2 Graph a line using its slope and y-intercept.

3 Use the point–slope form to write the equation of a line.

4 Write equations of vertical and horizontal lines.

5 Find equations of parallel and perpendicular lines.

1 In the last section, we learned that the slope–intercept form of a linear equation is $y = mx + b$. When a linear equation is written in this form, the slope of the line is the same as the coefficient m of x. Also, the y-intercept of the line is $(0, b)$. For example, the slope of the line defined by $y = 2x + 3$ is, 2, and its y-intercept is $(0, 3)$.

We may also use the slope–intercept form to write the equation of a line given its slope and y-intercept. The equation of a line is a linear equation in 2 variables that, if graphed, would produce the line described.

EXAMPLE 1

Write an equation of the line with y-intercept $(0, -3)$ and slope of $\dfrac{1}{4}$.

Solution We want to write a linear equation in 2 variables that describes the line with y-intercept $(0, -3)$ and has a slope of $\dfrac{1}{4}$. We are given the slope and the y-intercept. Let $m = \dfrac{1}{4}$ and $b = -3$, and write the equation in slope–intercept form, $y = mx + b$.

$$y = mx + b$$
$$y = \dfrac{1}{4}x + (-3) \qquad \text{Let } m = \dfrac{1}{4} \text{ and } b = -3.$$
$$y = \dfrac{1}{4}x - 3 \qquad \text{Simplify.}$$

✔ **CONCEPT CHECK**

What is wrong with the following equation of a line with y-intercept $(0, 4)$ and slope 2?

$$y = 4x + 2$$

Concept Check Answer:
y-intercept and slope were switched, should be $y = 2x + 4$

2 Given the slope and y-intercept of a line, we may graph the line as well as write its equation. Let's graph the line from Example 1.

EXAMPLE 2

Graph $y = \dfrac{1}{4}x - 3$.

Solution Recall that the slope of the graph of $y = \dfrac{1}{4}x - 3$ is $\dfrac{1}{4}$ and the y-intercept is $(0, -3)$. To graph the line, we first plot the y-intercept $(0, -3)$. To find another point on the line, we recall that slope is $\dfrac{\text{rise}}{\text{run}} = \dfrac{1}{4}$. Another point may then be plotted by starting at $(0, -3)$ rising 1 unit up, and then running 4 units to the right. We are now at the point $(4, -2)$. The graph is the line through these two points.

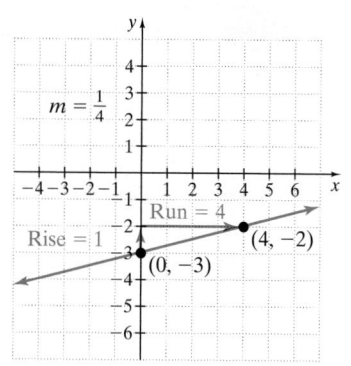

Notice that the line does have a y-intercept of $(0, -3)$ and a slope of $\dfrac{1}{4}$.

EXAMPLE 3

Graph $2x + 3y = 12$.

Solution First, we solve the equation for y to write it in slope–intercept form. In slope–intercept form, the equation is $y = -\dfrac{2}{3}x + 4$. Next we plot the y-intercept $(0, 4)$. To find another point on the line, we use the slope $-\dfrac{2}{3}$, which can be written as $\dfrac{\text{rise}}{\text{run}} = \dfrac{-2}{3}$. We start at $(0, 4)$ and move down 2 units since the numerator of the slope is -2; then we move 3 units to the right since the denominator of the slope is 3. We arrive at the point $(3, 2)$. The line through these points is the graph, shown below to the left.

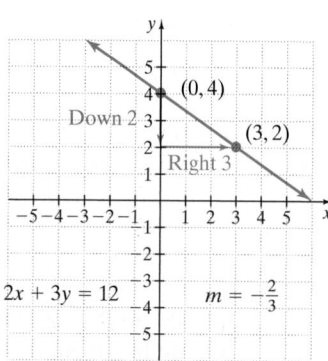
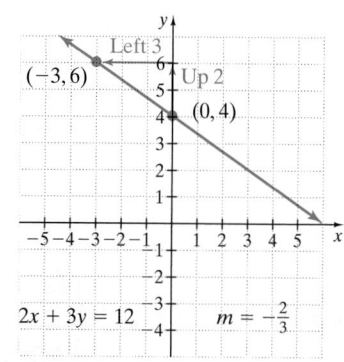

The slope $\dfrac{-2}{3}$ can also be written as $\dfrac{2}{-3}$, so to find another point in Example 3 we could start at $(0, 4)$ and move up 2 units and then 3 units to the left. We would arrive at the point $(-3, 6)$. The line through $(-3, 6)$ and $(0, 4)$ is the same line as shown previously through $(3, 2)$ and $(0, 4)$. See the graph on the previous page to the right. ⬭

3   When the slope of a line and a point on the line are known, the equation of the line can also be found. To do this, use the slope formula to write the slope of a line that passes through points (x_1, y_1) and (x, y). We have

$$m = \frac{y - y_1}{x - x_1}$$

Multiply both sides of this equation by $x - x_1$ to obtain

$$y - y_1 = m(x - x_1)$$

This form is called the **point–slope form** of the equation of a line.

> ### Point–Slope Form of the Equation of a Line
>
> The point–slope form of the equation of a line is $y - y_1 = m(x - x_1)$, where m is the slope of the line and (x_1, y_1) is a point on the line.

EXAMPLE 4

Find an equation of the line with slope -3 containing the point $(1, -5)$. Write the equation in slope–intercept form $y = mx + b$.

Solution   Because we know the slope and a point of the line, we use the point–slope form with $m = -3$ and $(x_1, y_1) = (1, -5)$.

$$
\begin{aligned}
y - y_1 &= m(x - x_1) && \text{Point–slope form.} \\
y - (-5) &= -3(x - 1) && \text{Let } m = -3 \text{ and } (x_1, y_1) = (1, -5). \\
y + 5 &= -3x + 3 && \text{Apply the distributive property.} \\
y &= -3x - 2 && \text{Write in slope–intercept form.}
\end{aligned}
$$

In slope–intercept form, the equation is $y = -3x - 2$. ⬭

> ### ▶ Helpful Hint
>
> Remember, "slope-intercept form" means the equation is "solved for y."

EXAMPLE 5

Find an equation of the line through points $(4, 0)$ and $(-4, -5)$. Write the equation using function notation.

Solution First, find the slope of the line.

$$m = \frac{-5 - 0}{-4 - 4} = \frac{-5}{-8} = \frac{5}{8}$$

Next, make use of the point–slope form. Replace (x_1, y_1) by either $(4, 0)$ or $(-4, -5)$ in the point–slope equation. We will choose the point $(4, 0)$. The line through $(4, 0)$ with slope $\frac{5}{8}$ is

$$
\begin{aligned}
y - y_1 &= m(x - x_1) &&\text{Point–slope form.} \\
y - 0 &= \frac{5}{8}(x - 4) &&\text{Let } m = \frac{5}{8} \text{ and } (x_1, y_1) = (4, 0). \\
8y &= 5(x - 4) &&\text{Multiply both sides by } 8. \\
8y &= 5x - 20 &&\text{Apply the distributive property.}
\end{aligned}
$$

To write the equation using function notation, we solve for y.

$$
\begin{aligned}
8y &= 5x - 20 \\
y &= \frac{5}{8}x - \frac{20}{8} &&\text{Divide both sides by } 8. \\
f(x) &= \frac{5}{8}x - \frac{5}{2} &&\text{Write using function notation.}
\end{aligned}
$$

> **Helpful Hint**
>
> If two points of a line are given, either one may be used with the point-slope form to write an equation of the line.

The point–slope form of an equation is very useful for solving real-world problems.

EXAMPLE 6

PREDICTING SALES

Southern Star Realty is an established real estate company that has enjoyed constant growth in sales since 1995. In 1997 the company sold 200 houses, and in 2002 the company sold 275 houses. Use these figures to predict the number of houses this company will sell in the year 2011.

Solution 1. UNDERSTAND. Read and reread the problem. Then let
$x = $ the number of years after 1995 and
$y = $ the number of houses sold in the year corresponding to x.
The information provided then gives the ordered pairs $(2, 200)$ and $(7, 275)$. To better visualize the sales of Southern Star Realty, we graph the linear equation that passes through the points $(2, 200)$ and $(7, 275)$.

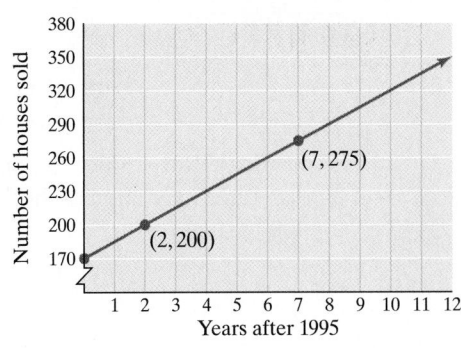

2. TRANSLATE.   We write a linear equation that passes through the points $(2, 200)$ and $(7, 275)$. To do so, we first find the slope of the line.

$$m = \frac{275 - 200}{7 - 2} = \frac{75}{5} = 15$$

Then, using the point–slope form and the point $(2, 200)$ to write the equation, we have

$$y - y_1 = m(x - x_1)$$

$$y - 200 = 15(x - 2) \quad \text{Let } m = 15 \text{ and } (x_1, y_1) = (2, 200).$$

$$y - 200 = 15x - 30 \quad \text{Multiply.}$$

$$y = 15x + 170 \quad \text{Add } 200 \text{ to both sides.}$$

3. SOLVE.   To predict the number of houses sold in the year 2011, we use $y = 15x + 170$ and complete the ordered pair $(16, \ )$, since $2011 - 1995 = 16$.

$$y = 15(16) + 170 \quad \text{Let } x = 16.$$
$$y = 410$$

4. INTERPRET.
Check: Verify that the point $(16, 410)$ is a point on the line graphed in step 1.
State: Southern Star Realty should expect to sell 410 houses in the year 2011. ⬭

4   A few special types of linear equations are linear equations whose graphs are vertical and horizontal lines.

EXAMPLE 7

Find an equation of the horizontal line containing the point $(2, 3)$.

Solution   Recall that a horizontal line has an equation of the form $y = b$. Since the line contains the point $(2, 3)$, the equation is $y = 3$.

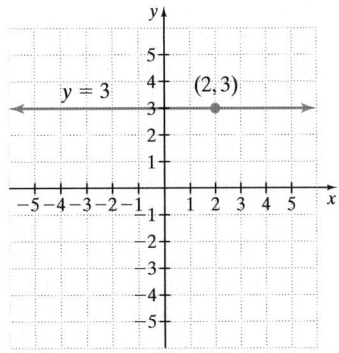

EXAMPLE 8

Find an equation of the line containing the point $(2, 3)$ with undefined slope.

Solution Since the line has undefined slope, the line must be vertical. A vertical line has an equation of the form $x = c$, and since the line contains the point $(2, 3)$, the equation is $x = 2$.

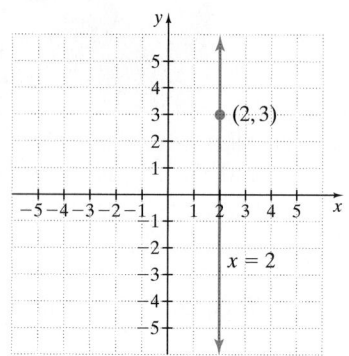

5 Next, we find equations of parallel and perpendicular lines.

EXAMPLE 9

Find an equation of the line containing the point $(4, 4)$ and parallel to the line $2x + 3y = -6$. Write the equation in standard form.

Solution Because the line we want to find is *parallel* to the line $2x + 3y = -6$, the two lines must have equal slopes. Find the slope of $2x + 3y = -6$ by writing it in the form $y = mx + b$. In other words, solve the equation for y.

$$2x + 3y = -6$$
$$3y = -2x - 6 \qquad \text{Subtract } 2x \text{ from both sides.}$$
$$y = \frac{-2x}{3} - \frac{6}{3} \qquad \text{Divide by } 3.$$
$$y = -\frac{2}{3}x - 2 \qquad \text{Write in slope-intercept form.}$$

The slope of this line is $-\frac{2}{3}$. Thus, a line parallel to this line will also have a slope of $-\frac{2}{3}$.

The equation we are asked to find describes a line containing the point $(4, 4)$ with a slope of $-\frac{2}{3}$. We use the point-slope form.

$$y - y_1 = m(x - x_1)$$
$$y - 4 = -\frac{2}{3}(x - 4) \qquad \text{Let } m = -\frac{2}{3}, x_1 = 4, \text{ and } y_1 = 4.$$
$$3(y - 4) = -2(x - 4) \qquad \text{Multiply both sides by } 3.$$
$$3y - 12 = -2x + 8 \qquad \text{Apply the distributive property.}$$
$$2x + 3y = 20 \qquad \text{Write in standard form.}$$

> ### Helpful Hint
> Multiply both sides of the equation $2x + 3y = 20$ by -1 and it becomes $-2x - 3y = -20$. Both equations are in standard form, and their graphs are the same line.

EXAMPLE 10

Write a function that describes the line containing the point $(4, 4)$ and is perpendicular to the line $2x + 3y = -6$.

Solution   In the previous example, we found that the slope of the line $2x + 3y = -6$ is $-\dfrac{2}{3}$. A line perpendicular to this line will have a slope that is the negative reciprocal of $-\dfrac{2}{3}$, or $\dfrac{3}{2}$.

From the point-slope equation, we have

$$y - y_1 = m(x - x_1)$$
$$y - 4 = \frac{3}{2}(x - 4) \qquad \text{Let } x_1 = 4, y_1 = 4 \text{ and } m = \frac{3}{2}.$$
$$2(y - 4) = 3(x - 4) \qquad \text{Multiply both sides by } 2.$$
$$2y - 8 = 3x - 12 \qquad \text{Apply the distributive property.}$$
$$2y = 3x - 4 \qquad \text{Add } 8 \text{ to both sides.}$$
$$y = \frac{3}{2}x - 2 \qquad \text{Divide both sides by } 2.$$
$$f(x) = \frac{3}{2}x - 2 \qquad \text{Write using function notation.}$$

Forms of Linear Equations

$Ax + By = C$	**Standard form** of a linear equation A and B are not both 0.
$y = mx + b$	**Slope–intercept form** of a linear equation The slope is m, and the y-intercept is $(0, b)$.
$y - y_1 = m(x - x_1)$	**Point–slope form** of a linear equation The slope is m, and (x_1, y_1) is a point on the line.
$y = c$	**Horizontal line** The slope is 0, and the y-intercept is $(0, c)$.
$x = c$	**Vertical line** The slope is undefined and the x-intercept is $(c, 0)$.

Parallel and Perpendicular Lines

Nonvertical parallel lines have the same slope. The product of the slopes of two nonvertical perpendicular lines is -1.

Spotlight on

DECISION
❀MAKING

Suppose you are a public health official. In 1993, the International Task Force for Disease Eradication (ITFDE) identified mumps as one of six infectious diseases that could probably be eradicated worldwide with current technology. The ITFDE defined "eradication" as reducing the incidence of a disease to zero. Does the graph of reported mumps cases in the United States support the possibility of U.S. mumps eradication? Explain.

Suppose U.S. officials would like to see mumps eradicated by 2010. If this goal does not currently seem possible, your department will increase eradication efforts with the launch of a new public awareness campaign. Will the new public awareness campaign be necessary? (*Hint:* Use the data for the years 2000 and 2001 to help you decide.)

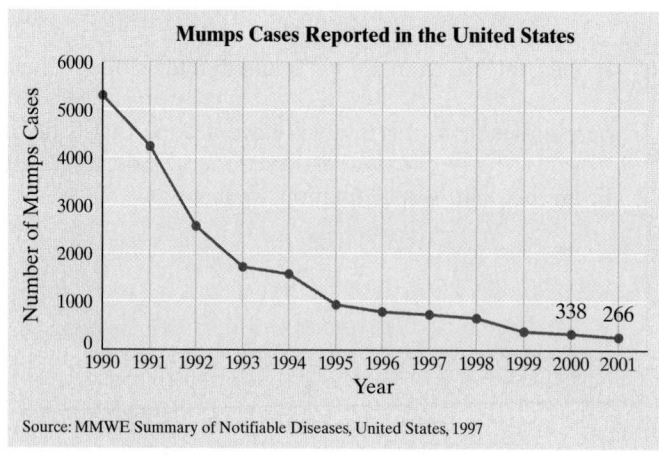

Source: MMWE Summary of Notifiable Diseases, United States, 1997

MENTAL MATH

State the slope and the y-intercept of each line with the given equation.

1. $y = -4x + 12$

2. $y = \frac{2}{3}x - \frac{7}{2}$

3. $y = 5x$

4. $y = -x$

5. $y = \frac{1}{2}x + 6$

6. $y = -\frac{2}{3}x + 5$

Decide whether the lines are parallel, perpendicular, or neither.

7. $y = 12x + 6$
  $y = 12x - 2$

8. $y = -5x + 8$
  $y = -5x - 8$

9. $y = -9x + 3$
  $y = \frac{3}{2}x - 7$

10. $y = 2x - 12$
  $y = \frac{1}{2}x - 6$

EXERCISE SET 3.5

STUDY GUIDE/SSM   CD/VIDEO   PH MATH TUTOR CENTER   MathXL®Tutorials ON CD   MathXL®   MyMathLab®

Use the slope–intercept form of the linear equation to write the equation of each line with the given slope and y-intercept. See Example 1.

1. Slope -1; y-intercept $(0, 1)$

2. Slope $\dfrac{1}{2}$; y-intercept $(0, -6)$

3. Slope 2; y-intercept $\left(0, \dfrac{3}{4}\right)$

4. Slope -3; y-intercept $\left(0, -\dfrac{1}{5}\right)$

5. Slope $\dfrac{2}{7}$; y-intercept $(0, 0)$

6. Slope $-\dfrac{4}{5}$; y-intercept $(0, 0)$

Graph each linear equation. See Examples 2 and 3.

7. $y = 5x$

8. $y = 2x + 12$

9. $x + y = 7$

10. $3x + y = 9$

11. $-3x + 2y = 3$

12. $-2x + 5y = -16$

Find an equation of the line with the given slope and containing the given point. Write the equation in slope–intercept form. See Example 4.

13. Slope 3; through $(1, 2)$

14. Slope 4; through $(5, 1)$

15. Slope -2; through $(1, -3)$

16. Slope -4; through $(2, -4)$

17. Slope $\dfrac{1}{2}$; through $(-6, 2)$

18. Slope $\dfrac{2}{3}$; through $(-9, 4)$

19. Slope $-\dfrac{9}{10}$; through $(-3, 0)$

20. Slope $-\dfrac{1}{5}$; through $(4, -6)$

Find an equation of each line graphed. Write the equation in standard form.

21.

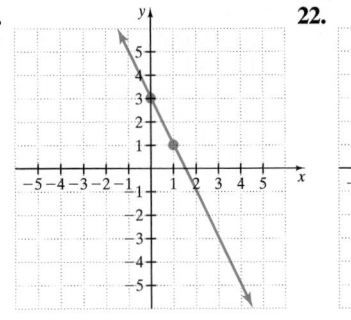

22.

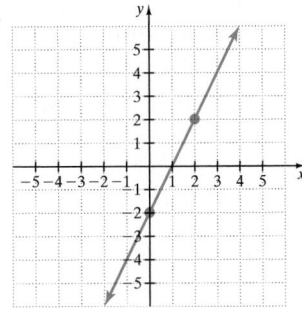

23.

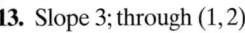

24.

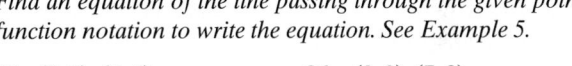

Find an equation of the line passing through the given points. Use function notation to write the equation. See Example 5.

25. $(2, 0), (4, 6)$

26. $(3, 0), (7, 8)$

27. $(-2, 5), (-6, 13)$

28. $(7, -4), (2, 6)$

29. $(-2, -4), (-4, -3)$

30. $(-9, -2), (-3, 10)$

31. $(-3, -8), (-6, -9)$

32. $(8, -3), (4, -8)$

33. Describe how to check to see if the graph of $2x - 4y = 7$ passes through the points $(1.4, -1.05)$ and $(0, -1.75)$. Then follow your directions and check these points.

Use the graph of the following function $f(x)$ to find each value.

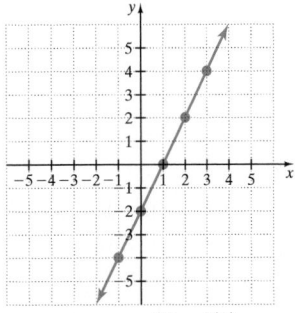

34. $f(1)$

35. $f(0)$

36. $f(-1)$

37. $f(2)$

38. Find x such that $f(x) = 4$.

39. Find x such that $f(x) = -6$.

Write an equation of each line. See Examples 7 and 8.

40. Vertical; through $(2, 6)$

41. Slope 0; through $(-2, -4)$

42. Horizontal; through $(-3, 1)$

43. Vertical; through $(4, 7)$

44. Undefined slope; through $(0, 5)$

45. Horizontal; through $(0, 5)$

△ 46. Answer the following true or false. A vertical line is always perpendicular to a horizontal line.

Find an equation of each line. Write the equation using function notation. See Examples 9 and 10.

△ 47. Through $(3, 8)$; parallel to $f(x) = 4x - 2$

△ 48. Through $(1, 5)$; parallel to $f(x) = 3x - 4$

🔒 49. Through $(2, -5)$; perpendicular to $3y = x - 6$

△ 50. Through $(-4, 8)$; perpendicular to $2x - 3y = 1$

△ 51. Through $(-2, -3)$; parallel to $3x + 2y = 5$

△ 52. Through $(-2, -3)$; perpendicular to $3x + 2y = 5$

MIXED PRACTICE

Find the equation of each line. Write the equation in standard form unless indicated otherwise.

53. Slope 2; through $(-2, 3)$

54. Slope 3; through $(-4, 2)$

55. Through $(1, 6)$ and $(5, 2)$; use function notation.

56. Through $(2, 9)$ and $(8, 6)$

57. With slope $-\dfrac{1}{2}$; y-intercept 11

58. With slope -4; y-intercept $\dfrac{2}{9}$; use function notation.

59. Through $(-7, -4)$ and $(0, -6)$

60. Through $(2, -8)$ and $(-4, -3)$

61. Slope $-\dfrac{4}{3}$; through $(-5, 0)$

62. Slope $-\dfrac{3}{5}$; through $(4, -1)$

63. Vertical line; through $(-2, -10)$

64. Horizontal line; through $(1, 0)$

△ 65. Through $(6, -2)$; parallel to the line $2x + 4y = 9$

△ 66. Through $(8, -3)$; parallel to the line $6x + 2y = 5$

67. Slope 0; through $(-9, 12)$

68. Undefined slope; through $(10, -8)$

△ 69. Through $(6, 1)$; parallel to the line $8x - y = 9$

△ 70. Through $(3, 5)$; perpendicular to the line $2x - y = 8$

△ 71. Through $(5, -6)$; perpendicular to $y = 9$

△ 72. Through $(-3, -5)$; parallel to $y = 9$

73. Through $(2, -8)$ and $(-6, -5)$; use function notation.

74. Through $(-4, -2)$ and $(-6, 5)$; use function notation.

Solve. See Example 6.

75. Del Monte Fruit Company recently released a new applesauce. By the end of its first year, profits on this product amounted to $30,000. The anticipated profit for the end of the fourth year is $66,000. The ratio of change in time to change in profit is constant. Let x be years and P be profit.

   a. Write a linear function $P(x)$ that expresses profit as a function of time.

   b. Use this function to predict the company's profit at the end of the seventh year.

   c. Predict when the profit should reach $126,000.

76. The value of a computer bought in 2000 depreciates, or decreases, as time passes. Two years after the computer was bought, it was worth $2600; 4 years after it was bought, it was worth $1000.

   a. If this relationship between number of years past 2000 and value of computer is linear, write an equation describing this relationship. [Use ordered pairs of the form (years past 2000, value of computer).]

   b. Use this equation to estimate the value of the computer in the year 2005.

77. The Pool Fun Company has learned that, by pricing a newly released Fun Noodle at $3, sales will reach 10,000 Fun Noodles per day during the summer. Raising the price to $5 will cause the sales to fall to 8000 Fun Noodles per day.

   a. Assume that the relationship between sales price and number of Fun Noodles sold is linear and write an equation describing this relationship.

   b. Predict the daily sales of Fun Noodles if the price is $3.50.

78. The value of a building bought in 1990 appreciates, or increases, as time passes. Seven years after the building was bought, it was worth $165,000; 12 years after it was bought, it was worth $180,000.

   a. If this relationship between number of years past 1990 and value of building is linear, write an equation describing this relationship. [Use ordered pairs of the form (years past 1980, value of building).]

   b. Use this equation to estimate the value of the building in the year 2010.

79. In 2002, the median price of an existing home in the United States was approximately $147,802. In 1999, the median price of an existing home was $133,300. Let y be the median price of an existing home in the year x, where $x = 0$ represents 1999. (*Source:* National Association of REALTORS®)

   a. Write a linear equation that models the median existing home price in terms of the year x. [*Hint:* The line must pass through the points $(0, 133{,}300)$ and $(3, 147{,}802)$]

b. Use this equation to predict the median existing home price for the year 2008.

c. Interpret the slope of the equation found in part **a**.

80. The number of births (in thousands) in the United States in 2000 was 4060. The number of births (in thousands) in the United States in 1997 was 3895. Let y be the number of births (in thousands) in the year x, where $x = 0$ represents 1997. (*Source*: National Center for Health Statistics)

a. Write a linear equation that models the number of births (in thousands) in terms of the year x. (See hint for Exercise 79a.)

b. Use this equation to predict the number of births in the United States for the year 2010.

c. Interpret the slope of the equation in part **a**.

81. The number of people employed in the United States as medical assistants was 757 thousand in 2000. By the year 2010, this number is expected to rise to 1052 thousand. Let y be the number of medical assistants (in thousands) employed in the United States in the year x, where $x = 0$ represents 2000. (*Source*: Bureau of Labor Statistics)

a. Write a linear equation that models the number of people (in thousands) employed as medical assistants in the year x. (See hint for Exercise 79a.)

b. Use this equation to estimate the number of people who will be employed as medical assistants in the year 2004.

82. The number of people employed in the United States as systems analysts was 431 thousand in 2000. By the year 2010, this number is expected to rise to 689 thousand. Let y be the number of systems analysts (in thousands) employed in the United States in the year x, where $x = 0$ represents 2000. (*Source*: Bureau of Labor Statistics)

a. Write a linear equation that models the number of people (in thousands) employed as systems analysts in the year x. (See hint for Exercise 79a.)

b. Use this equation to estimate the number of people who will be employed as systems analysts in the year 2008.

REVIEW AND PREVIEW

Solve and graph the solution. See Section 2.4.

83. $2x - 7 \le 21$

84. $-3x + 1 > 0$

85. $5(x - 2) \ge 3(x - 1)$

86. $-2(x + 1) \le -x + 10$

87. $\dfrac{x}{2} + \dfrac{1}{4} < \dfrac{1}{8}$

88. $\dfrac{x}{5} - \dfrac{3}{10} \ge \dfrac{x}{2} - 1$

Concept Extensions

Example:

Find an equation of the perpendicular bisector of the line segment whose endpoints are $(2, 6)$ and $(0, -2)$.

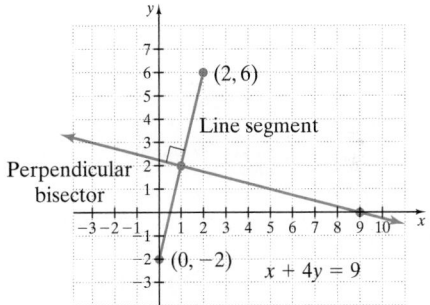

Solution:

A perpendicular bisector is a line that contains the midpoint of the given segment and is perpendicular to the segment.

Step 1: The midpoint of the segment with endpoints $(2, 6)$ and $(0, -2)$ is $(1, 2)$.

Step 2: The slope of the segment containing points $(2, 6)$ and $(0, -2)$ is 4.

Step 3: A line perpendicular to this line segment will have slope of $-\dfrac{1}{4}$.

Step 4: The equation of the line through the midpoint $(1, 2)$ with a slope of $-\dfrac{1}{4}$ will be the equation of the perpendicular bisector. This equation in standard form is $x + 4y = 9$.

Find an equation of the perpendicular bisector of the line segment whose endpoints are given. See the previous example.

△ **89.** $(3, -1); (-5, 1)$ △ **90.** $(-6, -3); (-8, -1)$

△ **91.** $(-2, 6); (-22, -4)$ △ **92.** $(5, 8); (7, 2)$

△ **93.** $(2, 3); (-4, 7)$ △ **94.** $(-6, 8); (-4, -2)$

Use a graphing calculator with a TRACE feature to see the results of each exercise.

95. Exercise 55; graph the function and verify that it passes through $(1, 6)$ and $(5, 2)$.

96. Exercise 56; graph the equation and verify that it passes through $(2, 9)$ and $(8, 6)$.

97. Exercise 61; graph the equation. See that it has a negative slope and passes through $(-5, 0)$.

98. Exercise 62; graph the equation. See that it has a negative slope and passes through $(4, -1)$.

Answer true or false.

99. A vertical line is always perpendicular to a horizontal line.

100. A vertical line is always parallel to a vertical line.

Use a grapher with a TRACE feature to see the results of eac exercise.

101. Exercise 47: Graph the equation and verify that it passe through $(3, 8)$ and is parallel to $y = 4x - 2$.

102. Exercise 48: Graph the equation and verify that it passe through $(1, 5)$ and is parallel to $y = 3x - 4$.

INTEGRATED REVIEW · LINEAR EQUATIONS IN TWO VARIABLES

Below is a review of equations of lines.

Forms of Linear Equations

$Ax + By = C$	**Standard form** of a linear equation A and B are not both 0.
$y = mx + b$	**Slope-intercept form** of a linear equation The slope is m, and the y-intercept is $(0, b)$.
$y - y_1 = m(x - x_1)$	**Point-slope form** of a linear equation The slope is m, and (x_1, y_1) is a point on the line.
$y = c$	**Horizontal line** The slope is 0, and the y-intercept is $(0, c)$.
$x = c$	**Vertical line** The slope is undefined and the x-intercept is $(c, 0)$.

Parallel and Perpendicular Lines

Nonvertical parallel lines have the same slope. The product of the slopes of two nonvertical perpendicular lines is -1.

Graph each linear equation.

1. $y = -2x$ **2.** $3x - 2y = 6$ **3.** $x = -3$ **4.** $y = 1.5$

Find the slope of the line containing each pair of points.

5. $(-2, -5), (3, -5)$ **6.** $(5, 2), (0, 5)$

Find the slope and y-intercept of each line.

7. $y = 3x - 5$ **8.** $5x - 2y = 7$

Determine whether each pair of lines is parallel, perpendicular, or neither.

9. $y = 8x - 6$

$\quad y = 8x + 6$

10. $y = \dfrac{2}{3}x + 1$

$\quad 2y + 3x = 1$

Find the equation of each line. Write the equation in the form $x = a$, $y = b$, or $y = mx + b$. For Exercises 14 through 17, write the equation in the form $f(x) = mx + b$.

11. Through $(1, 6)$ and $(5, 2)$

12. Vertical line; through $(-2, -10)$

13. Horizontal line; through $(1, 0)$

14. Through $(2, -8)$ and $(-6, -5)$

15. Through $(-2, 4)$ with slope -5

16. Slope -4; y-intercept $\left(0, \dfrac{1}{3}\right)$

17. Slope $\dfrac{1}{2}$; y-intercept $(0, -1)$

18. Through $\left(\dfrac{1}{2}, 0\right)$ with slope 3

19. Through $(-1, -5)$; parallel to $3x - y = 5$

20. Through $(0, 4)$; perpendicular to $4x - 5y = 10$

21. Through $(2, -3)$; perpendicular to $4x + y = \dfrac{2}{3}$

22. Through $(-1, 0)$; parallel to $5x + 2y = 2$

23. Undefined slope; through $(-1, 3)$

24. $m = 0$; through $(-1, 3)$

3.6 *GRAPHING LINEAR INEQUALITIES*

Objectives

1 Graph linear inequalities.

2 Graph the intersection or union of two linear inequalities.

1 Recall that the graph of a linear equation in two variables is the graph of all ordered pairs that satisfy the equation, and we determined that the graph is a line. Here we graph **linear inequalities** in two variables; that is, we graph all the ordered pairs that satisfy the inequality.

If the equal sign in a linear equation in two variables is replaced with an inequality symbol, the result is a linear inequality in two variables.

Examples of Linear Inequalities in Two Variables

$$3x + 5y \geq 6 \qquad 2x - 4y < -3$$
$$4x > 2 \qquad y \leq 5$$

To graph the linear inequality $x + y < 3$, for example, we first graph the related **boundary** equation $x + y = 3$. The resulting boundary line contains all ordered pairs the sum of whose coordinates is 3. This line separates the plane into two **half-planes**. All points "above" the boundary line $x + y = 3$ have coordinates that satisfy the inequality $x + y > 3$, and all points "below" the line have coordinates that satisfy the inequality $x + y < 3$.

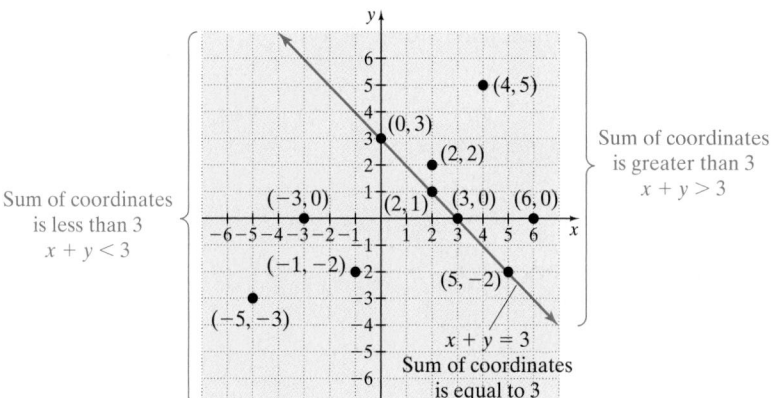

The graph, or **solution region**, for $x + y < 3$, then, is the half-plane below the boundary line and is shown shaded in the graph on the next page. The boundary line is shown dashed since it is not a part of the solution region. These ordered pairs on this line satisfy $x + y = 3$ and not $x + y < 3$.

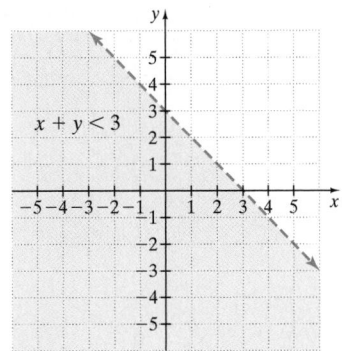

The following steps may be used to graph linear inequalities in two variables.

Graphing a Linear Inequality in Two Variables

Step 1: Graph the boundary line found by replacing the inequality sign with an equal sign. If the inequality sign is $<$ or $>$, graph a dashed line indicating that points on the line are not solutions of the inequality. If the inequality sign is $\leq$ or $\geq$, graph a solid line indicating that points on the line are solutions of the inequality.

Step 2: Choose a **test point not on the boundary line** and substitute the coordinates of this test point into the **original inequality.**

Step 3: If a true statement is obtained in Step 2, shade the half-plane that contains the test point. If a false statement is obtained, shade the half-plane that does not contain the test point.

EXAMPLE 1

Graph $2x - y < 6$.

Solution First, the boundary line for this inequality is the graph of $2x - y = 6$. Graph a dashed boundary line because the inequality symbol is $<$. Next, choose a test point on either side of the boundary line. The point $(0, 0)$ is not on the boundary line, so we use this point. Replacing x with 0 and y with 0 in the *original inequality* $2x - y < 6$ leads to the following:

$$2x - y < 6$$
$$2(0) - 0 < 6 \quad \text{Let } x = 0 \text{ and } y = 0.$$
$$0 < 6 \quad \text{True.}$$

Because $(0, 0)$ satisfies the inequality, so does every point on the same side of the boundary line as $(0, 0)$. Shade the half-plane that contains $(0, 0)$. The half-plane graph of the inequality is shown at the top of the following page.

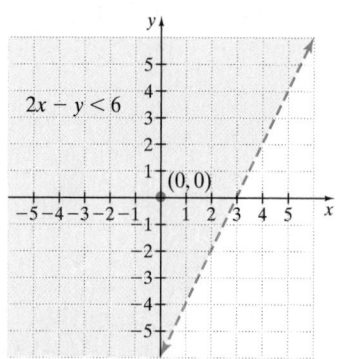

Every point in the shaded half-plane satisfies the original inequality. Notice that the in
equality $2x - y < 6$ does not describe a function since its graph does not pass the ver
tical line test.

In general, linear inequalities of the form $Ax + By \leq C$, when A and B are no
both 0, do not describe functions.

EXAMPLE 2

Graph $3x \geq y$.

Solution   First, graph the boundary line $3x = y$. Graph a solid boundary line because the in
equality symbol is $\geq$. Test a point not on the boundary line to determine which half
plane contains points that satisfy the inequality. We choose $(0, 1)$ as our test point.

$$3x \geq y$$

$$3(0) \geq 1 \quad \text{Let } x = 0 \text{ and } y = 1.$$

$$0 \geq 1 \quad \text{False.}$$

This point does not satisfy the inequality, so the correct half-plane is on the opposite
side of the boundary line from $(0, 1)$. The graph of $3x \geq y$ is the boundary line togethe
with the shaded region shown.

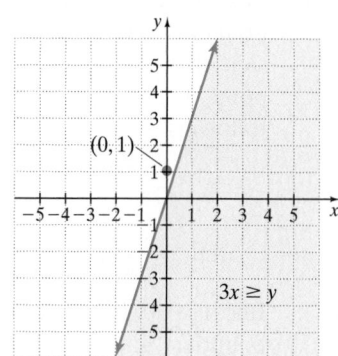

✔ **CONCEPT CHECK**

Concept Check Answer:
Solid

If a point on the boundary line is included in the solution of an inequality in two variables, should the
graph of the boundary line be solid or dashed?

2   The intersection and the union of linear inequalities can also be graphed, as shown in the next two examples.

EXAMPLE 3

Graph the intersection of $x \geq 1$ and $y \geq 2x - 1$.

Solution   Graph each inequality. The intersection of the two graphs is all points common to both regions, as shown by the dark pink shading in the third graph.

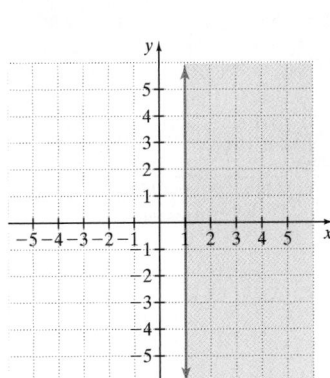
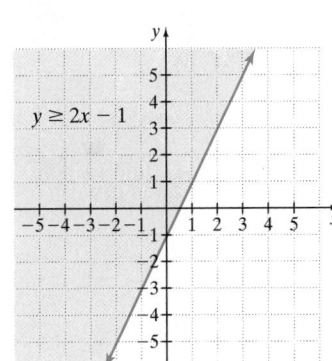
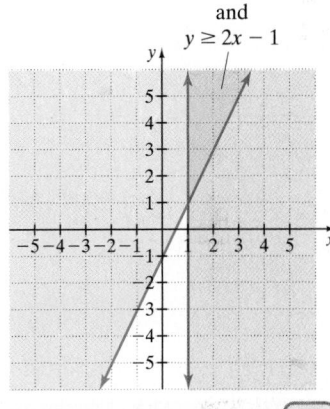

EXAMPLE 4

Graph the union of $x + \dfrac{1}{2}y \geq -4$ or $y \leq -2$.

Solution   Graph each inequality. The union of the two inequalities is both shaded regions, including the solid boundary lines shown in the third graph.

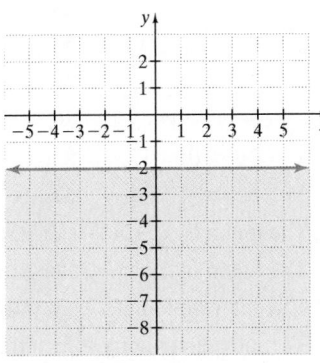
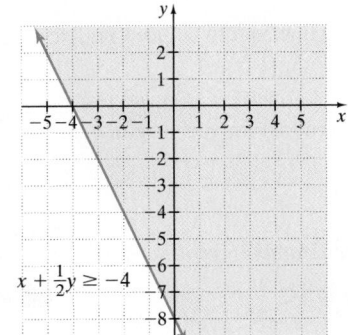
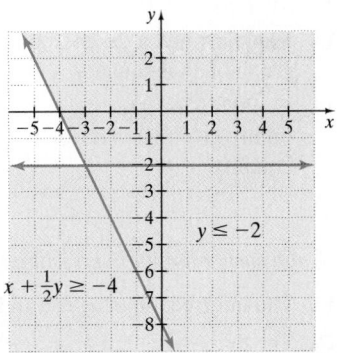

Spotlight on
DECISION
✓MAKING

Suppose you are a customer service representative for a mail-order medical supply company that sells support stockings. A customer, whose weight is 160 pounds and whose height is 5 feet 9 inches, places an order for support stockings and has asked your assistance in selecting the correct size. What size would you recommend that this customer order? Explain.

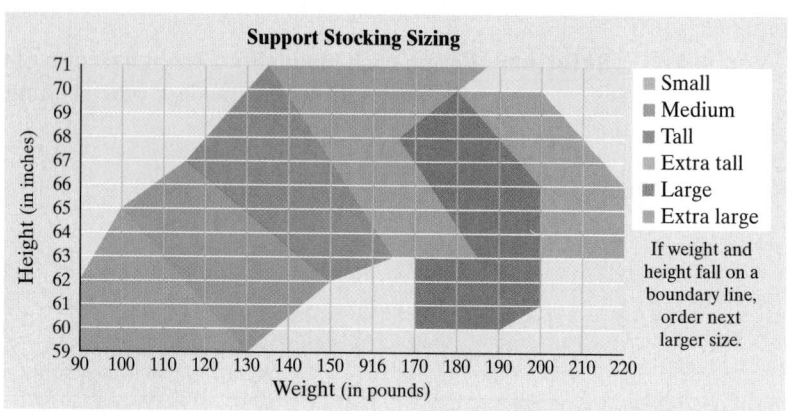

Support Stocking Sizing

Height (in inches) / Weight (in pounds)

- Small
- Medium
- Tall
- Extra tall
- Large
- Extra large

If weight and height fall on a boundary line, order next larger size.

EXERCISE SET 3.6

STUDY GUIDE/SSM · CD/VIDEO · PH MATH TUTOR CENTER · MathXL®Tutorials ON CD · MathXL® · MyMathLab®

Graph each inequality. See Examples 1 and 2.

1. $x < 2$

2. $x > -3$

3. $x - y \geq 7$

4. $3x + y \leq 1$

5. $3x + y > 6$

6. $2x + y > 2$

7. $y \leq -2x$

8. $y \leq 3x$

9. $2x + 4y \geq 8$

10. $2x + 6y \leq 12$

11. $5x + 3y > -15$

12. $2x + 5y < -20$

13. Explain when a dashed boundary line should be used in the graph of an inequality.

14. Explain why, after the boundary line is sketched, we test a point on either side of this boundary in the original inequality.

Graph each union or intersection. See Examples 3 and 4.

15. The intersection of $x \geq 3$ and $y \leq -2$

16. The union of $x \geq 3$ or $y \leq -2$

17. The union of $x \leq -2$ or $y \geq 4$

18. The intersection of $x \leq -2$ and $y \geq 4$

19. The intersection of $x - y < 3$ and $x > 4$

20. The intersection of $2x > y$ and $y > x + 2$

21. The union of $x + y \leq 3$ or $x - y \geq 5$

22. The union of $x - y \leq 3$ or $x + y > -1$

MIXED PRACTICE

Graph each inequality.

23. $y \geq -2$

24. $y \leq 4$

25. $x - 6y < 12$

26. $x - 4y < 8$

27. $x > 5$

28. $y \geq -2$

29. $-2x + y \leq 4$

30. $-3x + y \leq 9$

31. $x - 3y < 0$

32. $x + 2y > 0$

33. $3x - 2y \leq 12$

34. $2x - 3y \leq 9$

35. The union of $x - y > 2$ or $y < 5$

36. The union of $x - y < 3$ or $x > 4$

37. The intersection of $x + y \leq 1$ and $y \leq -1$

38. The intersection of $y \geq x$ and $2x - 4y \geq 6$

39. The union of $2x + y > 4$ or $x \geq 1$

40. The union of $3x + y < 9$ or $y \leq 2$

41. The intersection of $x \geq -2$ and $x \leq 1$

42. The intersection of $x \geq -4$ and $x \leq 3$

43. The union of $x + y \leq 0$ or $3x - 6y \geq 12$

44. The intersection of $x + y \leq 0$ and $3x - 6y \geq 12$

45. The intersection of $2x - y > 3$ and $x > 0$

46. The union of $2x - y > 3$ or $x > 0$

Match each inequality with its graph.

A

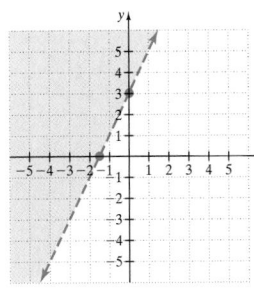

B

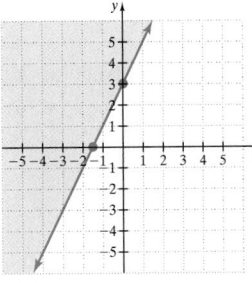

C

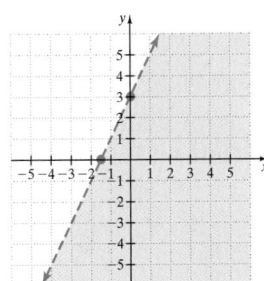

D

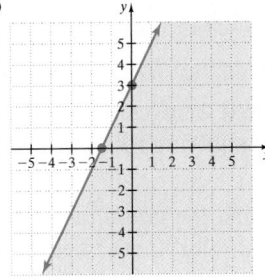

47. $y \leq 2x + 3$ **48.** $y < 2x + 3$

49. $y > 2x + 3$ **50.** $y \geq 2x + 3$

Write the inequality whose graph is given.

51.

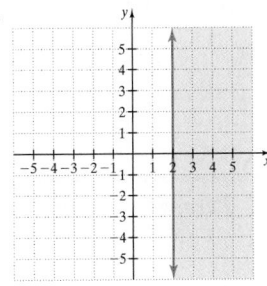

52.

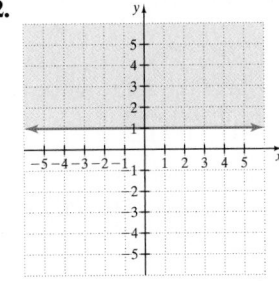

53.

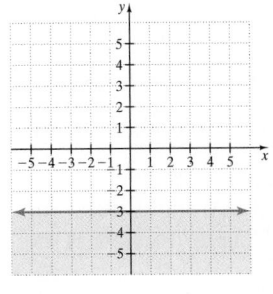

54.

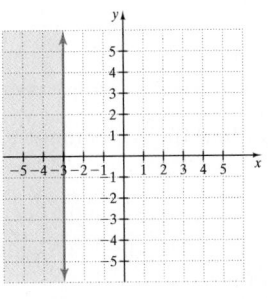

55.

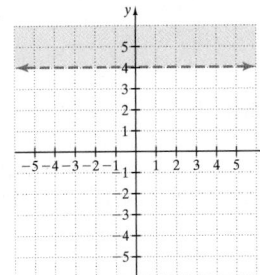

56.

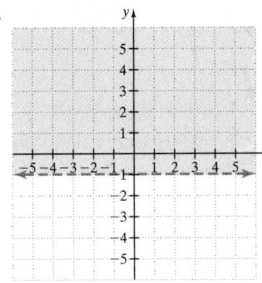

57.

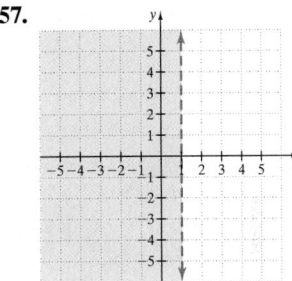

58.

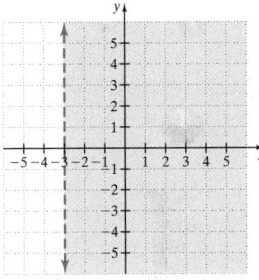

REVIEW AND PREVIEW

Evaluate each expression. See Sections 1.3 and 1.4.

59. 2^3 **60.** 3^2

61. -5^2 **62.** $(-5)^2$

63. $(-2)^4$ **64.** -2^4

65. $\left(\dfrac{3}{5}\right)^3$ **66.** $\left(\dfrac{2}{7}\right)^2$

Find the domain and the range of each relation. Determine whether the relation is also a function. See Section 3.2.

67.

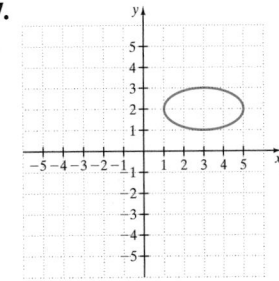

68.

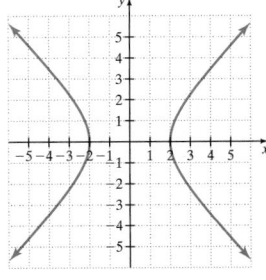

Concept Extensions

Solve.

69. Rheem Abo-Zahrah decides that she will study at most 20 hours every week and that she must work at least 10 hours every week. Let x represent the hours studying and y represent the hours working. Write two inequalities that model this situation and graph their intersection.

70. The movie and TV critic for the *New York Times* spends between 2 and 6 hours daily reviewing movies and fewer than 5 hours reviewing TV shows. Let x represent the hours watching movies and y represent the time spent watching TV. Write two inequalities that model this situation and graph their intersection.

71. Chris-Craft manufactures boats out of Fiberglas and wood. Fiberglas hulls require 2 hours work, whereas wood hulls require 4 hours work. Employees work at most 40 hours a week. The following inequalities model these restrictions, where x represents the number of Fiberglas hulls produced and y represents the number of wood hulls produced.

$$\begin{cases} x \geq 0 \\ y \geq 0 \\ 2x + 4y \leq 40 \end{cases}$$

Graph the intersection of these inequalities.

STUDY SKILLS REMINDER

Are You Preparing for a Test on Chapter 3?

Below I have listed some common trouble areas for students in Chapter 3. After studying for your test—but before taking your test—read these.

▶ Don't forget that the graph of an ordered pair is a *single* point in the rectangular coordinate plane.

▶ Remember that the slope of a horizontal line is 0 while a vertical line has undefined slope or no slope.

▶ For a linear equation such as $2y = 3x - 6$, the slope is not the coefficient of x unless the equation is solved for y. Solving this equation for y, we have $y = \dfrac{3}{2}x - 3$. The slope is $\dfrac{3}{2}$ and the y-intercept is $(0, -3)$.

▶ Parallel lines have the same slope while perpendicular lines have negative reciprocal slopes.

Slope	Parallel line	Perpendicular line
$m = 6$	$m = 6$	$m = -\dfrac{1}{6}$
$m = -\dfrac{2}{3}$	$m = -\dfrac{2}{3}$	$m = \dfrac{3}{2}$

▶ Don't forget that the statement $f(2) = 3$ corresponds to the ordered pair $(2, 3)$.

Remember: this is simply a checklist of common trouble areas. For a review of Chapter 3, see the Highlights and Chapter Review at the end of this chapter.

CHAPTER 3 TEST

Remember to use your Chapter Test Prep Video CD to help you study and view solutions to the test questions you need help with.

1. Plot the points, and name the quadrant in which each is located: $A(6, -2)$, $B(4, 0)$, $C(-1, 6)$.

Graph each line.

2. $2x - 3y = -6$

3. $4x + 6y = 7$

4. $f(x) = \dfrac{2}{3}x$

5. $y = -3$

6. Find the slope of the line that passes through $(5, -8)$ and $(-7, 10)$.

7. Find the slope and the y-intercept of the line $3x + 12y = 8$.

Graph each nonlinear function. Suggested x-values have been given for ordered pair solutions.

8. $f(x) = (x - 1)^2$ Let $x = -2, -1, 0, 1, 2, 3, 4$

9. $g(x) = |x| + 2$ Let $x = -3, -2, -1, 0, 1, 2, 3$

Find an equation of each line satisfying the conditions given. Write Exercises 11–15 in standard form. Write Exercises 16–18 using function notation.

10. Horizontal; through $(2, -8)$

11. Vertical; through $(-4, -3)$

12. Perpendicular to $x = 5$; through $(3, -2)$

13. Through $(4, -1)$; slope -3

14. Through $(0, -2)$; slope 5

15. Through $(4, -2)$ and $(6, -3)$

16. Through $(-1, 2)$; perpendicular to $3x - y = 4$

17. Parallel to $2y + x = 3$; through $(3, -2)$

18. Line L_1 has the equation $2x - 5y = 8$. Line L_2 passes through the points $(1, 4)$ and $(-1, -1)$. Determine whether these lines are parallel lines, perpendicular lines, or neither.

Graph each inequality.

19. $x \le -4$

20. $2x - y > 5$

21. The intersection of $2x + 4y < 6$ and $y \le -4$

Find the domain and range of each relation. Also determine whether the relation is a function.

22.

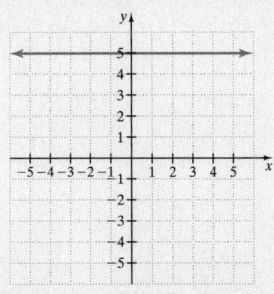

23.

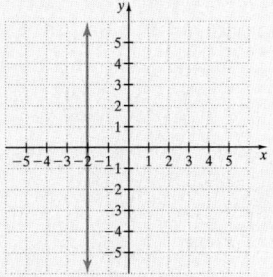

24.

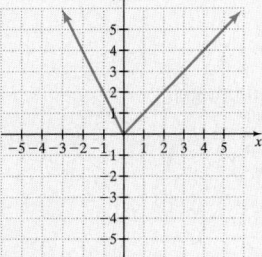

25.

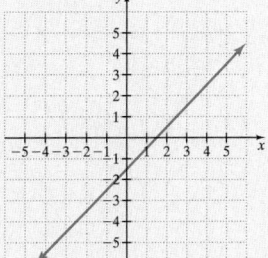

26. The average yearly earnings for high school graduates age 18 and older is given by the linear function

$$f(x) = 732x + 21{,}428$$

where x is the number of years since 1996 that a person graduated. (*Source:* U.S. Census Bureau)

a. Find the average earnings in 1998 for high school graduates.

b. Predict the average earnings for high school graduates in the year 2005.

c. Predict the first year that the average earnings for high school graduates will be greater than $30,000.

d. Find and interpret the slope of this equation.

e. Find and interpret the y-intercept of this equation.

CHAPTER CUMULATIVE REVIEW

1. Evaluate: $3x - y$ when $x = 15$ and $y = 4$.

2. Add.

   a. $-4 + (-3)$

   b. $\dfrac{1}{2} - \left(-\dfrac{1}{3}\right)$

   c. $7 - 20$

3. Determine whether the following statements are true or false.

   a. 3 is a real number.

   b. $\dfrac{1}{5}$ is an irrational number.

   c. Every rational number is an integer.

   d. $\{1, 5\} \subseteq \{2, 3, 4, 5\}$

4. Write the opposite of each.

   a. -7

   b. 0

   c. $\dfrac{1}{4}$

5. Subtract.

   a. $2 - 8$

   b. $-8 - (-1)$

   c. $-11 - 5$

   d. $10.7 - (-9.8)$

   e. $\dfrac{2}{3} - \dfrac{1}{2}$

   f. $1 - 0.06$

   g. Subtract 7 from 4.

6. Multiply or divide.

   a. $\dfrac{-42}{-6}$

   b. $\dfrac{0}{14}$

   c. $-1(-5)(-2)$

7. Simplify each expression.

   a. 3^2

   b. $\left(\dfrac{1}{2}\right)^4$

   c. -5^2

   d. $(-5)^2$

   e. -5^3

   f. $(-5)^3$

8. Which property is illustrated?

   a. $5(x + 7) = 5 \cdot x + 5 \cdot 7$

   b. $5(x + 7) = 5(7 + x)$

9. Insert $<$, $>$, or $=$ between each pair of numbers to form a true statement.

   a. $-1 \quad -2$

   b. $\dfrac{12}{4} \quad 3$

   c. $-5 \quad 0$

   d. $-3.5 \quad -3.05$

10. Evaluate $2x^2$ for

   a. $x = 7$

   b. $x = -7$

11. Write the multiplicative inverse, or reciprocal, of each.

   a. 11

   b. -9

   c. $\dfrac{7}{4}$

12. Simplify $-2 + 3[5 - (7 - 10)]$.

13. Solve: $0.6 = 2 - 3.5c$

14. Solve: $2(x - 3) = -40$.

15. Solve for x: $3x + 5 = 3(x + 2)$

16. Solve: $5(x - 7) = 4x - 35 + x$.

17. Find 16% of 25.

18. Find 25% of 16.

19. Kelsey Ohleger was helping her friend Benji Burnstin study for an algebra exam. Kelsey told Benji that her three latest art history quiz scores are three consecutive even integers whose sum is 264. Help Benji find the scores.

20. Find 3 consecutive odd integers whose sum is 213.

21. Solve $V = lwh$ for h.

22. Solve $7x + 3y = 21$ for y.

23. Solve: $x - 2 < 5$.

24. Solve: $-x - 17 \geq 9$.

25. Solve: $\frac{2}{5}(x - 6) \geq x - 1$

26. $3x + 10 > \frac{5}{2}(x - 1)$.

27. Solve: $2x \geq 0$ and $4x - 1 \leq -9$

28. Solve: $x - 2 < 6$ and $3x + 1 > 1$.

29. Solve: $5x - 3 \leq 10$ or $x + 1 \geq 5$

30. Solve: $x - 2 < 6$ or $3x + 1 > 1$.

31. Solve: $|5w + 3| = 7$

32. Solve: $|5x - 2| = 3$.

33. Solve: $|3x + 2| = |5x - 8|$

34. $|7x - 2| = |7x + 4|$

35. Solve for x: $|5x + 1| + 1 \leq 10$

36. $|-x + 8| - 2 \leq 8$

37. Solve for y: $|y - 3| > 7$

38. Solve for x: $|x + 3| > 1$.

39. Determine whether $(0, -12)$, $(1, 9)$, and $(2, -6)$ are solutions of the equation $3x - y = 12$.

40. Find the slope and y-intercept of $7x + 2y = 10$.

41. Is the relation $y = 2x + 1$ also a function?

42. Determine whether the graph below is the graph of a function.

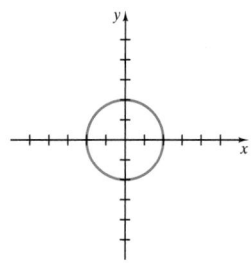

43. Find the y-intercept of the graph of each equation.
  a. $f(x) = \frac{1}{2}x + \frac{3}{7}$
  b. $y = -2.5x - 3.2$

44. Find the slope of the line through $(-1, 6)$ and $(0, 9)$.

45. Find the slope of the line whose equation is $f(x) = \frac{2}{3}x + 4$.

46. Find an equation of the vertical line through $\left(-2, -\frac{3}{4}\right)$.

47. Write an equation of the line with y-intercept $(0, -3)$ and slope of $\frac{1}{4}$.

48. Find an equation of the horizontal line through $\left(-2, -\frac{3}{4}\right)$.

49. Graph: $2x - y < 6$.

50. Write an equation of the line through $(-2, 5)$ and $(-4, 7)$.

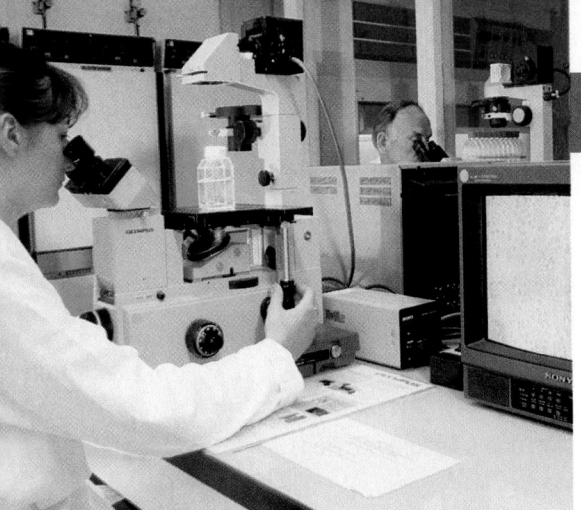

Exponents, Polynomials, and Polynomial Functions

Linear equations are important for solving problems. They are not sufficient, however, to solve all problems. Many real-world phenomena are modeled by polynomials. We begin this chapter by reviewing exponents. We will then study operations on polynomials and how polynomials can be used in problem solving.

TOO SMALL TO BE SEEN WITH THE NAKED EYE

A microbe is a tiny living organism that is too small to be seen with the naked eye. Microbes are everywhere, both indoors and outdoors. A single gram of ordinary soil may contain up to one billion microbes belonging to over 10,000 different species of microbes. We even find microbes in our food: Bread, chocolate, yogurt, and cheese are produced with the help of certain microbes.

A microbiologist is a person who studies microbes. Microbiologists identify harmful microbes, develop vaccines or treatments for disease, protect the environment, and conduct research. They need an understanding of the sciences, especially biology, chemistry, and physics, as well as mathematics.

In the Spotlight on Decision Making feature on page 281, you will have the opportunity to make a decision about microscope magnification as a microbiologist.

Source of text : American Society for Microbiology website

5.1 EXPONENTS AND SCIENTIFIC NOTATION

Objectives

1. Use the product rule for exponents.
2. Evaluate expressions raised to the 0 power.
3. Use the quotient rule for exponents.
4. Evaluate expressions raised to the negative *n*th power.
5. Convert between scientific notation and standard notation.

1 Recall that exponents may be used to write repeated factors in a more compact form. As we have seen in the previous chapters, exponents can be used when the repeated factor is a number or a variable. For example,

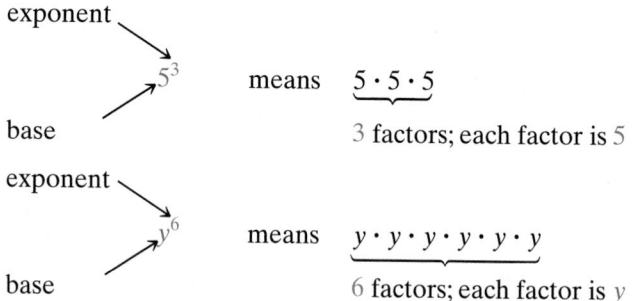

exponent

5^3 means $\underline{5 \cdot 5 \cdot 5}$

base   3 factors; each factor is 5

exponent

y^6 means $\underline{y \cdot y \cdot y \cdot y \cdot y \cdot y}$

base   6 factors; each factor is y

Expressions such as 5^3 and y^6 that contain exponents are called **exponential expressions**.
Exponential expressions can be multiplied, divided, added, subtracted, and themselves raised to powers. In this section, we review operations on exponential expressions.

We review multiplication first. To multiply x^2 by x^3, use the definition of an exponent.

$$x^2 \cdot x^3 = \underbrace{(x \cdot x)(x \cdot x \cdot x)}_{x \text{ is a factor 5 times}}$$

$$= x^5$$

Notice that the result is exactly the same if we add the exponents.

$$x^2 \cdot x^3 = x^{2+3} = x^5$$

This suggests the following.

Product Rule for Exponents

If m and n are positive integers and a is a real number, then

$$a^m \cdot a^n = a^{m+n}$$

In other words, the *product* of exponential expressions with a common base is the common base raised to a power equal to the *sum* of the exponents of the factors.

EXAMPLE 1

Use the product rule to simplify.

a. $2^2 \cdot 2^5$ **b.** $x^7 x^3$ **c.** $y \cdot y^2 \cdot y^4$

Solution   **a.** $2^2 \cdot 2^5 = 2^{2+5} = 2^7$

b. $x^7 x^3 = x^{7+3} = x^{10}$

c. $y \cdot y^2 \cdot y^4 = (y^1 \cdot y^2) \cdot y^4$
$$= y^3 \cdot y^4$$
$$= y^7$$

EXAMPLE 2

Use the product rule to simplify.

a. $(3x^6)(5x)$ **b.** $(-2x^3 p^2)(4xp^{10})$

Solution   Here, we use properties of multiplication to group together like bases.

a. $(3x^6)(5x) = 3(5)x^6 x^1 = 15x^7$

b. $(-2x^3 p^2)(4xp^{10}) = -2(4)x^3 x^1 p^2 p^{10} = -8x^4 p^{12}$

2   The definition of a^n does not include the possibility that n might be 0. But if it did, then, by the product rule,

$$\underbrace{a^0 \cdot a^n} = a^{0+n} = a^n = \underbrace{1 \cdot a^n}$$

From this, we reasonably define that $a^0 = 1$, as long as a does not equal 0.

Zero Exponent

If a does not equal 0, then $a^0 = 1$.

EXAMPLE 3

Evaluate the following.

Solution   **a.** 7^0 **b.** -7^0 **c.** $(2x + 5)^0$ **d.** $2x^0$

a. $7^0 = 1$

b. Without parentheses, only 7 is raised to the 0 power.

$$-7^0 = -(7^0) = -(1) = -1$$

c. $(2x + 5)^0 = 1$

d. $2x^0 = 2(1) = 2$

3 To find quotients of exponential expressions, we again begin with the definition of a^n to simplify $\dfrac{x^9}{x^2}$. For example,

$$\frac{x^9}{x^2} = \frac{x \cdot x \cdot x \cdot x \cdot x \cdot x \cdot x \cdot x \cdot x}{x \cdot x} = x^7$$

(Assume for the next two sections that denominators containing variables are not 0. Notice that the result is exactly the same if we subtract the exponents.

$$\frac{x^9}{x^2} = x^{9-2} = x^7$$

This suggests the following.

Quotient Rule for Exponents

If a is a nonzero real number and n and m are integers, then

$$\frac{a^m}{a^n} = a^{m-n}$$

In other words, the *quotient* of exponential expressions with a common base is the common base raised to a power equal to the *difference* of the exponents.

EXAMPLE 4

Use the quotient rule to simplify.

a. $\dfrac{x^7}{x^4}$
b. $\dfrac{5^8}{5^2}$
c. $\dfrac{20x^6}{4x^5}$
d. $\dfrac{12y^{10}z^7}{14y^8z^7}$

Solution

a. $\dfrac{x^7}{x^4} = x^{7-4} = x^3$

b. $\dfrac{5^8}{5^2} = 5^{8-2} = 5^6$

c. $\dfrac{20x^6}{4x^5} = 5x^{6-5} = 5x^1$, or $5x$

d. $\dfrac{12y^{10}z^7}{14y^8z^7} = \dfrac{6}{7}y^{10-8} \cdot z^{7-7} = \dfrac{6}{7}y^2z^0 = \dfrac{6}{7}y^2$, or $\dfrac{6y^2}{7}$

4 When the exponent of the denominator is larger than the exponent of the numerator, applying the quotient rule yields a negative exponent. For example,

$$\frac{x^3}{x^5} = x^{3-5} = x^{-2}$$

Using the definition of a^n, though, gives us

$$\frac{x^3}{x^5} = \frac{x \cdot x \cdot x}{x \cdot x \cdot x \cdot x \cdot x} = \frac{1}{x^2}$$

From this, we reasonably define $x^{-2} = \dfrac{1}{x^2}$ or, in general, $a^{-n} = \dfrac{1}{a^n}$.

Negative Exponents

If a is a real number other than 0 and n is a positive integer, then

$$a^{-n} = \frac{1}{a^n}$$

EXAMPLE 5

Simplify and write with positive exponents only.

a. 5^{-2} **b.** $(-4)^{-4}$ **c.** $2x^{-3}$ **d.** $(3x)^{-1}$

e. $\dfrac{m^5}{m^{15}}$ **f.** $\dfrac{3^3}{3^6}$ **g.** $2^{-1} + 3^{-2}$ **h.** $\dfrac{1}{t^{-5}}$

Solution   **a.** $5^{-2} = \dfrac{1}{5^2} = \dfrac{1}{25}$

b. $(-4)^{-4} = \dfrac{1}{(-4)^4} = \dfrac{1}{256}$

c. $2x^{-3} = 2 \cdot \dfrac{1}{x^3} = \dfrac{2}{x^3}$ Without parentheses, only x is raised to the -3 power.

d. $(3x)^{-1} = \dfrac{1}{(3x)^1} = \dfrac{1}{3x}$ With parentheses, both 3 and x are raised to the -1 power.

e. $\dfrac{m^5}{m^{15}} = m^{5-15} = m^{-10} = \dfrac{1}{m^{10}}$

f. $\dfrac{3^3}{3^6} = 3^{3-6} = 3^{-3} = \dfrac{1}{3^3} = \dfrac{1}{27}$

g. $2^{-1} + 3^{-2} = \dfrac{1}{2^1} + \dfrac{1}{3^2} = \dfrac{1}{2} + \dfrac{1}{9} = \dfrac{9}{18} + \dfrac{2}{18} = \dfrac{11}{18}$

h. $\dfrac{1}{t^{-5}} = \dfrac{1}{\dfrac{1}{t^5}} = 1 \div \dfrac{1}{t^5} = 1 \cdot \dfrac{t^5}{1} = t^5$

> **Helpful Hint**
>
> Notice that when a factor containing an exponent is moved from the numerator to the denominator or from the denominator to the numerator, the sign of its exponent changes.
>
> $$x^{-3} = \frac{1}{x^3}, \qquad 5^{-2} = \frac{1}{5^2} = \frac{1}{25}$$
>
> $$\frac{1}{y^{-4}} = y^4, \qquad \frac{1}{2^{-3}} = 2^3 = 8$$

EXAMPLE 6

Simplify and write with positive exponents only.

a. $\dfrac{x^{-9}}{x^2}$ **b.** $\dfrac{p^4}{p^{-3}}$ **c.** $\dfrac{2^{-3}}{2^{-1}}$ **d.** $\dfrac{2x^{-7}y^2}{10xy^{-5}}$ **e.** $\dfrac{(3x^{-3})(x^2)}{x^6}$

Solution   **a.** $\dfrac{x^{-9}}{x^2} = x^{-9-2} = x^{-11} = \dfrac{1}{x^{11}}$

b. $\dfrac{p^4}{p^{-3}} = p^{4-(-3)} = p^7$

c. $\dfrac{2^{-3}}{2^{-1}} = 2^{-3-(-1)} = 2^{-2} = \dfrac{1}{2^2} = \dfrac{1}{4}$

d. $\dfrac{2x^{-7}y^2}{10xy^{-5}} = \dfrac{x^{-7-1} \cdot y^{2-(-5)}}{5} = \dfrac{x^{-8}y^7}{5} = \dfrac{y^7}{5x^8}$

e. Simplify the numerator first.

$$\frac{(3x^{-3})(x^2)}{x^6} = \frac{3x^{-3+2}}{x^6} = \frac{3x^{-1}}{x^6} = 3x^{-1-6} = 3x^{-7} = \frac{3}{x^7}$$

✔ **CONCEPT CHECK**

Find and correct the error in the following:

$$\frac{y^{-6}}{y^{-2}} = y^{-6-2} = y^{-8} = \frac{1}{y^8}$$

EXAMPLE 7

Simplify. Assume that a and t are nonzero integers and that x is not 0.

Concept Check Answer:

$$\dfrac{y^{-6}}{y^{-2}} = y^{-6-(-2)} = y^{-4} = \dfrac{1}{y^4}$$

a. $x^{2a} \cdot x^3$ **b.** $\dfrac{x^{2t-1}}{x^{t-5}}$

Solution   **a.** $x^{2a} \cdot x^3 = x^{2a+3}$ *Use the product rule.*

b. $\dfrac{x^{2t-1}}{x^{t-5}} = x^{(2t-1)-(t-5)}$ *Use the quotient rule.*

$= x^{2t-1-t+5} = x^{t+4}$

5   Very large and very small numbers occur frequently in nature. For example, the distance between the Earth and the Sun is approximately 150,000,000 kilometers. A helium atom has a diameter of 0.000 000 022 centimeters. It can be tedious to write these very large and very small numbers in standard notation like this. **Scientific notation** is a convenient shorthand notation for writing very large and very small numbers.

Helium atom

0.000 000 022 centimeters

150,000,000 km

Scientific Notation

A positive number is written in **scientific notation** if it is written as the product of a number a, where $1 \le a < 10$ and an integer power r of 10:

$$a \times 10^r$$

The following are examples of numbers written in scientific notation.

diameter of helium atom $\rightarrow 2.2 \times 10^{-8}$ cm; 1.5×10^8 Km $\leftarrow$ approximate distance between Earth and Sun

Writing a Number in Scientific Notation

Step 1: Move the decimal point in the original number until the new number has a value between 1 and 10.

Step 2: Count the number of decimal places the decimal point was moved in Step 1. If the original number is 10 or greater, the count is positive. If the original number is less than 1, the count is negative.

Step 3: Write the product of the new number in Step 1 by 10 raised to an exponent equal to the count found in Step 2.

EXAMPLE 8

Write each number in scientific notation.

a. 730,000　　　　　　　　　　**b.** 0.00000104

Solution　**a. Step 1:** Move the decimal point until the number is between 1 and 10.

$$730,000.$$

Step 2: The decimal point is moved 5 places and the original number is 10 or greater, so the count is positive 5.

Step 3: $730,000 = 7.3 \times 10^5$.

b. Step 1: Move the decimal point until the number is between 1 and 10.

$$0.00000104$$

Step 2: The decimal point is moved 6 places and the original number is less then 1, so the count is -6.

Step 3: $0.00000104 = 1.04 \times 10^{-6}$.

To write a scientific notation number in standard form, we reverse the preceding steps.

Writing a Scientific Notation Number in Standard Notation

Move the decimal point in the number the same number of places as the exponent on 10. If the exponent is positive, move the decimal point to the right. If the exponent is negative, move the decimal point to the left.

EXAMPLE 9

Write each number in standard notation.

a. 7.7×10^8　　　　　　　　　**b.** 1.025×10^{-3}

Solution　**a.** $7.7 \times 10^8 = 770,000,000$　　*Since the exponent is positive, move the decimal point 8 places to the right. Add zeros as needed.*

b. $1.025 \times 10^{-3} = 0.001025$　　*Since the exponent is negative, move the decimal point 3 places to the left. Add zeros as needed.*

✔ **CONCEPT CHECK**

Which of the following numbers have values that are less than 1?

a. 3.5×10^{-5}　　　　　　　**b.** 3.5×10^5

c. -3.5×10^5　　　　　　**d.** -3.5×10^{-5}

Multiply 5,000,000 by 700,000 on your calculator. The display should read $\boxed{3.5 \quad 12}$ or $\boxed{3.5 \text{ E } 12}$, which is the product written in scientific notation. Both these notations mean 3.5×10^{12}.

To enter a number written in scientific notation on a calculator, find the key marked $\boxed{\text{EE}}$. (On some calculators, this key may be marked $\boxed{\text{EXP}}$.)

To enter 7.26×10^{13}, press the keys

$$\boxed{7.26} \quad \boxed{\text{EE}} \quad \boxed{13}$$

The display will read $\boxed{7.26 \quad 13}$ or $\boxed{7.26 \text{ E } 13}$.

Use your calculator to perform each operation indicated.

1. Multiply 3×10^{11} and 2×10^{32}.
2. Divide 6×10^{14} by 3×10^9.
3. Multiply 5.2×10^{23} and 7.3×10^4.
4. Divide 4.38×10^{41} by 3×10^{17}.

Spotlight on
DECISION
MAKING

Suppose you are a microbiologist. You know that when an image is viewed through a microscope, its magnification is the number of times the image is enlarged. For example, if a 4-millimeter-long object is viewed at five times magnification (denoted $5 \times$ magnification), it appears as an object that is $5 \times 4 = 20$ millimeters long.

Suppose you are studying the *Ebola Zaire* virus, which has an average length of 9.2×10^{-5} centimeters. You would like to view an Ebola virus with a microscope so that it appears to be 4 centimeters long. Decide what magnification setting (rounded to the nearest thousand) you will need to use on the microscope.

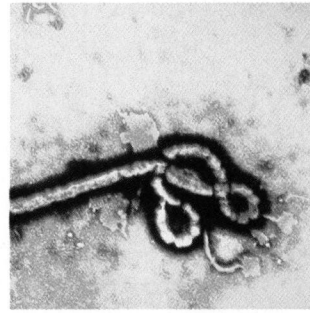

MENTAL MATH

Use positive exponents to state each expression.

1. $5x^{-1}y^{-2}$

2. $7xy^{-4}$

3. $a^2b^{-1}c^{-5}$

4. $a^{-4}b^2c^{-6}$

5. $\dfrac{y^{-2}}{x^{-4}}$

6. $\dfrac{x^{-7}}{z^{-3}}$

EXERCISE SET 5.1

STUDY GUIDE/SSM — CD/VIDEO — PH MATH TUTOR CENTER — MathXL®Tutorials ON CD — MathXL® — MyMathLab®

Use the product rule to simplify each expression. See Examples 1 and 2.

1. $4^2 \cdot 4^3$

2. $3^3 \cdot 3^5$

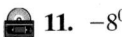 **3.** $x^5 \cdot x^3$

4. $a^2 \cdot a^9$

5. $-7x^3 \cdot 20x^9$

6. $-3y \cdot -9y^4$

7. $(4xy)(-5x)$

8. $(7xy)(7aby)$

9. $(-4x^3p^2)(4y^3x^3)$

10. $(-6a^2b^3)(-3ab^3)$

Evaluate the following. See Example 3.

11. -8^0

12. $(-9)^0$

13. $(4x + 5)^0$

14. $8x^0 + 1$

15. $(5x)^0 + 5x^0$

16. $4y^0 - (4y)^0$

17. Explain why $(-5)^0$ simplifies to 1 but -5^0 simplifies to -1.

18. Explain why both $4x^0 - 3y^0$ and $(4x - 3y)^0$ simplify to 1.

Find each quotient. See Example 4.

19. $\dfrac{a^5}{a^2}$

20. $\dfrac{x^9}{x^4}$

21. $\dfrac{x^9y^6}{x^8y^6}$

22. $\dfrac{a^{12}b^2}{a^9b}$

23. $-\dfrac{26z^{11}}{2z^7}$

24. $\dfrac{16x^5}{8x}$

25. $\dfrac{-36a^5b^7c^{10}}{6ab^3c^4}$

26. $\dfrac{49a^3bc^{14}}{-7abc^8}$

Simplify each expression. Write answers with positive exponents. See Examples 5 and 6.

27. 4^{-2}

28. 2^{-3}

29. $\dfrac{x^7}{x^{15}}$

30. $\dfrac{z}{z^3}$

31. $5a^{-4}$

32. $10b^{-1}$

33. $\dfrac{x^{-2}}{x^5}$

34. $\dfrac{y^{-6}}{y^{-9}}$

35. $\dfrac{8r^4}{2r^{-4}}$

36. $\dfrac{3s^3}{15s^{-3}}$

37. $\dfrac{x^{-9}x^4}{x^{-5}}$

38. $\dfrac{y^{-7}y}{y^8}$

MIXED PRACTICE

Simplify the following. Write answers with positive exponents.

39. $4^{-1} + 3^{-2}$

40. $1^{-3} - 4^{-2}$

41. $4x^0 + 5$

42. $-5x^0$

43. $x^7 \cdot x^8 \cdot x$

44. $y^6 \cdot y \cdot y^4$

45. $2x^3 \cdot 5x^7$

46. $-3z^4 \cdot 10z^7$

47. $\dfrac{z^{12}}{z^{15}}$

48. $\dfrac{x^{11}}{x^{20}}$

49. $\dfrac{y^{-3}}{y^{-7}}$

50. $\dfrac{z^{-12}}{z^{10}}$

51. $3x^{-1}$

52. $(4x)^{-1}$

53. $3^0 - 3t^0$

54. $4^0 + 4x^0$

55. $\dfrac{r^4}{r^{-4}}$

56. $\dfrac{x^{-5}}{x^3}$

57. $\dfrac{x^{-7}y^{-2}}{x^2y^2}$

58. $\dfrac{a^{-5}b^7}{a^{-2}b^{-3}}$

59. $\dfrac{2a^{-6}b^2}{18ab^{-5}}$

60. $\dfrac{18ab^{-6}}{3a^{-3}b^6}$

61. $\dfrac{(24x^8)(x)}{20x^{-7}}$

62. $\dfrac{(30z^2)(z^5)}{55z^{-4}}$

Write each number in scientific notation. See Example 8.

63. 31,250,000   **64.** 678,000

65. 0.016   **66.** 0.007613

67. 67,413   **68.** 36,800,000

69. 0.0125   **70.** 0.00084

71. 0.000053   **72.** 98,700,000,000

Write each number in scientific notation.

73. The approximate distance between Jupiter and the sun is 778,300,000 kilometers. (*Source:* National Space Data Center)

74. Total revenues for Wal-Mart in fiscal year 2003 were $245,525,000,000. (*Source:* Wal-Mart Stores, Inc.)

75. At the various hotels at the Walt Disney World Resort in Florida, there are 737,000 square feet of meeting facilities. (*Source:* The Walt Disney Company)

76. In 2002, the American toy industry had retail sales of $30,606,000,000. (*Source:* Toy Industry Asso.)

77. In 2002, the New York City subway system carried a total of 1,410,000,000 passengers. (*Source:* Metropolitan Transit Authority)

78. The center of the sun is about 27,000,000° F.

79. A pulsar is a rotating neutron star that gives off sharp, regular pulses of radio waves. For one particular pulsar, the rate of pulses is every 0.001 second.

80. To convert from cubic inches to cubic meters, multiply by 0.0000164.

Write each number in standard notation, without exponents. See Example 9.

81. 3.6×10^{-9} **82.** 2.7×10^{-5}

83. 9.3×10^{7} **84.** 6.378×10^{8}

85. 1.278×10^{6} **86.** 7.6×10^{4}

87. 7.35×10^{12} **88.** 1.66×10^{-5}

89. 4.03×10^{-7} **90.** 8.007×10^{8}

Write each number in standard notation.

91. The estimated world population in 1 A.D. was 2.0×10^{8}. (*Source: World Almanac and Book of Facts*)

92. There are 3.949×10^{6} miles of highways, roads, and streets in the United States. (*Source:* Bureau of Transportation Statistics)

93. In 2005, teenagers and children are expected to spend 4.9×10^{9} dollars on purchases and transactions made online. (*Source:* Jupiter Research)

94. Each day, an estimated 2.0×10^{7} adults in America drink gourmet coffee beverages. (*Source:* National Coffee Association)

REVIEW AND PREVIEW

Evaluate. See Sections 1.3 and 5.1.

95. $(5 \cdot 2)^2$ **96.** $5^2 \cdot 2^2$

97. $\left(\dfrac{3}{4}\right)^3$ **98.** $\dfrac{3^3}{4^3}$

99. $(2^3)^2$ **100.** $(2^2)^3$

101. $(2^{-1})^4$ **102.** $(2^4)^{-1}$

Concept Extensions

103. Explain how to convert a number from standard notation to scientific notation.

104. Explain how to convert a number from scientific notation to standard notation.

105. Simplify where possible.

   a. $x^a \cdot x^a$ **b.** $x^a + x^a$

   c. $\dfrac{x^a}{x^b}$ **d.** $x^a \cdot x^b$

   e. $x^a + x^b$

106. Which numbers are equal to 36,000? Of these, which is written in scientific notation?

   a. 36×10^3 **b.** 360×10^2

   c. 0.36×10^5 **d.** 3.6×10^4

Without calculating, determine which number is larger.

107. 7^{11} or 7^{13} **108.** 5^{10} or 5^9

109. 7^{-11} or 7^{-13} **110.** 5^{-10} or 5^{-9}

Simplify. Assume that variables in the exponent represent nonzero integers and that x, y, and z are not 0. See Example 7.

111. $x^5 \cdot x^{7a}$ **112.** $y^{2p} \cdot y^{9p}$

113. $\dfrac{x^{3t-1}}{x^t}$ **114.** $\dfrac{y^{4p-2}}{y^{3p}}$

115. $x^{4a} \cdot x^7$ **116.** $x^{9y} \cdot x^{-7y}$

117. $\dfrac{z^{6x}}{z^7}$ **118.** $\dfrac{y^6}{y^{4z}}$

119. $\dfrac{x^{3t} \cdot x^{4t-1}}{x^t}$ **120.** $\dfrac{z^{5x} \cdot z^{x-7}}{z^x}$

121. $x^{9+b} \cdot x^{3a-b}$ **122.** $z^{2a-b} \cdot z^{5a-b}$

5.2   MORE WORK WITH EXPONENTS AND SCIENTIFIC NOTATION

Objectives

1 Use the power rules for exponents.

2 Use exponent rules and definitions to simplify exponential expressions.

3 Compute, using scientific notation.

1 The volume of the cube shown whose side measures x^2 units is $(x^2)^3$ cubic units. To simplify an expression such as $(x^2)^3$, we use the definition of a^n. Then

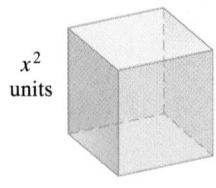

x^2 units

$$(x^2)^3 = \underbrace{(x^2)(x^2)(x^2)}_{x^2 \text{ is a factor 3 times}} = x^{2+2+2} = x^6$$

Notice that the result is exactly the same if the exponents are multiplied.

$$(x^2)^3 = x^{2 \cdot 3} = x^6$$

This suggests that the power of an exponential expression raised to a power is the product of the exponents. Two additional rules for exponents are given in the following box.

The Power Rule and Power of a Product or Quotient Rules for Exponents

If a and b are real numbers and m and n are integers, then

$$(a^m)^n = a^{m \cdot n} \qquad \text{Power rule}$$

$$(ab)^m = a^m b^m \qquad \text{Power of a product}$$

$$\left(\frac{a}{b}\right)^n = \frac{a^n}{b^n} \, (b \neq 0) \qquad \text{Power of a quotient}$$

EXAMPLE 1

Use the power rule to simplify the following expressions. Use positive exponents to write all results.

a. $(x^5)^7$ **b.** $(2^2)^3$ **c.** $(5^{-1})^2$ **d.** $(y^{-3})^{-4}$

Solution

a. $(x^5)^7 = x^{5\cdot7} = x^{35}$

b. $(2^2)^3 = 2^{2\cdot3} = 2^6 = 64$

c. $(5^{-1})^2 = 5^{-1\cdot2} = 5^{-2} = \dfrac{1}{5^2} = \dfrac{1}{25}$

d. $(y^{-3})^{-4} = y^{-3(-4)} = y^{12}$

EXAMPLE 2

Use the power rules to simplify the following. Use positive exponents to write all results.

a. $(5x^2)^3$ **b.** $\left(\dfrac{2}{3}\right)^3$ **c.** $\left(\dfrac{3p^4}{q^5}\right)^2$

d. $\left(\dfrac{2^{-3}}{y}\right)^{-2}$ **e.** $(x^{-5}y^2z^{-1})^7$

Solution

a. $(5x^2)^3 = 5^3 \cdot (x^2)^3 = 5^3 \cdot x^{2\cdot3} = 125x^6$

b. $\left(\dfrac{2}{3}\right)^3 = \dfrac{2^3}{3^3} = \dfrac{8}{27}$

c. $\left(\dfrac{3p^4}{q^5}\right)^2 = \dfrac{(3p^4)^2}{(q^5)^2} = \dfrac{3^2 \cdot (p^4)^2}{(q^5)^2} = \dfrac{9p^8}{q^{10}}$

d. $\left(\dfrac{2^{-3}}{y}\right)^{-2} = \dfrac{(2^{-3})^{-2}}{y^{-2}}$

$$= \dfrac{2^6}{y^{-2}} = 64y^2 \quad \text{Use the negative exponent rule.}$$

e. $(x^{-5}y^2z^{-1})^7 = (x^{-5})^7 \cdot (y^2)^7 \cdot (z^{-1})^7$

$$= x^{-35}y^{14}z^{-7} = \dfrac{y^{14}}{x^{35}z^7}$$

2   In the next few examples, we practice the use of several of the rules and definitions for exponents. The following is a summary of these rules and definitions.

Summary of Rules for Exponents

If a and b are real numbers and m and n are integers, then

Product rule	$a^m \cdot a^n = a^{m+n}$	
Zero exponent	$a^0 = 1$	$(a \neq 0)$
Negative exponent	$a^{-n} = \dfrac{1}{a^n}$	$(a \neq 0)$
Quotient rule	$\dfrac{a^m}{a^n} = a^{m-n}$	$(a \neq 0)$
Power rule	$(a^m)^n = a^{m \cdot n}$	
Power of a product	$(ab)^m = a^m \cdot b^m$	
Power of a quotient	$\left(\dfrac{a}{b}\right)^m = \dfrac{a^m}{b^m}$	$(b \neq 0)$

EXAMPLE 3

Simplify each expression. Use positive exponents to write the answers.

a. $(2x^0y^{-3})^{-2}$ **b.** $\left(\dfrac{x^{-5}}{x^{-2}}\right)^{-3}$ **c.** $\left(\dfrac{2}{7}\right)^{-2}$ **d.** $\dfrac{5^{-2}x^{-3}y^{11}}{x^2y^{-5}}$

Solution   **a.** $(2x^0y^{-3})^{-2} = 2^{-2}(x^0)^{-2}(y^{-3})^{-2}$

$$= 2^{-2}x^0y^6$$

$$= \dfrac{1(y^6)}{2^2} \qquad \text{Write } x^0 \text{ as 1.}$$

$$= \dfrac{y^6}{4}$$

b. $\left(\dfrac{x^{-5}}{x^{-2}}\right)^{-3} = \dfrac{(x^{-5})^{-3}}{(x^{-2})^{-3}} = \dfrac{x^{15}}{x^6} = x^{15-6} = x^9$

c. $\left(\dfrac{2}{7}\right)^{-2} = \dfrac{2^{-2}}{7^{-2}} = \dfrac{7^2}{2^2} = \dfrac{49}{4}$

d. $\dfrac{5^{-2}x^{-3}y^{11}}{x^2y^{-5}} = (5^{-2})\left(\dfrac{x^{-3}}{x^2}\right)\left(\dfrac{y^{11}}{y^{-5}}\right) = 5^{-2}x^{-3-2}y^{11-(-5)} = 5^{-2}x^{-5}y^{16}$

$$= \dfrac{y^{16}}{5^2x^5} = \dfrac{y^{16}}{25x^5}$$

EXAMPLE 4

Simplify each expression. Use positive exponents to write the answers.

a. $\left(\dfrac{3x^2y}{y^{-9}z}\right)^{-2}$ **b.** $\left(\dfrac{3a^2}{2x^{-1}}\right)^3\left(\dfrac{x^{-3}}{4a^{-2}}\right)^{-1}$

Solution There is often more than one way to simplify exponential expressions. Here, we will simplify inside the parentheses if possible before we apply the power rules for exponents.

a. $\left(\dfrac{3x^2y}{y^{-9}z}\right)^{-2} = \left(\dfrac{3x^2y^{10}}{z}\right)^{-2} = \dfrac{3^{-2}x^{-4}y^{-20}}{z^{-2}} = \dfrac{z^2}{3^2x^4y^{20}} = \dfrac{z^2}{9x^4y^{20}}$

b. $\left(\dfrac{3a^2}{2x^{-1}}\right)^3\left(\dfrac{x^{-3}}{4a^{-2}}\right)^{-1} = \dfrac{27a^6}{8x^{-3}} \cdot \dfrac{x^3}{4^{-1}a^2}$

$= \dfrac{27 \cdot 4 \cdot a^6 x^3 x^3}{8 \cdot a^2} = \dfrac{27a^4x^6}{2}$

EXAMPLE 5

Simplify each expression. Assume that a and b are integers and that x and y are not 0.

a. $x^{-b}(2x^b)^2$

b. $\dfrac{(y^{3a})^2}{y^{a-6}}$

Solution **a.** $x^{-b}(2x^b)^2 = x^{-b}2^2x^{2b} = 4x^{-b+2b} = 4x^b$

b. $\dfrac{(y^{3a})^2}{y^{a-6}} = \dfrac{y^{6a}}{y^{a-6}} = y^{6a-(a-6)} = y^{6a-a+6} = y^{5a+6}$

3   To perform operations on numbers written in scientific notation, we use properties of exponents.

EXAMPLE 6

Perform the indicated operations. Write each result in scientific notation.

a. $(8.1 \times 10^5)(5 \times 10^{-7})$

b. $\dfrac{1.2 \times 10^4}{3 \times 10^{-2}}$

Solution **a.** $(8.1 \times 10^5)(5 \times 10^{-7}) = 8.1 \times 5 \times 10^5 \times 10^{-7}$

$= 40.5 \times 10^{-2}$
Not in scientific notation because 40.5 is not between 1 and 10.

$= (4.05 \times 10^1) \times 10^{-2}$

$= 4.05 \times 10^{-1}$

b. $\dfrac{1.2 \times 10^4}{3 \times 10^{-2}} = \left(\dfrac{1.2}{3}\right)\left(\dfrac{10^4}{10^{-2}}\right) = 0.4 \times 10^{4-(-2)}$

$= 0.4 \times 10^6 = (4 \times 10^{-1}) \times 10^6 = 4 \times 10^5$

EXAMPLE 7

Use scientific notation to simplify $\dfrac{2000 \times 0.000021}{700}$. Write the result in scientific notation.

Solution

$$\frac{2000 \times 0.000021}{700} = \frac{(2 \times 10^3)(2.1 \times 10^{-5})}{7 \times 10^2} = \frac{2(2.1)}{7} \cdot \frac{10^3 \cdot 10^{-5}}{10^2}$$
$$= 0.6 \times 10^{-4}$$
$$= (6 \times 10^{-1}) \times 10^{-4}$$
$$= 6 \times 10^{-5}$$

STUDY SKILLS REMINDER

Are You Satisfied with Your Performance on a Particular Quiz or Exam?

If not, analyze your quiz or exam like you would a good mystery novel. Look for common themes in your errors.

Were most of your errors a result of

▶ *Carelessness*? If your errors were careless, did you turn in your work before the allotted time expired? If so, resolve next time to use the entire time allotted. Any extra time can be spent checking your work.

▶ *Running out of time*? If so, make a point to better manage your time on your next exam. A few suggestions are to work any questions that you are unsure of last and to check your work after all of the questions have been answered.

▶ *Not understanding a concept*? If so, review that concept and correct your work. Remember next time to make sure that all concepts on a quiz or exam are understood before the exam.

MENTAL MATH

Simplify. See Examples 1 through 4.

1. $(x^4)^5$
2. $(5^6)^2$
3. $x^4 \cdot x^5$
4. $x^7 \cdot x^8$
5. $(y^6)^7$

6. $(x^3)^4$
7. $(z^4)^9$
8. $(z^3)^7$
9. $(z^{-6})^{-3}$
10. $(y^{-4})^{-2}$

EXERCISE SET 5.2

| STUDY GUIDE/SSM | CD/ VIDEO | PH MATH TUTOR CENTER | MathXL®Tutorials ON CD | MathXL® | MyMathLab® |

Simplify. Write each answer using positive exponents only. See Examples 1 and 2.

1. $(3^{-1})^2$

2. $(2^{-2})^2$

3. $(x^4)^{-9}$

4. $(y^7)^{-3}$

5. $(y)^{-5}$

6. $(z^{-1})^{10}$

7. $(3x^2y^3)^2$

8. $(4x^3yz)^2$

9. $\left(\dfrac{2x^5}{y^{-3}}\right)^4$

10. $\left(\dfrac{3a^{-4}}{b^7}\right)^3$

11. $(a^2bc^{-3})^{-6}$

12. $(6x^{-6}y^7z^0)^{-2}$

13. $\left(\dfrac{x^7y^{-3}}{z^{-4}}\right)^{-5}$

14. $\left(\dfrac{a^{-2}b^{-5}}{c^{-11}}\right)^{-6}$

15. $(5^{-1})^3$

Simplify. Write each answer using positive exponents only. See Examples 3 and 4.

16. $\left(\dfrac{a^{-4}}{a^{-5}}\right)^{-2}$

17. $\left(\dfrac{x^{-9}}{x^{-4}}\right)^{-3}$

18. $\left(\dfrac{2a^{-2}b^5}{4a^2b^7}\right)^{-2}$

19. $\left(\dfrac{5x^7y^4}{10x^3y^{-2}}\right)^{-3}$

20. $\dfrac{4^{-1}x^2yz}{x^{-2}yz^3}$

21. $\dfrac{8^{-2}x^{-3}y^{11}}{x^2y^{-5}}$

22. $\left(\dfrac{6p^6}{p^{12}}\right)^2$

23. $\left(\dfrac{4p^6}{p^9}\right)^3$

24. $(-8y^3xa^{-2})^{-3}$

25. $(-xy^0x^2a^3)^{-3}$

26. $\left(\dfrac{x^{-2}y^{-2}}{a^{-3}}\right)^{-7}$

27. $\left(\dfrac{x^{-1}y^{-2}}{5^{-3}}\right)^{-5}$

MIXED PRACTICE

Simplify. Write each answer using positive exponents.

28. $(8^2)^{-1}$

29. $(x^7)^{-9}$

30. $(y^{-4})^5$

31. $\left(\dfrac{7}{8}\right)^3$

32. $\left(\dfrac{4}{3}\right)^2$

33. $(4x^2)^2$

34. $(-8x^3)^2$

35. $(-2^{-2}y)^3$

36. $(-4^{-6}y^{-6})^{-4}$

37. $\left(\dfrac{4^{-4}}{y^3x}\right)^{-2}$

38. $\left(\dfrac{7^{-3}}{ab^2}\right)^{-2}$

39. $\left(\dfrac{1}{4}\right)^{-3}$

40. $\left(\dfrac{1}{8}\right)^{-2}$

41. $\left(\dfrac{3x^5}{6x^4}\right)^4$

42. $\left(\dfrac{8^{-3}}{y^2}\right)^{-2}$

43. $\dfrac{(y^3)^{-4}}{y^3}$

44. $\dfrac{2(y^3)^{-3}}{y^{-3}}$

45. $\left(\dfrac{2x^{-3}}{y^{-1}}\right)^{-3}$

46. $\left(\dfrac{n^5}{2m^{-2}}\right)^{-4}$

47. $\dfrac{3^{-2}a^{-5}b^6}{4^{-2}a^{-7}b^{-3}}$

48. $\dfrac{2^{-3}m^{-4}n^{-5}}{5^{-2}m^{-5}n}$

49. $(4x^6y^5)^{-2}(6x^4y^3)$

50. $(5xy)^3(z^{-2})^{-3}$

51. $x^6(x^6bc)^{-6}$

52. $2(y^2b)^{-4}$

53. $\dfrac{2^{-3}x^2y^{-5}}{5^{-2}x^7y^{-1}}$

54. $\dfrac{7^{-1}a^{-3}b^5}{a^2b^{-2}}$

55. $\left(\dfrac{2x^2}{y^4}\right)^3\left(\dfrac{2x^5}{y}\right)^{-2}$

56. $\left(\dfrac{3z^{-2}}{y}\right)^2\left(\dfrac{9y^{-4}}{z^{-3}}\right)^{-1}$

Perform each indicated operation. Write each answer in scientific notation. See Example 6.

57. $(5 \times 10^{11})(2.9 \times 10^{-3})$

58. $(3.6 \times 10^{-12})(6 \times 10^9)$

59. $(2 \times 10^5)^3$

60. $(3 \times 10^{-7})^3$

61. $\dfrac{3.6 \times 10^{-4}}{9 \times 10^2}$

62. $\dfrac{1.2 \times 10^9}{2 \times 10^{-5}}$

63. $\dfrac{0.0069}{0.023}$

64. $\dfrac{0.00048}{0.0016}$

65. $\dfrac{18{,}200 \times 100}{91{,}000}$

66. $\dfrac{0.0003 \times 0.0024}{0.0006 \times 20}$

67. $\dfrac{6000 \times 0.006}{0.009 \times 400}$

68. $\dfrac{0.00016 \times 300}{0.064 \times 100}$

69. $\dfrac{0.00064 \times 2000}{16{,}000}$

70. $\dfrac{0.00072 \times 0.003}{0.00024}$

71. $\dfrac{66{,}000 \times 0.001}{0.002 \times 0.003}$

72. $\dfrac{0.0007 \times 11{,}000}{0.001 \times 0.0001}$

73. $\dfrac{1.25 \times 10^{15}}{(2.2 \times 10^{-2})(6.4 \times 10^{-5})}$

74. $\dfrac{(2.6 \times 10^{-3})(4.8 \times 10^{-4})}{1.3 \times 10^{-12}}$

Solve.

75. A computer can add two numbers in about 10^{-8} second. Express in scientific notation how long it would take this computer to do this task 200,000 times.

△ **76.** To convert from square inches to square meters, multiply by 6.452×10^{-4}. The area of the following square is 4×10^{-2} square inches. Convert this area to square meters.

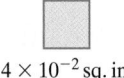

4×10^{-2} sq. in.

△ **77.** To convert from cubic inches to cubic meters, multiply by 1.64×10^{-5}. A grain of salt is in the shape of a cube. If an average size of a grain of salt is 3.8×10^{-6} cubic inches, convert this volume to cubic meters.

REVIEW AND PREVIEW

Simplify each expression. See Section 1.4.

78. $-5y + 4y - 18 - y$

79. $12m - 14 - 15m - 1$

80. $-3x - (4x - 2)$

81. $-9y - (5 - 6y)$

82. $3(z - 4) - 2(3z + 1)$

83. $5(x - 3) - 4(2x - 5)$

Concept Extensions

Simplify the following. Assume that variables in the exponents represent integers and that all other variables are not 0. See Example 5.

84. $(x^{3a+6})^3$

85. $(x^{2b+7})^2$

86. $\dfrac{x^{4a}(x^{4a})^3}{x^{4a-2}}$

87. $\dfrac{x^{-5y+2}x^{2y}}{x}$

88. $(b^{5x-2})^{2x}$

89. $(c^{2a+3})^3$

90. $\dfrac{(y^{2a})^8}{y^{a-3}}$

91. $\dfrac{(y^{4a})^7}{y^{2a-1}}$

92. $\left(\dfrac{2x^{3t}}{x^{2t-1}}\right)^4$

93. $\left(\dfrac{3y^{5a}}{y^{-a+1}}\right)^2$

94. $\dfrac{(z^{a+2})^b}{(z^{b-1})^a}$

95. $\dfrac{(y^{3-a})^b}{(y^{1-b})^a}$

96. $\dfrac{x^{2a+1}y^{a-1}}{x^{3a+1}y^{2a-3}}$

97. $\dfrac{x^{-5-3a}y^{-2a-b}}{x^{-5+3b}y^{-2b-a}}$

△ **98.** Each side of the cube shown is $\dfrac{2x^{-2}}{y}$ meters. Find its volume.

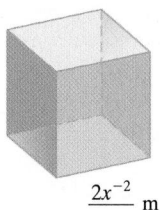

$\dfrac{2x^{-2}}{y}$ m

△ **99.** The lot shown is in the shape of a parallelogram with base $\dfrac{3x^{-1}}{y^{-3}}$ feet and height $5x^{-7}$ feet. Find its area.

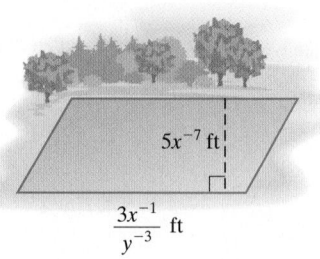

$5x^{-7}$ ft

$\dfrac{3x^{-1}}{y^{-3}}$ ft

100. The density D of an object is equivalent to the quotient of its mass M and volume V. Thus $D = \dfrac{M}{V}$. Express in scientific notation the density of an object whose mass is 500,000 pounds and whose volume is 250 cubic feet.

101. The density of ordinary water is 3.12×10^{-2} tons per cubic foot. The volume of water in the largest of the Great Lakes, Lake Superior, is 4.269×10^{14} cubic feet. Use the formula $D = \dfrac{M}{V}$ (see Exercise 100) to find the mass (in tons) of the water in Lake Superior. Express your answer in scientific notation. (*Source*: National Ocean Service)

102. Is there a number a such that $a^{-1} = a^1$? If so, give the value of a.

103. Is there a number a such that a^{-2} is a negative number? If so, give the value of a.

✎ **104.** Explain whether 0.4×10^{-5} is written in scientific notation.

105. The estimated population of the United States in 2003 was 2.927×10^8 people. The land area of the United States is 3.536×10^6 square miles. Find the population density (number of people per square mile) for the United States in 2003. Round to the nearest whole number. (*Source*: U.S. Census Bureau)

106. In 2002, the value of goods and services imported into the United States was $\$1.141 \times 10^{12}$. The estimated population of the United States in 2002 was 2.821×10^8 people. Find the average value of imports per person in the United States for 2002. Round to the nearest dollar. (*Sources*: U.S. Census Bureau, Bureau of Economic Analysis)

107. In 2002, the population of Japan was 1.27×10^8 people. At the same time, the population of Oceania (including the countries of Australia, Fiji, New Zealand, etc.) was 3.22×10^7 people. How many times greater was the population of Japan than the population of Oceania? Round to the nearest tenth. (*Source*: Population Reference Bureau)

108. Explain whether 0.4×10^{-5} is written in scientific notation.

109. The Moscow subway system has a passenger volume of 3.16×10^9 passengers. The São Paulo subway system has a passenger volume of 7.01×10^8 passengers. How many times greater is the Moscow subway volume than the São Paulo volume? Round to the nearest tenth. (*Source*: New York City Transit Authority)

110. China's fighting force numbers 2.93×10^6 soldiers. Taiwan's fighting force numbers 4.25×10^5. How many times greater is China's armed forces than Taiwan's? Round to the nearest whole number. (*Source*: Russell Ash, *The Top 10 of Everything*)

5.3   POLYNOMIALS AND POLYNOMIAL FUNCTIONS

Objectives

1 Identify term, constant, polynomial, monomial, binomial, trinomial, and the degree of a term and of a polynomial.

2 Define polynomial functions.

3 Review combining like terms.

4 Add polynomials.

5 Subtract polynomials.

6 Recognize the graph of a polynomial function from the degree of the polynomial.

1 A **term** is a number or the product of a number and one or more variables raised to powers. The **numerical coefficient**, or simply the **coefficient**, is the numerical factor of a term.

Term	Numerical Coefficient
$-12x^5$	-12
x^3y	1
$-z$	-1
2	2

If a term contains only a number, it is called a **constant term**, or simply a **constant**. A **polynomial** is a finite sum of terms in which all variables are raised to nonnegative integer powers and no variables appear in any denominator.

Polynomials	Not Polynomials	
$4x^5y + 7xz$	$5x^{-3} + 2x$	Negative integer exponent
$-5x^3 + 2x + \frac{2}{3}$	$\frac{6}{x^2} - 5x + 1$	Variable in denominator

A polynomial that contains only one variable is called a **polynomial in one variable**. For example, $3x^2 - 2x + 7$ is a **polynomial in x**. This polynomial in x is written in *descending order* since the terms are listed in descending order of the variable's exponents. (The term 7 can be thought of as $7x^0$.) The following examples are polynomials in one variable written in **descending order**.

$$4x^3 - 7x^2 + 5 \qquad y^2 - 4 \qquad 8a^4 - 7a^2 + 4a$$

A **monomial** is a polynomial consisting of one term. A **binomial** is a polynomial consisting of two terms. A **trinomial** is a polynomial consisting of three terms.

Monomials	*Binomials*	*Trinomials*
ax^2	$x + y$	$x^2 + 4xy + y^2$
$-3x$	$6y^2 - 2$	$-x^4 + 3x^3 + 1$
4	$\dfrac{5}{7}z^3 - 2z$	$8y^2 - 2y - 10$

By definition, all monomials, binomials, and trinomials are also polynomials.
Each term of a polynomial has a **degree**.

Degree of a Term

The **degree of a term** is the sum of the exponents on the *variables* contained in the term.

EXAMPLE 1

Find the degree of each term.

a. $3x^2$ **b.** -2^3x^5 **c.** y **d.** $12x^2yz^3$ **e.** 5

Solution

a. The exponent on x is 2, so the degree of the term is 2.

b. The exponent on x is 5, so the degree of the term is 5. (Recall that the degree is the sum of the exponents on only the *variables*.)

c. The degree of y, or y^1, is 1.

d. The degree is the sum of the exponents on the variables, or $2 + 1 + 3 = 6$.

e. The degree of 5, which can be written as $5x^0$, is 0.

From the preceding example, we can say that the degree of a constant is 0. Also, the term 0 has no degree.
Each polynomial also has a degree.

> ### Degree of a Polynomial
> The **degree of a polynomial** is the largest degree of all its terms.

EXAMPLE 2

Find the degree of each polynomial and indicate whether the polynomial is also a monomial, binomial, or trinomial.

	Polynomial	*Degree*	*Classification*
a.	$7x^3 - 3x + 2$	3	Trinomial
b.	$-xyz$	$1 + 1 + 1 = 3$	Monomial
c.	$x^4 - 16$	4	Binomial

EXAMPLE 3

Find the degree of the polynomial

$$3xy + x^2y^2 - 5x^2 - 6.$$

Solution   The degree of each term is

$$3xy + x^2y^2 - 5x^2 - 6$$
$$\downarrow \quad \downarrow \quad \downarrow \quad \downarrow$$

Degree: 2   4   2   0

The largest degree of any term is 4, so the degree of this polynomial is 4.

2   At times, it is convenient to use function notation to represent polynomials. For example, we may write $P(x)$ to represent the polynomial $3x^2 - 2x - 5$. In symbols, this is

$$P(x) = 3x^2 - 2x - 5$$

This function is called a **polynomial function** because the expression $3x^2 - 2x - 5$ is a polynomial.

> ### Helpful Hint
> Recall that the symbol $P(x)$ **does not mean** P times x. It is a special symbol used to denote a function.

EXAMPLE 4

If $P(x) = 3x^2 - 2x - 5$, find the following.

a. $P(1)$ **b.** $P(-2)$

Solution **a.** Substitute 1 for x in $P(x) = 3x^2 - 2x - 5$ and simplify.

$$P(x) = 3x^2 - 2x - 5$$
$$P(1) = 3(1)^2 - 2(1) - 5 = -4$$

b. Substitute -2 for x in $P(x) = 3x^2 - 2x - 5$ and simplify.

$$P(x) = 3x^2 - 2x - 5$$
$$P(-2) = 3(-2)^2 - 2(-2) - 5 = 11$$

Many real-world phenomena are modeled by polynomial functions. If the polynomial function model is given, we can often find the solution of a problem by evaluating the function at a certain value.

EXAMPLE 5

FINDING THE HEIGHT OF AN OBJECT

The world's highest bridge, Royal Gorge suspension bridge in Colorado, is 1053 feet above the Arkansas River. An object is dropped from the top of this bridge. Neglecting air resistance, the height of the object at time t seconds is given by the polynomial function $P(t) = -16t^2 + 1053$. Find the height of the object when $t = 1$ second and when $t = 8$ seconds.

Solution To find the height of the object at 1 second, we find $P(1)$.

$$P(t) = -16t^2 + 1053$$
$$P(1) = -16(1)^2 + 1053$$
$$P(1) = 1037$$

When $t = 1$ second, the height of the object is 1037 feet.

To find the height of the object at 8 seconds, we find $P(8)$.

$$P(t) = -16t^2 + 1053$$
$$P(8) = -16(8)^2 + 1053$$
$$P(8) = -1024 + 1053$$
$$P(8) = 29$$

When $t = 8$ seconds, the height of the object is 29 feet. Notice that as time t increases, the height of the object decreases.

3   Before we add polynomials, recall that terms are considered to be **like terms** if they contain exactly the same variables raised to exactly the same powers.

Like Terms	*Unlike Terms*
$-5x^2, -x^2$	$4x^2, 3x$
$7xy^3z, -2xzy^3$	$12x^2y^3, -2xy^3$

To simplify a polynomial, **combine like terms** by using the distributive property. For example, by the distributive property,

$$5x + 7x = (5 + 7)x = 12x$$

EXAMPLE 6

Simplify by combining like terms.

a. $-12x^2 + 7x^2 - 6x$ **b.** $3xy - 2x + 5xy - x$

Solution   By the distributive property,

a. $-12x^2 + 7x^2 - 6x = (-12 + 7)x^2 - 6x = -5x^2 - 6x$

b. Use the associative and commutative properties to group together like terms; then combine.

$$3xy - 2x + 5xy - x = 3xy + 5xy - 2x - x$$
$$= (3 + 5)xy + (-2 - 1)x$$
$$= 8xy - 3x$$

4   Now we have reviewed the necessary skills to add polynomials.

> ## Adding Polynomials
> Combine all like terms.

EXAMPLE 7

Add.

a. $(7x^3y - xy^3 + 11) + (6x^3y - 4)$ **b.** $(3a^3 - b + 2a - 5) + (a + b + 5)$

Solution   **a.** To add, remove the parentheses and group like terms.

$$(7x^3y - xy^3 + 11) + (6x^3y - 4)$$
$$= 7x^3y - xy^3 + 11 + 6x^3y - 4$$
$$= 7x^3y + 6x^3y - xy^3 + 11 - 4 \quad \text{Group like terms.}$$
$$= 13x^3y - xy^3 + 7 \quad\quad\quad \text{Combine like terms.}$$

b.

$$(3a^3 - b + 2a - 5) + (a + b + 5)$$
$$= 3a^3 - b + 2a - 5 + a + b + 5$$

$$= 3a^3 - b + b + 2a + a - 5 + 5 \quad \text{Group like terms.}$$

$$= 3a^3 + 3a \quad \text{Combine like terms.}$$

EXAMPLE 8

Add $11x^3 - 12x^2 + x - 3$ and $x^3 - 10x + 5$.

Solution $(11x^3 - 12x^2 + x - 3) + (x^3 - 10x + 5)$

$$= 11x^3 + x^3 - 12x^2 + x - 10x - 3 + 5 \quad \text{Group like terms.}$$

$$= 12x^3 - 12x^2 - 9x + 2 \quad \text{Combine like terms.}$$

Sometimes it is more convenient to add polynomials vertically. To do this, line up like terms beneath one another and add like terms.

5   The definition of subtraction of real numbers can be extended to apply to polynomials. To subtract a number, we add its opposite.

$$a - b = a + (-b)$$

Likewise, to subtract a polynomial, we add its opposite. In other words, if P and Q are polynomials, then

$$P - Q = P + (-Q)$$

The polynomial $-Q$ is the **opposite**, or **additive inverse**, of the polynomial Q. We can find $-Q$ by writing the opposite of each term of Q.

> ## Subtracting Polynomials
>
> To subtract a polynomial, add its opposite.

For example,

To subtract, add its opposite (found by writing the opposite of each term).

$$(3x^2 + 4x - 7) - (3x^2 - 2x - 5) = (3x^2 + 4x - 7) + (-3x^2 + 2x + 5)$$

$$= 3x^2 + 4x - 7 - 3x^2 + 2x + 5$$

$$= 6x - 2 \quad \text{Combine like terms.}$$

✔ **CONCEPT CHECK**

Which polynomial is the opposite of $16x^3 - 5x + 7$?

a. $-16x^3 - 5x + 7$ **b.** $-16x^3 + 5x - 7$

c. $16x^3 + 5x + 7$ **d.** $-16x^3 + 5x + 7$

Concept Check Answer:
b

EXAMPLE 9

Subtract: $(12z^5 - 12z^3 + z) - (-3z^4 + z^3 + 12z)$

Solution To subtract, add the opposite of the second polynomial to the first polynomial.

$(12z^5 - 12z^3 + z) - (-3z^4 + z^3 + 12z)$

$= 12z^5 - 12z^3 + z + 3z^4 - z^3 - 12z)$ *Add the opposite of the polynomial being subtracted.*

$= 12z^5 + 3z^4 - 12z^3 - z^3 + z - 12z$ *Group like terms.*

$= 12z^5 + 3z^4 - 13z^3 - 11z$ *Combine like terms.*

✔ **CONCEPT CHECK**

Why is the following subtraction incorrect?

$$(7z - 5) - (3z - 4)$$
$$= 7z - 5 - 3z - 4$$
$$= 4z - 9$$

EXAMPLE 10

Subtract $4x^3y^2 - 3x^2y^2 + 2y^2$ from $10x^3y^2 - 7x^2y^2$.

Solution If we subtract 2 from 8, the difference is $8 - 2 = 6$. Notice the order of the numbers, and then write "Subtract $4x^3y^2 - 3x^2y^2 + 2y^2$ from $10x^3y^2 - 7x^2y^2$" as a mathematical expression.

$(10x^3y^2 - 7x^2y^2) - (4x^3y^2 - 3x^2y^2 + 2y^2)$

$= 10x^3y^2 - 7x^2y^2 - 4x^3y^2 + 3x^2y^2 - 2y^2$ *Remove parentheses.*

$= 6x^3y^2 - 4x^2y^2 - 2y^2$ *Combine like terms.*

To add or subtract polynomials vertically, just remember to line up like terms. For example, perform the subtraction $(10x^3y^2 - 7x^2y^2) - (4x^3y^2 - 3x^2y^2 + 2y^2)$ vertically. Add the opposite of the second polynomial.

$$\begin{array}{r} 10x^3y^2 - 7x^2y^2 \\ -(4x^3y^2 - 3x^2y^2 + 2y^2) \\ \hline \end{array}$$ is equivalent to $$\begin{array}{r} 10x^3y^2 - 7x^2y^2 \\ -4x^3y^2 + 3x^2y^2 - 2y^2 \\ \hline 6x^3y^2 - 4x^2y^2 - 2y^2 \end{array}$$

Polynomial functions, like polynomials, can be added, subtracted, multiplied, and divided. For example, if

$$P(x) = x^2 + x + 1$$

then

$$2P(x) = 2(x^2 + x + 1) = 2x^2 + 2x + 2$$ *Use the distributive property.*

Concept Check Answer:
With parentheses removed, the expression should be
$7z - 5 - 3z + 4 = 4z - 1$

Also, if $Q(x) = 5x^2 - 1$, then $P(x) + Q(x) = (x^2 + x + 1) + (5x^2 - 1)$
$= 6x^2 + x$.

A useful business and economics application of subtracting polynomial functions is finding the profit function $P(x)$ when given a revenue function $R(x)$ and a cost function $C(x)$. In business, it is true that

$$\text{profit} = \text{revenue} - \text{cost, or}$$
$$P(x) = R(x) - C(x)$$

For example, if the revenue function is $R(x) = 7x$ and the cost function is $C(x) = 2x + 5000$, then the profit function is

$$P(x) = R(x) - C(x)$$

or

$$P(x) = 7x - (2x + 5000) \quad \text{Substitute } R(x) = 7x$$
$$P(x) = 5x - 5000 \quad\quad\quad \text{and } C(x) = 2x + 5000.$$

Problem-solving exercises involving profit are in the exercise set.

6 In this section, we reviewed how to find the degree of a polynomial. Knowing the degree of a polynomial can help us recognize the graph of the related polynomial function. For example, we know from Section 3.1 that the graph of the polynomial function $f(x) = x^2$ is a parabola as shown to the left.

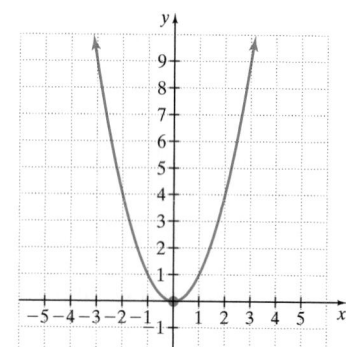

The polynomial x^2 has degree 2. The graphs of all polynomial functions of degree 2 will have this same general shape—opening upward, as shown, or downward. Graphs of polynomial functions of degree 2 or 3 will, in general, resemble one of the graphs shown next.

General Shapes of Graphs of Polynomial Functions

Degree 2

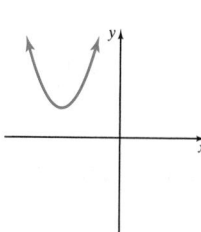

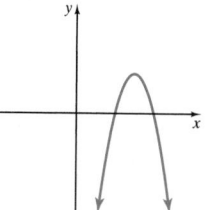

Coefficient of x^2
is a positive number.

Coefficient of x^2
is a negative number.

Degree 3

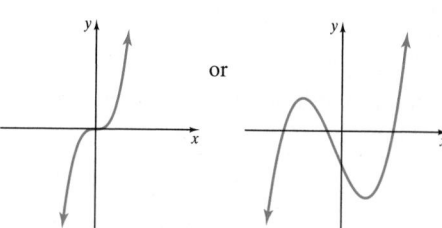

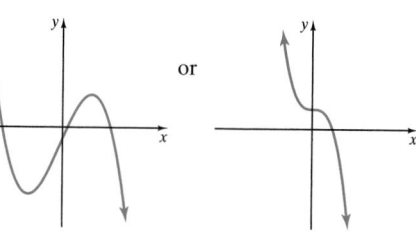

Coefficient of x^3
is a positive number.

Coefficient of x^3
is a negative number.

EXAMPLE 11

Determine which of the following graphs most closely resembles the graph of $f(x) = 5x^3 - 6x^2 + 2x + 3$

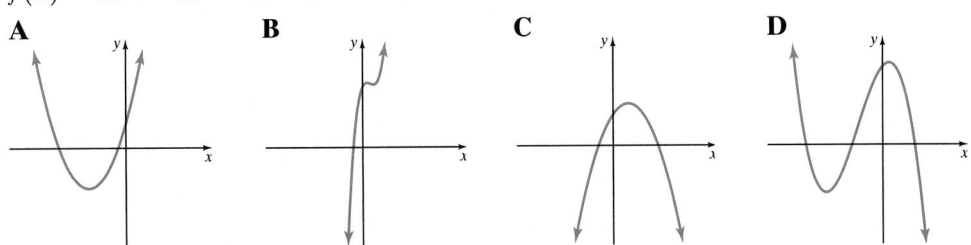

A **B** **C** **D**

Solution   The degree of $f(x)$ is 3, which means that its graph has the shape of B or D. The coefficient of x^3 is 5, a positive number, so the graph has the shape of B.

Graphing Calculator Explorations

A graphing calculator may be used to visualize addition and subtraction of polynomials in one variable. For example, to visualize the following polynomial subtraction statement

$$(3x^2 - 6x + 9) - (x^2 - 5x + 6) = 2x^2 - x + 3$$

graph both

$$Y_1 = (3x^2 - 6x + 9) - (x^2 - 5x + 6) \quad \text{Left side of equation}$$

and

$$Y_2 = 2x^2 - x + 3 \quad \text{Right side of equation}$$

on the same screen and see that their graphs coincide. (*Note:* If the graphs do not coincide, we can be sure that a mistake has been made in combining polynomials or in calculator keystrokes. If the graphs appear to coincide, we cannot be sure that our work is correct. This is because it is possible for the graphs to differ so slightly that we do not notice it.)

The graphs of Y_1 and Y_2 are shown. The graphs appear to coincide, so the subtraction statement

$$(3x^2 - 6x + 9) - (x^2 - 5x + 6) = 2x^2 - x + 3$$

appears to be correct.

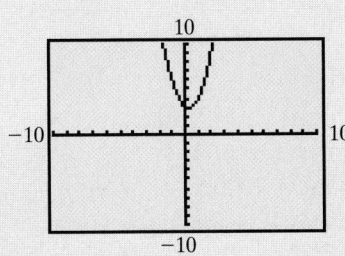

Perform the indicated operations. Then visualize by using the procedure described above.

1. $(2x^2 + 7x + 6) + (x^3 - 6x^2 - 14)$

2. $(-14x^3 - x + 2) + (-x^3 + 3x^2 + 4x)$

3. $(1.8x^2 - 6.8x - 1.7) - (3.9x^2 - 3.6x)$

4. $(-4.8x^2 + 12.5x - 7.8) - (3.1x^2 - 7.8x)$

5. $(1.29x - 5.68) + (7.69x^2 - 2.55x + 10.98)$

6. $(-0.98x^2 - 1.56x + 5.57) + (4.36x - 3.71)$

EXERCISE SET 5.3

STUDY GUIDE/SSM CD/VIDEO PH MATH TUTOR CENTER MathXL®Tutorials ON CD MathXL® MyMathLab®

Find the degree of each term. See Example 1.

1. 4

2. 7

3. $5x^2$

4. $-z^3$

5. $-3xy^2$

6. $12x^3z$

Find the degree of each polynomial and indicate whether the polynomial is a monomial, binomial, trinomial, or none of these. See Examples 2 and 3.

7. $6x + 3$

8. $7x - 8$

9. $3x^2 - 2x + 5$

10. $5x^2 - 3x^2y - 2x^3$

11. $-xyz$

12. -9

13. $x^2y - 4xy^2 + 5x + y$

14. $-2x^2y - 3y^2 + 4x + y^5$

15. In your own words, describe how to find the degree of a term.

16. In your own words, describe how to find the degree of a polynomial.

If $P(x) = x^2 + x + 1$ and $Q(x) = 5x^2 - 1$, find the following. See Example 4.

17. $P(7)$

18. $Q(4)$

19. $Q(-10)$

20. $P(-4)$

21. $P(0)$

22. $Q(0)$

23. $Q\left(\frac{1}{4}\right)$

24. $P\left(\frac{1}{2}\right)$

Refer to Example 5 for Exercises 25 through 28.

25. Find the height of the object at $t = 2$ seconds.

26. Find the height of the object at $t = 4$ seconds.

27. Find the height of the object at $t = 6$ seconds.

28. Approximate (to the nearest second) how long it takes before the object hits the ground. (*Hint:* The object hits the ground when $P(x) = 0$.)

Simplify by combining like terms. See Example 6.

29. $5y + y$

30. $-x + 3x$

31. $4x + 7x - 3$

32. $-8y + 9y + 4y^2$

33. $4xy + 2x - 3xy - 1$

34. $-8xy^2 + 4x - x + 2xy^2$

35. $7x^2 - 2xy + 5y^2 - x^2 + xy + 11y^2$

36. $-a^2 + 18ab - 2b^2 + 14a^2 - 12ab - b^2$

MIXED PRACTICE

Perform the indicated operations. See Examples 7 through 10.

37. $(9y^2 - 8) + (9y^2 - 9)$

38. $(x^2 + 4x - 7) + (8x^2 + 9x - 7)$

39. Add $(x^2 + xy - y^2)$ and $(2x^2 - 4xy + 7y^2)$.

40. Add $(4x^3 - 6x^2 + 5x + 7)$ and $(2x^2 + 6x - 3)$.

41. $x^2 - 6x + 3$
$\underline{+\ (2x + 5)}$

42. $-2x^2 + 3x - 9$
$\underline{+\ \ (2x - 3)}$

43. $(9y^2 - 7y + 5) - (8y^2 - 7y + 2)$

44. $(2x^2 + 3x + 12) - (5x - 7)$

45. Subtract $(6x^2 - 3x)$ from $(4x^2 + 2x)$.

46. Subtract $(xy + x - y)$ from $(xy + x - 3)$.

47. $3x^2 - 4x + 8$
$\underline{-\ (5x^2 - 7)}$

48. $-3x^2 - 4x + 8$
$\underline{-\ \ \ (5x + 12)}$

49. $(5x - 11) + (-x - 2)$

50. $(3x^2 - 2x) + (5x^2 - 9x)$

51. $(7x^2 + x + 1) - (6x^2 + x - 1)$

52. $(4x - 4) - (-x - 4)$

53. $(7x^3 - 4x + 8) + (5x^3 + 4x + 8x)$

54. $(9xyz + 4x - y) + (-9xyz - 3x + y + 2)$

55. $(9x^3 - 2x^2 + 4x - 7) - (2x^3 - 6x^2 - 4x + 3)$

56. $(3x^2 + 6xy + 3y^2) - (8x^2 - 6xy - y^2)$

57. Add $(y^2 + 4yx + 7)$ and $(-19y^2 + 7yx + 7)$.

58. Subtract $(x - 4)$ from $(3x^2 - 4x + 5)$.

59. $(3x^3 - b + 2a - 6) + (-4x^3 + b + 6a - 6)$

60. $(5x^2 - 6) + (2x^2 - 4x + 8)$

61. $(4x^2 - 6x + 2) - (-x^2 + 3x + 5)$

62. $(5x^2 + x + 9) - (2x^2 - 9)$

63. $(-3x + 8) + (-3x^2 + 3x - 5)$

64. $(5y^2 - 2y + 4) + (3y + 7)$

65. $(-3 + 4x^2 + 7xy^2) + (2x^3 - x^2 + xy^2)$

66. $(-3x^2y + 4) - (-7x^2y - 8y)$

67. $6y^2 - 6y + 4$
$\underline{-(-y^2 - 6y + 7)}$

68. $-4x^3 + 4x^2 - 4x$
$\underline{-(2x^3 - 2x^2 + 3x)}$

69. $3x^2 + 15x + 8$
$\underline{+(2x^2 + 7x + 8)}$

70. $9x^2 + 9x - 4$
$\underline{+(7x^2 - 3x - 4)}$

71. $\left(\frac{1}{2}x^2 - \frac{1}{3}x^2y + 2y^3\right) + \left(\frac{1}{4}x^2 - \frac{8}{3}x^2y^2 - \frac{1}{2}y^3\right)$

72. $\left(\frac{2}{5}a^2 - ab + \frac{4}{3}b^2\right) + \left(\frac{1}{5}a^2b - ab + \frac{5}{6}b^2\right)$

73. Find the sum of $(5q^4 - 2q^2 - 3q)$ and $(-6q^4 + 3q^2 + 5)$.

74. Find the sum of $(5y^4 - 7y^2 + x^2 - 3)$ and $(-3y^4 + 2y^2 + 4)$.

75. Subtract $(3x + 7)$ from the sum of $(7x^2 + 4x + 9)$ and $(8x^2 + 7x - 8)$.

76. Subtract $(9x + 8)$ from the sum of $(3x^2 - 2x - x^3 + 2)$ and $(5x^2 - 8x - x^3 + 4)$.

77. Find the sum of $(4x^4 - 7x^2 + 3)$ and $(2 - 3x^4)$.

78. Find the sum of $(8x^4 - 14x^2 + 6)$ and $(-12x^6 - 21x^4 - 9x^2)$.

79. $\left(\frac{2}{3}x^2 - \frac{1}{6}x + \frac{5}{6}\right) - \left(\frac{1}{3}x^2 + \frac{5}{6}x - \frac{1}{6}\right)$

80. $\left(\frac{3}{16}x^2 + \frac{5}{8}x - \frac{1}{4}\right) - \left(\frac{5}{16}x^2 - \frac{3}{8}x + \frac{3}{4}\right)$

Solve. See Example 5.

The surface area of a rectangular box is given by the polynomial

$$2HL + 2LW + 2HW$$

and is measured in square units. In business, surface area is often calculated to help determine cost of materials.

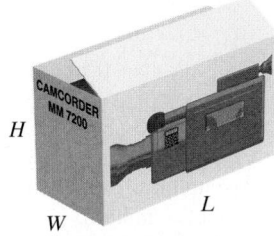

81. A rectangular box is to be constructed to hold a new camcorder. The box is to have dimensions 5 inches by 4 inches by 9 inches. Find the surface area of the box.

82. Suppose it has been determined that a box of dimensions 4 inches by 4 inches by 8.5 inches can be used to contain the camcorder in Exercise 81. Find the surface area of this box and calculate the square inches of material saved by using this box instead of the box in Exercise 81.

83. A projectile is fired upward from the ground with an initial velocity of 300 feet per second. Neglecting air resistance, the height of the projectile at any time t can be described by the polynomial function $P(t) = -16t^2 + 300t$. Find the height of the projectile at each given time.

  a. $t = 1$ second   **b.** $t = 2$ seconds

  c. $t = 3$ seconds   **d.** $t = 4$ seconds

  e. Explain why the height increases and then decreases as time passes.

  f. Approximate (to the nearest second) how long before the object hits the ground.

84. An object is thrown upward with an initial velocity of 25 feet per second from the top of the 984-foot-high Eiffel Tower in Paris, France. The height of the object at any time t can be described by the polynomial function $P(t) = -16t^2 + 25t + 984$. Find the height of the projectile at each given time.(*Source:* Council on Tall Buildings and Urban Habitat, Lehigh University)

  a. $t = 1$ second

  b. $t = 3$ seconds

  c. $t = 5$ seconds

  d. Approximate (to the nearest second) how long before the object hits the ground.

85. The polynomial function $P(x) = 45x - 100,000$ models the relationship between the number of computer briefcases x that a company sells and the profit the company makes, $P(x)$. Find $P(4000)$, the profit from selling 4000 computer briefcases.

86. The total cost (in dollars) for MCD, Inc., Manufacturing Company to produce x blank audiocassette tapes per week is given by the polynomial function $C(x) = 0.8x + 10,000$. Find the total cost of producing 20,000 tapes per week.

87. The total revenues (in dollars) for MCD, Inc., Manufacturing Company to sell x blank audiocasette tapes per week is given by the polynomial function $R(x) = 2x$. Find the total revenue from selling 20,000 tapes per week.

88. In business, profit equals revenue minus cost, or $P(x) = R(x) - C(x)$. Find the profit function for MCD, Inc. by subtracting the given functions in Exercises 86 and 87.

Match each equation with its graph. See Example 11.

89. $f(x) = 3x^2 - 2$

90. $h(x) = 5x^3 - 6x + 2$

91. $g(x) = -2x^3 - 3x^2 + 3x - 2$

92. $g(x) = -2x^2 - 6x + 2$

A
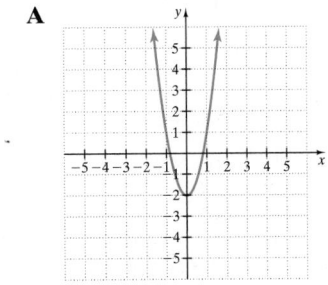

B
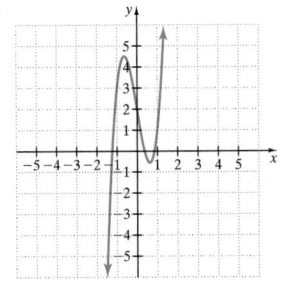

C
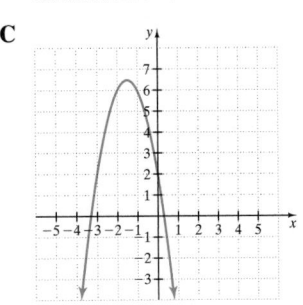

D
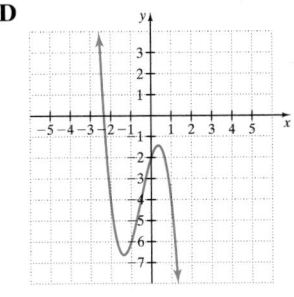

REVIEW AND PREVIEW

Multiply. See Section 1.4.

93. $5(3x - 2)$

94. $-7(2z - 6y)$

95. $-2(x^2 - 5x + 6)$

96. $5(-3y^2 - 2y + 7)$

Concept Extensions

Perform indicated operations.

97. $(4x^{2a} - 3x^a + 0.5) - (x^{2a} - 5x^a - 0.2)$

98. $(9y^{5a} - 4y^{3a} + 1.5y) - (6y^{5a} - y^{3a} + 4.7y)$

99. $(8x^{2y} - 7x^y + 3) + (-4x^{2y} + 9x^y - 14)$

100. $(14z^{5x} + 3z^{2x} + z) - (2z^{5x} - 10z^{2x} + 3z)$

Find each perimeter.

 101.

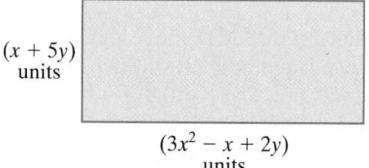

$(x + 5y)$ units

$(3x^2 - x + 2y)$ units

 102.

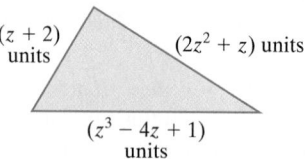

$(z + 2)$ units

$(2z^2 + z)$ units

$(z^3 - 4z + 1)$ units

If $P(x) = 3x + 3$, $Q(x) = 4x^2 - 6x + 3$, and $R(x) = 5x^2 - 7$, find the following.

103. $P(x) + Q(x)$

104. $R(x) + P(x)$

105. $Q(x) - R(x)$

106. $P(x) - Q(x)$

107. $2[Q(x)] - R(x)$

108. $-5[P(x)] - Q(x)$

109. $3[R(x)] + 4[P(x)]$

110. $2[Q(x)] + 7[R(x)]$

*If $P(x)$ is the polynomial given, find **a.** $P(a)$, **b.** $P(-x)$, and **c.** $P(x + h)$.*

111. $P(x) = 2x - 3$

112. $P(x) = 8x + 3$

113. $P(x) = 4x$

114. $P(x) = -4x$

115. $P(x) = 4x - 1$

116. $P(x) = 3x - 2$

117. The function $f(x) = -246.7x^2 + 1887.9x + 1016.9$ can be used to approximate the increasing number of radio stations on the Internet during the years 1998–2003 where x is the number of years after 1998 and $f(x)$ is the number of stations. Round answers to the nearest whole. (*Source:* BRS Media, Inc.)

a. Approximate the number of radio stations on the Internet in 1998.

b. Approximate the number of radio stations on the Internet in 2000.

c. Use the function to predict the number of radio stations on the Internet in 2006.

d. From parts (a), (b), and (c), determine whether the number of radio stations on the Internet is increasing at a steady rate. Explain why or why not.

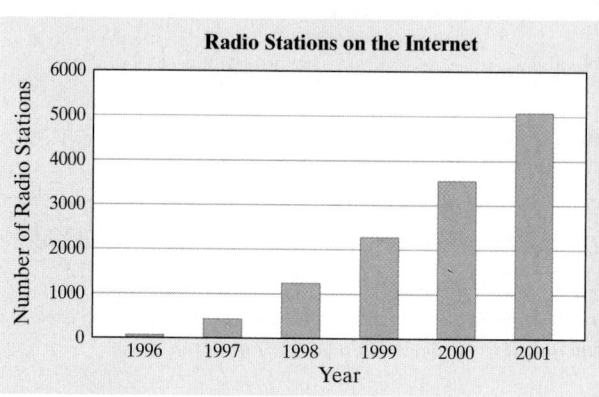

Radio Stations on the Internet

118. The function $f(x) = 0.21x^2 - 0.55x + 8.57$ can be used to approximate the number of Americans enrolled in health maintenance organizations (HMOs) during the period 1980–2001 where x is the number of years after 1980 and $f(x)$ is the number of millions of Americans. Round answers to the nearest tenth of a million. (*Source:* Based on data from *Health, United States, 2001*, National Center for Health Statistics)

a. Approximate the number of Americans enrolled in HMOs in 1995.

b. Approximate the number of Americans enrolled in HMOs in 2000.

c. Use the function to predict the number of Americans enrolled in HMOs in 2005.

d. From parts (a), (b), and (c), determine whether the number of Americans enrolled in HMOs is changing at a steady rate. Explain why or why not.

19. Sport utility vehicle (SUV) sales in the Uninted States. have increased since 1992. The function $f(x) = 0.014x^2 + 0.12x + 0.85$ can be used to approximate the number of SUV sales during the years 1990–2000 where x is the number of years after 1990 and $f(x)$ is the SUV sales (in millions). Round answers to the nearest tenth of a million. (*Source:* Wards Communications)

a. Approximate the number of SUVs sold in 1999.

b. Use the function to predict the number of SUVs sold in 2005.

20. Digital camera sales have increased since 1996. The function $f(x) = 34.7x^2 + 68.2x + 377.3$ can be used to approximate the revenue from selling digital cameras for the years 1996–2001 where x is the number of years after 1996 and $f(x)$ is the sales revenue (in million of dollars). Round answers to the nearest whole million. (*Source:* International Data Corporation)

a. Approximate the revenue from digital camera sales in 2000.

b. Use the function to predict the revenue from digital camera sales in 2004.

121. The function $f(x) = 1.4x^2 + 129.6x + 939$ can be used to approximate spending for health care in the United States, where x is the number of years since 1980 and $f(x)$ is the amount of money spent per capita. (*Source:* U.S. Health Care Financing Administration)

a. Approximate the amount of money spent on health care per capita in the year 1985.

b. Approximate the amount of money spent on health care per capita in the year 1995.

c. Use the given function to predict the amount of money that will be spent on health care per capita in the year 2010.

d. From parts **a**, **b**, and **c**, is the amount of money spent rising at a steady rate? Why or why not?

122. The function $f(x) = 904x^2 - 10,311x + 70,479$ can be used to approximate the number of AIDS cases reported in the United States from 1995 to 2002, where x is the number of years since 1995. (*Source:* Based on data from the U.S. Centers for Disease Control and Prevention)

a. Approximate the number of AIDS cases reported in the United States in 1995.

b. Approximate the number of AIDS cases reported in the United States in 2002.

c. Approximate the number of AIDS cases reported in the United States in 2000.

d. Describe the trend in the number of AIDS cases reported during the period covered by the model.

5.4   *MULTIPLYING POLYNOMIALS*

Objectives

1. Multiply two polynomials.
2. Multiply binomials.
3. Square binomials.
4. Multiply the sum and difference of two terms.
5. Multiply three or more polynomials.
6. Evaluate polynomial functions.

1   Properties of real numbers and exponents are used continually in the process of multiplying polynomials. To multiply monomials, for example, we apply the commutative and associative properties of real numbers and the product rule for *exponents*.

EXAMPLE 1

Multiply.

a. $(2x^3)(5x^6)$ **b.** $(7y^4z^4)(-xy^{11}z^5)$

Solution   Group like bases and apply the product rule for exponents.

a. $(2x^3)(5x^6) = 2(5)(x^3)(x^6) = 10x^9$

b. $(7y^4z^4)(-xy^{11}z^5) = 7(-1)x(y^4y^{11})(z^4z^5) = -7xy^{15}z^9$

> ### Helpful Hint
> See Sections 5.1 and 5.2 to review exponential expressions further.

To multiply a monomial by a polynomial other than a monomial, we use an expanded form of the distributive property.

$$a(b + c + d + \cdots + z) = ab + ac + ad + \cdots + az$$

Notice that the monomial a is multiplied by each term of the polynomial.

EXAMPLE 2

Multiply.

a. $2x(5x - 4)$ **b.** $-3x^2(4x^2 - 6x + 1)$ **c.** $-xy(7x^2y + 3xy - 11)$

Solution   Apply the distributive property.

a. $2x(5x - 4) = 2x(5x) + 2x(-4)$ Use the distributive property.

$\qquad\qquad\qquad = 10x^2 - 8x$ Multiply.

b. $-3x^2(4x^2 - 6x + 1) = -3x^2(4x^2) + (-3x^2)(-6x) + (-3x^2)(1)$

$\qquad\qquad\qquad\qquad\quad = -12x^4 + 18x^3 - 3x^2$

c. $-xy(7x^2y + 3xy - 11) = -xy(7x^2y) + (-xy)(3xy) + (-xy)(-11)$

$\qquad\qquad\qquad\qquad\qquad = -7x^3y^2 - 3x^2y^2 + 11xy$

To multiply any two polynomials, we can use the following.

> ## Multiplying Two Polynomials
>
> To multiply any two polynomials, use the distributive property and multiply each term of one polynomial by each term of the other polynomial. Then combine any like terms.

✔ **CONCEPT CHECK**

Find the error:

$\qquad 4x(x - 5) + 2x$

$\qquad\quad = 4x(x) + 4x(-5) + 4x(2x)$

$\qquad\quad = 4x^2 - 20x + 8x^2$

$\qquad\quad = 12x^2 - 20x$

Concept Check Answer:

$4x(x - 5) + 2x$

$\quad = 4x(x) + 4x(-5) + 2x$

$\quad = 4x^2 - 20x + 2x$

$\quad = 4x^2 - 18x$

EXAMPLE 3

Multiply and simplify the product if possible.

a. $(x + 3)(2x + 5)$ **b.** $(2x - 3)(5x^2 - 6x + 7)$

Solution   **a.** Multiply each term of $(x + 3)$ by $(2x + 5)$.

$$(x + 3)(2x + 5) = x(2x + 5) + 3(2x + 5)$$ Apply the distributive property.
$$= 2x^2 + 5x + 6x + 15$$ Apply the distributive property again.
$$= 2x^2 + 11x + 15$$ Combine like terms.

b. Multiply each term of $(2x - 3)$ by each term of $(5x^2 - 6x + 7)$.

$$(2x - 3)(5x^2 - 6x + 7) = 2x(5x^2 - 6x + 7) + (-3)(5x^2 - 6x + 7)$$

$$= 10x^3 - 12x^2 + 14x - 15x^2 + 18x - 21$$

$$= 10x^3 - 27x^2 + 32x - 21$$ Combine like terms.

Sometimes polynomials are easier to multiply vertically, in the same way we multiply real numbers. When multiplying vertically, we line up like terms in the **partial products** vertically. This makes combining like terms easier.

EXAMPLE 4

Multiply vertically $(4x^2 + 7)(x^2 + 2x + 8)$.

Solution

$$
\begin{array}{r}
x^2 + 2x + 8 \\
4x^2 + 7 \\
\hline
7x^2 + 14x + 56 \\
4x^4 + 8x^3 + 32x^2 \\
\hline
4x^4 + 8x^3 + 39x^2 + 14x + 56
\end{array}
$$

$7(x^2 + 2x + 8)$
$4x^2(x^2 + 2x + 8)$
Combine like terms.

2   When multiplying a binomial by a binomial, we can use a special order of multiplying terms, called the **FOIL** order. The letters of FOIL stand for "First-**O**uter-**I**nner-**L**ast." To illustrate this method, let's multiply $(2x - 3)$ by $(3x + 1)$.

Multiply the **F**irst terms of each binomial. $(2x - 3)(3x + 1)$ **F** $2x(3x) = 6x^2$

Multiply the **O**uter terms of each binomial. $(2x - 3)(3x + 1)$ **O** $2x(1) = 2x$

Multiply the **I**nner terms of each binomial. $(2x - 3)(3x + 1)$ **I** $-3(3x) = -9x$

Multiply the **L**ast terms of each binomial. $(2x - 3)(3x + 1)$ **L** $-3(1) = -3$
Combine like terms.

$$6x^2 + 2x - 9x - 3 = 6x^2 - 7x - 3$$

EXAMPLE 5

Use the FOIL order to multiply $(x - 1)(x + 2)$.

Solution

$$
\begin{array}{cccc}
\text{First} & \text{Outer} & \text{Inner} & \text{Last} \\
\downarrow & \downarrow & \downarrow & \downarrow
\end{array}
$$

$$(x - 1)(x + 2) = x \cdot x \ + \ 2 \cdot x \ + \ (-1)x \ + \ (-1)(2)$$

$$= x^2 + 2x - x - 2$$

$$= x^2 + x - 2 \quad \text{Combine like terms.}$$

EXAMPLE 6

Multiply.

a. $(2x - 7)(3x - 4)$ **b.** $(3x + y)(5x - 2y)$

Solution

$$
\begin{array}{cccc}
\text{First} & \text{Outer} & \text{Inner} & \text{Last} \\
\downarrow & \downarrow & \downarrow & \downarrow
\end{array}
$$

a. $(2x - 7)(3x - 4) = 2x(3x) + 2x(-4) + (-7)(3x) + (-7)(-4)$

$$= 6x^2 - 8x - 21x + 28$$

$$= 6x^2 - 29x + 28$$

$$
\begin{array}{cccc}
\text{F} & \text{O} & \text{I} & \text{L} \\
\downarrow & \downarrow & \downarrow & \downarrow
\end{array}
$$

b. $(3x + y)(5x - 2y) = 15x^2 - 6xy + 5xy - 2y^2$

$$= 15x^2 - xy - 2y^2$$

3 The **square of a binomial** is a special case of the product of two binomials. By the FOIL order for multiplying two binomials, we have

$$(a + b)^2 = (a + b)(a + b)$$

$$
\begin{array}{cccc}
\text{F} & \text{O} & \text{I} & \text{L} \\
\downarrow & \downarrow & \downarrow & \downarrow
\end{array}
$$

$$= a^2 + ab + ba + b^2$$

$$= a^2 + 2ab + b^2$$

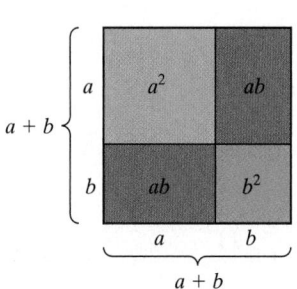

This product can be visualized geometrically by analyzing areas.

Area of larger square: $(a + b)^2$

Sum of areas of smaller rectangles: $a^2 + 2ab + b^2$

Thus, $(a + b)^2 = a^2 + 2ab + b^2$

The same pattern occurs for the square of a difference. In general,

---

Square of a Binomial

$$(a + b)^2 = a^2 + 2ab + b^2 \qquad (a - b)^2 = a^2 - 2ab + b^2$$

In other words, a binomial squared is the sum of the first term squared, twice the product of both terms, and the second term squared.

EXAMPLE 7

Multiply.

a. $(x + 5)^2$ **b.** $(x - 9)^2$ **c.** $(3x + 2z)^2$ **d.** $(4m^2 - 3n)^2$

Solution

a.
$$(a + b)^2 = a^2 + 2 \cdot a \cdot b + b^2$$
$$(x + 5)^2 = x^2 + 2 \cdot x \cdot 5 + 5^2 = x^2 + 10x + 25$$

b. $(x - 9)^2 = x^2 - 2 \cdot x \cdot 9 + 9^2 = x^2 - 18x + 81$

c. $(3x + 2z)^2 = (3x)^2 + 2(3x)(2z) + (2z)^2 = 9x^2 + 12xz + 4z^2$

d. $(4m^2 - 3n)^2 = (4m^2)^2 - 2(4m^2)(3n) + (3n)^2 = 16m^4 - 24m^2n + 9n^2$

Helpful Hint

Note that $(a + b)^2 = a^2 + 2ab + b^2$, **not** $a^2 + b^2$. Also, $(a - b)^2 = a^2 - 2ab + b^2$, **not** $a^2 - b^2$.

---

4   Another special product applies to the sum and difference of the same two terms. Multiply $(a + b)(a - b)$ to see a pattern.

$$(a + b)(a - b) = a^2 - ab + ba - b^2$$
$$= a^2 - b^2$$

Product of the Sum and Difference of Two Terms

$$(a + b)(a - b) = a^2 - b^2$$

The product of the sum and difference of the same two terms is the difference of the first term squared and the second term squared.

EXAMPLE 8

Multiply.

a. $(x - 3)(x + 3)$

b. $(4y + 1)(4y - 1)$

c. $(x^2 + 2y)(x^2 - 2y)$

d. $\left(3m^2 - \dfrac{1}{2}\right)\left(3m^2 + \dfrac{1}{2}\right)$

Solution

a. $(a + b)(a - b) = a^2 - b^2$

$(x + 3)(x - 3) = x^2 - 3^2 = x^2 - 9$

b. $(4y + 1)(4y - 1) = (4y)^2 - 1^2 = 16y^2 - 1$

c. $(x^2 + 2y)(x^2 - 2y) = (x^2)^2 - (2y)^2 = x^4 - 4y^2$

d. $\left(3m^2 - \dfrac{1}{2}\right)\left(3m^2 + \dfrac{1}{2}\right) = (3m^2)^2 - \left(\dfrac{1}{2}\right)^2 = 9m^4 - \dfrac{1}{4}$

EXAMPLE 9

Multiply $[3 + (2a + b)]^2$.

Solution

Think of 3 as the first term and $(2a + b)$ as the second term, and apply the method for squaring a binomial.

$$[a \quad + \quad b]^2 = a^2 + 2(a) \cdot \quad b \quad + \quad b^2$$

$$[3 + (2a + b)]^2 = 3^2 + 2(3)(2a + b) + (2a + b)^2$$

$$= 9 + 6(2a + b) + (2a + b)^2$$

$$= 9 + 12a + 6b + (2a)^2 + 2(2a)(b) + b^2 \quad \text{Square } (2a + b).$$

$$= 9 + 12a + 6b + 4a^2 + 4ab + b^2$$

EXAMPLE 10

Multiply $[(5x - 2y) - 1][(5x - 2y) + 1]$.

Solution

Think of $(5x - 2y)$ as the first term and 1 as the second term, and apply the method for the product of the sum and difference of two terms.

$$(a \quad - b) \quad (a \quad + b) = \quad a^2 \quad - b^2$$

$$[(5x - 2y) - 1][(5x - 2y) + 1] = (5x - 2y)^2 - 1^2$$

$$= (5x)^2 - 2(5x)(2y) + (2y)^2 - 1 \quad \text{Square} \ (5x - 2y).$$

$$= 25x^2 - 20xy + 4y^2 - 1$$

5 To multiply three or more polynomials, more than one method may be needed

EXAMPLE 11

Multiply: $(x - 3)(x + 3)(x^2 - 9)$

Solution   We multiply the first two binomials, the sum and difference of two terms. Then we multiply the resulting two binomials, the square of a binomial.

$$(x - 3)(x + 3)(x^2 - 9) = (x^2 - 9)(x^2 - 9) \quad \text{Multiply } (x - 3)(x + 3).$$
$$= (x^2 - 9)^2$$
$$= x^4 - 18x^2 + 81 \quad \text{Square } (x^2 - 9).$$

6   Our work in multiplying polynomials is often useful in evaluating polynomial functions.

EXAMPLE 12

If $f(x) = x^2 + 5x - 2$, find $f(a + 1)$.

Tyler Johnson

Solution   To find $f(a + 1)$, replace x with the expression $a + 1$ in the polynomial function $f(x)$.

$$f(x) = x^2 + 5x - 2$$
$$f(a + 1) = (a + 1)^2 + 5(a + 1) - 2$$
$$= a^2 + 2a + 1 + 5a + 5 - 2$$
$$= a^2 + 7a + 4$$

Graphing Calculator Explorations

In the previous section, we used a graphing calculator to visualize addition and subtraction of polynomials in one variable. In this section, the same method is used to visualize multiplication of polynomials in one variable. For example, to see that

$$(x - 2)(x + 1) = x^2 - x - 2,$$

graph both $Y_1 = (x - 2)(x + 1)$ and $Y_2 = x^2 - x - 2$ on the same screen and see whether their graphs coincide.

By tracing along both graphs, we see that the graphs of Y_1 and Y_2 appear to coincide, and thus $(x - 2)(x + 1) = x^2 - x - 2$ appears to be correct.

Multiply. Then use a graphing calculator to visualize the results.

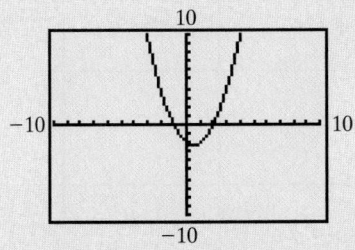

1. $(x + 4)(x - 4)$ 2. $(x + 3)(x + 3)$
3. $(3x - 7)^2$ 4. $(5x - 2)^2$
5. $(5x + 1)(x^2 - 3x - 2)$ 6. $(7x + 4)(2x^2 + 3x - 5)$

Spotlight on
DECISION
MAKING

Suppose you would like to sign up for an online service and have received the following advertisements from internet service providers in the mail.

US Online

Try our Internet service FREE for 30 days! See why everyone is talking about us:
- Unlimited Internet access and e-mail for a low monthly fee of $21.95
- No set-up fee
- Your own 6 MB Web site
- Thousands of local access numbers across the nation
- Around-the-clock help with our toll-free 888 number

Give us a call to set up your service today!

Interconnect

When you sign up with Interconnect as your Internet service provider, you get:
- Unlimited access to the Internet and e-mail
- Local access numbers in major metropolitan areas
- Online expert help

all for just $11.95 per month*! And, for a limited time, you can try Interconnect for a full month for FREE!
*A one-time $20 set-up fee applies, however.

e-Link

The sky's the limit with e-Link! If you act now, you can get your first 60 days for FREE, as well as a waiver of the $25 set-up fee. For just $19.95 per month, you get:
- 150 hours of Internet access and e-mail*
- a personal 3 MB Web page
- toll-free help, 24 hours a day, 7 days a week
- local access numbers around the country

*Each additional hour costs $2.95.

You construct a decision grid to help make your choice. In the decision grid, give each of the decision criteria a rank reflecting its importance to you, with 1 being not important to 10 being very important. Then for each online service, decide how well the criteria are supported, assigning a 1 in the rating column for poor support to a rating of 10 for excellent support. For US Online, fill in the Score column by multiplying rank by rating for each criteria. Repeat for each online service. Finally, total the scores in each column for each online service. The service with the highest score is likely to be the best choice for you.

Based on your decision-grid analysis, which online service would you choose? Explain.

Criteria	Rank	US Online		Interconnect		e-Link	
		Rating	Score	Rating	Score	Rating	Score
Free Trial Period							
Monthly Fee							
Unlimited Access							
Includes E-mail							
Includes Personal Web Page							
Set-up Fee							
Toll-free Help							
Local Access Numbers							
TOTAL							

EXERCISE SET 5.4

STUDY GUIDE/SSM CD/VIDEO PH MATH TUTOR CENTER MathXL®Tutorials ON CD MathXL® MyMathLab®

Multiply. See Examples 1 through 4.

1. $(-4x^3)(3x^2)$ **2.** $(-6a)(4a)$

3. $3x(4x + 7)$ **4.** $5x(6x - 4)$

5. $-6xy(4x + y)$ **6.** $-8y(6xy + 4x)$

7. $-4ab(xa^2 + ya^2 - 3)$ **8.** $-6b^2z(z^2a + baz - 3b)$

9. $(x - 3)(2x + 4)$ **10.** $(y + 5)(3y - 2)$

11. $(2x + 3)(x^3 - x + 2)$ **12.** $(a + 2)(3a^2 - a + 5)$

13.
$$\begin{array}{r} 3x - 2 \\ \times\ 5x + 1 \end{array}$$

14.
$$\begin{array}{r} 2z - 4 \\ \times\ 6z - 2 \end{array}$$

15.
$$\begin{array}{r} 3m^2 + 2m - 1 \\ \times\ \qquad 5m + 2 \end{array}$$

16.
$$\begin{array}{r} 2x^2 - 3x - 4 \\ \times\ \qquad x + 5 \end{array}$$

17. Explain how to multiply a polynomial by a polynomial.

18. Explain why $(3x + 2)^2$ does not equal $9x^2 + 4$.

Multiply the binomials. See Examples 5 and 6.

19. $(x - 3)(x + 4)$ **20.** $(c - 3)(c + 1)$

21. $(5x + 8y)(2x - y)$ **22.** $(2n - 9m)(n - 7m)$

23. $(3x - 1)(x + 3)$ **24.** $(5d - 3)(d + 6)$

25. $\left(3x + \dfrac{1}{2}\right)\left(3x - \dfrac{1}{2}\right)$ **26.** $\left(2x - \dfrac{1}{3}\right)\left(2x + \dfrac{1}{3}\right)$

Multiply, using special product methods. See Examples 7 and 8.

27. $(x + 4)^2$ **28.** $(x - 5)^2$

29. $(6y - 1)(6y + 1)$ **30.** $(x - 9)(x + 9)$

31. $(3x - y)^2$ **32.** $(4x - z)^2$

33. $(3b - 6y)(3b + 6y)$ **34.** $(2x - 4y)(2x + 4y)$

Multiply, using special product methods. See Examples 9 and 10.

35. $[3 + (4b + 1)]^2$

36. $[5 - (3b - 3)]^2$

37. $[(2s - 3) - 1][(2s - 3) + 1]$

38. $[(2y + 5) + 6][(2y + 5) - 6]$

39. $[(xy + 4) - 6]^2$

40. $[(2a^2 + 4a) + 1]^2$

41. Explain when the FOIL method can be used to multiply polynomials.

42. Explain why the product of $(a + b)$ and $(a - b)$ is not a trinomial.

Multiply. See Example 11.

43. $(x + y)(2x - 1)(x + 1)$

44. $(z + 2)(z - 3)(2z + 1)$

45. $(x - 2)^4$

46. $(x - 1)^4$

47. $(x - 5)(x + 5)(x^2 + 25)$

48. $(x + 3)(x - 3)(x^2 + 9)$

MIXED PRACTICE

Multiply.

49. $(3x + 1)(3x + 5)$

50. $(4x - 5)(5x + 6)$

51. $(2x^3 + 5)(5x^2 + 4x + 1)$

52. $(3y^3 - 1)(3y^3 - 6y + 1)$

53. $(7x - 3)(7x + 3)$

54. $(4x + 1)(4x - 1)$

55.
$$\begin{array}{r} 3x^2 + 4x - 4 \\ \times\ \qquad 3x + 6 \end{array}$$

56.
$$\begin{array}{r} 6x^2 + 2x - 1 \\ \times\ \qquad 3x - 6 \end{array}$$

57. $\left(4x + \dfrac{1}{3}\right)\left(4x - \dfrac{1}{2}\right)$

58. $\left(4y - \dfrac{1}{3}\right)\left(3y - \dfrac{1}{8}\right)$

59. $(6x + 1)^2$

60. $(4x + 7)^2$

61. $(x^2 + 2y)(x^2 - 2y)$

62. $(3x + 2y)(3x - 2y)$

63. $-6a^2b^2[5a^2b^2 - 6a - 6b]$

64. $7x^2y^3(-3ax - 4xy + z)$

65. $(a - 4)(2a - 4)$

66. $(2x - 3)(x + 1)$

67. $(7ab + 3c)(7ab - 3c)$

68. $(3xy - 2b)(3xy + 2b)$

69. $(m - 4)^2$

70. $(x + 2)^2$

71. $(3x + 1)^2$

72. $(4x + 6)^2$

73. $(y - 4)(y - 3)$

74. $(c - 8)(c + 2)$

75. $(x + y)(2x - 1)(x + 1)$

76. $(z + 2)(z - 3)(2z + 1)$ **77.** $(3x^2 + 2x - 1)^2$

78. $(4x^2 + 4x - 4)^2$

79. $(3x + 1)(4x^2 - 2x + 5)$

80. $(2x - 1)(5x^2 - x - 2)$

If $f(x) = x^2 - 3x$, find the following. See Example 12.

81. $f(a)$

82. $f(c)$

83. $f(a + h)$

84. $f(a + 5)$

85. $f(b - 2)$

86. $f(a - b)$

REVIEW AND PREVIEW

Use the slope-intercept form of a line, $y = mx + b$, to find the slope of each line. See Section 3.4.

87. $y = -2x + 7$

88. $y = \dfrac{3}{2}x - 1$

89. $3x - 5y = 14$

90. $x + 7y = 2$

Use the vertical line test to determine which of the following are graphs of functions. See Section 3.2.

91.

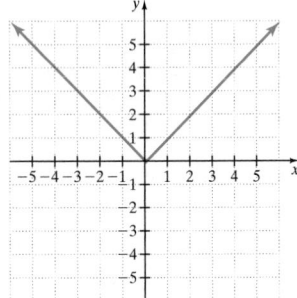

92.

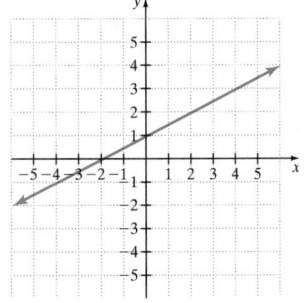

Concept Extensions

93. If $F(x) = x^2 + 3x + 2$, find

   a. $F(a + h)$

   b. $F(a)$

   c. $F(a + h) - F(a)$

94. If $g(x) = x^2 + 2x + 1$, find

   a. $g(a + h)$

   b. $g(a)$

   c. $g(a + h) - g(a)$

Multiply. Assume that variables represent positive integers.

95. $5x^2y^n(6y^{n+1} - 2)$

96. $-3yz^n(2y^3z^{2n} - 1)$

97. $(x^a + 5)(x^{2a} - 3)$

98. $(x^a + y^{2b})(x^a - y^{2b})$

For Exercises 99 through 102, write the result as a simplified polynomial.

△ **99.** Find the area of the circle. Do not approximate π.

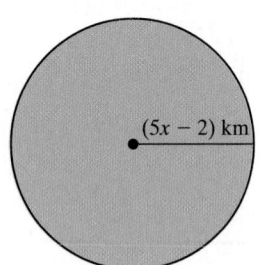

$(5x - 2)$ km

△ **100.** Find the volume of the cylinder. Do not approximate π.

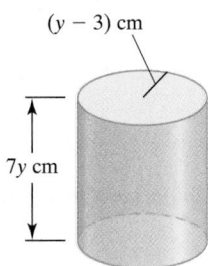

$(y - 3)$ cm

$7y$ cm

Find the area of each shaded region.

△ **101.**

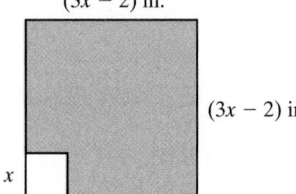

$(3x - 2)$ in.

$(3x - 2)$ in.

x

x

102.

103. Perform each indicated operation. Explain the difference between the two problems.

a. $(3x + 5) + (3x + 7)$

b. $(3x + 5)(3x + 7)$

104. Explain when the FOIL method can be used to multiply polynomials.

If $R(x) = x + 5, Q(x) = x^2 - 2,$ and $P(x) = 5x,$ find the following.

105. $P(x) \cdot R(x)$

106. $P(x) \cdot Q(x)$

107. $[Q(x)]^2$

108. $[R(x)]^2$

109. $R(x) \cdot Q(x)$

110. $P(x) \cdot R(x) \cdot Q(x)$

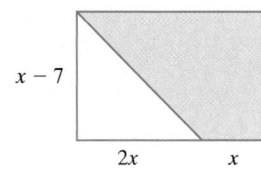

STUDY SKILLS REMINDER

Are You Getting all the Mathematics Help that You Need?

Remember that, in addition to your instructor, there are many places to get help with your mathematics course. For example, see which of the list below are available.

▶ This text has an accompanying video lesson for every section in this text.

▶ The back of this book contains answers to odd-numbered exercises.

▶ A tutorial software program with lessons corresponding to each section in the text is available.

▶ A student solutions manual is available that contains worked-out solutions to odd-numbered exercises as well as solutions to every exercise in the Integrated Reviews, Chapter Reviews, Chapter Tests, and Cumulative Reviews.

▶ Don't forget to check with your instructor for other local resources available to you, such as a tutor center.

5.5   THE GREATEST COMMON FACTOR AND FACTORING BY GROUPING

Objectives

1. Identify the GCF.
2. Factor out the GCF of a polynomial's terms.
3. Factor polynomials by grouping.

1   **Factoring** is the reverse process of multiplying. It is the process of writing a polynomial as a product.

$$6x^2 + 13x - 5 = (3x - 1)(2x + 5)$$

factoring

multiplying

In the next few sections, we review techniques for factoring polynomials. These techniques are used at the end of this chapter to solve polynomial equations.

To factor a polynomial, we first factor out the greatest common factor (GCF) of its terms, using the distributive property. The GCF of a list of terms or monomials is the product of the GCF of the numerical coefficients and each GCF of the powers of a common variable.

Finding the GCF of a List of Monomials

Step 1: Find the GCF of the numerical coefficients.

Step 2: Find the GCF of the variable factors.

Step 3: The product of the factors found in Steps 1 and 2 is the GCF of the monomials.

EXAMPLE 1

Find the GCF of $20x^3y$, $10x^2y^2$, and $35x^3$.

Solution   The GCF of the numerical coefficients 20, 10, and 35 is 5, the largest integer that is a factor of each integer. The GCF of the variable factors x^3, x^2, and x^3 is x^2 because x^2 is the largest factor common to all three powers of x. The variable y is not a common factor because it does not appear in all three monomials. The GCF is thus

$$5 \cdot x^2, \quad \text{or} \quad 5x^2$$

To see this in factored form,

$$20x^3y = 2 \cdot 2 \cdot 5 \cdot x^2 \cdot x \cdot y$$
$$10x^2y^2 = 2 \cdot 5 \cdot x^2 \cdot y$$
$$35x^3 = 3 \cdot 5 \cdot x^2 \cdot x$$
$$\text{GCF} = 5 \cdot x^2$$

2   A first step in factoring polynomials is to use the distributive property and write the polynomial as a product of the GCF of its monomial terms and a simpler polynomial. This is called **factoring out** the GCF.

EXAMPLE 2

Factor.

a. $8x^2 + 4$ **b.** $5y - 2z^4$ **c.** $6x^2 - 3x^3$

Solution   **a.** The GCF of terms $8x^2$ and 4 is 4.

$$8x^2 + 4 = 4 \cdot 2x^2 + 4 \cdot 1 \quad \text{Factor out 4 from each term.}$$
$$= 4(2x^2 + 1) \quad \text{Apply the distributive property.}$$

The factored form of $8x^2 + 4$ is $4(2x^2 + 1)$. To check, multiply $4(2x^2 + 1)$ to see that the product is $8x^2 + 4$.

b. There is no common factor of the terms $5y$ and $-2z^4$ other than 1 (or -1).

c. The greatest common factor of $6x^2$ and $-3x^3$ is $3x^2$. Thus,

$$6x^2 - 3x^3 = 3x^2 \cdot 2 - 3x^2 \cdot x$$
$$= 3x^2(2 - x)$$

> **Helpful Hint**
> To verity that the GCF has been factored out correctly, multiply the factors together and see that their product is the original polynomial.

EXAMPLE 3

Factor $17x^3y^2 - 34x^4y^2$.

Solution   The GCF of the two terms is $17x^3y^2$, which we factor out of each term.

$$17x^3y^2 - 34x^4y^2 = 17x^3y^2 \cdot 1 - 17x^3y^2 \cdot 2x$$
$$= 17x^3y^2(1 - 2x)$$

> **Helpful Hint**
> If the GCF happens to be one of the terms in the polynomial, a factor of 1 will remain for this term when the GCF is factored out. For example, in the polynomial $21x^2 + 7x$, the GCF of $21x^2$ and $7x$ is $7x$, so
>
> $$21x^2 + 7x = 7x \cdot 3x + 7x \cdot 1 = 7x(3x + 1)$$

✔ **CONCEPT CHECK**

Which factorization of $12x^2 + 9x - 3$ is correct?

a. $3(4x^2 + 3x + 1)$ **b.** $3(4x^2 + 3x - 1)$ **c.** $3(4x^2 + 3x - 3)$ **d.** $3(4x^2 + 3x$

EXAMPLE 4

Factor $-3x^3y + 2x^2y - 5xy$.

Solution Two possibilities are shown for factoring this polynomial. First, the common factor xy factored out.

$$-3x^3y + 2x^2y - 5xy = xy(-3x^2 + 2x - 5)$$

Also, the common factor $-xy$ can be factored out as shown.

$$-3x^3y + 2x^2y - 5xy = -xy(3x^2) + (-xy)(-2x) + (-xy)(5)$$
$$= -xy(3x^2 - 2x + 5)$$

Both of these alternatives are correct.

EXAMPLE 5

Factor $2(x - 5) + 3a(x - 5)$.

Solution The greatest common factor is the binomial factor $(x - 5)$.

$$2(x - 5) + 3a(x - 5) = (x - 5)(2 + 3a)$$

EXAMPLE 6

Factor $7x(x^2 + 5y) - (x^2 + 5y)$.

Solution
$$7x(x^2 + 5y) - (x^2 + 5y) = 7x(x^2 + 5y) - 1(x^2 + 5y)$$
$$= (x^2 + 5y)(7x - 1)$$

> ▶ **Helpful Hint**
> Notice that we wrote $-(x^2 + 5y)$ as $-1(x^2 + 5y)$ to aid in factoring.

Concept Check Answer:
b

3   Sometimes it is possible to factor a polynomial by grouping the terms of the polynomial and looking for common factors in each group. This method of factoring is called **factoring by grouping**.

EXAMPLE 7

Factor $ab - 6a + 2b - 12$.

Solution   First look for the GCF of all four terms. The GCF of all four terms is 1. Next group the first two terms and the last two terms and factor out common factors from each group.

$$ab - 6a + 2b - 12 = (ab - 6a) + (2b - 12)$$

Factor a from the first group and 2 from the second group.

$$= a(b - 6) + 2(b - 6)$$

Now we see a GCF of $(b - 6)$. Factor out $(b - 6)$ to get

$$a(b - 6) + 2(b - 6) = (b - 6)(a + 2)$$

Check: To check, multiply $(b - 6)$ and $(a + 2)$ to see that the product is $ab - 6a + 2b - 12$.

> **Helpful Hint**
> Notice that the polynomial $a(b - 6) + 2(b - 6)$ is *not* in factored form. It is a *sum*, not a *product*. The factored form is $(b - 6)(a + 2)$.

EXAMPLE 8

Factor $x^3 + 5x^2 + 3x + 15$.

Solution
$$
\begin{aligned}
x^3 + 5x^2 + 3x + 15 &= (x^3 + 5x^2) + (3x + 15) && \text{Group pairs of terms.}\\
&= x^2(x + 5) + 3(x + 5) && \text{Factor each binomial.}\\
&= (x + 5)(x^2 + 3) && \text{Factor out the common factor,}\\
& && (x + 5).
\end{aligned}
$$

EXAMPLE 9

Factor $m^2n^2 + m^2 - 2n^2 - 2$.

Solution
$$
\begin{aligned}
m^2n^2 + m^2 - 2n^2 - 2 &= (m^2n^2 + m^2) + (-2n^2 - 2) && \text{Group pairs of terms.}\\
&= m^2(n^2 + 1) - 2(n^2 + 1) && \text{Factor each binomial.}\\
&= (n^2 + 1)(m^2 - 2) && \text{Factor out the common factor,}\\
& && (n^2 + 1).
\end{aligned}
$$

EXAMPLE 10

Factor $xy + 2x - y - 2$.

Solution

$$xy + 2x - y - 2 = (xy + 2x) + (-y - 2) \quad \text{Group pairs of terms.}$$
$$= x(y + 2) - 1(y + 2) \quad \text{Factor each binomial.}$$
$$= (y + 2)(x - 1) \quad \text{Factor out the common factor}$$
$$(y + 2).$$

MENTAL MATH

Find the GCF of each list of monomials.

1. $6, 12$ **2.** $9, 27$ **3.** $15x, 10$ **4.** $9x, 12$

5. $13x, 2x$ **6.** $4y, 5y$ **7.** $7x, 14x$ **8.** $8z, 4z$

EXERCISE SET 5.5

STUDY GUIDE/SSM   CD/VIDEO   PH MATH TUTOR CENTER   MathXL®Tutorials ON CD   MathXL®   MyMathLab®

Find the GCF of each list of monomials. See Example 1.

1. a^8, a^5, a^3 **2.** b^9, b^2, b^5

3. $x^2y^3z^3, y^2z^3, xy^2z^2$ **4.** $xy^2z^3, x^2y^2z^2, x^2y^3$

5. $6x^3y, 9x^2y^2, 12x^2y$ **6.** $4xy^2, 16xy^3, 8x^2y^2$

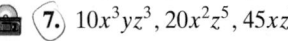 **7.** $10x^3yz^3, 20x^2z^5, 45xz^3$ **8.** $12y^2z^4, 9xy^3z^4, 15x^2y^2z^3$

Factor out the GCF in each polynomial. See Examples 2 through 6.

9. $18x - 12$ **10.** $21x + 14$

11. $4y^2 - 16xy^3$ **12.** $3z - 21xz^4$

13. $6x^5 - 8x^4 + 2x^3$ **14.** $9x + 3x^2 - 6x^3$

15. $8a^3b^3 - 4a^2b^2 + 4ab + 16ab^2$

16. $12a^3b - 6ab + 18ab^2 - 18a^2b$

17. $6(x + 3) + 5a(x + 3)$ **18.** $2(x - 4) + 3y(x - 4)$

19. $2x(z + 7) + (z + 7)$ **20.** $x(y - 2) + (y - 2)$

21. $3x(x^2 + 5) - 2(x^2 + 5)$ **22.** $4x(2y + 3) - 5(2y + 3)$

23. When $3x^2 - 9x + 3$ is factored, the result is $3(x^2 - 3x + 1)$. Explain why it is necessary to include the term 1 in this factored form.

24. Construct a trinomial whose GCF is $5x^2y^3$.

Factor each polynomial by grouping. See Examples 7 through 10

25. $ab + 3a + 2b + 6$ **26.** $ab + 2a + 5b + 10$

27. $ac + 4a - 2c - 8$ **28.** $bc + 8b - 3c - 24$

29. $2xy - 3x - 4y + 6$ **30.** $12xy - 18x - 10y + 15$

31. $12xy - 8x - 3y + 2$ **32.** $20xy - 15x - 4y + 3$

MIXED PRACTICE

Factor each polynomial

33. $6x^3 + 9$ **34.** $6x^2 - 8$

35. $x^3 + 3x^2$ **36.** $x^4 - 4x^3$

37. $8a^3 - 4a$ **38.** $12b^4 + 3b^2$

39. $-20x^2y + 16xy^3$

40. $-18xy^3 + 27x^4y$

41. $10a^2b^3 + 5ab^2 - 15ab^3$

42. $10ef - 20e^2f^3 + 30e^3f$

43. $9abc^2 + 6a^2bc - 6ab + 3bc$

44. $4a^2b^2c - 6ab^2c - 4ac + 8a$

45. $4x(y - 2) - 3(y - 2)$

46. $8y(z + 8) - 3(z + 8)$

47. $6xy + 10x + 9y + 15$

48. $15xy + 20x + 6y + 8$

49. $xy + 3y - 5x - 15$

50. $xy + 4y - 3x - 12$

51. $6ab - 2a - 9b + 3$

52. $16ab - 8a - 6b + 3$

53. $12xy + 18x + 2y + 3$

54. $20xy + 8x + 5y + 2$

55. $2m(n - 8) - (n - 8)$

56. $3a(b - 4) - (b - 4)$

57. $15x^3y^2 - 18x^2y^2$

58. $12x^4y^2 - 16x^3y^3$

59. $2x^2 + 3xy + 4x + 6y$

60. $3x^2 + 12x + 4xy + 16y$

61. $5x^2 + 5xy - 3x - 3y$

62. $4x^2 + 2xy - 10x - 5y$

63. $x^3 + 3x^2 + 4x + 12$

64. $x^3 + 4x^2 + 3x + 12$

65. $x^3 - x^2 - 2x + 2$

66. $x^3 - 2x^2 - 3x + 6$

REVIEW EXERCISES

Simplify the following. See Section 5.1.

67. $(5x^2)(11x^5)$

68. $(7y)(-2y^3)$

69. $(5x^2)^3$

70. $(-2y^3)^4$

Find each product by using the FOIL order of multiplying binomials. See Section 5.4.

71. $(x + 2)(x - 5)$

72. $(x - 7)(x - 1)$

73. $(x + 3)(x + 2)$

74. $(x - 4)(x + 2)$

75. $(y - 3)(y - 1)$

76. $(s + 8)(s + 10)$

Concept Extensions

77. A factored polynomial can be in many forms. For example, a factored form of $xy - 3x - 2y + 6$ is $(x - 2)(y - 3)$. Which of the following is not a factored form of $xy - 3x - 2y + 6$?

a. $(2 - x)(3 - y)$

b. $(-2 + x)(-3 + y)$

c. $(x - 2)(y - 3)$

d. $(-x + 2)(-y + 3)$

78. Consider the following sequence of algebraic steps:

$$x^3 - 6x^2 + 2x - 10 = (x^3 - 6x^2) + (2x - 10)$$
$$= x^2(x - 6) + 2(x - 5)$$

Explain whether the final result is the factored form of the original polynomial.

79. Which factorization of $12x^2 + 9x + 3$ is correct?

a. $3(4x^2 + 3x + 1)$

b. $3(4x^2 + 3x - 1)$

c. $3(4x^2 + 3x - 3)$

d. $3(4x^2 + 3x)$

Solve.

△ **80.** The material needed to manufacture a tin can is given by the polynomial $2\pi r^2 + 2\pi rh$ where the radius is r and height is h. Factor this expression.

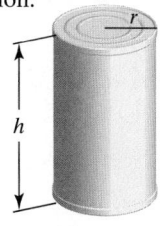

81. The amount E of voltage in an electrical circuit is given by the formula

$$IR_1 + IR_2 = E$$

Write an equivalent equation by factoring the expression $IR_1 + IR_2$.

82. At the end of T years, the amount of money A in a savings account earning simple interest from an initial investment of P dollars at rate R is given by the formula

$$A = P + PRT$$

Write an equivalent equation by factoring the expression $P + PRT$.

△ **83.** An open-topped box has a square base and a height of 10 inches. If each of the bottom edges of the box has length x inches, find the amount of material needed to construct the box. Write the answer in factored form.

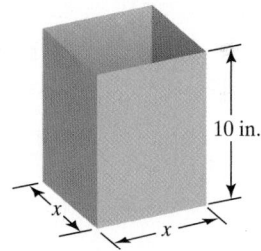

10 in.

84. An object is thrown upward from the ground with an initial velocity of 64 feet per second. The height $h(t)$ of the object after t seconds is given by the polynomial function

$$h(t) = -16t^2 + 64t$$

a. Write an equivalent factored expression for the function $h(t)$ by factoring $-16t^2 + 64t$.

b. Find $h(1)$ by using $h(t) = -16t^2 + 64t$ and then by using the factored form of $h(t)$.

c. Explain why the values found in part **b** are the same.

85. An object is dropped from the gondola of a hot-air balloon at a height of 224 feet. The height $h(t)$ of the object after t seconds is given by the polynomial function

$$h(t) = -16t^2 + 224$$

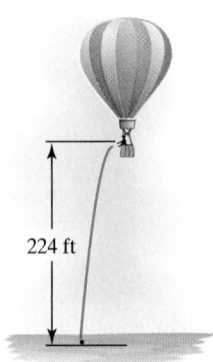

224 ft

a. Write an equivalent factored expression for the function $h(t)$ by factoring $-16t^2 + 224$.

b. Find $h(2)$ by using $h(t) = -16t^2 + 224$ and then by using the factored form of the function.

c. Explain why the values found in part **b** are the same.

Factor. Assume that variables used as exponents represent positive integers.

86. $x^{3n} - 2x^{2n} + 5x^n$

87. $3y^n + 3y^{2n} + 5y^{8n}$

88. $6x^{8a} - 2x^{5a} - 4x^{3a}$

89. $3x^{5a} - 6x^{3a} + 9x^{2a}$

5.6 FACTORING TRINOMIALS

Objectives

1 Factor trinomials of the form $x^2 + bx + c$.

2 Factor trinomials of the form $ax^2 + bx + c$.

   a. Method 1 - Trial and Check

   b. Method 2 - Grouping

3 Factor by substitution.

1   In the previous section, we used factoring by grouping to factor four-term polynomials. In this section, we present techniques for factoring trinomials. Since $(x - 2)(x + 5) = x^2 + 3x - 10$, we say that $(x - 2)(x + 5)$ is a factored form of $x^2 + 3x - 10$. Taking a close look at how $(x - 2)$ and $(x + 5)$ are multiplied suggests a pattern for factoring trinomials of the form

$$x^2 + bx + c$$

$$(x - 2)(x + 5) = x^2 + 3x - 10$$

$$-2 + 5$$
$$-2 \cdot 5$$

The pattern for factoring is summarized next.

> **Factoring a Trinomial of the Form $x^2 + bx + c$**
>
> Find two numbers whose product is c and whose sum is b. The factored form of $x^2 + bx + c$ is
>
> $$(x + \text{one number})(x + \text{other number})$$

EXAMPLE 1

Factor $x^2 + 10x + 16$.

Solution   We look for two integers whose product is 16 and whose sum is 10. Since our integers must have a positive product and a positive sum, we look at only positive factors of 16.

Positive Factors of 16	Sum of Factors	
1, 16	$1 + 16 = 17$	
4, 4	$4 + 4 = 8$	
2, 8	$2 + 8 = 10$	Correct pair

The correct pair of numbers is 2 and 8 because their product is 16 and their sum is 10. Thus,

$$x^2 + 10x + 16 = (x + 2)(x + 8)$$

Check: To check, see that $(x + 2)(x + 8) = x^2 + 10x + 16$.

EXAMPLE 2

Factor $x^2 - 12x + 35$.

Solution   We need to find two integers whose product is 35 and whose sum is -12. Since our integers must have a positive product and a negative sum, we consider only negative factors of 35.

Negative Factors of 35	Sum of Factors	
$-1, -35$	$-1 + (-35) = -36$	
$-5, -7$	$-5 + (-7) = -12$	Correct pair

The numbers are -5 and -7.

$$x^2 - 12x + 35 = [x + (-5)][x + (-7)]$$
$$= (x - 5)(x - 7)$$

Check: To check, see that $(x - 5)(x - 7) = x^2 - 12x + 35$.

EXAMPLE 3

Factor $5x^3 - 30x^2 - 35x$.

Solution First we factor out the greatest common factor, $5x$.

$$5x^3 - 30x^2 - 35x = 5x(x^2 - 6x - 7)$$

Next we try to factor $x^2 - 6x - 7$ by finding two numbers whose product is -7 and whose sum is -6. The numbers are 1 and -7.

$$5x^3 - 30x^2 - 35x = 5x(x^2 - 6x - 7)$$
$$= 5x(x + 1)(x - 7)$$

> **Helpful Hint**
> If the polynomial to be factored contains a common factor that is factored out, don't forget to include that common factor in the final factored form of the original polynomial.

EXAMPLE 4

Factor $2n^2 - 38n + 80$.

Solution The terms of this polynomial have a greatest common factor of 2, which we factor out first.

$$2n^2 - 38n + 80 = 2(n^2 - 19n + 40)$$

Next we factor $n^2 - 19n + 40$ by finding two numbers whose product is 40 and whose sum is -19. Both numbers must be negative since their sum is -19. Possibilities are

$$-1 \text{ and } -40, \quad -2 \text{ and } -20, \quad -4 \text{ and } -10, \quad -5 \text{ and } -8$$

None of the pairs has a sum of -19, so no further factoring with integers is possible. The factored form of $2n^2 - 38n + 80$ is

$$2n^2 - 38n + 80 = 2(n^2 - 19n + 40)$$

We call a polynomial such as $n^2 - 19n + 40$ that cannot be factored further, a **prime polynomial**.

2 Next, we factor trinomials of the form $ax^2 + bx + c$, where the coefficient a of x^2 is not 1. Don't forget that the first step in factoring any polynomial is to factor out the greatest common factor of its terms. We will review two methods here. The first method we'll call trial and check.

EXAMPLE 5

METHOD 1—TRIAL AND CHECK

Factor $2x^2 + 11x + 15$.

Solution   Factors of $2x^2$ are $2x$ and x. Let's try these factors as first terms of the binomials.

$$2x^2 + 11x + 15 = (2x + \quad)(x + \quad)$$

Next we try combinations of factors of 15 until the correct middle term, $11x$, is obtained. We will try only positive factors of 15 since the coefficient of the middle term, 11, is positive. Positive factors of 15 are 1 and 15 and 3 and 5.

$(2x + 1)(x + 15)$
$1x$
$30x$
$31x$ *Incorrect middle term*

$(2x + 3)(x + 5)$
$3x$
$10x$
$13x$ *Incorrect middle term*

$(2x + 15)(x + 1)$
$15x$
$2x$
$17x$ *Incorrect middle term*

$(2x + 5)(x + 3)$
$5x$
$6x$
$11x$ *Correct middle term*

Thus, the factored form of $2x^2 + 11x + 15$ is $(2x + 5)(x + 3)$.

Factoring a Trinomial of the Form $ax^2 + bx + c$

Step 1: Write all pairs of factors of ax^2.

Step 2: Write all pairs of factors of c, the constant term.

Step 3: Try various combinations of these factors until the correct middle term bx is found.

Step 4: If no combination exists, the polynomial is **prime**.

EXAMPLE 6

Factor $3x^2 - x - 4$.

Solution   Factors of $3x^2$: $3x \cdot x$
Factors of -4: $-1 \cdot 4$, $1 \cdot -4$, $-2 \cdot 2$, $2 \cdot -2$

Let's try possible combinations of these factors.

$(3x - 1)(x + 4)$
$-1x$
$12x$
$11x$ *Incorrect middle term*

$(3x + 4)(x - 1)$
$4x$
$-3x$
$1x$ *Incorrect middle term*

$(3x - 4)(x + 1)$
$-4x$
$3x$
$-1x$ *Correct middle term*

Thus, $3x^2 - x - 4 = (3x - 4)(x + 1)$.

> **Helpful Hint—Sign Patterns**
>
> A positive constant in a trinomial tells us to look for two numbers with the same sign. The sign of the coefficient of the middle term tells us whether the signs are both positive or both negative.
>
> both   same   both   same
> positive sign   negative sign
> $\downarrow$ $\downarrow$ $\downarrow$ $\downarrow$
>
> $2x^2 + 7x + 3 = (2x + 1)(x + 3)$ $2x^2 - 7x + 3 = (2x - 1)(x - 3)$
>
> A negative constant in a trinomial tells us to look for two numbers with opposite signs.
>
> opposite   opposite
> signs   signs
> $\downarrow$ $\downarrow$
>
> $2x^2 - 5x - 3 = (2x + 1)(x - 3)$ $2x^2 + 5x - 3 = (2x - 1)(x + 3)$

EXAMPLE 7

Factor $12x^3y - 22x^2y + 8xy$.

Solution   First we factor out the greatest common factor of the terms of this trinomial, $2xy$.

$$12x^3y - 22x^2y + 8xy = 2xy(6x^2 - 11x + 4)$$

Now we try to factor the trinomial $6x^2 - 11x + 4$.
Factors of $6x^2$: $2x \cdot 3x$, $6x \cdot x$

Let's try $2x$ and $3x$.

$$2xy(6x^2 - 11x + 4) = 2xy(2x + \quad)(3x + \quad)$$

The constant term, 4, is positive and the coefficient of the middle term, -11, is negative, so we factor 4 into negative factors only.
Negative factors of 4: $-4(-1)$, $-2(-2)$

Let's try -4 and -1.

$$2xy(2x - 4)(3x - 1)$$
$$\underbrace{}_{-12x}$$
$$\underline{-2x}$$
$$-14x \qquad \text{\textit{Incorrect middle term}}$$

This combination cannot be correct, because one of the factors, $(2x - 4)$, has a common factor of 2. This cannot happen if the polynomial $6x^2 - 11x + 4$ has no common factors.

Now let's try -1 and -4.

$$2xy(2x - 1)(3x - 4)$$
$$\underbrace{}_{-3x}$$
$$\underline{-8x}$$
$$-11x \qquad \text{\textit{Correct middle term}}$$

Thus,

$$12x^3y - 22x^2y + 8xy = 2xy(2x - 1)(3x - 4)$$

If this combination had not worked, we would have tried -2 and -2 as factors of 4 and then $6x$ and x as factors of $6x^2$.

> **Helpful Hint**
>
> If a trinomial has no common factor (other than 1), then none of its binomial factors will contain a common factor (other than 1).

EXAMPLE 8

Factor $16x^2 + 24xy + 9y^2$.

Solution   No greatest common factor can be factored out of this trinomial.

Factors of $16x^2$: $16x \cdot x$, $8x \cdot 2x$, $4x \cdot 4x$

Factors of $9y^2$: $y \cdot 9y$, $3y \cdot 3y$

We try possible combinations until the correct factorization is found.

$$16x^2 + 24xy + 9y^2 = (4x + 3y)(4x + 3y)   \text{or}   (4x + 3y)^2$$

The trinomial $16x^2 + 24xy + 9y^2$ in Example 8 is an example of a **perfect square trinomial** since its factors are two identical binomials. In the next section, we examine a special method for factoring perfect square trinomials.

Method 2— Grouping   There is another method we can use when factoring trinomials of the form $ax^2 + bx + c$: Write the trinomial as a four-term polynomial, and then factor by grouping.

Factoring a Trinomial of the Form $ax^2 + bx + c$ by Grouping

Step 1: Find two numbers whose product is $a \cdot c$ and whose sum is b.

Step 2: Write the term bx as a sum by using the factors found in Step 1.

Step 3: Factor by grouping.

EXAMPLE 9

Factor $6x^2 + 13x + 6$.

In this trinomial, $a = 6, b = 13$, and $c = 6$.

Solution   **Step 1:** Find two numbers whose product is $a \cdot c$, or $6 \cdot 6 = 36$, and whose sum is b, 13. The two numbers are 4 and 9.

Step 2: Write the middle term, $13x$, as the sum $4x + 9x$.

$$6x^2 + 13x + 6 = 6x^2 + 4x + 9x + 6$$

Step 3: Factor $6x^2 + 4x + 9x + 6$ by grouping.

$$(6x^2 + 4x) + (9x + 6) = 2x(3x + 2) + 3(3x + 2)$$
$$= (3x + 2)(2x + 3)$$

✔ **CONCEPT CHECK**

Name one way that a factorization can be checked.

EXAMPLE 10

Factor $18x^2 - 9x - 2$.

Solution In this trinomial, $a = 18$, $b = -9$, and $c = -2$.

Step 1: Find two numbers whose product is $a \cdot c$ or $18(-2) = -36$ and whose sum is b, -9. The two numbers are -12 and 3.

Step 2: Write the middle term, $-9x$, as the sum $-12x + 3x$.

$$18x^2 - 9x - 2 = 18x^2 - 12x + 3x - 2$$

Step 3: Factor by grouping.

$$(18x^2 - 12x) + (3x - 2) = 6x(3x - 2) + 1(3x - 2)$$
$$= (3x - 2)(6x + 1).$$

3 A complicated looking polynomial may be a simpler trinomial "in disguise." Revealing the simpler trinomial is possible by substitution.

EXAMPLE 11

Factor $2(a + 3)^2 - 5(a + 3) - 7$.

Solution The quantity $(a + 3)$ is in two of the terms of this polynomial. *Substitute x for $(a + 3)$* and the result is the following simpler trinomial.

$$2(a + 3)^2 - 5(a + 3) - 7 \quad \text{Original trinomial.}$$
$$\downarrow \qquad\qquad \downarrow$$
$$= 2(x)^2 - 5(x) - 7 \quad \text{Substitute } x \text{ for } (a + 3).$$

Now factor $2x^2 - 5x - 7$.

$$2x^2 - 5x - 7 = (2x - 7)(x + 1)$$

But the quantity in the original polynomial was $(a + 3)$, not x. Thus, we need to reverse the substitution and replace x with $(a + 3)$.

$$(2x - 7)(x + 1) \qquad \text{Factored expression.}$$

$$= [2(a + 3) - 7][(a + 3) + 1] \quad \text{Substitute } (a + 3) \text{ for } x.$$
$$= (2a + 6 - 7)(a + 3 + 1) \quad \text{Remove inside parentheses.}$$
$$= (2a - 1)(a + 4) \quad \text{Simplify.}$$

Thus, $2(a + 3)^2 - 5(a + 3) - 7 = (2a - 1)(a + 4)$.

Concept Check Answer:
Answers may vary. A sample is: By multiplying the factors to see that the product is the original polynomial.

EXAMPLE 12

Factor $5x^4 + 29x^2 - 42$.

Solution Again, substitution may help us factor this polynomial more easily. Since this polynomial contains the variable x, we will choose a different substitution variable. Let $y = x^2$, so $y^2 = (x^2)^2$, or x^4. Then

$$5x^4 + 29x^2 - 42$$
$$\downarrow \qquad \downarrow$$

becomes

$$5y^2 + 29y - 42$$

which factors as

$$5y^2 + 29y - 42 = (5y - 6)(y + 7)$$

Next, replace y with x^2 to get

$$(5x^2 - 6)(x^2 + 7)$$

MENTAL MATH

1. Find two numbers whose product is 10 and whose sum is 7.
2. Find two numbers whose product is 12 and whose sum is 8.
3. Find two numbers whose product is 24 and whose sum is 11.
4. Find two numbers whose product is 30 and whose sum is 13.

EXERCISE SET 5.6

STUDY GUIDE/SSM   CD/ VIDEO   PH MATH TUTOR CENTER   MathXL®Tutorials ON CD   MathXL®   MyMathLab®

Factor each trinomial. See Examples 1 through 4.

1. $x^2 + 9x + 18$
2. $x^2 + 9x + 20$
3. $x^2 - 12x + 32$
4. $x^2 - 12x + 27$
5. $x^2 + 10x - 24$
6. $x^2 + 3x - 54$
7. $x^2 - 2x - 24$
8. $x^2 - 9x - 36$
9. $3x^2 - 18x + 24$
10. $x^2y^2 + 4xy^2 + 3y^2$
11. $4x^2z + 28xz + 40z$
12. $5x^2 - 45x + 70$
13. $2x^2 + 30x - 108$
14. $3x^2 + 12x - 96$

15. Find all positive and negative integers b such that $x^2 + bx + 6$ factors.
16. Find all positive and negative integers b such that $x^2 + bx - 10$ factors.

Factor each trinomial. See Examples 5 through 10.

17. $5x^2 + 16x + 3$
18. $3x^2 + 8x + 4$
19. $2x^2 - 11x + 12$
20. $3x^2 - 19x + 20$
21. $2x^2 + 25x - 20$
22. $6x^2 - 13x - 8$
23. $4x^2 - 12x + 9$
24. $25x^2 - 30x + 9$

25. $12x^2 + 10x - 50$

26. $12y^2 - 48y + 45$

27. $3y^4 - y^3 - 10y^2$

28. $2x^2z + 5xz - 12z$

29. $6x^3 + 8x^2 + 24x$

30. $18y^3 + 12y^2 + 2y$

31. $x^2 + 8xz + 7z^2$

32. $a^2 - 2ab - 15b^2$

33. $2x^2 - 5xy - 3y^2$

34. $6x^2 + 11xy + 4y^2$

35. $x^2 - x - 12$

36. $x^2 + 4x - 5$

37. $28y^2 + 22y + 4$

38. $24y^3 - 2y^2 - y$

39. $2x^2 + 15x - 27$

40. $3x^2 + 14x + 15$

41. Find all positive and negative integers b such that $3x^2 + bx + 5$ factors.

42. Find all positive and negative integers b such that $2x^2 + bx + 7$ factors.

Use substitution to factor each polynomial completely. See Examples 11 and 12.

43. $x^4 + x^2 - 6$

44. $x^4 - x^2 - 20$

45. $(5x + 1)^2 + 8(5x + 1) + 7$

46. $(3x - 1)^2 + 5(3x - 1) + 6$

47. $x^6 - 7x^3 + 12$

48. $x^6 - 4x^3 - 12$

49. $(a + 5)^2 - 5(a + 5) - 24$

50. $(3c + 6)^2 + 12(3c + 6) - 28$

Solve.

△ **51.** The volume $V(x)$ of a box in terms of its height x is given by the function $V(x) = 3x^3 - 2x^2 - 8x$. Factor this expression for $V(x)$.

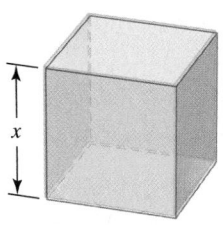

x

△ **52.** Based on your results from Exercise 51, find the length and width of the box if the height is 5 inches and the dimensions of the box are whole numbers.

MIXED PRACTICE

Factor each polynomial completely.

53. $x^2 - 24x - 81$

54. $x^2 - 48x - 100$

55. $x^2 - 15x - 54$

56. $x^2 - 15x + 54$

57. $3x^2 - 6x + 3$

58. $8x^2 - 8x + 2$

🔒 **59.** $3x^2 - 5x - 2$

60. $5x^2 - 14x - 3$

61. $8x^2 - 26x + 15$

62. $12x^2 - 17x + 6$

🔒 **63.** $18x^4 + 21x^3 + 6x^2$

64. $20x^5 + 54x^4 + 10x^3$

65. $3a^2 + 12ab + 12b^2$

66. $2x^2 + 16xy + 32y^2$

67. $x^2 + 4x + 5$

68. $x^2 + 6x + 8$

69. $2(x + 4)^2 + 3(x + 4) - 5$

70. $3(x + 3)^2 + 2(x + 3) - 5$

71. $6x^2 - 49x + 30$

72. $4x^2 - 39x + 27$

73. $x^4 - 5x^2 - 6$

74. $x^4 - 5x^2 + 6$

75. $6x^3 - x^2 - x$

76. $12x^3 + x^2 - x$

77. $12a^2 - 29ab + 15b^2$

78. $16y^2 + 6yx - 27x^2$

79. $9x^2 + 30x + 25$

80. $4x^2 + 6x + 9$

81. $3x^2y - 11xy + 8y$

82. $5xy^2 - 9xy + 4x$

83. $2x^2 + 2x - 12$

84. $3x^2 + 6x - 45$

85. $(x - 4)^2 + 3(x - 4) - 18$

86. $(x - 3)^2 - 2(x - 3) - 8$

87. $2x^6 + 3x^3 - 9$

88. $3x^6 - 14x^3 + 8$

89. $72xy^4 - 24xy^2z + 2xz^2$

90. $36xy^2 - 48xyz^2 + 16xz^4$

REVIEW AND PREVIEW

Multiply. See Section 5.4.

91. $(x - 3)(x + 3)$

92. $(x - 4)(x + 4)$

93. $(2x + 1)^2$

94. $(3x + 5)^2$

95. $(x - 2)(x^2 + 2x + 4)$

96. $(y + 1)(y^2 - y + 1)$

Concept Extensions

97. Suppose that a movie is being filmed in New York City. An action shot requires an object to be thrown upward with an initial velocity of 80 feet per second off the top of 1 Madison Square Plaza, a height of 576 feet. The height $h(t)$ in feet of the object after t seconds is given by the function $h(t) = -16t^2 + 80t + 576$. (*Source:* The World Almanac, 2001)

   a. Find the height of the object at $t = 0$ seconds, $t = 2$ seconds, $t = 4$ seconds, and $t = 6$ seconds.

   b. Explain why the height of the object increases and then decreases as time passes.

   c. Factor the polynomial $-16t^2 + 80t + 576$.

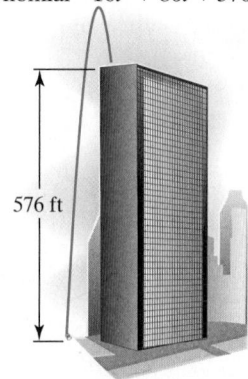

576 ft

98. Suppose that an object is thrown upward with an initial velocity of 64 feet per second off the edge of a 960-foot-cliff. The height $h(t)$ in feet of the object after t seconds is given by the function

$$h(t) = -16t^2 + 64t + 960$$

a. Find the height of the object at $t = 0$ seconds, $t = 3$ seconds, $t = 6$ seconds, and $t = 9$ seconds.

b. Explain why the height of the object increases and then decreases as time passes.

c. Factor the polynomial $-16t^2 + 64t + 960$.

Factor. Assume that variables used as exponents represent positive integers.

99. $x^{2n} + 10x^n + 16$

100. $x^{2n} - 7x^n + 12$

101. $x^{2n} - 3x^n - 18$

102. $x^{2n} + 7x^n - 18$

103. $2x^{2n} + 11x^n + 5$

104. $3x^{2n} - 8x^n + 4$

105. $4x^{2n} - 12x^n + 9$

106. $9x^{2n} + 24x^n + 16$

Recall that a graphing calculator may be used to check addition, subtraction, and multiplication of polynomials. In the same manner, a graphing calculator may be used to check factoring of polynomials in one variable. For example, to see that

$$2x^3 - 9x^2 - 5x = x(2x + 1)(x - 5)$$

graph $Y_1 = 2x^3 - 9x^2 - 5x$ and $Y_2 = x(2x + 1)(x - 5)$. Then trace along both graphs to see that they coincide. Factor the following and use this method to check your results.

107. $x^4 + 6x^3 + 5x^2$

108. $x^3 + 6x^2 + 8x$

109. $30x^3 + 9x^2 - 3x$

110. $-6x^4 + 10x^3 - 4x^2$

5.7   FACTORING BY SPECIAL PRODUCTS

Objectives

1 Factor a perfect square trinomial.

2 Factor the difference of two squares.

3 Factor the sum or difference of two cubes.

1 In the previous section, we considered a variety of ways to factor trinomials of the form $ax^2 + bx + c$. In one particular example, we factored $16x^2 + 24xy + 9y^2$ as

$$16x^2 + 24xy + 9y^2 = (4x + 3y)^2$$

Recall that $16x^2 + 24xy + 9y^2$ is a perfect square trinomial because its factors are two identical binomials. A perfect square trinomial can be factored quickly if you recognize the trinomial as a perfect square.

A trinomial is a perfect square trinomial if it can be written so that its first term is the square of some quantity a, its last term is the square of some quantity b, and its middle term is twice the product of the quantities a and b. The following special formulas can be used to factor perfect square trinomials.

Perfect Square Trinomials

$$a^2 + 2ab + b^2 = (a + b)^2$$
$$a^2 - 2ab + b^2 = (a - b)^2$$

Notice that these formulas above are the same special products from Section 5.4 for the square of a binomial.

From

$$a^2 + 2ab + b^2 = (a + b)^2,$$

we see that

$$16x^2 + 24xy + 9y^2 = (4x)^2 + 2(4x)(3y) + (3y)^2 = (4x + 3y)^2$$

EXAMPLE 1

Factor $m^2 + 10m + 25$.

Solution Notice that the first term is a square: $m^2 = (m)^2$, the last term is a square: $25 = 5^2$; and $10m = 2 \cdot 5 \cdot m$.

Thus,

$$m^2 + 10m + 25 = m^2 + 2(m)(5) + 5^2 = (m + 5)^2$$

EXAMPLE 2

Factor $3a^2x - 12abx + 12b^2x$.

Solution The terms of this trinomial have a GCF of $3x$, which we factor out first.

$$3a^2x - 12abx + 12b^2x = 3x(a^2 - 4ab + 4b^2)$$

Now, the polynomial $a^2 - 4ab + 4b^2$ is a perfect square trinomial. Notice that the first term is a square: $a^2 = (a)^2$; the last term is a square: $4b^2 = (2b)^2$; and $4ab = 2(a)(2b)$. The factoring can now be completed as

$$3x(a^2 - 4ab + 4b^2) = 3x(a - 2b)^2$$

> **Helpful Hint**
> If you recognize a trinomial as a perfect square trinomial, use the special formulas to factor. However, methods for factoring trinomials in general from Section 5.6 will also result in the correct factored form.

2 We now factor special types of binomials, beginning with the **difference of two squares.** The special product pattern presented in Section 5.4 for the product of a sum and a difference of two terms is used again here. However, the emphasis is now on factoring rather than on multiplying.

> **Difference of Two Squares**
> $$a^2 - b^2 = (a + b)(a - b)$$

Notice that a binomial is a difference of two squares when it is the difference of the square of some quantity a and the square of some quantity b.

EXAMPLE 3

Factor the following.

a. $x^2 - 9$ b. $16y^2 - 9$ c. $50 - 8y^2$ d. $x^2 - \dfrac{1}{4}$

Solution a. $x^2 - 9 = x^2 - 3^2$ b. $16y^2 - 9 = (4y)^2 - 3^2$
$= (x + 3)(x - 3)$ $= (4y + 3)(4y - 3)$

c. First factor out the common factor of 2.
$50 - 8y^2 = 2(25 - 4y^2)$
$= 2(5 + 2y)(5 - 2y)$

d. $x^2 - \dfrac{1}{4} = x^2 - \left(\dfrac{1}{2}\right)^2 = \left(x + \dfrac{1}{2}\right)\left(x - \dfrac{1}{2}\right)$

The binomial $x^2 + 9$ is a **sum of two squares** and cannot be factored by using real numbers. **In general, except for factoring out a GCF, the sum of two squares usually cannot be factored by using real numbers.**

> **Helpful Hint**
>
> The sum of two squares whose GCF is 1 usually cannot be factored by using real numbers. For example, $x^2 + 9$ is called a prime polynomial.

EXAMPLE 4

Factor the following.

a. $p^4 - 16$ b. $(x + 3)^2 - 36$

Solution a. $p^4 - 16 = (p^2)^2 - 4^2$
$= (p^2 + 4)(p^2 - 4)$

The binomial factor $p^2 + 4$ cannot be factored by using real numbers, but the binomial factor $p^2 - 4$ is a difference of squares.

$(p^2 + 4)(p^2 - 4) = (p^2 + 4)(p + 2)(p - 2)$

b. Factor $(x + 3)^2 - 36$ as the difference of squares.

$(x + 3)^2 - 36 = (x + 3)^2 - 6^2$
$= [(x + 3) + 6][(x + 3) - 6]$ Factor.
$= [x + 3 + 6][x + 3 - 6]$ Remove parentheses.
$= (x + 9)(x - 3)$ Simplify.

✔ **CONCEPT CHECK**

Is $(x - 4)(y^2 - 9)$ completely factored? Why or why not?

Concept Check Answer:
o; $(y^2 - 9)$ can be factored

EXAMPLE 5

Factor $x^2 + 4x + 4 - y^2$.

Solution Factoring by grouping comes to mind since the sum of the first three terms of this polynomial is a perfect square trinomial.

$$x^2 + 4x + 4 - y^2 = (x^2 + 4x + 4) - y^2 \quad \text{Group the first three terms.}$$
$$= (x + 2)^2 - y^2 \quad \text{Factor the perfect square trinomial.}$$

This is not factored yet since we have a *difference*, not a *product*. Since $(x + 2)^2 - y^2$ is a difference of squares, we have

$$(x + 2)^2 - y^2 = [(x + 2) + y][(x + 2) - y]$$
$$= (x + 2 + y)(x + 2 - y)$$

3 Although the sum of two squares usually cannot be factored, the sum of two cubes, as well as the difference of two cubes, can be factored as follows.

> **Sum and Difference of Two Cubes**
> $$a^3 + b^3 = (a + b)(a^2 - ab + b^2)$$
> $$a^3 - b^3 = (a - b)(a^2 + ab + b^2)$$

To check the first pattern, let's find the product of $(a + b)$ and $(a^2 - ab + b^2)$.

$$(a + b)(a^2 - ab + b^2) = a(a^2 - ab + b^2) + b(a^2 - ab + b^2)$$
$$= a^3 - a^2b + ab^2 + a^2b - ab^2 + b^3$$
$$= a^3 + b^3$$

EXAMPLE 6

Factor $x^3 + 8$.

Solution First we write the binomial in the form $a^3 + b^3$. Then we use the formula

$$a^3 + b^3 = (a + b)(a^2 - a \cdot b + b^2), \quad \text{where } a \text{ is } x \text{ and } b \text{ is } 2.$$
$$\downarrow \quad \downarrow \quad \downarrow \quad \downarrow \quad \downarrow \quad \downarrow \quad \downarrow \quad \downarrow$$
$$x^3 + 8 = x^3 + 2^3 = (x + 2)(x^2 - x \cdot 2 + 2^2)$$

Thus, $x^3 + 8 = (x + 2)(x^2 - 2x + 4)$

EXAMPLE 7

Factor $p^3 + 27q^3$.

Solution
$$p^3 + 27q^3 = p^3 + (3q)^3$$
$$= (p + 3q)[p^2 - (p)(3q) + (3q)^2]$$
$$= (p + 3q)(p^2 - 3pq + 9q^2)$$

EXAMPLE 8

Factor $y^3 - 64$.

Solution   This is a difference of cubes since $y^3 - 64 = y^3 - 4^3$.

From

$$a^3 - b^3 = (a - b)(a^2 + a \cdot b + b^2)$$
$$\downarrow \quad \downarrow \qquad \downarrow \quad \downarrow \quad \downarrow \qquad \downarrow \quad \downarrow \qquad \downarrow$$
$$y^3 - 4^3 = (y - 4)(y^2 + y \cdot 4 + 4^2)$$
$$= (y - 4)(y^2 + 4y + 16)$$

> **Helpful Hint**
>
> When factoring sums or differences of cubes, be sure to notice the sign patterns.
>
> same sign
>
> $$x^3 + y^3 = (x + y)(x^2 - xy + y^2)$$
>
> opposite sign   always positive
>
> same sign
>
> $$x^3 - y^3 = (x - y)(x^2 + xy + y^2)$$
>
> opposite sign   always positive

EXAMPLE 9

Factor $125q^2 - n^3q^2$.

Solution   First we factor out a common factor of q^2.

$$125q^2 - n^3q^2 = q^2(125 - n^3)$$
$$= q^2(5^3 - n^3)$$

opposite sign   positive

$$= q^2(5 - n)[5^2 + (5)(n) + n^2]$$
$$= q^2(5 - n)(25 + 5n + n^2)$$

Thus, $125q^2 - n^3q^2 = q^2(5 - n)(25 + 5n + n^2)$. The trinomial $25 + 5n + n^2$ cannot be factored further.

EXERCISE SET 5.7

STUDY   CD/   PH MATH   MathXL®Tutorials   MathXL®   MyMathLab®
GUIDE/SSM   VIDEO   TUTOR CENTER   ON CD

Factor the following. See Examples 1 and 2.

1. $x^2 + 6x + 9$

2. $x^2 - 10x + 25$

3. $4x^2 - 12x + 9$

4. $25x^2 + 10x + 1$

5. $3x^2 - 24x + 48$

6. $x^3 + 14x^2 + 49x$

7. $9y^2x^2 + 12yx^2 + 4x^2$

8. $32x^2 - 16xy + 2y^2$

Factor the following. See Examples 3 through 5.

9. $x^2 - 25$

10. $y^2 - 100$

11. $9 - 4z^2$

12. $16x^2 - y^2$

13. $(y + 2)^2 - 49$

14. $(x - 1)^2 - z^2$

15. $64x^2 - 100$

16. $4x^2 - 36$

Factor the following. See Examples 6 through 8.

17. $x^3 + 27$

18. $y^3 + 1$

19. $z^3 - 1$

20. $x^3 - 8$

21. $m^3 + n^3$

22. $r^3 + 125$

23. $x^3y^2 - 27y^2$

24. $64 - p^3$

25. $a^3b + 8b^4$

26. $8ab^3 + 27a^4$

27. $125y^3 - 8x^3$

28. $54y^3 - 128$

Factor the following. See Example 9.

29. $x^2 + 6x + 9 - y^2$

30. $x^2 + 12x + 36 - y^2$

31. $x^2 - 10x + 25 - y^2$

32. $x^2 - 18x + 81 - y^2$

33. $4x^2 + 4x + 1 - z^2$

34. $9y^2 + 12y + 4 - x^2$

MIXED PRACTICE

Factor each polynomial completely.

35. $9x^2 - 49$

36. $25x^2 - 4$

37. $x^2 - 12x + 36$

38. $x^2 - 18x + 81$

39. $x^4 - 81$

40. $x^4 - 256$

41. $x^2 + 8x + 16 - 4y^2$

42. $x^2 + 14x + 49 - 9y^2$

43. $(x + 2y)^2 - 9$

44. $(3x + y)^2 - 25$

45. $x^3 - 216$

46. $8 - a^3$

47. $x^3 + 125$

48. $x^3 + 216$

49. $4x^2 + 25$

50. $16x^2 + 25$

51. $4a^2 + 12a + 9$

52. $9a^2 - 30a + 25$

53. $18x^2y - 2y$

54. $12xy^2 - 108x$

55. $8x^3 + y^3$

56. $27x^3 - y^3$

57. $x^6 - y^3$

58. $x^3 - y^6$

59. $x^2 + 16x + 64 - x^4$

60. $x^2 + 20x + 100 - x^4$

61. $3x^6y^2 + 81y^2$

62. $x^2y^9 + x^2y^3$

63. $(x + y)^3 + 125$

64. $(x + y)^3 + 27$

65. $(2x + 3)^3 - 64$

66. $(4x + 2)^3 - 125$

REVIEW AND PREVIEW

Solve the following equations. See Section 2.1.

67. $x - 5 = 0$

68. $x + 7 = 0$

69. $3x + 1 = 0$

70. $5x - 15 = 0$

71. $-2x = 0$

72. $3x = 0$

73. $-5x + 25 = 0$

74. $-4x - 16 = 0$

Concept Extensions

△ **75.** A manufacturer of metal washers needs to determine the cross-sectional area of each washer. If the outer radius of the washer is R and the radius of the hole is r, express the area of the washer as a polynomial. Factor this polynomial completely.

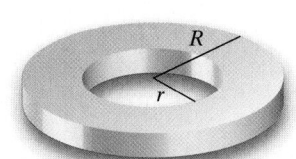

△ **76.** Express the area of the shaded region as a polynomial. Factor the polynomial completely.

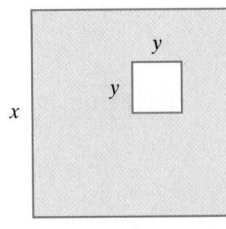

Express the volume of each solid as a polynomial. To do so, subtract the volume of the "hole" from the volume of the larger solid. Then factor the resulting polynomial.

7.

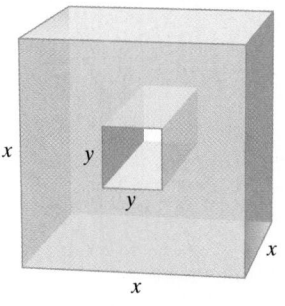

8.

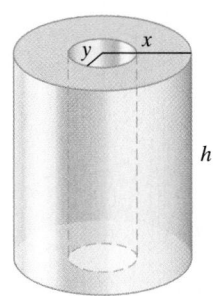

Find the value of c that makes each trinomial a perfect square trinomial.

79. $x^2 + 6x + c$ **80.** $y^2 + 10y + c$

81. $m^2 - 14m + c$ **82.** $n^2 - 2n + c$

83. $x^2 + cx + 16$ **84.** $x^2 + cx + 36$

85. Factor $x^6 - 1$ completely, using the following methods from this chapter.

     a. Factor the expression by treating it as the difference of two squares, $(x^3)^2 - 1^2$.

     b. Factor the expression treating it as the difference of two cubes, $(x^2)^3 - 1^3$.

     c. Are the answers to parts **a** and **b** the same? Why or why not?

Factor. Assume that variables used as exponents represent positive integers.

86. $x^{2n} - 25$

87. $x^{2n} - 36$

88. $36x^{2n} - 49$

89. $25x^{2n} - 81$

90. $x^{4n} - 16$

91. $x^{4n} - 625$

INTEGRATED REVIEW   OPERATIONS ON POLYNOMIALS AND FACTORING STRATEGIES

OPERATIONS ON POLYNOMIALS

Perform each indicated operation.

1. $(-y^2 + 6y - 1) + (3y^2 - 4y - 10)$ **2.** $(5z^4 - 6z^2 + z + 1) - (7z^4 - 2z + 1)$

3. Subtract $(x - 5)$ from $(x^2 - 6x + 2)$.   **4.** $(2x^2 + 6x - 5) \div (5x^2 - 10x)$

5. $(5x - 3)^2$ **6.** $(5x^2 - 14x - 3) + (5x + 1)$

7. $(2x^4 - 3x^2 + 5x - 2) \div (x + 2)$ **8.** $(4x - 1)(x^2 - 3x - 2)$

FACTORING STRATEGIES

The key to proficiency in factoring polynomials is to practice until you are comfortable with each technique. A strategy for factoring polynomials completely is given next.

Factoring a Polynomial

Step 1: Are there any common factors? If so, factor out the greatest common factor.

Step 2: How many terms are in the polynomial?

    a. If there are *two* terms, decide if one of the following formulas may be applied:

       i. Difference of two squares: $a^2 - b^2 = (a - b)(a + b)$

       ii. Difference of two cubes: $a^3 - b^3 = (a - b)(a^2 + ab + b^2)$

      iii. Sum of two cubes: $a^3 + b^3 = (a + b)(a^2 - ab + b^2)$

    b. If there are *three* terms, try one of the following:

       i. Perfect square trinomial: $a^2 + 2ab + b^2 = (a + b)^2$

$$a^2 - 2ab + b^2 = (a - b)^2$$

      ii. If not a perfect square trinomial, factor by using the methods presented in Section 5.5.

    c. If there are *four* or more terms, try factoring by grouping.

Step 3: See whether any factors in the factored polynomial can be factored further.

A few examples are worked for you below.

EXAMPLE 1

Factor each polynomial completely.

  a. $8a^2b - 4ab$ **b.** $36x^2 - 9$ **c.** $2x^2 - 5x - 7$

  d. $5p^2 + 5 + qp^2 + q$ **e.** $9x^2 + 24x + 16$ **f.** $y^2 + 25$

Solution

a. Step 1: The terms have a common factor of $4ab$, which we factor out.

$$8a^2b - 4ab = 4ab(2a - 1)$$

Step 2: There are two terms, but the binomial $2a - 1$ is not the difference of two squares or the sum or difference of two cubes.

Step 3: The factor $2a - 1$ cannot be factored further.

b. Step 1: Factor out a common factor of 9.

$$36x^2 - 9 = 9(4x^2 - 1)$$

Step 2: The factor $4x^2 - 1$ has two terms, and it is the difference of two squares.

$$9(4x^2 - 1) = 9(2x + 1)(2x - 1)$$

Step 3: No factor with more than one term can be factored further.

c. Step 1: The terms of $2x^2 - 5x - 7$ contain no common factor other than 1 or -1.

Step 2: There are three terms. The trinomial is not a perfect square, so we factor by methods from Section 5.6.

$$2x^2 - 5x - 7 = (2x - 7)(x + 1)$$

Step 3: No factor with more than one term can be factored further.

d. Step 1: There is no common factor of all terms of $5p^2 + 5 + qp^2 + q$.

Step 2: The polynomial has four terms, so try factoring by grouping.

$$\begin{aligned} 5p^2 + 5 + qp^2 + q &= (5p^2 + 5) + (qp^2 + q) && \text{Group the terms.}\\ &= 5(p^2 + 1) + q(p^2 + 1)\\ &= (p^2 + 1)(5 + q) \end{aligned}$$

Step 3: No factor can be factored further.

e. Step 1: The terms of $9x^2 + 24x + 16$ contain no common factor other than 1 or -1.

Step 2: The trinomial $9x^2 + 24x + 16$ is a perfect square trinomial, and $9x^2 + 24x + 16 = (3x + 4)^2$.

Step 3: No factor can be factored further.

f. Step 1: There is no common factor of $y^2 + 25$ other than 1.

Step 2: This binomial is the sum of two squares and is prime.

Step 3: The binomial $y^2 + 25$ cannot be factored further.

EXAMPLE 2

Factor each completely.

a. $27a^3 - b^3$ **b.** $3n^2m^4 - 48m^6$ **c.** $2x^2 - 12x + 18 - 2z^2$

d. $8x^4y^2 + 125xy^2$ **e.** $(x - 5)^2 - 49y^2$

Solution **a.** This binomial is the difference of two cubes.

$$\begin{aligned} 27a^3 - b^3 &= (3a)^3 - b^3\\ &= (3a - b)[(3a)^2 + (3a)(b) + b^2]\\ &= (3a - b)(9a^2 + 3ab + b^2) \end{aligned}$$

b. $\begin{aligned}[t] 3n^2m^4 - 48m^6 &= 3m^4(n^2 - 16m^2) && \text{Factor out the GCF, } 3m^4.\\ &= 3m^4(n + 4m)(n - 4m) && \text{Factor the difference of squares.} \end{aligned}$

c. $\begin{aligned}[t] 2x^2 - 12x + 18 - 2z^2 &= 2(x^2 - 6x + 9 - z^2) && \text{The GCF is 2.}\\ &= 2[(x^2 - 6x + 9) - z^2] && \text{Group the first three terms together.}\\ &= 2[(x - 3)^2 - z^2] && \text{Factor the perfect square trinomial.}\\ &= 2[(x - 3) + z][(x - 3) - z] && \text{Factor the difference of squares.}\\ &= 2(x - 3 + z)(x - 3 - z) \end{aligned}$

d. $8x^4y^2 + 125xy^2 = xy^2(8x^3 + 125)$ The GCF is xy^2.

$$= xy^2[(2x)^3 + 5^3]$$
$$= xy^2(2x + 5)[(2x)^2 - (2x)(5) + 5^2]$$ Factor the sum of cubes.
$$= xy^2(2x + 5)(4x^2 - 10x + 25)$$

e. This binomial is the difference of squares.

$$(x - 5)^2 - 49y^2 = (x - 5)^2 - (7y)^2$$
$$= [(x - 5) + 7y][(x - 5) - 7y]$$
$$= (x - 5 + 7y)(x - 5 - 7y)$$

Factor completely.

9. $x^2 - 8x + 16 - y^2$ **10.** $12x^2 - 22x - 20$ **11.** $x^4 - x$

12. $(2x + 1)^2 - 3(2x + 1) + 2$ **13.** $14x^2y - 2xy$ **14.** $24ab^2 - 6ab$

15. $4x^2 - 16$ **16.** $9x^2 - 81$ **17.** $3x^2 - 8x - 11$

18. $5x^2 - 2x - 3$ **19.** $4x^2 + 8x - 12$ **20.** $6x^2 - 6x - 12$

21. $4x^2 + 36x + 81$ **22.** $25x^2 + 40x + 16$ **23.** $8x^3 + 125y^3$

24. $27x^3 - 64y^3$ **25.** $64x^2y^3 - 8x^2$ **26.** $27x^5y^4 - 216x^2y$

27. $(x + 5)^3 + y^3$ **28.** $(y - 1)^3 + 27x^3$ **29.** $(5a - 3)^2 - 6(5a - 3) + 9$

30. $(4r + 1)^2 + 8(4r + 1) + 16$ **31.** $7x^2 - 63x$ **32.** $20x^2 + 23x + 6$

33. $ab - 6a + 7b - 42$

34. $20x^2 - 220x + 600$

35. $x^4 - 1$

36. $15x^2 - 20x$

37. $10x^2 - 7x - 33$

38. $45m^3n^3 - 27m^2n^2$

39. $5a^3b^3 - 50a^3b$

40. $x^4 + x$

41. $16x^2 + 25$

42. $20x^3 + 20y^3$

43. $10x^3 - 210x^2 + 1100x$

44. $9y^2 - 42y + 49$

45. $64a^3b^4 - 27a^3b$

46. $y^4 - 16$

47. $2x^3 - 54$

48. $2sr + 10s - r - 5$

49. $3y^5 - 5y^4 + 6y - 10$

50. $64a^2 + b^2$

51. $100z^3 + 100$

52. $250x^4 - 16x$

53. $4b^2 - 36b + 81$

54. $2a^5 - a^4 + 6a - 3$

55. $(y - 6)^2 + 3(y - 6) + 2$

56. $(c + 2)^2 - 6(c + 2) + 5$

△**57.** Express the area of the shaded region
as a polynomial. Factor the polynomial
completely.

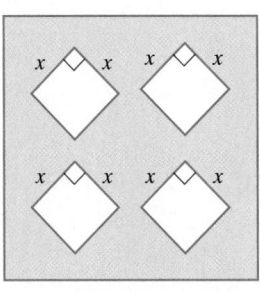

5.8 SOLVING EQUATIONS BY FACTORING AND PROBLEM SOLVING

Objectives

1. Solve polynomial equations by factoring.
2. Solve problems that can be modeled by polynomial equations.
3. Find the x-intercepts of a polynomial function.

1   In this section, your efforts to learn factoring start to pay off. We use factoring to solve polynomial equations, which in turn helps us solve problems that can be modeled by polynomial equations and also helps us sketch the graph of polynomial functions.

A **polynomial equation** is the result of setting two polynomials equal to each other. Examples of polynomial equations are

$$3x^3 - 2x^2 = x^2 + 2x - 1 \qquad 2.6x + 7 = -1.3 \qquad -5x^2 - 5 = -9x^2 - 2x + 1$$

A polynomial equation is in **standard form** if one side of the equation is 0. In standard form the polynomial equations above are

$$3x^3 - 3x^2 - 2x + 1 = 0 \qquad 2.6x + 8.3 = 0 \qquad 4x^2 + 2x - 6 = 0$$

The degree of a simplified polynomial equation in standard form is the same as the highest degree of any of its terms. A polynomial equation of degree 2 is also called a **quadratic equation**.

A solution of a polynomial equation in one variable is a value of the variable that makes the equation true. The method presented in this section for solving polynomial equations is called the **factoring method**. This method is based on the **zero-factor property**.

Zero-Factor Property

If a and b are real numbers and $a \cdot b = 0$, then $a = 0$ or $b = 0$. This property is true for three or more factors also.

In other words, if the product of two or more real numbers is zero, then at least one number must be zero.

EXAMPLE 1

Solve $(x + 2)(x - 6) = 0$.

Solution   By the zero-factor property, $(x + 2)(x - 6) = 0$ only if $x + 2 = 0$ or $x - 6 = 0$.

$$x + 2 = 0 \quad \text{or} \quad x - 6 = 0 \quad \text{\small Apply the zero-factor property.}$$
$$x = -2 \quad \text{or} \quad x = 6 \quad \text{\small Solve each linear equation.}$$

To check, let $x = -2$ and then let $x = 6$ in the original equation.

Let $x = -2$.	Let $x = 6$.
Then $(x + 2)(x - 6) = 0$	Then $(x + 2)(x - 6) = 0$
becomes $(-2 + 2)(-2 - 6) \stackrel{?}{=} 0$	becomes $(6 + 2)(6 - 6) \stackrel{?}{=} 0$
$(0)(-8) \stackrel{?}{=} 0$	$(8)(0) \stackrel{?}{=} 0$
$0 = 0$ True.	$0 = 0$ True.

Both -2 and 6 check, so they are both solutions. The solution set is $\{-2, 6\}$.

EXAMPLE 2

Solve $2x^2 + 9x - 5 = 0$.

Solution   To use the zero-factor property, one side of the equation must be 0, and the other side must be in factored form.

$$2x^2 + 9x - 5 = 0$$

$$(2x - 1)(x + 5) = 0 \qquad \text{Factor.}$$

$$2x - 1 = 0 \quad \text{or} \quad x + 5 = 0 \quad \text{Set each factor equal to zero.}$$

$$2x = 1$$

$$x = \frac{1}{2} \quad \text{or} \quad x = -5 \quad \text{Solve each linear equation.}$$

The solutions are -5 and $\frac{1}{2}$. To check, let $x = \frac{1}{2}$ in the original equation; then let $x = -5$ in the original equation. The solution set is $\left\{-5, \frac{1}{2}\right\}$.

Solving Polynomial Equations by Factoring

Step 1: Write the equation in standard form so that one side of the equation is 0.

Step 2: Factor the polynomial completely.

Step 3: Set each factor containing a variable equal to 0.

Step 4: Solve the resulting equations.

Step 5: Check each solution in the original equation.

Since it is not always possible to factor a polynomial, not all polynomial equations can be solved by factoring. Other methods of solving polynomial equations are presented in Chapter 8.

EXAMPLE 3

Solve $x(2x - 7) = 4$.

Solution First, write the equation in standard form; then, factor.

$$x(2x - 7) = 4$$

$$2x^2 - 7x = 4 \qquad \text{Multiply.}$$

$$2x^2 - 7x - 4 = 0 \qquad \text{Write in standard form.}$$

$$(2x + 1)(x - 4) = 0 \qquad \text{Factor.}$$

$$2x + 1 = 0 \quad \text{or} \quad x - 4 = 0 \quad \text{Set each factor equal to zero.}$$

$$2x = -1 \qquad \text{Solve.}$$

$$x = -\frac{1}{2} \quad \text{or} \quad x = 4$$

The solutions are $-\dfrac{1}{2}$ and 4. Check both solutions in the original equation. ⬭

> **Helpful Hint**
> To apply the zero-factor property, one side of the equation must be 0, and the other side of the equation must be factored. To solve the equation $x(2x - 7) = 4$, for example, you may **not** set each factor equal to 4.

EXAMPLE 4

Solve $3(x^2 + 4) + 5 = -6(x^2 + 2x) + 13$.

Solution Rewrite the equation so that one side is 0.

$$3(x^2 + 4) + 5 = -6(x^2 + 2x) + 13.$$

$$3x^2 + 12 + 5 = -6x^2 - 12x + 13 \qquad \text{Apply the distributive property.}$$

$$9x^2 + 12x + 4 = 0 \qquad \text{Rewrite the equation so that one side is } 0.$$

$$(3x + 2)(3x + 2) = 0 \qquad \text{Factor.}$$

$$3x + 2 = 0 \quad \text{or} \quad 3x + 2 = 0 \quad \text{Set each factor equal to } 0.$$

$$3x = -2 \quad \text{or} \quad 3x = -2$$

$$x = -\frac{2}{3} \quad \text{or} \quad x = -\frac{2}{3} \quad \text{Solve each equation.}$$

The solution is $-\dfrac{2}{3}$. Check by substituting $-\dfrac{2}{3}$ into the original equation. ⬭

If the equation contains fractions, we clear the equation of fractions as a first step.

EXAMPLE 5

Solve $2x^2 = \dfrac{17}{3}x + 1$.

Solution

$$2x^2 = \frac{17}{3}x + 1$$

$$3(2x^2) = 3\left(\frac{17}{3}x + 1\right) \qquad \text{\textit{Clear the equation of fractions.}}$$

$$6x^2 = 17x + 3 \qquad \text{\textit{Apply the distributive property.}}$$

$$6x^2 - 17x - 3 = 0 \qquad \text{\textit{Rewrite the equation in standard form.}}$$

$$(6x + 1)(x - 3) = 0 \qquad \text{\textit{Factor.}}$$

$$6x + 1 = 0 \quad \text{or} \quad x - 3 = 0 \quad \text{\textit{Set each factor equal to zero.}}$$

$$6x = -1$$

$$x = -\frac{1}{6} \quad \text{or} \quad x = 3 \quad \text{\textit{Solve each equation.}}$$

The solutions are $-\dfrac{1}{6}$ and 3.

EXAMPLE 6

Solve $x^3 = 4x$.

Solution

$$x^3 = 4x$$

$$x^3 - 4x = 0 \qquad \text{\textit{Rewrite the equation so that one side is 0.}}$$

$$x(x^2 - 4) = 0 \qquad \text{\textit{Factor out the GCF, x.}}$$

$$x(x + 2)(x - 2) = 0 \qquad \text{\textit{Factor the difference of squares.}}$$

$$x = 0 \quad \text{or} \quad x + 2 = 0 \quad \text{or} \quad x - 2 = 0 \quad \text{\textit{Set each factor equal to 0.}}$$

$$x = 0 \quad \text{or} \quad x = -2 \quad \text{or} \quad x = 2 \quad \text{\textit{Solve each equation.}}$$

The solutions are $-2, 0$, and 2. Check by substituting into the original equation.

Notice that the *third*-degree equation of Example 6 yielded *three* solutions.

EXAMPLE 7

Solve $x^3 + 5x^2 = x + 5$.

Solution   First, write the equation so that one side is 0.

$$x^3 + 5x^2 - x - 5 = 0$$

$$(x^3 - x) + (5x^2 - 5) = 0 \qquad \text{\textit{Factor by grouping.}}$$

$$x(x^2 - 1) + 5(x^2 - 1) = 0$$

$$(x^2 - 1)(x + 5) = 0$$

$$(x + 1)(x - 1)(x + 5) = 0 \qquad \text{\textit{Factor the difference of squares.}}$$

$$x + 1 = 0 \quad \text{or} \quad x - 1 = 0 \quad \text{or} \quad x + 5 = 0 \quad \text{\textit{Set each factor equal to 0.}}$$

$$x = -1 \quad \text{or} \quad x = 1 \quad \text{or} \quad x = -5 \quad \text{\textit{Solve each equation.}}$$

The solutions are $-5, -1$, and 1. Check in the original equation.

✔ **CONCEPT CHECK**

Which solution strategies are incorrect? Why?

a. Solve $(y - 2)(y + 2) = 4$ by setting each factor equal to 4.
b. Solve $(x + 1)(x + 3) = 0$ by setting each factor equal to 0.
c. Solve $z^2 + 5z + 6 = 0$ by factoring $z^2 + 5z + 6$ and setting each factor equal to 0.
d. Solve $x^2 + 6x + 8 = 10$ by factoring $x^2 + 6x + 8$ and setting each factor equal to 0.

2   Some problems may be modeled by polynomial equations. To solve these problems, we use the same problem-solving steps that were introduced in Section 2.2. When solving these problems, keep in mind that a solution of an equation that models a problem is not always a solution to the problem. For example, a person's weight or the length of a side of a geometric figure is always a positive number. Discard solutions that do not make sense as solutions of the problem.

EXAMPLE 8

FINDING THE RETURN TIME OF A ROCKET

An Alpha III model rocket is launched from the ground with an A8–3 engine. Without a parachute, the height of the rocket h at time t seconds is approximated by the equation,

$$h = -16t^2 + 144t$$

Find how long it takes the rocket to return to the ground.

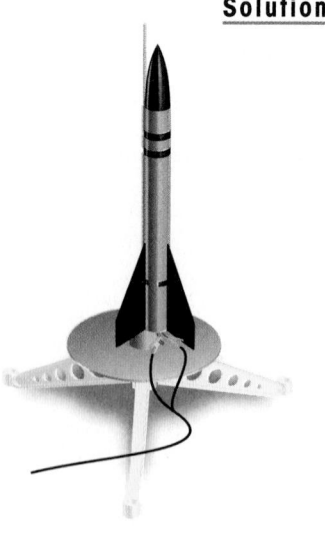

Solution   **1.** UNDERSTAND.   Read and reread the problem. The equation $h = -16t^2 + 144t$ models the height of the rocket. Familiarize yourself with this equation by finding a few values.

When $t = 1$ second, the height of the rocket is

$$h = -16(1)^2 + 144(1) = 128 \text{ feet}$$

When $t = 2$ seconds, the height of the rocket is

$$h = -16(2)^2 + 144(2) = 224 \text{ feet}$$

2. TRANSLATE.   To find how long it takes the rocket to return to the ground, we want to know what value of t makes the height h equal to 0. That is, we want to solve $h = 0$.

$$-16t^2 + 144t = 0$$

3. SOLVE   the quadratic equation by factoring.

$$-16t^2 + 144t = 0$$
$$-16t(t - 9) = 0$$
$$-16t = 0 \quad \text{or} \quad t - 9 = 0$$
$$t = 0 \qquad\qquad t = 9$$

4. INTERPRET.   The height h is 0 feet at time 0 seconds (when the rocket is launched) and at time 9 seconds.

Concept Check Answer:
a and d; the zero-factor property works only if one side of the equation is 0

Check: See that the height of the rocket at 9 seconds equals 0.

$$h = -16(9)^2 + 144(9) = -1296 + 1296 = 0$$

State: The rocket returns to the ground 9 seconds after it is launched.

Some of the exercises at the end of this section make use of the **Pythagorean theorem.** Before we review this theorem, recall that a **right triangle** is a triangle that contains a 90° angle, or right angle. The **hypotenuse** of a right triangle is the side opposite the right angle and is the longest side of the triangle. The **legs** of a right triangle are the other sides of the triangle.

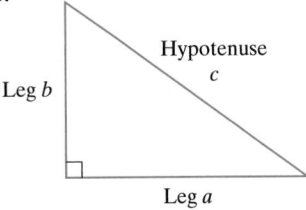

Pythagorean Theorem

In a right triangle, the sum of the squares of the lengths of the two legs is equal to the square of the length of the hypotenuse.

$$(\text{leg})^2 + (\text{leg})^2 = (\text{hypotenuse})^2 \qquad \text{or} \qquad a^2 + b^2 = c^2$$

△ **EXAMPLE 9**

USING THE PYTHAGOREAN THEOREM

While framing an addition to an existing home, Kim Menzies, a carpenter, used the Pythagorean theorem to determine whether a wall was "square"—that is, whether the wall formed a right angle with the floor. He used a triangle whose sides are three consecutive integers. Find a right triangle whose sides are three consecutive integers.

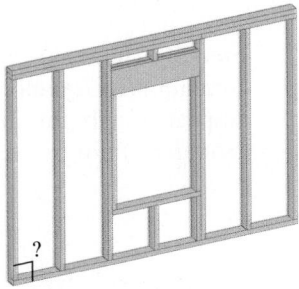

Solution **1.** UNDERSTAND.   Read and reread the problem.

Let x, $x + 1$, and $x + 2$ be three consecutive integers. Since these integers represent lengths of the sides of a right triangle, we have

$$x = \text{one leg}$$
$$x + 1 = \text{other leg}$$
$$x + 2 = \text{hypotenuse (longest side)}$$

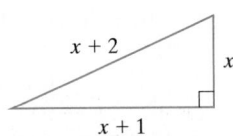

2. TRANSLATE. By the Pythagorean theorem, we have

In words:
$(\text{leg})^2$ + $(\text{leg})^2$ = $(\text{hypotenuse})^2$
↓ ↓ ↓

Translate:
$(x)^2$ + $(x + 1)^2$ = $(x + 2)^2$

3. SOLVE the equation.

$$x^2 + (x + 1)^2 = (x + 2)^2$$

$$x^2 + x^2 + 2x + 1 = x^2 + 4x + 4 \qquad \text{Multiply.}$$

$$2x^2 + 2x + 1 = x^2 + 4x + 4$$

$$x^2 - 2x - 3 = 0 \qquad \text{Write in standard form.}$$

$$(x - 3)(x + 1) = 0$$

$$x - 3 = 0 \quad \text{or} \quad x + 1 = 0$$

$$x = 3 \qquad\qquad x = -1$$

4. INTERPRET. Discard $x = -1$ since length cannot be negative. If $x = 3$, then $x + 1 = 4$ and $x + 2 = 5$.

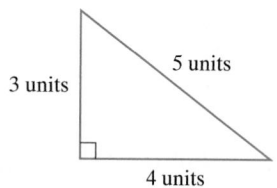

3 units | 5 units | 4 units

Check: To check, see that $(\text{leg})^2 + (\text{leg})^2 = (\text{hypotenuse})^2$

$$3^2 + 4^2 = 5^2$$

$$9 + 16 = 25 \quad \text{True.}$$

State: The lengths of the sides of the right triangle are 3, 4, and 5 units. Kim used this information, for example, by marking off lengths of 3 and 4 feet on the floor and framing respectively. If the diagonal length between these marks was 5 feet, the wall was "square." If not, adjustments were made.

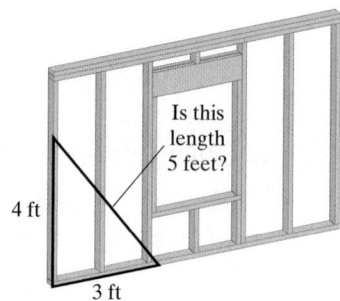

Is this length 5 feet?

4 ft

3 ft

3   Recall that to find the x-intercepts of the graph of a function, let $f(x) = 0$, or $y = 0$, and solve for x. This fact gives us a visual interpretation of the results of this section.

From Example 1, we know that the solutions of the equation $(x + 2)(x - 6) = 0$ are -2 and 6. These solutions give us important information about the related polynomial function $p(x) = (x + 2)(x - 6)$. We know that when x is -2 or when x is 6, the value of $p(x)$ is 0.

$$p(x) = (x + 2)(x - 6)$$
$$p(-2) = (-2 + 2)(-2 - 6) = (0)(-8) = 0$$
$$p(6) = (6 + 2)(6 - 6) = (8)(0) = 0$$

Thus, we know that $(-2, 0)$ and $(6, 0)$ are the x-intercepts of the graph of $p(x)$.

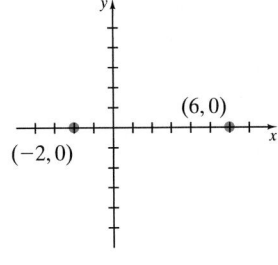

We also know that the graph of $p(x)$ does not cross the x-axis at any other point. For this reason, and the fact that $p(x) = (x + 2)(x - 6) = x^2 - 4x - 12$ has degree 2, we conclude that the graph of p must look something like one of these two graphs:

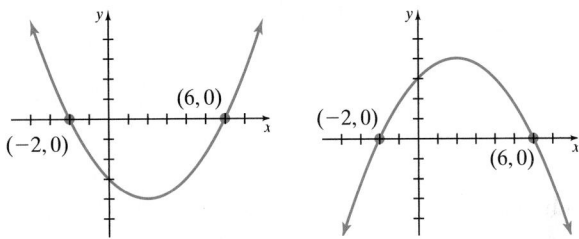

In a later chapter, we explore these graphs more fully. For the moment, know that the solutions of a polynomial equation are the x-intercepts of the graph of the related function and that the x-intercepts of the graph of a polynomial function are the solutions of the related polynomial equation. These values are also called **roots**, or **zeros**, of a polynomial function.

EXAMPLE 10

MATCH EACH FUNCTION WITH ITS GRAPH

$$f(x) = (x - 3)(x + 2) \qquad g(x) = x(x + 2)(x - 2) \qquad h(x) = (x - 2)(x + 2)(x - 1)$$

A 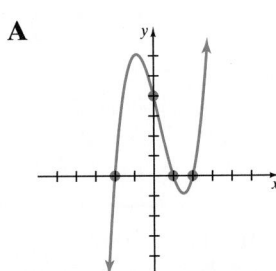   **B** 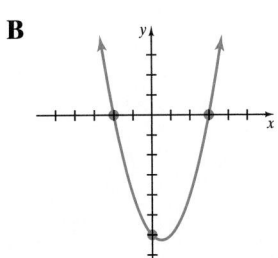   **C**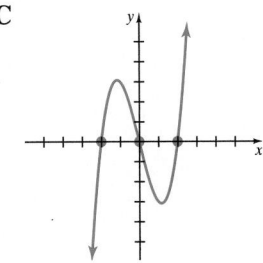

Solution   The graph of the function $f(x) = (x - 3)(x + 2)$ has two x-intercepts, $(3, 0)$ and $(-2, 0)$, because the equation $0 = (x - 3)(x + 2)$ has two solutions, 3 and -2.

The graph of $f(x)$ is graph B.

The graph of the function $g(x) = x(x + 2)(x - 2)$ has three x-intercepts $(0, 0)$, $(-2, 0)$, and $(2, 0)$, because the equation $0 = x(x + 2)(x - 2)$ has three solutions, 0, -2, and 2.

The graph of $g(x)$ is graph C.

The graph of the function $h(x) = (x - 2)(x + 2)(x - 1)$ has three x-intercepts, $(-2, 0)$, $(1, 0)$, and $(2, 0)$, because the equation $0 = (x - 2)(x + 2)(x - 1)$ has three solutions, -2, 1, and 2.

The graph of $h(x)$ is graph A.

Graphing Calculator Explorations

We can use a graphing calculator to approximate real number solutions of any quadratic equation in standard form, whether the associated polynomial is factorable or not. For example, let's solve the quadratic equation $x^2 - 2x - 4 = 0$. The solutions of this equation will be the x-intercepts of the graph of the function $f(x) = x^2 - 2x - 4$. (Recall that to find x-intercepts, we let $f(x) = 0$, or $y = 0$.) When we use a standard window, the graph of this function looks like this.

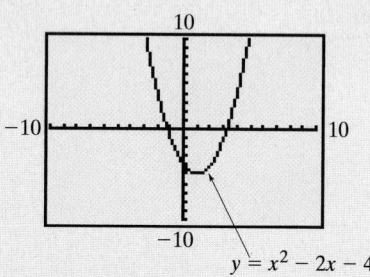

$$y = x^2 - 2x - 4$$

The graph appears to have one x-intercept between -2 and -1 and one between 3 and 4. To find the x-intercept between 3 and 4 to the nearest hundredth, we can use a zero feature, a Zoom feature, which magnifies a portion of the graph around the cursor, or we can redefine our window. If we redefine our window to

Xmin = 2	Ymin = -1
Xmax = 5	Ymax = 1
Xscl = 1	Yscl = 1

the resulting screen is

By using the Trace feature, we can now see that one of the intercepts is between 3.21 and 3.25. To approximate to the nearest hundredth, Zoom again or redefine the window to

Xmin = 3.2	Ymin = -0.1
Xmax = 3.3	Ymax = 0.1
Xscl = 1	Yscl = 1

If we use the Trace feature again, we see that, to the nearest hundredth, the x-intercept is 3.24. By repeating this process, we can approximate the other x-intercept to be -1.24.

To check, find $f(3.24)$ and $f(-1.24)$. Both of these values should be close to 0. (They will not be exactly 0 since we approximated these solutions.)

$$f(3.24) = 0.0176 \quad \text{and} \quad f(-1.24) = 0.0176$$

Solve each of these quadratic equations by graphing a related function and approximating the x-intercepts to the nearest thousandth.

1. $x^2 + 3x - 2 = 0$
2. $5x^2 - 7x + 1 = 0$
3. $2.3x^2 - 4.4x - 5.6 = 0$
4. $0.2x^2 + 6.2x + 2.1 = 0$
5. $0.09x^2 - 0.13x - 0.08 = 0$
6. $x^2 + 0.08x - 0.01 = 0$

STUDY SKILLS REMINDER

Continue your outline started in Section 2.1. Write how to recognize and how to solve quadratic and higher degree equations by factoring in your own words. For example:

Solving Equations and Inequalities

I. Equations

    A. Linear equations (Sec. 2.1)

    B. Absolute value equations (Sec. 2.6)

    C. Quadratic and Higher Degree Equations–Recognize: *highest power on variable in equation is at least 2 when written in standard form (one side 0)*–Solve: write in standard form and try to factor the polynomial on one side of the equation. If it factors, set each factor equal to 0.

II. Inequalities

    A. Linear inequalities (Sec. 2.4)

    B. Compound inequalities (Sec. 2.5)

    C. Absolute value inequalities (Sec. 2.7)

See Appendix A for summary exercises.

MENTAL MATH

Solve each equation for the variable. See Example 1.

1. $(x - 3)(x + 5) = 0$
2. $(y + 5)(y + 3) = 0$
3. $(z - 3)(z + 7) = 0$
4. $(c - 2)(c - 4) = 0$
5. $x(x - 9) = 0$
6. $w(w + 7) = 0$

EXERCISE SET 5.8

STUDY GUIDE/SSM CD/VIDEO PH MATH TUTOR CENTER MathXL®Tutorials ON CD MathXL® MyMathLab®

Solve each equation. See Example 1.

 1. $(x + 3)(3x - 4) = 0$

2. $(5x + 1)(x - 2) = 0$

3. $3(2x - 5)(4x + 3) = 0$

4. $8(3x - 4)(2x - 7) = 0$

Solve each equation. See Examples 2 through 5.

5. $x^2 + 11x + 24 = 0$

6. $y^2 - 10y + 24 = 0$

7. $12x^2 + 5x - 2 = 0$

8. $3y^2 - y - 14 = 0$

9. $z^2 + 9 = 10z$

10. $n^2 + n = 72$

 11. $x(5x + 2) = 3$

12. $n(2n - 3) = 2$

13. $x^2 - 6x = x(8 + x)$

14. $n(3 + n) = n^2 + 4n$

15. $\dfrac{z^2}{6} - \dfrac{z}{2} - 3 = 0$

16. $\dfrac{c^2}{20} - \dfrac{c}{4} + \dfrac{1}{5} = 0$

17. $\dfrac{x^2}{2} + \dfrac{x}{20} = \dfrac{1}{10}$

18. $\dfrac{y^2}{30} = \dfrac{y}{15} + \dfrac{1}{2}$

19. $\dfrac{4t^2}{5} = \dfrac{t}{5} + \dfrac{3}{10}$

20. $\dfrac{5x^2}{6} - \dfrac{7x}{2} + \dfrac{2}{3} = 0$

Solve each equation. See Examples 6 and 7.

21. $(x + 2)(x - 7)(3x - 8) = 0$

22. $(4x + 9)(x - 4)(x + 1) = 0$

23. $y^3 = 9y$

24. $n^3 = 16n$

 25. $x^3 - x = 2x^2 - 2$

26. $m^3 = m^2 + 12m$

27. Explain how solving $2(x - 3)(x - 1) = 0$ differs from solving $2x(x - 3)(x - 1) = 0$.

28. Explain why the zero-factor property works for more than two numbers whose product is 0.

MIXED PRACTICE

Solve each equation.

29. $(2x + 7)(x - 10) = 0$

30. $(x + 4)(5x - 1) = 0$

31. $3x(x - 5) = 0$

32. $4x(2x + 3) = 0$

33. $x^2 - 2x - 15 = 0$

34. $x^2 + 6x - 7 = 0$

35. $12x^2 + 2x - 2 = 0$

36. $8x^2 + 13x + 5 = 0$

37. $w^2 - 5w = 36$

38. $x^2 + 32 = 12x$

39. $25x^2 - 40x + 16 = 0$

40. $9n^2 + 30n + 25 = 0$

41. $2r^3 + 6r^2 = 20r$

42. $-2t^3 = 108t - 30t^2$

43. $z(5z - 4)(z + 3) = 0$

44. $2r(r + 3)(5r - 4) = 0$

 45. $2z(z + 6) = 2z^2 + 12z - 8$

46. $3c^2 - 8c + 2 = c(3c - 8)$

47. $(x - 1)(x + 4) = 24$

48. $(2x - 1)(x + 2) = -3$

49. $\dfrac{x^2}{4} - \dfrac{5}{2}x + 6 = 0$

50. $\dfrac{x^2}{18} + \dfrac{x}{2} + 1 = 0$

51. $y^2 + \dfrac{1}{4} = -y$

52. $\dfrac{x^2}{10} + \dfrac{5}{2} = x$

53. $y^3 + 4y^2 = 9y + 36$

54. $x^3 + 5x^2 = x + 5$

55. $2x^3 = 50x$

56. $m^5 = 36m^3$

57. $x^2 + (x + 1)^2 = 61$

58. $y^2 + (y + 2)^2 = 34$

59. $m^2(3m - 2) = m$

60. $x^2(5x + 3) = 26x$

61. $3x^2 = -x$

62. $y^2 = -5y$

63. $x(x - 3) = x^2 + 5x + 7$

64. $z^2 - 4z + 10 = z(z - 5)$

65. $3(t - 8) + 2t = 7 + t$

66. $7c - 2(3c + 1) = 5(4 - 2c)$

67. $-3(x - 4) + x = 5(3 - x)$

68. $-4(a + 1) - 3a = -7(2a - 3)$

69. Which solution strategies are incorrect? Why?

    a. Solve $(y - 2)(y + 2) = 4$ by setting each factor equal to 4.

    b. Solve $(x + 1)(x + 3) = 0$ by setting each factor equal to 0.

    c. Solve $z^2 + 5z + 6 = 0$ by factoring $z^2 + 5z + 6$ and setting each factor equal to 0.

    d. Solve $x^2 + 6x + 8 = 10$ by factoring $x^2 + 6x + 8$ and setting each factor equal to 0.

70. Describe two ways a linear equation differs from a quadratic equation.

olve. See Examples 8 and 9.

. One number exceeds another by five, and their product is 66. Find the numbers.

. If the sum of two numbers is 4 and their product is $\frac{15}{4}$, find the numbers.

. An electrician needs to run a cable from the top of a 60-foot tower to a transmitter box located 45 feet away from the base of the tower. Find how long he should make the cable.

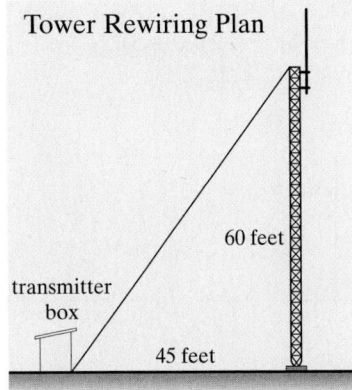

Tower Rewiring Plan

60 feet

transmitter box

45 feet

4. A stereo system installer needs to run speaker wire along the two diagonals of a rectangular room whose dimensions are 40 feet by 75 feet. Find how much speaker wire she needs.

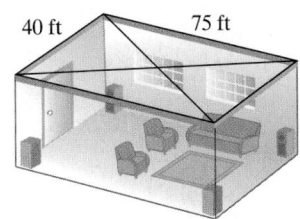

40 ft   75 ft

5. If the cost, $C(x)$, for manufacturing x units of a certain product is given by $C(x) = x^2 - 15x + 50$, find the number of units manufactured at a cost of $9500.

6. Determine whether any three consecutive integers represent the lengths of the sides of a right triangle.

7. The shorter leg of a right triangle is 3 centimeters less than the other leg. Find the length of the two legs if the hypotenuse is 15 centimeters.

8. The longer leg of a right triangle is 4 feet longer than the other leg. Find the length of the two legs if the hypotenuse is 20 feet.

△ 79. Marie Mulroney has a rectangular board 12 inches by 16 inches around which she wants to put a uniform border of shells. If she has enough shells for a border whose area is 128 square inches, determine the width of the border.

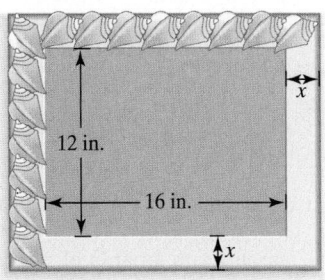

12 in.

16 in.

x

x

△ 80. A gardener has a rose garden that measures 30 feet by 20 feet. He wants to put a uniform border of pine bark around the outside of the garden. Find how wide the border should be if he has enough pine bark to cover 336 square feet.

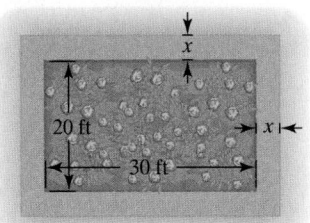

x

20 ft

30 ft

x

81. While hovering near the top of Ribbon Falls in Yosemite National Park at 1600 feet, a helicopter pilot accidentally drops his sunglasses. The height $h(t)$ of the sunglasses after t seconds is given by the polynomial function

$$h(t) = -16t^2 + 1600$$

When will the sunglasses hit the ground?

82. After t seconds, the height $h(t)$ of a model rocket launched from the ground into the air is given by the function

$$h(t) = -16t^2 + 80t$$

Find how long it takes the rocket to reach a height of 96 feet.

△ **83.** The floor of a shed has an area of 90 square feet. The floor is in the shape of a rectangle whose length is 3 feet less than twice the width. Find the length and the width of the floor of the shed.

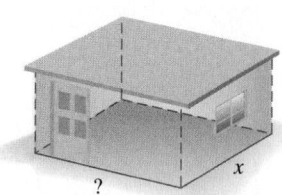

△ **84.** A vegetable garden with an area of 200 square feet is to be fertilized. If the length of the garden is 1 foot less than three times the width, find the dimensions of the garden.

85. The function $W(x) = 0.5x^2$ gives the number of servings of wedding cake that can be obtained from a two-layer x-inch square wedding cake tier. What size square wedding cake tier is needed to serve 50 people? (*Source:* Based on data from the *Wilton 2000 Yearbook of Cake Decorating*)

86. Use the function in Exercise 85 to determine what size wedding cake tier is needed to serve 200 people.

87. Suppose that a movie is being filmed in New York City. An action shot requires an object to be thrown upward with an initial velocity of 80 feet per second off the top of 1 Madison Square Plaza, a height of 576 feet. The height $h(t)$ in feet of the object after t seconds is given by the function

$$h(t) = -16t^2 + 80t + 576.$$

Determine how long before the object strikes the ground. (See Exercise 91, Section 5.5) (*Source: The World Almanac, 2001*)

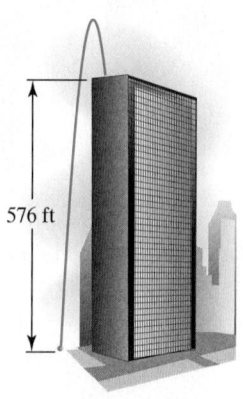

576 ft

88. Suppose that an object is thrown upward with an initial velocity of 64 feet per second off the edge of a 960-foot-cliff. The height $h(t)$ in feet of the object after t seconds is given by the function

$$h(t) = -16t^2 + 64t + 960$$

Determine how long before the object strikes the ground. (See Exercise 92, Section 5.5)

Match each polynomial function with its graph (A–F). See Example 10.

89. $f(x) = (x - 2)(x + 5)$

90. $g(x) = (x + 1)(x - 6)$

91. $h(x) = x(x + 3)(x - 3)$

92. $F(x) = (x + 1)(x - 2)(x + 5)$

93. $G(x) = 2x^2 + 9x + 4$

94. $H(x) = 2x^2 - 7x - 4$

A

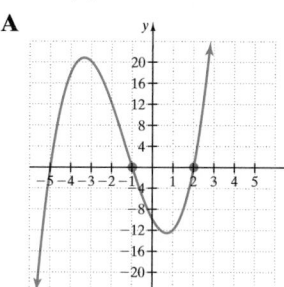

B

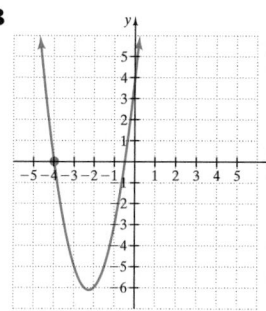

C

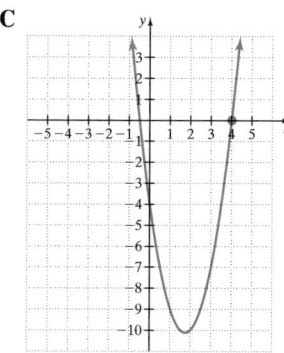

D

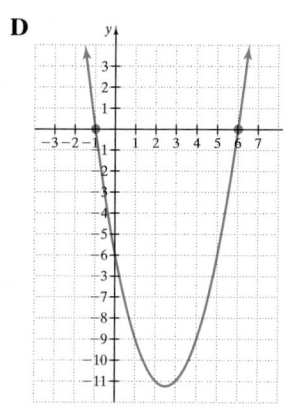

E

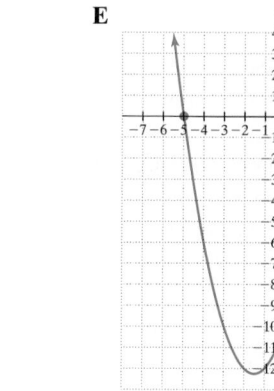

F

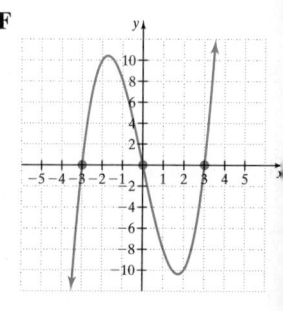

rite the x- and y-intercepts for each graph and determine whether e graph is the graph of a function. See Sections 3.1 and 3.2.

5.

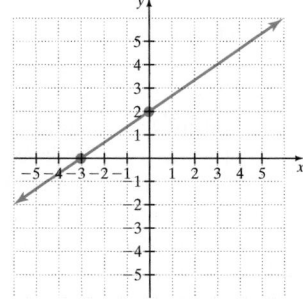

96.

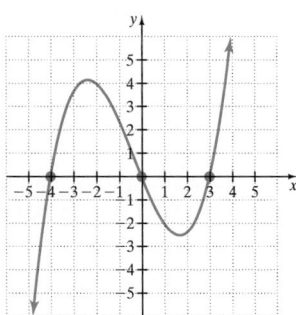

97.

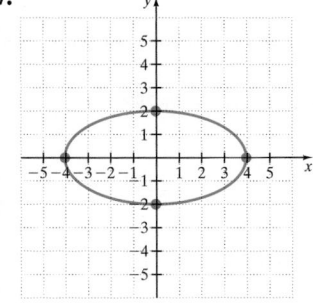

98.

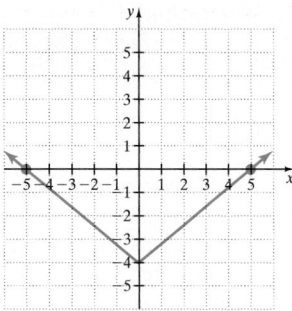

99. Draw a function with intercepts $(-3, 0)$, $(5, 0)$, and $(0, 4)$.

100. Draw a function with intercepts $(-7, 0)$, $\left(-\frac{1}{2}, 0\right)$, $(4, 0)$, and $(0, -1)$.

Concept Extensions

Solve.

101. $(x^2 + x - 6)(3x^2 - 14x - 5) = 0$

102. $(x^2 - 9)(x^2 + 8x + 16) = 0$

103. Is the following step correct? Why or why not?

$$x(x - 3) = 5$$
$$x = 5 \text{ or } x - 3 = 5$$

Write a quadratic equation that has the given numbers as solutions.

104. $5, 3$

105. $6, 7$

106. $-1, 2$

107. $4, -3$

CHAPTER 5 PROJECT

Investigating Earth's Water

Earth is covered by water. In fact, oceans cover nearly three-fourths of the surface of Earth. However, oceans aren't the only source of Earth's water. The melting of one of the other main sources of Earth's water, icecaps and glaciers, is expected to contribute to a global rise in ocean level due to global warming over the next 100 years. In this project, you will have the opportunity to investigate where Earth's water exists and how the ocean level will change. This project may be completed by working in groups or individually.

1. Refer to Table 1. Which accounts for more of Earth's water: groundwater or icecaps and glaciers?

2. Find the total volume of water that exists on planet Earth. Add this figure to the table.

3. Using the total you computed in Question 2, complete the percent column of the table. Discuss your findings.

Widespread industrialization during the nineteenth and twentieth centuries has led to an increase in the presence of carbon dioxide, methane, nitrous oxide, and chlorofluorocarbons in Earth's atmosphere. These so-called greenhouse gases are believed by some scientists to be responsible for an increase in the average global temperature of 0.2°C to 0.3°C in the last half of the twentieth century. If this global warming trend continues, one of its consequences may be a global increase in the level of the oceans. An overall increase in ocean level will be due to change in icecaps and glaciers, as well as thermal expansion. Higher global temperatures lead to warming in the top layers of the ocean causing the water to expand and elevate the sea level.

Table 2 lists each contributor to overall changes in ocean level along with a polynomial model describing the projected rise y (in centimeters) each is expected to contribute x years after 2000.

4. By 2020, how much will the ocean level have risen due to thermal expansion?

5. Using the polynomial models given in Table 2, find a single polynomial model that gives the overall rise in ocean level from 1990 to 2100.

6. Using your model from Question 5, find the projected overall increase in ocean level for
   a. 2025   b. 2050
   c. 2075   d. 2100

7. Discuss the impact of your findings in Question 6.

Table 1.   Where Earth's Water Exists

	Water Volume (cubic kilometers)	Percent
Atmosphere	1.3×10^4	
Average in stream channels	1.0×10^3	
Freshwater lakes	1.2×10^5	
Groundwater	8.3×10^6	
Icecaps and glaciers	2.9×10^7	
Oceans	1.32×10^9	
Saline lakes and inland seas	1.0×10^5	
Water in soil above groundwater	6.7×10^5	
Total		

(*Source:* Data from B.J. Skinner, *Earth Resources*, 2nd Ed., Prentice Hall, 1976)

Table 2.   Projections of Global Ocean Level Rise by Contributor, 1990–2100

Alpine glaciers:
$$y = 0.0006x^2 + 0.0936x + 0.8788$$

Greenland ice sheet:
$$y = 0.0004x^2 + 0.0164x + 0.1212$$

Antarctica ice sheet:
$$y = -0.0001x^2 - 0.0002x + 0.0076$$

Thermal expansion:
$$y = 0.0011x^2 + 0.1564x + 1.4545$$

(*Source:* Based on data from Frederick K. Lutgens, Edward J. Tarbuck, *The Atmosphere: An Introduction to Meteorology*, 7th Ed., Prentice Hall, 1998)

28. $\left(\dfrac{8p^6}{4p^4}\right)^{-2}$

29. $(-3x^{-2}y^2)^3$

30. $\left(\dfrac{x^{-5}y^{-3}}{z^3}\right)^{-5}$

31. $\dfrac{4^{-1}x^3yz}{x^{-2}yx^4}$

32. $(5xyz)^{-4}(x^{-2})^{-3}$

33. $\dfrac{2(3yz)^{-3}}{y^{-3}}$

Simplify each expression.

34. $x^{4a}(3x^{5a})^3$

35. $\dfrac{4y^{3x-3}}{2y^{2x+4}}$

Use scientific notation to find the quotient. Express each quotient in scientific notation.

36. $\dfrac{(0.00012)(144{,}000)}{0.0003}$

37. $\dfrac{(-0.00017)(0.00039)}{3000}$

Simplify. Use only positive exponents.

38. $\dfrac{27x^{-5}y^5}{18x^{-6}y^2}\cdot\dfrac{x^4y^{-2}}{x^{-2}y^3}$

39. $\dfrac{3x^5}{y^{-4}}\cdot\dfrac{(3xy^{-3})^{-2}}{(z^{-3})^{-4}}$

40. $\dfrac{(x^w)^2}{(x^{w-4})^{-2}}$

(5.3) Find the degree of each polynomial.

41. $x^2y - 3xy^3z + 5x + 7y$

42. $3x + 2$

Simplify by combining like terms.

43. $4x + 8x - 6x^2 - 6x^2y$

44. $-8xy^3 + 4xy^3 - 3x^3y$

Add or subtract as indicated.

45. $(3x + 7y) + (4x^2 - 3x + 7) + (y - 1)$

46. $(4x^2 - 6xy + 9y^2) - (8x^2 - 6xy - y^2)$

47. $(3x^2 - 4b + 28) + (9x^2 - 30) - (4x^2 - 6b + 20)$

48. Add $(9xy + 4x^2 + 18)$ and $(7xy - 4x^3 - 9x)$.

49. Subtract $(x - 7)$ from the sum of $(3x^2y - 7xy - 4)$ and $(9x^2y + x)$.

50. $x^2 - 5x + 7$
$\quad\underline{-(x + 4)}$

51. $x^3\quad + 2xy^2 - y$
$\quad\underline{+ (x - 4xy^2\ -7)}$

If $P(x) = 9x^2 - 7x + 8$, find the following.

52. $P(6)$

53. $P(-2)$

54. $P(-3)$

If $P(x) = 2x - 1$ and $Q(x) = x^2 + 2x - 5$, find the following.

55. $P(x) + Q(x)$

56. $2[P(x)] - Q(x)$

△ **57.** Find the perimeter of the rectangle.

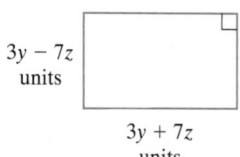

$x^2y + 5$
cm

$2x^2y - 6x + 1$
cm

(5.4) Multiply.

58. $-6x(4x^2 - 6x + 1)$

59. $-4ab^2(3ab^3 + 7ab + 1)$

60. $(x - 4)(2x + 9)$

61. $(-3xa + 4b)^2$

62. $(9x^2 + 4x + 1)(4x - 3)$

63. $(5x - 9y)(3x + 9y)$

64. $\left(x - \dfrac{1}{3}\right)\left(x + \dfrac{2}{3}\right)$

65. $(x^2 + 9x + 1)^2$

Multiply, using special products.

66. $(3x - y)^2$

67. $(4x + 9)^2$

68. $(x + 3y)(x - 3y)$

69. $[4 + (3a - b)][4 - (3a - b)]$

70. If $P(x) = 2x - 1$ and $Q(x) = x^2 + 2x - 5$, find $P(x)\cdot Q(x)$.

△ **71.** Find the area of the rectangle.

$3y - 7z$
units

$3y + 7z$
units

Multiply. Assume that all variable exponents represent integers.

72. $4a^b(3a^{b+2} - 7)$

73. $(4xy^z - b)^2$

74. $(3x^a - 4)(3x^a + 4)$

(5.5) Factor out the greatest common factor.

75. $16x^3 - 24x^2$

76. $36y - 24y^2$

77. $6ab^2 + 8ab - 4a^2b^2$

78. $14a^2b^2 - 21ab^2 + 7ab$

79. $6a(a + 3b) - 5(a + 3b)$ **80.** $4x(x - 2y) - 5(x - 2y)$

81. $xy - 6y + 3x - 18$

82. $ab - 8b + 4a - 32$

83. $pq - 3p - 5q + 15$ **84.** $x^3 - x^2 - 2x + 2$

△ **85.** A smaller square is cut from a larger rectangle. Write the area of the shaded region as a factored polynomial.

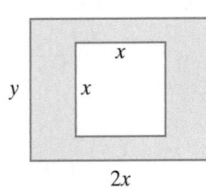

(5.6) Completely factor each polynomial.

86. $x^2 - 14x - 72$

87. $x^2 + 16x - 80$

88. $2x^2 - 18x + 28$

89. $3x^2 + 33x + 54$

90. $2x^3 - 7x^2 - 9x$

91. $3x^2 + 2x - 16$

92. $6x^2 + 17x + 10$

93. $15x^2 - 91x + 6$

94. $4x^2 + 2x - 12$

95. $9x^2 - 12x - 12$

96. $y^2(x + 6)^2 - 2y(x + 6)^2 - 3(x + 6)^2$

97. $(x + 5)^2 + 6(x + 5) + 8$

98. $x^4 - 6x^2 - 16$ **99.** $x^4 + 8x^2 - 20$

(5.7) Factor each polynomial completely.

100. $x^2 - 100$

101. $x^2 - 81$

102. $2x^2 - 32$

103. $6x^2 - 54$

104. $81 - x^4$

105. $16 - y^4$

106. $(y + 2)^2 - 25$

107. $(x - 3)^2 - 16$

108. $x^3 + 216$

109. $y^3 + 512$

110. $8 - 27y^3$

111. $1 - 64y^3$

112. $6x^4y + 48xy$

113. $2x^5 + 16x^2y^3$

114. $x^2 - 2x + 1 - y^2$

115. $x^2 - 6x + 9 - 4y^2$

116. $4x^2 + 12x + 9$

117. $16a^2 - 40ab + 25b^2$

△ **118.** The volume of the cylindrical shell is $\pi R^2h - \pi r^2h$ cubic units. Write this volume as a factored expression.

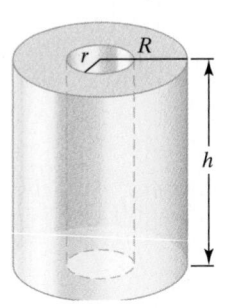

(5.8) Solve each polynomial equation for the variable.

119. $(3x - 1)(x + 7) = 0$

120. $3(x + 5)(8x - 3) = 0$

121. $5x(x - 4)(2x - 9) = 0$

122. $6(x + 3)(x - 4)(5x + 1) = 0$

123. $2x^2 = 12x$

124. $4x^3 - 36x = 0$

125. $(1 - x)(3x + 2) = -4x$

126. $2x(x - 12) = -40$

127. $3x^2 + 2x = 12 - 7x$

128. $2x^2 + 3x = 35$

129. $x^3 - 18x = 3x^2$

130. $19x^2 - 42x = -x^3$

131. $12x = 6x^3 + 6x^2$

132. $8x^3 + 10x^2 = 3x$

133. The sum of a number and twice its square is 105. Find the number.

△ **134.** The length of a rectangular piece of carpet is 5 meters less than twice its width. Find the dimensions of the carpet if it area is 33 square meters.

135. A scene from an adventure film calls for a stunt dummy to be dropped from above the second-story platform of the Eiffel Tower, a distance of 400 feet. Its height $h(t)$ at time t seconds is given by

$$h(t) = -16t^2 + 400$$

Determine when the stunt dummy will reach the ground.

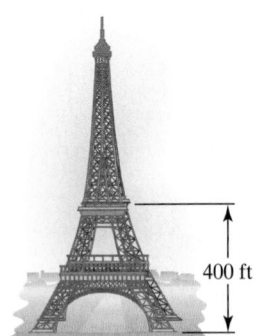

400 ft

CHAPTER 5 TEST

Remember to use your Chapter Test Prep Video CD to help you study and view solutions to the test questions you need help with.

Simplify. Use positive exponents to write the answers.

1. $(-9x)^{-2}$

2. $-3xy^{-2}(4xy^2)z$

3. $\dfrac{6^{-1}a^2b^{-3}}{3^{-2}a^{-5}b^2}$

4. $\left(\dfrac{-xy^{-5}z}{xy^3}\right)^{-5}$

Write in scientific notation.

5. 630,000,000

6. 0.01200

7. Write 5×10^{-6} without exponents.

8. Use scientific notation to find the quotient.

$$\frac{(0.0024)(0.00012)}{0.00032}$$

Perform the indicated operations.

9. $(4x^3y - 3x - 4) - (9x^3y + 8x + 5)$

10. $-3xy(4x + y)$

11. $(3x + 4)(4x - 7)$

12. $(5a - 2b)(5a + 2b)$

13. $(6m + n)^2$

14. $(2x - 1)(x^2 - 6x + 4)$

Factor each polynomial completely.

15. $16x^3y - 12x^2y^4$

16. $x^2 - 13x - 30$

17. $4y^2 + 20y + 25$

18. $6x^2 - 15x - 9$

19. $4x^2 - 25$

20. $x^3 + 64$

21. $3x^2y - 27y^3$

22. $6x^2 + 24$

23. $16y^3 - 2$

24. $x^2y - 9y - 3x^2 + 27$

Solve the equation for the variable.

25. $3n(7n - 20) = 96$

26. $(x + 2)(x - 2) = 5(x + 4)$

27. $2x^3 + 5x^2 = 8x + 20$

28. Write the area of the shaded region as a factored polynomial.

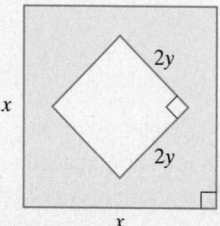

29. A pebble is hurled upward from the top of the Canada Trust Tower, which is 880 feet tall, with an initial velocity of 96 feet per second. Neglecting air resistance, the height $h(t)$ of the pebble after t seconds is given by the polynomial function

$$h(t) = -16t^2 + 96t + 880$$

a. Find the height of the pebble when $t = 1$.

b. Find the height of the pebble when $t = 5.1$.

c. When will the pebble hit the ground?

CHAPTER CUMULATIVE REVIEW

1. Find the roots.

a. $\sqrt[3]{27}$

b. $\sqrt[5]{1}$

c. $\sqrt[4]{16}$

2. Find the roots.

a. $\sqrt[3]{64}$

b. $\sqrt[4]{81}$

c. $\sqrt[5]{32}$

3. Solve: $2(x - 3) = 5x - 9$.

4. Solve. $0.3y + 2.4 = 0.1y + 4$

5. Karen Estes just received an inheritance of $10,000 and plans to place all the money in a savings account that pays 5% compounded quarterly to help her son go to college in 3 years. How much money will be in the account in 3 years?

6. A gallon of latex paint can cover 400 square feet. How many gallon containers of paint should be bought to paint two coats on each wall of a rectangular room whose dimensions are 14 feet by 18 feet? (Assume 8-foot ceilings).

7. Solve and graph the solution set.

a. $\dfrac{1}{4}x \le \dfrac{3}{8}$

b. $-2.3x < 6.9$

8. Solve. Graph the solution set and write it in interval notation. $x + 2 \le \frac{1}{4}(x - 7)$

Solve.

9. $-1 \le \frac{2x}{3} + 5 \le 2$

10. Solve. $-\frac{1}{3} < \frac{3x + 1}{6} \le \frac{1}{3}$

11. $|y| = 0$

12. Solve. $8 + |4c| = 24$

13. $\left|2x - \frac{1}{10}\right| < -13$

14. Solve. $|5x - 1| + 9 > 5$

15. Graph the linear equation $y = \frac{1}{3}x$.

16. Graph the linear equation $y = 3x$.

17. Is the relation $x = y^2$ also a function?

18. If $f(x) = 3x^2 + 2x + 3$, find $f(-3)$.

19. Graph $x = 2$.

20. Graph $y - 5 = 0$.

21. Find the slope of the line $y = 2$.

22. Find the slope of the line, $f(x) = -2x - 3$.

23. Find an equation of the horizontal line containing the point (2, 3).

24. Find the equation of the vertical line containing the point $(-3, 2)$.

25. Graph the union of $x + \frac{1}{2}y \ge -4$ or $y \le -2$.

26. Find the equation of the line containing the point $(-2, 3)$ and slope of 0.

27. Use the substitution method to solve the system.
$$\begin{cases} 2x + 4y = -6 \\ x = 2y - 5 \end{cases}$$

28. Use the substitution method to solve the system.
$$\begin{cases} 4x - 2y = 8 \\ y = 3x - 6 \end{cases}$$

29. Solve the system.
$$\begin{cases} 2x + 4y = 1 \\ 4x - 4z = -1 \\ y - 4z = -3 \end{cases}$$

30. Solve the system.
$$\begin{cases} x + y - \frac{3}{2}z = \frac{1}{2} \\ -y - 2z = 14 \\ x - \frac{2}{3}y = -\frac{1}{3} \end{cases}$$

31. A first number is 4 less than a second number. Four times the first number is 6 more than twice the second. Find the numbers.

32. One solution contains 20% acid and a second solution contains 60% acid. How many ounces of each solution should be mixed in order to have 50 ounces of a 30% acid solution

33. Use matrices to solve the system.
$$\begin{cases} 2x - y = 3 \\ 4x - 2y = 5 \end{cases}$$

34. Use matrices to solve the system.
$$\begin{cases} 4y = 8 \\ x + y = 7 \end{cases}$$

35. Use Cramer's rule to solve the system.
$$\begin{cases} x - 2y + z = 4 \\ 3x + y - 2z = 3 \\ 5x + 5y + 3z = -8 \end{cases}$$

36. Use Cramer's Rule to solve the system.
$$\begin{cases} x + y + z = 0 \\ 2x - 3y + z = 5 \\ 2x + y + 2z = 2 \end{cases}$$

37. Write each number in scientific notation.
   a. 730,000   b. 0.00000104

38. Write each number in scientific notation.
   a. 8,250,000   b. 0.0000346

39. Simplify each expression. Use positive exponents to write the answers.
   a. $(2x^0y^{-3})^{-2}$ b. $\left(\frac{x^{-5}}{x^{-2}}\right)^{-3}$
   c. $\left(\frac{2}{7}\right)^{-2}$ d. $\frac{5^{-2}x^{-3}y^{11}}{x^2y^{-5}}$

40. Simplify each expression. Use positive exponents to write the answers.
   a. $(4a^{-1}b^0)^{-3}$ b. $\left(\frac{a^{-6}}{a^{-8}}\right)^{-2}$
   c. $\left(\frac{2}{3}\right)^{-3}$ d. $\frac{3^{-2}a^{-2}b^{12}}{a^4b^{-5}}$

41. Find the degree of the polynomial $3xy + x^2y^2 - 5x^2 - 6$.

42. Subtract $(5x^2 + 3x)$ from $(3x^2 - 2x)$.

43. Multiply.
   a. $(2x^3)(5x^6)$ b. $(7y^4z^4)(-xy^{11}z^5)$

44. Multiply.
   a. $(3y^6)(4y^2)$ b. $(6a^3b^2)(-a^2bc^4)$

Factor.

45. $17x^3y^2 - 34x^4y^2$

46. Factor completely $12x^3y - 3xy^3$

47. $x^2 + 10x + 16$

48. Factor $5a^2 + 14a - 3$

49. Solve $2x^2 + 9x - 5 = 0$.

50. Solve $3x^2 - 10x - 8 = 0$

Rational Expressions

Have you ever thought about how many feet, or even miles, of wiring are needed in your house, dormitory, or apartment building to make all of your lights and electrical appliances work? Without electricians to wire our homes and buildings, we all would probably be in the dark right now.

In addition to installing wiring and coaxial or fiber-optic cable, electricians also may repair or maintain electrical components. Most electricians learn their trade through a four-or-five year apprenticeship program that includes both on-the-job training and classes such as electrical theory and mathematics. Electricians use math and problem-solving skills in tasks such as estimating job costs, testing circuits, and reading blueprints.

Polynomials are to algebra what integers are to arithmetic. We have added, subtracted, multiplied, and raised polynomials to powers, each operation yielding another polynomial, just as these operations on integers yield another integer. But when we divide one integer by another, the result may or may not be another integer. Likewise, when we divide one polynomial by another, we may or may not get a polynomial in return. The quotient $x \div (x + 1)$ is not a polynomial; it is a *rational expression* that can be written as $\dfrac{x}{x + 1}$.

In this chapter, we study these new algebraic forms known as rational expressions and the *rational functions* they generate.

In the Spotlight on Decision Making feature on page 371, you will have the opportunity to make a decision as an electrician about which resistor to use to repair a power supply.

Source: National Electrical Contractors Association Website

6.1 RATIONAL FUNCTIONS AND MULTIPLYING AND DIVIDING RATIONAL EXPRESSIONS

Objectives

1. Find the domain of a rational expression.
2. Simplify rational expressions.
3. Multiply rational expressions.
4. Divide rational expressions.
5. Use rational functions in applications.

Recall that a *rational number*, or *fraction*, is a number that can be written as the quotient $\frac{p}{q}$ of two integers p and q as long as q is not 0. A **rational expression** is an expression that can be written as the quotient $\frac{P}{Q}$ of two polynomials P and Q as long as Q is not 0.

Examples of Rational Expressions

$$\frac{3x + 7}{2} \qquad \frac{5x^2 - 3}{x - 1} \qquad \frac{7x - 2}{2x^2 + 7x + 6}$$

Rational expressions are sometimes used to describe functions. For example, we call the function $f(x) = \dfrac{x^2 + 2}{x - 3}$ a **rational function** since $\dfrac{x^2 + 2}{x - 3}$ is a rational expression.

1   As with fractions, a rational expression is **undefined** if the denominator is 0. If a variable in a rational expression is replaced with a number that makes the denominator 0, we say that the rational expression is **undefined** for this value of the variable. For example, the rational expression $\dfrac{x^2 + 2}{x - 3}$ is undefined when x is 3, because replacing x with 3 results in a denominator of 0. For this reason, we must exclude 3 from the domain of the function $f(x) = \dfrac{x^2 + 2}{x - 3}$.

The domain of f is then

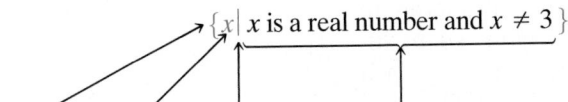

$$\{x \mid x \text{ is a real number and } x \neq 3\}$$

"The set of all x such that x is a real number and x is not equal to 3."
In this section, we will use this set builder notations to write domains.

Unless told otherwise, we assume that the domain of a function described by an equation is the set of all real numbers for which the equation is defined.

EXAMPLE 1

Find the domain of each rational function.

a. $f(x) = \dfrac{8x^3 + 7x^2 + 20}{2}$ **b.** $g(x) = \dfrac{5x^2 - 3}{x - 1}$ **c.** $f(x) = \dfrac{7x - 2}{x^2 - 2x - 15}$

Solution   The domain of each function will contain all real numbers except those values that make the denominator 0.

a. No matter what the value of x, the denominator of $f(x) = \dfrac{8x^3 + 7x^2 + 20}{2}$ is never 0, so the domain of f is $\{x \mid x \text{ is a real number}\}$.

b. To find the values of x that make the denominator of $g(x)$ equal to 0, we solve the equation "denominator = 0":

$$x - 1 = 0, \quad \text{or} \quad x = 1$$

The domain must exclude 1 since the rational expression is undefined when x is 1. The domain of g is $\{x \mid x \text{ is a real number and } x \neq 1\}$.

c. We find the domain by setting the denominator equal to 0.

$$\begin{aligned} x^2 - 2x - 15 &= 0 \qquad \text{Set the denominator equal to 0 and solve.} \\ (x - 5)(x + 3) &= 0 \end{aligned}$$

$$\begin{array}{rcl} x - 5 = 0 & \text{or} & x + 3 = 0 \\ x = 5 & \text{or} & x = -3 \end{array}$$

If x is replaced with 5 or with -3, the rational expression is undefined.

The domain of f is $\{x \mid x \text{ is a real number and } x \neq 5, x \neq -3\}$.

✔ **CONCEPT CHECK**

For which of these values (if any) is the rational expression $\dfrac{x - 3}{x^2 + 2}$ undefined?

a. 2

b. 3

c. −2

d. 0

e. None of these

2   Recall that a fraction is in lowest terms or simplest form if the numerator and denominator have no common factors other than 1 (or −1). For example, $\dfrac{3}{13}$ is in lowest terms since 3 and 13 have no common factors other than 1 (or −1).

To **simplify** a rational expression, or to write it in lowest terms, we use the fundamental principle of rational expressions.

Fundamental Principle of Rational Expressions

For any rational expression $\dfrac{P}{Q}$ and any polynomial R, where $R \neq 0$,

$$\frac{PR}{QR} = \frac{P}{Q}$$

Thus, the fundamental principle says that multiplying or dividing the numerator and denominator of a rational expression by the same nonzero polynomial yields an equivalent rational expression.

To simplify a rational expression such as $\dfrac{(x+2)^2}{x^2-4}$, factor the numerator and the denominator and then use the fundamental principle of rational expressions to divide out common factors.

$$\frac{(x+2)^2}{x^2-4} = \frac{(x+2)(x+2)}{(x+2)(x-2)} = \frac{x+2}{x-2}$$

This means that the rational expression $\dfrac{(x+2)^2}{x^2-4}$ has the same value as the rational expression $\dfrac{x+2}{x-2}$ for all values of x except 2 and -2. (Remember that when x is 2, the denominators of both rational expressions are 0 and that when x is -2, the original rational expression has a denominator of 0.)

As we simplify rational expressions, we will assume that the simplified rational expression is equivalent to the original rational expression for all real numbers except those for which either denominator is 0.

In general, the following steps may be used to simplify rational expressions or to write a rational expression in lowest terms.

Simplifying or Writing a Rational Expression in Lowest Terms

Step 1: Completely factor the numerator and denominator of the rational expression.

Step 2: Apply the fundamental principle of rational expressions to divide out factors common to both the numerator and denominator.

For now, we assume that variables in a rational expression do not represent values that make the denominator 0.

EXAMPLE 2

Simplify $\dfrac{2x^2}{10x^3-2x^2}$.

Solution Factor out the GCF of $2x^2$ from the denominator. Then divide numerator and denominator by their GCF, $2x^2$.

$$\frac{2x^2}{10x^3-2x^2} = \frac{2x^2 \cdot 1}{2x^2(5x-1)} = \frac{1}{5x-1}$$

When the terms in the numerator of a rational expression differ by sign from the terms of the denominator, the polynomials are opposites of each other and the expression simplifies to -1. To see this, study Example 3b on the next page.

EXAMPLE 3

Simplify each rational expression.

a. $\dfrac{2 + x}{x + 2}$ b. $\dfrac{2 - x}{x - 2}$

Solution

a. $\dfrac{2 + x}{x + 2} = \dfrac{x + 2}{x + 2} = 1$ By the commutative property of addition, $2 + x = x + 2$.

b. $\dfrac{2 - x}{x - 2}$

The terms in the numerator of $\dfrac{2 - x}{x - 2}$ differ by sign from the terms of the denominator, so the polynomials are opposites of each other and the expression simplifies to -1. To see this, we factor out -1 from the numerator or the denominator. If -1 is factored from the numerator, then

Helpful Hint

When the numerator and the denominator of a rational expression are opposites of each other, the expression simplifies to -1.

$$\dfrac{2 - x}{x - 2} = \dfrac{-1(-2 + x)}{x - 2} = \dfrac{-1(x - 2)}{x - 2} = \dfrac{-1}{1} = -1$$

If -1 is factored from the denominator, the result is the same.

$$\dfrac{2 - x}{x - 2} = \dfrac{2 - x}{-1(-x + 2)} = \dfrac{2 - x}{-1(2 - x)} = \dfrac{1}{-1} = -1$$

EXAMPLE 4

Simplify $\dfrac{18 - 2x^2}{x^2 - 2x - 3}$.

Solution

$$\dfrac{18 - 2x^2}{x^2 - 2x - 3} = \dfrac{2(9 - x^2)}{(x + 1)(x - 3)}$$ Factor.

$$= \dfrac{2(3 + x)(3 - x)}{(x + 1)(x - 3)}$$ Factor completely.

$$= \dfrac{2(3 + x) \cdot -1(x - 3)}{(x + 1)(x - 3)}$$ Notice the opposites $3 - x$ and $x - 3$. Write $3 - x$ as $-1(x - 3)$ and simplify.

$$= -\dfrac{2(3 + x)}{x + 1}$$

Helpful Hint

Recall that for a fraction $\dfrac{a}{b}$,

$$\dfrac{a}{-b} = \dfrac{-a}{b} = -\dfrac{a}{b}$$

For example

$$\dfrac{-(x + 1)}{(x + 2)} = \dfrac{(x + 1)}{-(x + 2)} = -\dfrac{x + 1}{x + 2}$$

✔ **CONCEPT CHECK**

Which of the following expressions are equivalent to $\dfrac{x}{8-x}$?

a. $\dfrac{-x}{x-8}$ b. $\dfrac{-x}{8-x}$ c. $\dfrac{x}{x-8}$ d. $\dfrac{-x}{-8+x}$

EXAMPLE 5

Simplify each rational expression.

a. $\dfrac{x^3+8}{2+x}$ b. $\dfrac{2y^2+2}{y^3-5y^2+y-5}$

Solution   a. $\dfrac{x^3+8}{2+x} = \dfrac{(x+2)(x^2-2x+4)}{x+2}$ Factor the sum of the two cubes.

$= x^2 - 2x + 4$ Divide out common factors.

b. $\dfrac{2y^2+2}{y^3-5y^2+y-5} = \dfrac{2(y^2+1)}{(y^3-5y^2)+(y-5)}$ Factor the numerator.

$= \dfrac{2(y^2+1)}{y^2(y-5)+1(y-5)}$ Factor the denominator by grouping.

$= \dfrac{2(y^2+1)}{(y-5)(y^2+1)}$

$= \dfrac{2}{y-5}$ Divide out common factors.

✔ **CONCEPT CHECK**

Does $\dfrac{n}{n+2}$ simplify to $\dfrac{1}{2}$? Why or why not?

3   Arithmetic operations on rational expressions are performed in the same way as they are on rational numbers.

Multiplying Rational Expressions

The rule for multiplying rational expressions is

$$\frac{P}{Q} \cdot \frac{R}{S} = \frac{PR}{QS} \quad \text{as long as } Q \neq 0 \text{ and } S \neq 0.$$

To multiply rational expressions, you may use these steps:

Step 1: Completely factor each numerator and denominator.
Step 2: Use the rule above and multiply the numerators and the denominators.
Step 3: Simplify the product by dividing the numerator and denominator by their common factors.

Concept Check Answer:
a and d

Concept Check Answer:
no; answers may vary.

When we multiply rational expressions, notice that we factor each numerator and denominator first. This helps when we apply the fundamental principle to write the product in simplest form.

EXAMPLE 6

Multiply.

a. $\dfrac{1 + 3n}{2n} \cdot \dfrac{2n - 4}{3n^2 - 2n - 1}$ **b.** $\dfrac{x^3 - 1}{-3x + 3} \cdot \dfrac{15x^2}{x^2 + x + 1}$

Solution

a. $\dfrac{1 + 3n}{2n} \cdot \dfrac{2n - 4}{3n^2 - 2n - 1} = \dfrac{1 + 3n}{2n} \cdot \dfrac{2(n - 2)}{(3n + 1)(n - 1)}$ *Factor.*

$= \dfrac{(1 + 3n) \cdot 2(n - 2)}{2n(3n + 1)(n - 1)}$ *Multiply.*

$= \dfrac{n - 2}{n(n - 1)}$ *Divide out common factors.*

b. $\dfrac{x^3 - 1}{-3x + 3} \cdot \dfrac{15x^2}{x^2 + x + 1} = \dfrac{(x - 1)(x^2 + x + 1)}{-3(x - 1)} \cdot \dfrac{15x^2}{x^2 + x + 1}$ *Factor.*

$= \dfrac{(x - 1)(x^2 + x + 1) \cdot 3 \cdot 5x^2}{-1 \cdot 3(x - 1)(x^2 + x + 1)}$ *Factor.*

$= \dfrac{5x^2}{-1}$ *Divide out common factors.*

$= -5x^2$

4   Recall that two numbers are reciprocals of each other if their product is 1. Similarly, if $\dfrac{P}{Q}$ is a rational expression, then $\dfrac{Q}{P}$ is its **reciprocal**, since

$$\frac{P}{Q} \cdot \frac{Q}{P} = \frac{P \cdot Q}{Q \cdot P} = 1$$

The following are examples of expressions and their reciprocals.

Expression	*Reciprocal*
$\dfrac{3}{x}$	$\dfrac{x}{3}$
$\dfrac{2 + x^2}{4x - 3}$	$\dfrac{4x - 3}{2 + x^2}$
x^3	$\dfrac{1}{x^3}$
0	no reciprocal

Dividing Rational Expressions

The rule for dividing rational expressions is

$$\frac{P}{Q} \div \frac{R}{S} = \frac{P}{Q} \cdot \frac{S}{R} = \frac{PS}{QR} \quad \text{as long as } Q \neq 0, S \neq 0, \text{ and } R \neq 0.$$

To divide by a rational expression, use the rule above and multiply by its reciprocal. Then simplify if possible.

Notice that division of rational expressions is the same as for rational numbers.

EXAMPLE 7

Divide.

a. $\dfrac{3x}{5y} \div \dfrac{9y}{x^5}$ **b.** $\dfrac{8m^2}{3m^2 - 12} \div \dfrac{40}{2 - m}$

Solution   **a.** $\dfrac{3x}{5y} \div \dfrac{9y}{x^5} = \dfrac{3x}{5y} \cdot \dfrac{x^5}{9y}$ *Multiply by the reciprocal of the divisor.*

$= \dfrac{x^6}{15y^2}$ *Simplify.*

b. $\dfrac{8m^2}{3m^2 - 12} \div \dfrac{40}{2 - m} = \dfrac{8m^2}{3m^2 - 12} \cdot \dfrac{2 - m}{40}$ *Multiply by the reciprocal of the divisor.*

$= \dfrac{8m^2(2 - m)}{3(m + 2)(m - 2) \cdot 40}$ *Factor and multiply.*

$= \dfrac{8m^2 \cdot -1(m - 2)}{3(m + 2)(m - 2) \cdot 8 \cdot 5}$ *Write $(2 - m)$ as $-1(m - 2)$.*

$= -\dfrac{m^2}{15(m + 2)}$ *Simplify.*

> **Helpful Hint**
>
> When dividing rational expressions, do not divide out common factors until the division problem is rewritten as a multiplication problem.

EXAMPLE 8

Perform each indicated operation.

$$\dfrac{x^2 - 25}{(x + 5)^2} \cdot \dfrac{3x + 15}{4x} \div \dfrac{x^2 - 3x - 10}{x}$$

Solution $\dfrac{x^2 - 25}{(x + 5)^2} \cdot \dfrac{3x + 15}{4x} \div \dfrac{x^2 - 3x - 10}{x}$

$= \dfrac{x^2 - 25}{(x + 5)^2} \cdot \dfrac{3x + 15}{4x} \cdot \dfrac{x}{x^2 - 3x - 10}$ *To divide, multiply by the reciprocal*

$= \dfrac{(x + 5)(x - 5)}{(x + 5)(x + 5)} \cdot \dfrac{3(x + 5)}{4x} \cdot \dfrac{x}{(x - 5)(x + 2)}$

$= \dfrac{3}{4(x + 2)}$

5   Rational functions occur often in real-life situations.

EXAMPLE 9

COST FOR PRESSING COMPACT DISCS

For the ICL Production Company, the rational function $C(x) = \dfrac{2.6x + 10,000}{x}$ describes the company's cost per disc of pressing x compact discs. Find the cost per disc for pressing

a. 100 compact discs

b. 1000 compact discs

Solution

a. $C(100) = \dfrac{2.6(100) + 10,000}{100} = \dfrac{10,260}{100} = 102.6$

The cost per disc for pressing 100 compact discs is $102.60.

b. $C(1000) = \dfrac{2.6(1000) + 10,000}{1000} = \dfrac{12,600}{1000} = 12.6$

The cost per disc for pressing 1000 compact discs is $12.60. Notice that as more compact discs are produced, the cost per disc decreases.

Spotlight on
DECISION
✕MAKING

Suppose you are an electrician at a small packaging plant. You are repairing machinery that heats the hot glue gun used for sealing boxes. You have determined that a resistor in the machinery's 50-volt direct current power supply must be replaced. To keep the glue warm, the power supply must dissipate about 2000 watts of power.

You know that the power P (in watts) dissipated by a resistor in a direct current circuit is given by the formula $P = \dfrac{V^2}{R}$, where V is the voltage (in volts) and R is the resistance (in ohms). Which of the three resistors shown in the parts list would you use to replace the faulty resistor? Why?

Parts List Resistors

Part Number	Material	Resistance (in ohms)
1298	Aluminum	0.95
3169	Nickel	1.81
4203	Tungsten	1.22

Graphing Calculator Explorations

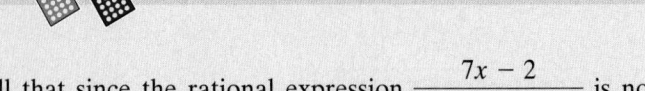

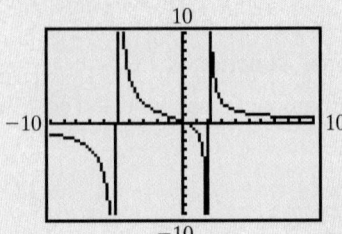

Recall that since the rational expression $\dfrac{7x - 2}{(x - 2)(x + 5)}$ is not defined when $x = 2$ or when $x = -5$, we say that the domain of the rational function $f(x) = \dfrac{7x - 2}{(x - 2)(x + 5)}$ is all real numbers except 2 and -5. This domain can be written as $\{x \mid x$ is a real number and $x \neq 2$, $x \neq -5\}$. This means that the graph of $f(x)$ should not cross the vertical lines $x = 2$ and $x = -5$. The graph of $f(x)$ in *connected* mode is to the left. In connected mode the graphing calculator tries to connect all dots of the graph so that the result is a smooth curve. This is what has happened in the graph. Notice that the graph appears to contain vertical lines at $x = 2$ and at $x = -5$. We know that this cannot happen because the function is not defined at $x = 2$ and at $x = -5$. We also know that this cannot happen because the graph of this function would not pass the vertical line test.

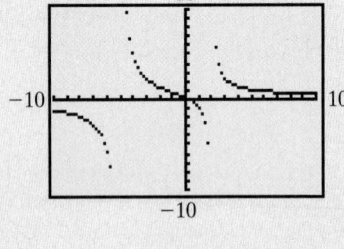

The graph of $f(x)$ in *dot* mode, is to the left. In dot mode the graphing calculator will not connect dots with a smooth curve. Notice that the vertical lines have disappeared, and we have a better picture of the graph. The graph, however, actually appears more like the hand-drawn graph below. By using a Table feature, a Calculate Value feature, or by tracing, we can see that the function is not defined at $x = 2$ and at $x = -5$.

Find the domain of each rational function. Then graph each rational function and use the graph to confirm the domain. **1.–4.** See graphing answer section.

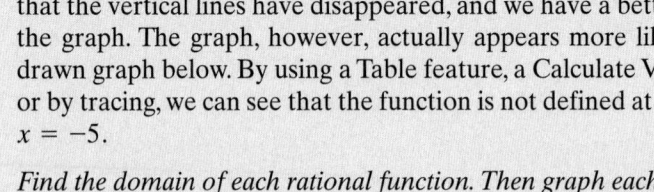

1. $f(x) = \dfrac{x + 1}{x^2 - 4}$

2. $g(x) = \dfrac{5x}{x^2 - 9}$

3. $h(x) = \dfrac{x^2}{2x^2 + 7x - 4}$

4. $f(x) = \dfrac{3x + 2}{4x^2 - 19x - 5}$

EXERCISE SET 6.1

STUDY GUIDE/SSM   CD/VIDEO   PH MATH TUTOR CENTER   MathXL®Tutorials ON CD   MathXL®   MyMathLab®

Find each function value. See Example 9.

 1. $f(x) = \dfrac{x + 8}{2x - 1}; f(2), f(0), f(-1)$

2. $f(y) = \dfrac{y - 2}{-5 + y}; f(-5), f(0), f(10)$

3. $g(x) = \dfrac{x^2 + 8}{x^3 - 25x}; g(3), g(-2), g(1)$

4. $s(t) = \dfrac{t^3 + 1}{t^2 + 1}; s(-1), s(1), s(2)$

Find the domain of each rational function. See Example 1.

5. $f(x) = \dfrac{5x - 7}{4}$

6. $g(x) = \dfrac{4 - 3x}{2}$

7. $s(t) = \dfrac{t^2 + 1}{2t}$

8. $v(t) = -\dfrac{5t + t^2}{3t}$

9. $f(x) = \dfrac{3x}{7 - x}$

10. $f(x) = \dfrac{-4x}{-2 + x}$

11. $f(x) = \dfrac{x}{3x - 1}$

12. $g(x) = \dfrac{-2}{2x + 5}$

13. $R(x) = \dfrac{3 + 2x}{x^3 + x^2 - 2x}$

14. $h(x) = \dfrac{5 - 3x}{2x^2 - 14x + 20}$

15. $C(x) = \dfrac{x + 3}{x^2 - 4}$

16. $R(x) = \dfrac{5}{x^2 - 7x}$

17. In your own words, explain how to find the domain of a rational function.

18. In your own words, explain how to simplify a rational expression or to write it in lowest terms.

Simplify each rational expression. See Examples 2 through 5.

19. $\dfrac{4x - 8}{3x - 6}$

20. $\dfrac{12 - 6x}{30 - 15x}$

21. $\dfrac{2x - 14}{7 - x}$

22. $\dfrac{9 - x}{5x - 45}$

23. $\dfrac{x^2 - 2x - 3}{x^2 - 6x + 9}$

24. $\dfrac{x^2 + 10x + 25}{x^2 + 8x + 15}$

25. $\dfrac{2x^2 + 12x + 18}{x^2 - 9}$

26. $\dfrac{x^2 - 4}{2x^2 + 8x + 8}$

27. $\dfrac{3x + 6}{x^2 + 2x}$

28. $\dfrac{3x + 4}{9x^2 + 4}$

29. $\dfrac{2x^2 - x - 3}{2x^3 - 3x^2 + 2x - 3}$

30. $\dfrac{3x^2 - 5x - 2}{6x^3 + 2x^2 + 3x + 1}$

31. $\dfrac{8q^2}{16q^3 - 16q^2}$

32. $\dfrac{3y}{6y^2 - 30y}$

33. $\dfrac{x^2 + 6x - 40}{10 + x}$

34. $\dfrac{x^2 - 8x + 16}{4 - x}$

35. $\dfrac{x^3 - 125}{5 - x}$

36. $\dfrac{4x + 4}{2x^3 + 2}$

37. $\dfrac{8x^3 - 27}{4x - 6}$

38. $\dfrac{9x^2 - 15x + 25}{27x^3 + 125}$

39. Which expression below does not simplify to 1?

   a. $\dfrac{2 + x}{x + 2}$ **b.** $\dfrac{5 - x}{-x + 5}$ **c.** $\dfrac{-x - y}{-y - x}$ **d.** $\dfrac{x - 3}{3 - x}$

40. Which expression below does not simplify to -1?

   a. $\dfrac{2 - x}{x - 2}$ **b.** $\dfrac{y + 5}{y - 5}$ **c.** $\dfrac{x + y}{-x - y}$ **d.** $\dfrac{-5 + z}{5 - z}$

MIXED PRACTICE

Multiply or divide as indicated. Simplify all answers. See Examples through 8.

41. $\dfrac{3xy^3}{4x^3y^2} \cdot \dfrac{-8x^3y^4}{9x^4y^7}$

42. $-\dfrac{2xyz^3}{5x^2z^2} \cdot \dfrac{10xy}{x^3}$

43. $\dfrac{8a}{3a^4b^2} \div \dfrac{4b^5}{6a^2b}$

44. $\dfrac{3y^3}{14x^4} \div \dfrac{8y^3}{7x}$

45. $\dfrac{a^2b}{a^2 - b^2} \cdot \dfrac{a + b}{4a^3b}$

46. $\dfrac{3ab^2}{a^2 - 4} \cdot \dfrac{a - 2}{6a^2b^2}$

🔒 **47.** $\dfrac{x^2 - 9}{4} \div \dfrac{x^2 - 6x + 9}{x^2 - x - 6}$

48. $\dfrac{a - 5b}{a^2 + ab} \div \dfrac{15b - 3a}{b^2 - a^2}$

🔒 **49.** $\dfrac{9x + 9}{4x + 8} \cdot \dfrac{2x + 4}{3x^2 - 3}$

50. $\dfrac{x^2 - 1}{10x + 30} \cdot \dfrac{12x + 36}{3x - 3}$

51. $\dfrac{a + b}{ab} \div \dfrac{a^2 - b^2}{4a^3b}$

52. $\dfrac{6a^2b^2}{a^2 - 4} \div \dfrac{3ab^2}{a - 2}$

53. $\dfrac{2x^2 - 4x - 30}{5x^2 - 40x - 75} \div \dfrac{x^2 - 8x + 15}{x^2 - 6x + 9}$

54. $\dfrac{4a + 36}{a^2 - 7a - 18} \div \dfrac{a^2 - a - 6}{a^2 - 81}$

55. $\dfrac{2x^3 - 16}{6x^2 + 6x - 36} \cdot \dfrac{9x + 18}{3x^2 + 6x + 12}$

56. $\dfrac{x^2 - 3x + 9}{5x^2 - 20x - 105} \cdot \dfrac{x^2 - 49}{x^3 + 27}$

57. $\dfrac{15b - 3a}{b^2 - a^2} \div \dfrac{a - 5b}{ab + b^2}$

58. $\dfrac{4x + 4}{x - 1} \div \dfrac{x^2 - 4x - 5}{x^2 - 1}$

59. $\dfrac{a^3 + a^2b + a + b}{a^3 + a} \cdot \dfrac{6a^2}{2a^2 - 2b^2}$

60. $\dfrac{a^2 - 2a}{ab - 2b + 3a - 6} \cdot \dfrac{8b + 24}{3a + 6}$

61. $\dfrac{5a}{12} \cdot \dfrac{2}{25a^2} \cdot \dfrac{15a}{2}$

62. $\dfrac{4a}{7} \div \dfrac{a^2}{14} \cdot \dfrac{3}{a}$

63. $\dfrac{3x - x^2}{x^3 - 27} \div \dfrac{x}{x^2 + 3x + 9}$

64. $\dfrac{x^2 - 3x}{x^3 - 27} \div \dfrac{2x}{2x^2 + 6x + 18}$

65. $\dfrac{4a}{7} \div \left(\dfrac{a^2}{14} \cdot \dfrac{3}{a} \right)$

66. $\dfrac{a^2}{14} \cdot \dfrac{3}{a} \div \dfrac{4a}{7}$

67. $\dfrac{8b + 24}{3a + 6} \div \dfrac{ab - 2b + 3a - 6}{a^2 - 4a + 4}$

68. $\dfrac{2a^2 - 2b^2}{a^3 + a^2b + a + b} \div \dfrac{6a^2}{a^3 + a}$

69. $\dfrac{4}{x} \div \dfrac{3xy}{x^2} \cdot \dfrac{6x^2}{x^4}$

70. $\dfrac{4}{x} \cdot \dfrac{3xy}{x^2} \div \dfrac{6x^2}{x^4}$

71. $\dfrac{3x^2 - 5x - 2}{y^2 + y - 2} \cdot \dfrac{y^2 + 4y - 5}{12x^2 + 7x + 1} \div \dfrac{5x^2 - 9x - 2}{8x^2 - 2x - 1}$

72. $\dfrac{x^2 + x - 2}{3y^2 - 5y - 2} \cdot \dfrac{12y^2 + y - 1}{x^2 + 4x - 5} \div \dfrac{8y^2 - 6y + 1}{5y^2 - 9y - 2}$

73. $\dfrac{5a^2 - 20}{3a^2 - 12a} \div \dfrac{a^3 + 2a^2}{2a^2 - 8a} \cdot \dfrac{9a^3 + 6a^2}{2a^2 - 4a}$

74. $\dfrac{5a^2 - 20}{3a^2 - 12a} \div \left(\dfrac{a^3 + 2a^2}{2a^2 - 8a} \cdot \dfrac{9a^3 + 6a^2}{2a^2 - 4a} \right)$

75. $\dfrac{5x^4 + 3x^2 - 2}{x - 1} \cdot \dfrac{x + 1}{x^4 - 1}$

76. $\dfrac{3x^4 - 10x^2 - 8}{x - 2} \cdot \dfrac{3x + 6}{15x^2 + 10}$

REVIEW AND PREVIEW

Perform the indicated operations. See Section 1.3.

77. $\dfrac{4}{5} + \dfrac{3}{5}$

78. $\dfrac{4}{10} - \dfrac{7}{10}$

79. $\dfrac{5}{28} - \dfrac{2}{21}$

80. $\dfrac{5}{13} + \dfrac{2}{7}$

81. $\dfrac{3}{8} + \dfrac{1}{2} - \dfrac{3}{16}$

82. $\dfrac{2}{9} - \dfrac{1}{6} + \dfrac{2}{3}$

Concept Extensions

△ **83.** Find the area of the rectangle.

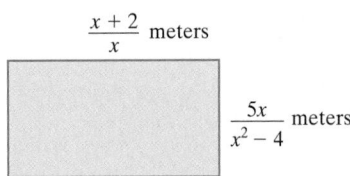

$\dfrac{x + 2}{x}$ meters

$\dfrac{5x}{x^2 - 4}$ meters

△ **84.** Find the area of the triangle.

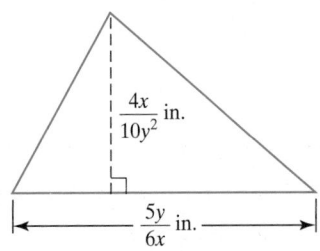

$\dfrac{4x}{10y^2}$ in.

$\dfrac{5y}{6x}$ in.

85. The function $f(x) = \dfrac{100{,}000x}{100 - x}$ models the cost in dollars for removing x percent of the pollutants from a bayou in which a nearby company dumped creosote.

a. What is the domain of $f(x)$?

b. Find the cost of removing 30% of the pollutants from the bayou. (*Hint:* Find $f(30)$.)

c. Find the cost of removing 60% of the pollutants and then 80% of the pollutants.

✎ **d.** Find $f(90)$, then $f(95)$, and then $f(99)$. What happens to the cost as x approaches 100%?

86. The total revenue from the sale of a popular book is approximated by the rational function $R(x) = \dfrac{1000x^2}{x^2 + 4}$ where x is the number of years since publication and $R(x)$ is the total revenue in millions of dollars.

a. Find the total revenue at the end of the first year.

b. Find the total revenue at the end of the second year.

c. Find the revenue during the second year only.

✎ **87.** In our definition of division for

$$\dfrac{P}{Q} \div \dfrac{R}{S}$$

we stated that $Q \neq 0$, $S \neq 0$, and $R \neq 0$. Explain why R cannot equal 0.

88. Find the polynomial in the second numerator such that the following statement is true.

$$\dfrac{x^2 - 4}{x^2 - 7x + 10} \cdot \dfrac{?}{2x^2 + 11x + 14} = 1$$

△ **89.** A parallelogram has area $\dfrac{x^2 + x - 2}{x^3}$ square feet and height $\dfrac{x^2}{x - 1}$ feet. Express the length of its base as a rational expression in x. (*Hint:* Since $A = b \cdot h$, then $b = \dfrac{A}{h}$ or $b = A \div h$.)

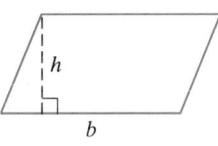

h

b

0. A lottery prize of $\dfrac{15x^3}{y^2}$ dollars is to be divided among $5x$ people. Express the amount of money each person is to receive as a rational expression in x and y.

1. Graph a portion of the function $f(x) = \dfrac{20x}{100 - x}$. To do so, complete the given table, plot the points, and then connect the plotted points with a smooth curve.

x	0	10	30	50	70	90	95	99
y or $f(x)$								

2. The domain of the function $f(x) = \dfrac{1}{x}$ is all real numbers except 0. This means that the graph of this function will be in two pieces: one piece corresponding to x values less than 0 and one piece corresponding to x values greater than 0. Graph the function by completing the following tables, separately plotting the points, and connecting each set of plotted points with a smooth curve.

x	$\frac{1}{4}$	$\frac{1}{2}$	1	2	4
y or $f(x)$					

x	-4	-2	-1	$-\frac{1}{2}$	$-\frac{1}{4}$
y or $f(x)$					

Perform the indicated operation. Write all answers in lowest terms.

93. $\dfrac{x^{2n} - 4}{7x} \cdot \dfrac{14x^3}{x^n - 2}$

94. $\dfrac{x^{2n} + 4x^n + 4}{4x - 3} \cdot \dfrac{8x^2 - 6x}{x^n + 2}$

95. $\dfrac{y^{2n} + 9}{10y} \cdot \dfrac{y^n - 3}{y^{4n} - 81}$

96. $\dfrac{y^{4n} - 16}{y^{2n} + 4} \cdot \dfrac{6y}{y^n + 2}$

97. $\dfrac{y^{2n} - y^n - 2}{2y^n - 4} \div \dfrac{y^{2n} - 1}{1 + y^n}$

98. $\dfrac{y^{2n} + 7y^n + 10}{10} \div \dfrac{y^{2n} + 4y^n + 4}{5y^n + 25}$

6.2   ADDING AND SUBTRACTING RATIONAL EXPRESSIONS

Objectives

1   Add or subtract rational expressions with common denominators.

2   Identify the least common denominator of two or more rational expressions.

3   Add or subtract rational expressions with unlike denominators.

1   Rational expressions, like rational numbers, can be added or subtracted. We define the sum or difference of rational expressions in the same way that we defined the sum or difference of rational numbers (fractions).

> ### Adding or Subtracting Rational Expressions with Common Denominators
>
> If $\dfrac{P}{Q}$ and $\dfrac{R}{Q}$ are rational expressions, then
>
> $$\frac{P}{Q} + \frac{R}{Q} = \frac{P+R}{Q} \quad \text{and} \quad \frac{P}{Q} - \frac{R}{Q} = \frac{P-R}{Q}$$

To add or subtract rational expressions with common denominators, add or subtract the numerators and write the sum or difference over the common denominator.

EXAMPLE 1

Add or subtract.

a. $\dfrac{x}{4} + \dfrac{5x}{4}$ **b.** $\dfrac{x^2}{x+7} - \dfrac{49}{x+7}$ **c.** $\dfrac{x}{3y^2} - \dfrac{x+1}{3y^2}$

Solution The rational expressions have common denominators, so add or subtract their numerators and place the sum or difference over their common denominator.

a. $\dfrac{x}{4} + \dfrac{5x}{4} = \dfrac{x+5x}{4} = \dfrac{6x}{4} = \dfrac{3x}{2}$ Add the numerators and write the result over the common denominator.

b. $\dfrac{x^2}{x+7} - \dfrac{49}{x+7} = \dfrac{x^2 - 49}{x+7}$ Subtract the numerators and write the result over the common denominator.

$\qquad = \dfrac{(x+7)(x-7)}{x+7}$ Factor the numerator.

$\qquad = x - 7$ Simplify.

c. $\dfrac{x}{3y^2} - \dfrac{x+1}{3y^2} = \dfrac{x - (x+1)}{3y^2}$ Subtract the numerators.

$\qquad = \dfrac{x - x - 1}{3y^2}$ Use the distributive property.

$\qquad = -\dfrac{1}{3y^2}$ Simplify.

> **Helpful Hint**
>
> Be sure to insert parentheses here so that the entire numerator is subtracted.

✔ **CONCEPT CHECK**

Find and correct the **error**.

$$\frac{3+2y}{y^2 - 1} - \frac{y+3}{y^2 - 1}$$

$$= \frac{3 + 2y - y + 3}{y^2 - 1}$$

$$= \frac{y + 6}{y^2 - 1}$$

Concept Check Answer:

$\dfrac{3+2y}{y^2 - 1} - \dfrac{y+3}{y^2 - 1} =$

$\dfrac{3 + 2y - y - 3}{y^2 - 1} = \dfrac{y}{y^2 - 1}$

2 To add or subtract rational expressions with unlike denominators, first write the rational expressions as equivalent rational expressions with common denominators.

The **least common denominator (LCD)** is usually the easiest common denominator to work with. The LCD of a list of rational expressions is a polynomial of least degree whose factors include the denominator factors in the list.

Use the following steps to find the LCD.

Finding the Least Common Denominator (LCD)

Step 1: Factor each denominator completely.

Step 2: The LCD is the product of all unique factors each raised to the greatest power that appears in any factored denominator.

EXAMPLE 2

Find the LCD of the rational expressions in each list.

a. $\dfrac{2}{3x^5y^2}, \dfrac{3z}{5xy^3}$

b. $\dfrac{7}{z+1}, \dfrac{z}{z-1}$

c. $\dfrac{m-1}{m^2-25}, \dfrac{2m}{2m^2-9m-5}, \dfrac{7}{m^2-10m+25}$

d. $\dfrac{x}{x^2-4}, \dfrac{11}{6-3x}$

Solution

a. First we factor each denominator.

$$3x^5y^2 = 3 \cdot x^5 \cdot y^2$$
$$5xy^3 = 5 \cdot x \cdot y^3$$
$$\text{LCD} = 3 \cdot 5 \cdot x^5 \cdot y^3 = 15x^5y^3$$

> **Helpful Hint**
>
> The greatest power of x is 5, so we have a factor of x^5. The greatest power of y is 3, so we have a factor of y^3.

b. The denominators $z+1$ and $z-1$ do not factor further. Thus,

$$\text{LCD} = (z+1)(z-1)$$

c. We first factor each denominator.

$$m^2 - 25 = (m+5)(m-5)$$
$$2m^2 - 9m - 5 = (2m+1)(m-5)$$
$$m^2 - 10m + 25 = (m-5)(m-5)$$
$$\text{LCD} = (m+5)(2m+1)(m-5)^2$$

d. Factor each denominator.

$$x^2 - 4 = (x+2)(x-2)$$
$$6 - 3x = 3(2-x) = 3(-1)(x-2)$$
$$\text{LCD} = 3(-1)(x+2)(x-2)$$
$$= -3(x+2)(x-2)$$

> **Helpful Hint**
>
> $(x-2)$ and $(2-x)$ are opposite factors. Notice that -1 was factored from $(2-x)$ so that the factors are identical.

> **Helpful Hint**
>
> If opposite factors occur, do not use both in the LCD. Instead, factor -1 from one of the opposite factors so that the factors are then identical.

3 To add or subtract rational expressions with unlike denominators, we write each rational expression as an equivalent rational expression so that their denominators are alike.

Adding or Subtracting Rational Expressions with Unlike Denominators

Step 1: Find the LCD of the rational expressions.

Step 2: Write each rational expression as an equivalent rational expression whose denominator is the LCD found in Step 1.

Step 3: Add or subtract numerators, and write the result over the common denominator.

Step 4: Simplify the resulting rational expression.

EXAMPLE 3

Perform the indicated operation.

a. $\dfrac{2}{x^2y} + \dfrac{5}{3x^3y}$ **b.** $\dfrac{3x}{x+2} + \dfrac{2x}{x-2}$ **c.** $\dfrac{x}{x-1} - \dfrac{4}{1-x}$

Solution **a.** The LCD is $3x^3y$. Write each fraction as an equivalent fraction with denominator $3x^3y$. To do this, we multiply both the numerator and denominator of each fraction by the factors needed to obtain the LCD as denominator.

The first fraction is multiplied by $\dfrac{3x}{3x}$ so that the new denominator is the LCD.

$$\frac{2}{x^2y} + \frac{5}{3x^3y} = \frac{2 \cdot 3x}{x^2y \cdot 3x} + \frac{5}{3x^3y} \quad \text{\textit{The second expression already has a denominator of } } 3x^3y.$$

$$= \frac{6x}{3x^3y} + \frac{5}{3x^3y}$$

$$= \frac{6x+5}{3x^3y} \quad \text{\textit{Add the numerators.}}$$

b. The LCD is the product of the two denominators: $(x+2)(x-2)$.

$$\frac{3x}{x+2} + \frac{2x}{x-2} = \frac{3x \cdot (x-2)}{(x+2) \cdot (x-2)} + \frac{2x \cdot (x+2)}{(x-2) \cdot (x+2)} \quad \text{\textit{Write equivalent rational expressions.}}$$

$$= \frac{3x(x-2) + 2x(x+2)}{(x+2)(x-2)} \quad \text{\textit{Add the numerators.}}$$

$$= \frac{3x^2 - 6x + 2x^2 + 4x}{(x+2)(x-2)} \quad \text{\textit{Apply the distributive property.}}$$

$$= \frac{5x^2 - 2x}{(x+2)(x-2)} \quad \text{\textit{Simplify the numerator.}}$$

c. The LCD is either $x - 1$ or $1 - x$. To get a common denominator of $x - 1$, we factor -1 from the denominator of the second rational expression.

$$\frac{x}{x-1} - \frac{4}{1-x} = \frac{x}{x-1} - \frac{4}{-1(x-1)} \qquad \text{Write } 1 - x \text{ as } -1(x-1).$$

$$= \frac{x}{x-1} - \frac{-1 \cdot 4}{x-1} \qquad \text{Write } \frac{4}{-1(x-1)} \text{ as } \frac{-1 \cdot 4}{x-1}.$$

$$= \frac{x - (-4)}{x-1}$$

$$= \frac{x + 4}{x-1} \qquad \text{Simplify.}$$

EXAMPLE 4

Subtract $\dfrac{5k}{k^2 - 4} - \dfrac{2}{k^2 + k - 2}$.

Solution $\dfrac{5k}{k^2 - 4} - \dfrac{2}{k^2 + k - 2} = \dfrac{5k}{(k+2)(k-2)} - \dfrac{2}{(k+2)(k-1)}$ Factor each denominator to find the LCD.

The LCD is $(k + 2)(k - 2)(k - 1)$. We write equivalent rational expressions with the LCD as denominators.

$$\frac{5k}{(k+2)(k-2)} - \frac{2}{(k+2)(k-1)} = \frac{5k \cdot (k-1)}{(k+2)(k-2) \cdot (k-1)} - \frac{2 \cdot (k-2)}{(k+2)(k-1) \cdot (k-2)} \qquad \text{Subtract the numerators.}$$

$$= \frac{5k(k-1) - 2(k-2)}{(k+2)(k-2)(k-1)}$$

$$= \frac{5k^2 - 5k - 2k + 4}{(k+2)(k-2)(k-1)} \qquad \text{Multiply in the numerator.}$$

$$= \frac{5k^2 - 7k + 4}{(k+2)(k-2)(k-1)} \qquad \text{Simplify.}$$

EXAMPLE 5

Add $\dfrac{2x - 1}{2x^2 - 9x - 5} + \dfrac{x + 3}{6x^2 - x - 2}$.

Solution $\dfrac{2x - 1}{2x^2 - 9x - 5} + \dfrac{x + 3}{6x^2 - x - 2} = \dfrac{2x - 1}{(2x + 1)(x - 5)} + \dfrac{x + 3}{(2x + 1)(3x - 2)}$ Factor the denominators.

The LCD is $(2x + 1)(x - 5)(3x - 2)$.

$$= \frac{(2x - 1) \cdot (3x - 2)}{(2x + 1)(x - 5) \cdot (3x - 2)} + \frac{(x + 3) \cdot (x - 5)}{(2x + 1)(3x - 2) \cdot (x - 5)}$$

$$= \frac{(2x - 1)(3x - 2) + (x + 3)(x - 5)}{(2x + 1)(x - 5)(3x - 2)} \qquad \text{Add the numerators.}$$

$$= \frac{6x^2 - 7x + 2 + x^2 - 2x - 15}{(2x + 1)(x - 5)(3x - 2)} \qquad \text{Multiply in the numerator.}$$

$$= \frac{7x^2 - 9x - 13}{(2x + 1)(x - 5)(3x - 2)} \qquad \text{Simplify.}$$

EXAMPLE 6

Perform each indicated operation.

$$\frac{7}{x-1} + \frac{10x}{x^2-1} - \frac{5}{x+1}$$

Solution

$$\frac{7}{x-1} + \frac{10x}{x^2-1} - \frac{5}{x+1} = \frac{7}{x-1} + \frac{10x}{(x-1)(x+1)} - \frac{5}{x+1} \qquad \text{Factor the denominators.}$$

The LCD is $(x-1)(x+1)$.

$$= \frac{7 \cdot (x+1)}{(x-1) \cdot (x+1)} + \frac{10x}{(x-1)(x+1)} - \frac{5 \cdot (x-1)}{(x+1) \cdot (x-1)}$$

$$= \frac{7(x+1) + 10x - 5(x-1)}{(x-1)(x+1)} \qquad \text{Add and subtract the numerators.}$$

$$= \frac{7x + 7 + 10x - 5x + 5}{(x-1)(x+1)} \qquad \text{Multiply in the numerator.}$$

$$= \frac{12x + 12}{(x-1)(x+1)} \qquad \text{Simplify.}$$

$$= \frac{12(x+1)}{(x-1)(x+1)} \qquad \text{Factor the numerator.}$$

$$= \frac{12}{x-1} \qquad \text{Divide out common factors.}$$

STUDY SKILLS REMINDER

Is Your Notebook Still Organized?

Is your notebook still organized? It it's not, it's not too late to start organizing it. Start writing your notes and completing your homework assignment in a notebook with pockets (spiral or ring binder). Take class notes in this notebook, and then follow the notes with your completed homework assignment. When you receive graded papers or handouts, place them in the notebook pocket so that you will not lose them.

Remember to mark (possibly with an exclamation point) any note(s) that seem extra important to you. Also remember to mark (possibly with a question mark) any notes or homework that you are having trouble with. Don't forget to see your instructor or a math tutor to help you with the concepts or exercises that you are having trouble understanding.

Also don't forget to write neatly and keep a positive attitude.

Graphing Calculator Explorations

A graphing calculator can be used to support the results of operations on rational expressions. For example, to verify the result of Example 3b, graph

$$Y_1 = \frac{3x}{x+2} + \frac{2x}{x-2} \quad \text{and} \quad Y_2 = \frac{5x^2 - 2x}{(x+2)(x-2)}$$

on the same set of axes. The graphs should be the same. Use a Table feature or a Trace feature to see that this is true.

MENTAL MATH

Name the operation(s) below that make each statement true.

a. Addition   **b.** Subtraction   **c.** Multiplication   **d.** Division

1. The denominators must be the same before performing the operation.

2. To perform this operation, you multiply the first rational expression by the reciprocal of the second rational expression.

3. Numerator times numerator all over denominator times denominator.

4. These operations are commutative (order doesn't matter.)

For the rational expressions $\dfrac{5}{y}$ and $\dfrac{7}{y}$, perform each operation mentally.

5. Addition   **6.** Subtraction   **7.** Multiplication   **8.** Division

EXERCISE SET 6.2

STUDY GUIDE/SSM   CD/ VIDEO   PH MATH TUTOR CENTER   MathXL®Tutorials ON CD   MathXL®   MyMathLab®

Perform the indicated operation. If possible, simplify your answer. See Example 1.

1. $\dfrac{2}{x} - \dfrac{5}{x}$

2. $\dfrac{4}{x^2} + \dfrac{2}{x^2}$

3. $\dfrac{2}{x-2} + \dfrac{x}{x-2}$

4. $\dfrac{x}{5-x} + \dfrac{2}{5-x}$

5. $\dfrac{x^2}{x+2} - \dfrac{4}{x+2}$

6. $\dfrac{4}{x-2} - \dfrac{x^2}{x-2}$

7. $\dfrac{2x-6}{x^2+x-6} + \dfrac{3-3x}{x^2+x-6}$

8. $\dfrac{5x+2}{x^2+2x-8} + \dfrac{2-4x}{x^2+2x-8}$

△ **9.** Find the perimeter and the area of the square.

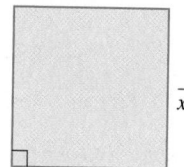

$\dfrac{x}{x+5}$ ft

△ **10.** Find the perimeter of the quadrilateral.

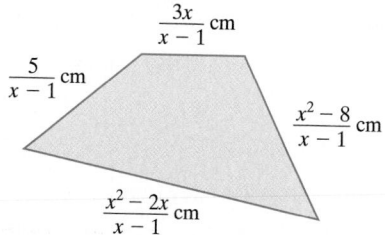

$\dfrac{3x}{x-1}$ cm

$\dfrac{5}{x-1}$ cm

$\dfrac{x^2-8}{x-1}$ cm

$\dfrac{x^2-2x}{x-1}$ cm

Find the LCD of the rational expressions in each list. See Example 2.

11. $\dfrac{2}{7}, \dfrac{3}{5x}$

12. $\dfrac{4}{5y}, \dfrac{3}{4y^2}$

13. $\dfrac{3}{x}, \dfrac{2}{x+1}$

14. $\dfrac{5}{2x}, \dfrac{7}{2+x}$

15. $\dfrac{12}{x+7}, \dfrac{8}{x-7}$

16. $\dfrac{1}{2x-1}, \dfrac{x}{2x+1}$

17. $\dfrac{5}{3x+6}, \dfrac{2x}{2x-4}$

18. $\dfrac{2}{3a+9}, \dfrac{5}{5a-15}$

19. $\dfrac{5+x}{(3x-1)(x+2)}, \dfrac{2}{3x-1}$

20. $\dfrac{6-x}{(x+3)(x-3)}, \dfrac{9}{x+3}$

21. $\dfrac{2a}{a^2-b^2}, \dfrac{1}{a^2-2ab+b^2}$

22. $\dfrac{2a}{a^2+8a+16}, \dfrac{7a}{a^2+a-12}$

23. $\dfrac{x}{x^2-9}, \dfrac{5x}{x}, \dfrac{7}{12-4x}$

24. $\dfrac{9}{x^2-25}, \dfrac{1}{50-10x}, \dfrac{6}{x}$

25. When is the LCD of two rational expressions equal to the product of their denominators? (*Hint:* What is the LCD of $\dfrac{1}{x}$ and $\dfrac{7}{x+5}$?)

26. When is the LCD of two rational expressions with different denominators equal to one of the denominators?(*Hint:* What is the LCD of $\dfrac{3x}{x+2}$ and $\dfrac{7x+1}{(x+2)^3}$?)

Perform the indicated operation. If possible, simplify your answer. See Example 3a and 3b.

27. $\dfrac{4}{3x} + \dfrac{3}{2x}$

28. $\dfrac{10}{7x} - \dfrac{5}{2x}$

29. 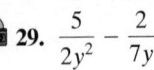 $\dfrac{5}{2y^2} - \dfrac{2}{7y}$

30. $\dfrac{4}{11x^4y} - \dfrac{1}{4x^2y^3}$

31. $\dfrac{x-3}{x+4} - \dfrac{x+2}{x-4}$

32. $\dfrac{x-1}{x-5} - \dfrac{x+2}{x+5}$

33. $\dfrac{1}{x-5} + \dfrac{x}{x^2-x-20}$

34. $\dfrac{x+1}{x^2-x-20} - \dfrac{2}{x+4}$

Perform the indicated operation. If possible, simplify your answer. See Example 3c.

35. $\dfrac{1}{a-b} + \dfrac{1}{b-a}$

36. $\dfrac{1}{a-3} - \dfrac{1}{3-a}$

37. $\dfrac{x+1}{1-x} + \dfrac{1}{x-1}$

38. $\dfrac{5}{1-x} - \dfrac{1}{x-1}$

39. $\dfrac{5}{x-2} + \dfrac{x+4}{2-x}$

40. $\dfrac{3}{5-x} + \dfrac{x+2}{x-5}$

Perform each indicated operation. If possible, simplify your answer. See Examples 4 through 6.

41. $\dfrac{y+1}{y^2-6y+8} - \dfrac{3}{y^2-16}$

42. $\dfrac{x+2}{x^2-36} - \dfrac{x}{x^2+9x+18}$

43. $\dfrac{x+4}{3x^2+11x+6} + \dfrac{x}{2x^2+x-15}$

44. $\dfrac{x+3}{5x^2+12x+4} + \dfrac{6}{x^2-x-6}$

45. $\dfrac{7}{x^2-x-2} + \dfrac{x}{x^2+4x+3}$

46. $\dfrac{a}{a^2+10a+25} + \dfrac{4}{a^2+6a+5}$

47. $\dfrac{2}{x+1} - \dfrac{3x}{3x+3} + \dfrac{1}{2x+2}$

48. $\dfrac{5}{3x-6} - \dfrac{x}{x-2} + \dfrac{3+2x}{5x-10}$

49. $\dfrac{3}{x+3} + \dfrac{5}{x^2+6x+9} - \dfrac{x}{x^2-9}$

50. $\dfrac{x+2}{x^2-2x-3} + \dfrac{x}{x-3} - \dfrac{4}{x+1}$

MIXED PRACTICE

Add or subtract as indicated. If possible, simplify your answer.

51. $\dfrac{4}{3x^2y^3} + \dfrac{5}{3x^2y^3}$

52. $\dfrac{7}{2xy^4} + \dfrac{1}{2xy^4}$

53. $\dfrac{x-5}{2x} - \dfrac{x+5}{2x}$

54. $\dfrac{x+4}{4x} - \dfrac{x-4}{4x}$

55. $\dfrac{3}{2x+10} + \dfrac{8}{3x+15}$

56. $\dfrac{10}{3x-3} + \dfrac{1}{7x-7}$

57. $\dfrac{-2}{x^2-3x} - \dfrac{1}{x^3-3x^2}$

58. $\dfrac{-3}{2a+8} - \dfrac{8}{a^2+4a}$

59. $\dfrac{ab}{a^2-b^2} + \dfrac{b}{a+b}$

60. $\dfrac{x}{25-x^2} + \dfrac{2}{3x-15}$

61. $\dfrac{5}{x^2-4} - \dfrac{3}{x^2+4x+4}$

62. $\dfrac{3z}{z^2-9} - \dfrac{2}{3-z}$

63. $\dfrac{2}{a^2+2a+1} + \dfrac{3}{a^2-1}$

64. $\dfrac{9x+2}{3x^2-2x-8} + \dfrac{7}{3x^2+x-4}$

65. In your own words, explain how to add rational expressions with different denominators.

6. In your own words, explain how to multiply rational expressions.

7. In your own words, explain how to divide rational expressions.

8. In your own words, explain how to subtract rational expressions with different denominators.

Perform the indicated operation. If possible, simplify your answer.

9. $\left(\dfrac{2}{3} - \dfrac{1}{x}\right) \cdot \left(\dfrac{3}{x} + \dfrac{1}{2}\right)$

70. $\left(\dfrac{2}{3} - \dfrac{1}{x}\right) \div \left(\dfrac{3}{x} + \dfrac{1}{2}\right)$

71. $\left(\dfrac{1}{x} + \dfrac{2}{3}\right) - \left(\dfrac{1}{x} - \dfrac{2}{3}\right)$ **72.** $\left(\dfrac{1}{2} + \dfrac{2}{x}\right) - \left(\dfrac{1}{2} - \dfrac{1}{x}\right)$

73. $\left(\dfrac{2a}{3}\right)^2 \div \left(\dfrac{a^2}{a+1} - \dfrac{1}{a+1}\right)$

74. $\left(\dfrac{x+2}{2x} - \dfrac{x-2}{2x}\right) \cdot \left(\dfrac{5x}{4}\right)^2$

75. $\left(\dfrac{2x}{3}\right)^2 \div \left(\dfrac{x}{3}\right)^2$ **76.** $\left(\dfrac{2x}{3}\right)^2 \cdot \left(\dfrac{3}{x}\right)^2$

77. $\dfrac{x}{x^2-9} + \dfrac{3}{x^2-6x+9} - \dfrac{1}{x+3}$

78. $\dfrac{3}{x^2-9} - \dfrac{x}{x^2-6x+9} + \dfrac{1}{x+3}$

79. $\left(\dfrac{x}{x+1} - \dfrac{x}{x-1}\right) \div \dfrac{x}{2x+2}$

80. $\dfrac{x}{2x+2} \div \left(\dfrac{x}{x+1} + \dfrac{x}{x-1}\right)$

81. $\dfrac{4}{x} \cdot \left(\dfrac{2}{x+2} - \dfrac{2}{x-2}\right)$

82. $\dfrac{1}{x+1} \cdot \left(\dfrac{5}{x} + \dfrac{2}{x-3}\right)$

REVIEW AND PREVIEW

Use the distributive property to multiply the following. See Section 1.4.

83. $12\left(\dfrac{2}{3} + \dfrac{1}{6}\right)$ **84.** $14\left(\dfrac{1}{7} + \dfrac{3}{14}\right)$

85. $x^2\left(\dfrac{4}{x^2} + 1\right)$ **86.** $5y^2\left(\dfrac{1}{y^2} - \dfrac{1}{5}\right)$

Find each root. See Section 1.3.

87. $\sqrt{100}$ **88.** $\sqrt{25}$

89. $\sqrt[3]{8}$ **90.** $\sqrt[3]{27}$

91. $\sqrt[4]{81}$ **92.** $\sqrt[4]{16}$

Use the Pythagorean theorem to find each unknown length of a right triangle. See Section 5.8.

△ **93.**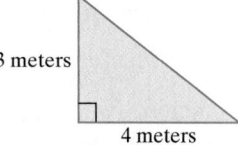

△ **94.**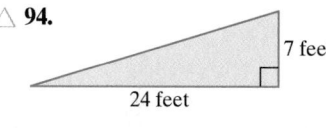

Concept Extensions

Perform the indicated operation. Begin by writing each term with positive exponents only.

95. $x^{-1} + (2x)^{-1}$ **96.** $3y^{-1} + (4y)^{-1}$

97. $4x^{-2} - 3x^{-1}$ **98.** $(4x)^{-2} - (3x)^{-1}$

99. $x^{-3}(2x+1) - 5x^{-2}$ **100.** $4x^{-3} + x^{-4}(5x+7)$

 Use a graphing calculator to support the results of each exercise.

101. Exercise 3 **102.** Exercise 4

103. Exercise 31 **104.** Exercise 32

6.3 *SIMPLIFYING COMPLEX FRACTIONS*

Objectives

1 Simplify complex fractions by simplifying the numerator and denominator and then dividing.

2 Simplify complex fractions by multiplying by a common denominator.

3 Simplify expressions with negative exponents.

1 A rational expression whose numerator, denominator, or both contain one o
more rational expressions is called a **complex rational expression** or a **complex fraction**

Complex Fractions

$$\frac{\dfrac{1}{a}}{\dfrac{b}{2}} \qquad \frac{\dfrac{x}{2y^2}}{6x-2} \qquad \frac{x+\dfrac{1}{y}}{y+1}$$

The parts of a complex fraction are

$$\left.\frac{\left.\dfrac{x}{y+2}\right\}}{7+\dfrac{1}{y}\Biggr\}}\right.$$

← Numerator of complex fraction.

← Main fraction bar.

← Denominator of complex fraction.

Our goal in this section is to simplify complex fractions. A complex fraction is simpli
fied when it is in the form $\dfrac{P}{Q}$, where P and Q are polynomials that have no common

factors. Two methods of simplifying complex fractions are introduced. The first method
evolves from the definition of a fraction as a quotient.

Simplifying A Complex Fraction: Method I

Step 1: Simplify the numerator and the denominator of the complex fraction so
that each is a single fraction.

Step 2: Perform the indicated division by multiplying the numerator of the
complex fraction by the reciprocal of the denominator of the complex
fraction.

Step 3: Simplify if possible.

EXAMPLE 1

Simplify each complex fraction.

a. $\dfrac{\dfrac{2x}{27y^2}}{\dfrac{6x^2}{9}}$ **b.** $\dfrac{\dfrac{5x}{x+2}}{\dfrac{10}{x-2}}$ **c.** $\dfrac{\dfrac{x}{y^2}+\dfrac{1}{y}}{\dfrac{y}{x^2}+\dfrac{1}{x}}$

Solution **a.** The numerator of the complex fraction is already a single fraction, and so is the de
nominator. Perform the indicated division by multiplying the numerator, $\dfrac{2x}{27y^2}$, by
the reciprocal of the denominator, $\dfrac{6x^2}{9}$. Then simplify.

$$\frac{\dfrac{2x}{27y^2}}{\dfrac{6x^2}{9}} = \frac{2x}{27y^2} \div \frac{6x^2}{9}$$

$$= \frac{2x}{27y^2} \cdot \frac{9}{6x^2} \qquad \text{Multiply by the reciprocal of } \frac{6x^2}{9}.$$

$$= \frac{2x \cdot 9}{27y^2 \cdot 6x^2}$$

$$= \frac{1}{9xy^2}$$

Helpful Hint

Both the numerator and denominator are single fractions, so we perform the indicated division.

b. $\dfrac{\left\{\dfrac{5x}{x+2}\right.}{\left\{\dfrac{10}{x-2}\right.} = \dfrac{5x}{x+2} \div \dfrac{10}{x-2} = \dfrac{5x}{x+2} \cdot \dfrac{x-2}{10}$ Multiply by the reciprocal of $\dfrac{10}{x-2}$.

$$= \frac{5x(x-2)}{2 \cdot 5(x+2)}$$

$$= \frac{x(x-2)}{2(x+2)} \qquad \text{Simplify.}$$

c. First simplify the numerator and the denominator of the complex fraction separately so that each is a single fraction. Then perform the indicated division.

$$\frac{\dfrac{x}{y^2} + \dfrac{1}{y}}{\dfrac{y}{x^2} + \dfrac{1}{x}} = \frac{\dfrac{x}{y^2} + \dfrac{1 \cdot y}{y \cdot y}}{\dfrac{y}{x^2} + \dfrac{1 \cdot x}{x \cdot x}} \qquad \begin{array}{l}\text{Simplify the numerator. The LCD is } y^2.\\ \text{Simplify the denominator. The LCD is } x^2.\end{array}$$

$$= \frac{\dfrac{x+y}{y^2}}{\dfrac{y+x}{x^2}} \qquad \text{Add.}$$

$$= \frac{x+y}{y^2} \div \frac{y+x}{x^2} \qquad \text{Add.}$$

$$= \frac{x+y}{y^2} \cdot \frac{x^2}{y+x} \qquad \text{Multiply by the reciprocal of } \frac{y+x}{x^2}.$$

$$= \frac{x^2(x+y)}{y^2(y+x)}$$

$$= \frac{x^2}{y^2} \qquad \text{Simplify.}$$

✔ **CONCEPT CHECK**

Which of the following are equivalent to $\dfrac{\dfrac{1}{x}}{\dfrac{3}{y}}$?

a. $\dfrac{1}{x} \div \dfrac{3}{y}$ **b.** $\dfrac{1}{x} \cdot \dfrac{y}{3}$ **c.** $\dfrac{1}{x} \div \dfrac{y}{3}$

2   Next we look at another method of simplifying complex fractions. With this method we multiply the numerator and the denominator of the complex fraction by the LCD of all fractions in the complex fraction.

Simplifying A Complex Fraction: Method II

Step 1: Multiply the numerator and the denominator of the complex fraction by the LCD of the fractions in both the numerator and the denominator.

Step 2: Simplify.

EXAMPLE 2

Simplify each complex fraction.

a. $\dfrac{\dfrac{5x}{x+2}}{\dfrac{10}{x-2}}$ **b.** $\dfrac{\dfrac{x}{y^2}+\dfrac{1}{y}}{\dfrac{y}{x^2}+\dfrac{1}{x}}$

Solution   **a.** The least common denominator of $\dfrac{5x}{x+2}$ and $\dfrac{10}{x-2}$ is $(x+2)(x-2)$. Multiply both the numerator, $\dfrac{5x}{x+2}$, and the denominator, $\dfrac{10}{x-2}$, by the LCD.

$$\dfrac{\dfrac{5x}{x+2}}{\dfrac{10}{x-2}} = \dfrac{\left(\dfrac{5x}{x+2}\right)\cdot(x+2)(x-2)}{\left(\dfrac{10}{x-2}\right)\cdot(x+2)(x-2)}$$ Multiply numerator and denominator by the LCD

$$= \dfrac{5x\cdot(x-2)}{2\cdot5\cdot(x+2)}$$ Simplify.

$$= \dfrac{x(x-2)}{2(x+2)}$$ Simplify.

b. The least common denominator of $\dfrac{x}{y^2}, \dfrac{1}{y}, \dfrac{y}{x^2},$ and $\dfrac{1}{x}$ is x^2y^2.

$$\frac{\dfrac{x}{y^2} + \dfrac{1}{y}}{\dfrac{y}{x^2} + \dfrac{1}{x}} = \frac{\left(\dfrac{x}{y^2} + \dfrac{1}{y}\right) \cdot x^2y^2}{\left(\dfrac{y}{x^2} + \dfrac{1}{x}\right) \cdot x^2y^2}$$ Multiply the numerator and denominator by the LCD.

$$= \frac{\dfrac{x}{y^2} \cdot x^2y^2 + \dfrac{1}{y} \cdot x^2y^2}{\dfrac{y}{x^2} \cdot x^2y^2 + \dfrac{1}{x} \cdot x^2y^2}$$ Use the distributive property.

$$= \frac{x^3 + x^2y}{y^3 + xy^2}$$ Simplify.

$$= \frac{x^2(x + y)}{y^2(y + x)}$$ Factor.

$$= \frac{x^2}{y^2}$$ Simplify.

3   If an expression contains negative exponents, write the expression as an equivalent expression with positive exponents.

EXAMPLE 3

Simplify.

$$\frac{x^{-1} + 2xy^{-1}}{x^{-2} - x^{-2}y^{-1}}$$

Solution   This fraction does not appear to be a complex fraction. If we write it by using only positive exponents, however, we see that it is a complex fraction.

$$\frac{x^{-1} + 2xy^{-1}}{x^{-2} - x^{-2}y^{-1}} = \frac{\dfrac{1}{x} + \dfrac{2x}{y}}{\dfrac{1}{x^2} - \dfrac{1}{x^2y}}$$

The LCD of $\dfrac{1}{x}, \dfrac{2x}{y}, \dfrac{1}{x^2},$ and $\dfrac{1}{x^2y}$ is x^2y. Multiply both the numerator and denominator by x^2y.

$$= \frac{\left(\dfrac{1}{x} + \dfrac{2x}{y}\right) \cdot x^2y}{\left(\dfrac{1}{x^2} - \dfrac{1}{x^2y}\right) \cdot x^2y}$$

$$= \frac{\dfrac{1}{x} \cdot x^2y + \dfrac{2x}{y} \cdot x^2y}{\dfrac{1}{x^2} \cdot x^2y - \dfrac{1}{x^2y} \cdot x^2y}$$ Apply the distributive property.

$$= \frac{xy + 2x^3}{y - 1} \quad \text{or} \quad \frac{x(y + 2x^2)}{y - 1}$$ Simplify.

EXAMPLE 4

Simplify: $\dfrac{(2x)^{-1} + 1}{2x^{-1} - 1}$

Solution

Helpful Hint

Don't forget that

$(2x)^{-1} = \dfrac{1}{2x}$, but

$2x^{-1} = 2 \cdot \dfrac{1}{x} = \dfrac{2}{x}$.

$$\frac{(2x)^{-1} + 1}{2x^{-1} - 1} = \frac{\dfrac{1}{2x} + 1}{\dfrac{2}{x} - 1}$$

Write using positive exponents.

$$= \frac{\left(\dfrac{1}{2x} + 1\right) \cdot 2x}{\left(\dfrac{2}{x} - 1\right) \cdot 2x}$$

The LDC of $\dfrac{1}{2x}$ and $\dfrac{2}{x}$ is 2x.

$$= \frac{\dfrac{1}{2x} \cdot 2x + 1 \cdot 2x}{\dfrac{2}{x} \cdot 2x - 1 \cdot 2x}$$

Use distributive property.

$$= \frac{1 + 2x}{4 - 2x} \quad \text{or} \quad \frac{1 + 2x}{2(2 - x)}$$

Simplify.

STUDY SKILLS REMINDER

Are You Satisfied With Your Performance in this Course thus Far?

If not, ask yourself the following questions:

▶ Am I attending all class periods and arriving on time?

▶ Am I working and checking my homework assignments?

▶ Am I getting help when I need it?

▶ In addition to my instructor, am I using the supplements to this text that could help me? For example, the tutorial video lessons? The tutorial software?

▶ Am I satisfied with my performance on quizzes and tests?

If you answered no to *any* of these questions, read or reread Section 1.1 for suggestions in these areas. Also, you may want to contact your instructor for additional feedback.

EXERCISE SET 6.3

STUDY   CD/   PH MATH   MathXL®Tutorials   MathXL®   MyMathLab®
GUIDE/SSM   VIDEO   TUTOR CENTER   ON CD

Simplify each complex fraction. See Examples 1 and 2.

1. $\dfrac{\dfrac{10}{3x}}{\dfrac{5}{6x}}$

2. $\dfrac{\dfrac{15}{2x}}{\dfrac{5}{6x}}$

3. $\dfrac{1 + \dfrac{2}{5}}{2 + \dfrac{3}{5}}$

4. $\dfrac{2 + \dfrac{1}{7}}{3 - \dfrac{4}{7}}$

5. $\dfrac{\dfrac{4}{x-1}}{\dfrac{x}{x-1}}$

6. $\dfrac{\dfrac{x}{x+2}}{\dfrac{2}{x+2}}$

7. $\dfrac{1 - \dfrac{2}{x}}{x + \dfrac{4}{9x}}$

8. $\dfrac{5 - \dfrac{3}{x}}{x + \dfrac{2}{3x}}$

9. $\dfrac{\dfrac{4x^2 - y^2}{xy}}{\dfrac{2}{y} - \dfrac{1}{x}}$

10. $\dfrac{\dfrac{x^2 - 9y^2}{xy}}{\dfrac{1}{y} - \dfrac{3}{x}}$

11. $\dfrac{\dfrac{x+1}{3}}{\dfrac{2x-1}{6}}$

12. $\dfrac{\dfrac{x+3}{12}}{\dfrac{4x-5}{15}}$

13. $\dfrac{\dfrac{2}{x} + \dfrac{3}{x^2}}{\dfrac{4}{x^2} - \dfrac{9}{x}}$

14. $\dfrac{\dfrac{2}{x^2} + \dfrac{1}{x}}{\dfrac{4}{x^2} - \dfrac{1}{x}}$

15. $\dfrac{\dfrac{1}{x} + \dfrac{2}{x^2}}{x + \dfrac{8}{x^2}}$

16. $\dfrac{\dfrac{1}{y} + \dfrac{3}{y^2}}{y + \dfrac{27}{y^2}}$

17. $\dfrac{\dfrac{4}{5-x} + \dfrac{5}{x-5}}{\dfrac{2}{x} + \dfrac{3}{x-5}}$

18. $\dfrac{\dfrac{3}{x-4} - \dfrac{2}{4-x}}{\dfrac{2}{x-4} - \dfrac{2}{x}}$

19. $\dfrac{\dfrac{x+2}{x} - \dfrac{2}{x-1}}{\dfrac{x+1}{x} + \dfrac{x+1}{x-1}}$

20. $\dfrac{\dfrac{5}{a+2} - \dfrac{1}{a-2}}{\dfrac{3}{2+a} + \dfrac{6}{2-a}}$

21. $\dfrac{\dfrac{2}{x} + 3}{\dfrac{4}{x^2} - 9}$

22. $\dfrac{2 + \dfrac{1}{x}}{4x - \dfrac{1}{x}}$

23. $\dfrac{1 - \dfrac{x}{y}}{\dfrac{x^2}{y^2} - 1}$

24. $\dfrac{1 - \dfrac{2}{x}}{x - \dfrac{4}{x}}$

25. $\dfrac{\dfrac{-2x}{x-y}}{\dfrac{y}{x^2}}$

26. $\dfrac{\dfrac{7y}{x^2 + xy}}{\dfrac{y^2}{x^2}}$

27. $\dfrac{\dfrac{2}{x} + \dfrac{1}{x^2}}{\dfrac{y}{x^2}}$

28. $\dfrac{\dfrac{5}{x^2} - \dfrac{2}{x}}{\dfrac{1}{x} + 2}$

29. $\dfrac{\dfrac{x}{9} - \dfrac{1}{x}}{1 + \dfrac{3}{x}}$

30. $\dfrac{\dfrac{x}{4} - \dfrac{4}{x}}{1 - \dfrac{4}{x}}$

31. $\dfrac{\dfrac{x-1}{x^2-4}}{1 + \dfrac{1}{x-2}}$

32. $\dfrac{\dfrac{2}{x+5} + \dfrac{4}{x+3}}{\dfrac{3x+13}{x^2+8x+15}}$

Simplify. See Examples 3 and 4.

33. $\dfrac{x^{-1}}{x^{-2} + y^{-2}}$

34. $\dfrac{a^{-3} + b^{-1}}{a^{-2}}$

35. $\dfrac{2a^{-1} + 3b^{-2}}{a^{-1} - b^{-1}}$

36. $\dfrac{x^{-1} + y^{-1}}{3x^{-2} + 5y^{-2}}$

37. $\dfrac{1}{x - x^{-1}}$

38. $\dfrac{x^{-2}}{x + 3x^{-1}}$

39. $\dfrac{a^{-1} + 1}{a^{-1} - 1}$

40. $\dfrac{a^{-1} - 4}{4 + a^{-1}}$

41. $\dfrac{3x^{-1} + (2y)^{-1}}{x^{-2}}$

42. $\dfrac{5x^{-2} - 3y^{-1}}{x^{-1} + y^{-1}}$

43. $\dfrac{2a^{-1} + (2a)^{-1}}{a^{-1} + 2a^{-2}}$

44. $\dfrac{a^{-1} + 2a^{-2}}{2a^{-1} + (2a)^{-1}}$

45. $\dfrac{5x^{-1} + 2y^{-1}}{x^{-2}y^{-2}}$

46. $\dfrac{x^{-2}y^{-2}}{5x^{-1} + 2y^{-1}}$

47. $\dfrac{5x^{-1} - 2y^{-1}}{25x^{-2} - 4y^{-2}}$

48. $\dfrac{3x^{-1} + 3y^{-1}}{4x^{-2} - 9y^{-2}}$

REVIEW AND PREVIEW

Simplify. See Sections 5.1 and 5.2.

49. $\dfrac{3x^3y^2}{12x}$

50. $\dfrac{-36xb^3}{9xb^2}$

51. $\dfrac{144x^5y^5}{-16x^2y}$

52. $\dfrac{48x^3y^2}{-4xy}$

Solve the following. See Section 2.6.

53. $|x - 5| = 9$

54. $|2y + 1| = 1$

Concept Extensions

55. When the source of a sound is traveling toward a listener, the pitch that the listener hears due to the Doppler effect is given by the complex rational compression $\dfrac{a}{1 - \dfrac{s}{770}}$, where

a is the actual pitch of the sound and s is the speed of the sound source. Simplify this expression.

56. In baseball, the earned run average (ERA) statistic gives the average number of earned runs scored on a pitcher per game. It is computed with the following expression: $\dfrac{E}{\dfrac{I}{9}}$,

where E is the number of earned runs scored on a pitcher and I is the total number of innings pitched by the pitcher.

Simplify this expression.

57. Which of the following are equivalent to $\dfrac{\dfrac{1}{x}}{\dfrac{3}{y}}$?

a. $\dfrac{1}{x} \div \dfrac{3}{y}$ **b.** $\dfrac{1}{x} \cdot \dfrac{y}{3}$ **c.** $\dfrac{1}{x} \div \dfrac{y}{3}$

58. In your own words, explain one method for simplifying a complex fraction.

Simplify.

59. $\dfrac{1}{1 + (1 + x)^{-1}}$

60. $\dfrac{(x + 2)^{-1} + (x - 2)^{-1}}{(x^2 - 4)^{-1}}$

61. $\dfrac{x}{1 - \dfrac{1}{1 + \dfrac{1}{x}}}$

62. $\dfrac{x}{1 - \dfrac{1}{1 - \dfrac{1}{x}}}$

63. $\dfrac{\dfrac{2}{y^2} - \dfrac{5}{xy} - \dfrac{3}{x^2}}{\dfrac{2}{y^2} + \dfrac{7}{xy} + \dfrac{3}{x^2}}$

64. $\dfrac{\dfrac{2}{x^2} - \dfrac{1}{xy} - \dfrac{1}{y^2}}{\dfrac{1}{x^2} - \dfrac{3}{xy} + \dfrac{2}{y^2}}$

65. $\dfrac{3(a + 1)^{-1} + 4a^{-2}}{(a^3 + a^2)^{-1}}$

66. $\dfrac{9x^{-1} - 5(x - y)^{-1}}{4(x - y)^{-1}}$

*In the study of calculus, the difference quotient $\dfrac{f(a + h) - f(a)}{h}$ is often found and simplified. Find and simplify this quotient for each function f(x) by following steps **a** through **d**.*

a. *Find* $(a + h)$.

b. *Find* $f(a)$.

c. *Use steps **a** and **b** to find* $\dfrac{f(a + h) - f(a)}{h}$

d. *Simplify the result of step **c**.*

67. $f(x) = \dfrac{1}{x}$

68. $f(x) = \dfrac{5}{x}$

69. $\dfrac{3}{x + 1}$

70. $\dfrac{2}{x^2}$

6.4   DIVIDING POLYNOMIALS

Objectives

1   Divide a polynomial by a monomial.

2   Divide by a polynomial.

1   Recall that a rational expression is a quotient of polynomials. An equivalent form of a rational expression can be obtained by performing the indicated division. For example, the rational expression $\dfrac{10x^3 - 5x^2 + 20x}{5x}$ can be thought of as the polynomial $10x^3 - 5x^2 + 20x$ divided by the monomial $5x$. To perform this division of a polynomial by a monomial (which we do below) recall the following addition fact for fractions with a common denominator.

$$\frac{a}{c} + \frac{b}{c} = \frac{a + b}{c}$$

If a, b, and c are monomials, we might read this equation from right to left and gain insight into dividing a polynomial by a monomial.

Dividing A Polynomial by a Monomial

Divide each term in the polynomial by the monomial.

$$\frac{a + b}{c} = \frac{a}{c} + \frac{b}{c}, \text{ where } c \neq 0$$

EXAMPLE 1

Divide $10x^3 - 5x^2 + 20x$ by $5x$.

Solution   We divide each term of $10x^3 - 5x^2 + 20x$ by $5x$ and simplify.

$$\frac{10x^3 - 5x^2 + 20x}{5x} = \frac{10x^3}{5x} - \frac{5x^2}{5x} + \frac{20x}{5x} = 2x^2 - x + 4$$

Check: To check, see that (quotient) (divisor) = dividend, or

$$(2x^2 - x + 4)(5x) = 10x^3 - 5x^2 + 20x.$$

EXAMPLE 2

Divide $\dfrac{3x^5y^2 - 15x^3y - x^2y - 6x}{x^2y}$

Solution   We divide each term in the numerator by x^2y.

$$\frac{3x^5y^2 - 15x^3y - x^2y - 6x}{x^2y} = \frac{3x^5y^2}{x^2y} - \frac{15x^3y}{x^2y} - \frac{x^2y}{x^2y} - \frac{6x}{x^2y}$$

$$= 3x^3y - 15x - 1 - \frac{6}{xy}$$

2   To divide a polynomial by a polynomial other than a monomial, we use **long division.** Polynomial long division is similar to long division of real numbers. We review long division of real numbers by dividing 7 into 296.

$$\begin{array}{r} 42 \\ 7\overline{)296} \\ \underline{-28} \\ 16 \\ \underline{-14} \\ 2 \end{array}$$

Divisor:

$4(7) = 28.$

Subtract and bring down the next digit in the dividend.

$2(7) = 14.$

Subtract. The remainder is 2.

The quotient is $42\dfrac{2\ \text{(remainder)}}{7\ \text{(divisor)}}$.

Check: To check, notice that

$$42(7) + 2 = 296, \text{ the dividend.}$$

This same division process can be applied to polynomials, as shown next.

EXAMPLE 3

Divide $2x^2 - x - 10$ by $x + 2$.

Solution $2x^2 - x - 10$ is the dividend, and $x + 2$ is the divisor.

Step 1: Divide $2x^2$ by x.

$$x + 2\overline{)2x^2 - x - 10}$$
quotient: $2x$

$\dfrac{2x^2}{x} = 2x$, so $2x$ is the first term of the quotient.

Step 2: Multiply $2x(x + 2)$.

$$\begin{array}{r} 2x \\ x + 2\overline{)2x^2 - x - 10} \\ 2x^2 + 4x \end{array}$$

$2x(x + 2)$

Like terms are lined up vertically.

Step 3: Subtract $(2x^2 + 4x)$ from $(2x^2 - x - 10)$ by changing the signs of $(2x^2 + 4x)$ and adding.

$$
\begin{array}{r}
2x \\
x + 2 \overline{)\,2x^2 - x - 10\,} \\
\underline{-2x^2 - 4x} \\
-5x
\end{array}
$$

Step 4: Bring down the next term, -10, and start the process over.

$$
\begin{array}{r}
2x \\
x + 2 \overline{)\,2x^2 - x - 10\,} \\
\underline{-2x^2 - 4x} \\
-5x - 10
\end{array}
$$

Step 5: Divide $-5x$ by x.

$$
\begin{array}{r}
2x - 5 \\
x + 2 \overline{)\,2x^2 - x - 10\,} \\
\underline{-2x^2 - 4x} \\
-5x - 10
\end{array}
$$

$\dfrac{-5x}{x} = -5$, so -5 is the second term of the quotient.

Step 6: Multiply $-5(x + 2)$.

$$
\begin{array}{r}
2x - 5 \\
x + 2 \overline{)\,2x^2 - x - 10\,} \\
\underline{-2x^2 - 4x} \\
-5x - 10 \\
-5x - 10
\end{array}
$$

$-5(x + 2)$

Like terms are lined up vertically.

Step 7: Subtract $(-5x - 10)$ from $(-5x - 10)$.

$$
\begin{array}{r}
2x - 5 \\
x + 2 \overline{)\,2x^2 - x - 10\,} \\
\underline{-2x^2 - 4x} \\
-5x - 10 \\
\underline{+5x + 10} \\
0
\end{array}
$$

Then $\dfrac{2x^2 - x - 10}{x + 2} = 2x - 5$. There is no remainder.

Check: Check this result by multiplying $2x - 5$ by $x + 2$. Their product is $(2x - 5)(x + 2) = 2x^2 - x - 10$, the dividend.

EXAMPLE 4

Divide: $(6x^2 - 19x + 12) \div (3x - 5)$

Solution

$$\begin{array}{r} 2x \\ 3x - 5 \overline{)6x^2 - 19x + 12} \\ \underline{6x^2 - 10x} \\ -9x + 12 \end{array}$$

Divide $\dfrac{6x^2}{3x} = 2x$.

Multiply $2x(3x - 5)$.
Subtract by adding the opposite.
Bring down the next term, $+12$.

$$\begin{array}{r} 2x - 3 \\ 3x - 5 \overline{)6x^2 - 19x + 12} \\ \underline{6x^2 - 10x} \\ -9x + 12 \\ \underline{-9x + 15} \\ -3 \end{array}$$

Divide $\dfrac{-9x}{3x} = -3$.

Multiply $-3(3x - 5)$.
Subtract by adding the opposite.

Check:

divisor	·	quotient	+	remainder

$$(3x - 5) \qquad (2x - 3) \qquad + 1(-3) = 6x^2 - 19x + 15 - 3$$
$$= 6x^2 - 19x + 12 \qquad \text{The dividend}$$

The division checks, so

$$\frac{6x^2 - 19x + 12}{3x - 5} = 2x - 3 - \frac{3}{3x - 5}$$

> **Helpful Hint**
> This fraction is the remainder over the divisor.

EXAMPLE 5

Divide: $(7x^3 + 16x^2 + 2x - 1) \div (x + 4)$.

Solution

$$\begin{array}{r} 7x^2 - 12x + 50 \\ x + 4 \overline{)7x^3 + 16x^2 + 2x - 1} \\ \underline{7x^3 + 28x^2} \\ -12x^2 + 2x \\ \underline{-12x^2 - 48x} \\ 50x - 1 \\ \underline{50x + 200} \\ -201 \end{array}$$

Divide $\dfrac{7x^3}{x} = 7x^2$.

$7x^2(x + 4)$

Subtract. Bring down $2x$.
$\dfrac{-12x^2}{x} = -12x$, a term of the quotient.
$-12x(x + 4)$

Subtract. Bring down -1.
$\dfrac{50x}{x} = 50$, a term of the quotient.
$50(x + 4)$.
Subtract.

Thus, $\dfrac{7x^3 + 16x^2 + 2x - 1}{x + 4} = 7x^2 - 12x + 50 + \dfrac{-201}{x + 4}$ or

$$7x^2 - 12x + 50 + \frac{201}{x + 4}.$$

EXAMPLE 6

Divide $3x^4 + 2x^3 - 8x + 6$ by $x^2 - 1$.

Solution Before dividing, we represent any "missing powers" by the product of 0 and the variable raised to the missing power. There is no x^2 term in the dividend, so we include $0x^2$ to represent the missing term. Also, there is no x term in the divisor, so we include $0x$ in the divisor.

$$
\begin{array}{r}
3x^2 + 2x + 3 \\
x^2 + 0x - 1\overline{)3x^4 + 2x^3 + 0x^2 - 8x + 6} \\
\underline{3x^4 + 0x^3 - 3x^2} \\
2x^3 + 3x^2 - 8x \\
\underline{2x^3 - 0x^2 - 2x} \\
3x^2 - 6x + 6 \\
\underline{3x^2 + 0x - 3} \\
-6x + 9
\end{array}
$$

$\dfrac{3x^4}{x^2} = 3x^2$

$3x^2(x^2 + 0x - 1)$

Subtract. Bring down $-8x$.

$\dfrac{2x^3}{x^2} = 2x$, a term of the quotient.

$2x(x^2 + 0x - 1)$

Subtract. Bring down 6.

$\dfrac{3x^2}{x^2} = 3$, a term of the quotient.

$3(x^2 + 0x - 1)$

Subtract.

The division process is finished when the degree of the remainder polynomial is less than the degree of the divisor. Thus,

$$\frac{3x^4 + 2x^3 - 8x + 6}{x^2 - 1} = 3x^2 + 2x + 3 + \frac{-6x + 9}{x^2 - 1}$$

EXAMPLE 7

Divide $27x^3 + 8$ by $3x + 2$.

Solution We replace the missing terms in the dividend with $0x^2$ and $0x$.

$$
\begin{array}{r}
9x^2 - 6x + 4 \\
3x + 2\overline{)27x^3 + 0x^2 + 0x + 8} \\
\underline{27x^3 + 18x^2} \\
-18x^2 + 0x \\
\underline{-18x^2 - 12x} \\
12x + 8 \\
\underline{-12x + 8}
\end{array}
$$

$9x^2(3x + 2)$

Subtract. Bring down $0x$.

$-6x(3x + 2)$

Subtract. Bring down 8.

$4(3x + 2)$

Thus, $\dfrac{27x^3 + 8}{3x + 2} = 9x^2 - 6x + 4$.

✔ **CONCEPT CHECK**

In a division problem, the divisor is $4x^3 - 5$. The division process can be stopped when which of these possible remainder polynomials is reached?

a. $2x^4 + x^2 - 3$

b. $x^3 - 5^2$

c. $4x^2 + 25$

EXERCISE SET 6.4

STUDY GUIDE/SSM   CD/VIDEO   PH MATH TUTOR CENTER   MathXL®Tutorials ON CD   MathXL®   MyMathLab®

Divide. See Examples 1 and 2

1. Divide $4a^2 + 8a$ by $2a$.

2. Divide $6x^4 - 3x^3$ by $3x^2$.

3. $\dfrac{12a^5b^2 + 16a^4b}{4a^4b}$

4. $\dfrac{4x^3y + 12x^2y^2 - 4xy^3}{4xy}$

 5. $\dfrac{4x^2y^2 + 6xy^2 - 4y^2}{2x^2y}$

6. $\dfrac{6x^5 + 74x^4 + 24x^3}{2x^3}$

7. $\dfrac{4x^2 + 8x + 4}{4}$

8. $\dfrac{15x^3 - 5x^2 + 10x}{5x^2}$

9. A board of length A $(3x^4 + 6x^2 - 18)$ meters is to be cut into three pieces of the same length. Find the length of each piece.

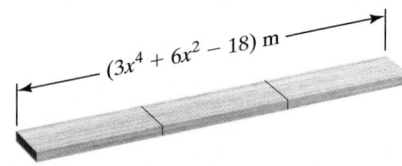

$(3x^4 + 6x^2 - 18)$ m

10. The perimeter of a regular hexagon is given to be $12x^5 - 48x^3 + 3$ miles. Find the length of each side.

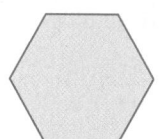

Divide. See Examples 3 through 7.

 11. $(x^2 + 3x + 2) \div (x + 2)$

12. $(y^2 + 7y + 10) \div (y + 5)$

13. $(2x^2 - 6x - 7) \div (x + 1)$

14. $(3x^2 + 19x + 18) \div (x + 5)$

15. $2x^2 + 3x - 2$ by $2x + 4$

16. $6x^2 - 17x - 3$ by $3x - 9$

17. $(4x^3 + 7x^2 + 8x + 20) \div (2x + 4)$

18. $(18x^3 + x^2 - 90x - 5) \div (9x^2 - 45)$

△ **19.** If the area of the rectangle is $(15x^2 - 29x - 14)$ square inches and its length is $(5x + 2)$ inches, find its width.

?

$(5x + 2)$ in.

△ **20.** If the area of a parallelogram is $(2x^2 - 17x + 35)$ square centimeters and its base is $(2x - 7)$ centimeters, find its height.

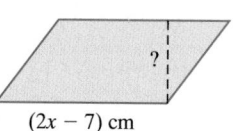

?

$(2x - 7)$ cm

MIXED PRACTICE

Divide.

21. $25a^2b^{12}$ by $10a^5b^7$

22. $12a^2b^3$ by $8a^7b$

23. $(x^6y^6 - x^3y^3) \div x^3y^3$

24. $(25xy^2 + 75xyz + 125x^2yz) \div -5x^2y$

25. $(a^2 + 4a + 3) \div (a + 1)$

26. $(3x^2 - 14x + 16) \div (x - 2)$

27. $(2x^2 + x - 10) \div (x - 2)$

28. $(x^2 - 7x + 12) \div (x - 5)$

29. $-16y^3 + 24y^4$ by $-4y^2$

30. $-20a^2b + 12ab^2$ by $-4ab$

31. $(2x^2 + 13x + 15) \div (x - 5)$

32. $(2x^2 + 13x + 5) \div (2x + 3)$

33. $(20x^2y^3 + 6xy^4 - 12x^3y^5) \div 2xy^3$

34. $(3x^2y + 6x^2y^2 + 3xy) \div 3xy$

35. $(6x^2 + 16x + 8) \div (3x + 2)$

36. $(x^2 - 25) \div (x + 5)$

37. $(2y^2 + 7y - 15) \div (2y - 3)$

38. $(3x^2 - 4x + 6) \div (x - 2)$

39. $4x^2 - 9$ by $2x - 3$ **40.** $8x^2 + 6x - 27$ by $4x + 9$

41. $2x^3 + 6x - 4$ by $x + 4$ **42.** $4x^3 - 5x$ by $2x - 1$

43. $3x^2 - 4$ by $x - 1$ **44.** $x^2 - 9$ by $x + 4$

45. $(-13x^3 + 2x^4 + 16x^2 - 9x + 20) \div (5 - x)$

46. $(5x^2 - 5x + 2x^3 + 20) \div (4 + x)$

47. $3x^5 - x^3 + 4x^2 - 12x - 8$ by $x^2 - 2$

48. $-8x^3 + 2x^4 + 19x^2 - 33x + 15$ by $x^2 - x + 5$

49. $(3x^3 - 5) \div 3x^2$

50. $(14x^3 - 2) \div (7x - 1)$

REVIEW AND PREVIEW

Insert $<, >,$ *or* $=$ *to make each statement true. See Section 1.2.*

51. 3^2 $(-3)^2$ **52.** $(-5)^2$ 5^2

53. -2^3 $(-2)^3$ **54.** 3^4 $(-3)^4$

Solve each inequality. See Section 2.7.

55. $|x + 5| < 4$ **56.** $|x - 1| \le 8$

57. $|2x + 7| \ge 9$ **58.** $|4x + 2| > 10$

Concept Extensions

59. Find $P(1)$ for the polynomial function
$P(x) = 3x^3 + 2x^2 - 4x + 3$. Next, divide
$3x^3 + 2x^2 - 4x + 3$ by $x - 1$. Compare the remainder with $P(1)$.

60. Find $P(-2)$ for the polynomial function
$P(x) = x^3 - 4x^2 - 3x + 5$. Next, divide
$x^3 - 4x^2 - 3x + 5$ by $x + 2$. Compare the remainder with $P(-2)$.

61. Find $P(-3)$ for the polynomial
$P(x) = 5x^4 - 2x^2 + 3x - 6$. Next, divide
$5x^4 - 2x^2 + 3x - 6$ by $x + 3$. Compare the remainder with $P(-3)$.

62. Find $P(2)$ for the polynomial function
$P(x) = -4x^4 + 2x^3 - 6x + 3$. Next, divide
$-4x^4 + 2x^3 - 6x + 3$ by $x - 2$. Compare the remainder with $P(2)$.

63. Write down any patterns you noticed from Exercises 59–62.

64. Explain how to check polynomial long division.

Divide.

65. $\left(x^4 + \dfrac{2}{3}x^3 + x \right) \div (x - 1)$

66. $\left(2x^3 + \dfrac{9}{2}x^2 - 4x - 10 \right) \div (x + 2)$

67. $\left(3x^4 - x - x^3 + \dfrac{1}{2} \right) \div (2x - 1)$

68. $\left(2x^4 + \dfrac{1}{2}x^3 + x^2 + x \right) \div (x - 2)$

69. $(5x^4 - 2x^2 + 10x^3 - 4x) \div (5x + 10)$

70. $(9x^5 + 6x^4 - 6x^2 - 4x) \div (3x + 2)$

For each given $f(x)$ and $g(x)$, find $\dfrac{f(x)}{g(x)}$. Also find any x-values that are not in the domain of $\dfrac{f(x)}{g(x)}$. (Note: Since $g(x)$ is in the denominator, $g(x)$ cannot be 0).

71. $f(x) = 25x^2 - 5x + 30;\ g(x) = 5x$

72. $f(x) = 12x^4 - 9x^3 + 3x - 1;\ g(x) = 3x$

73. $f(x) = 7x^4 - 3x^2 + 2;\ g(x) = x - 2$

74. $f(x) = 2x^3 - 4x^2 + 1;\ g(x) = x + 3$

75. Try performing the following division without changing the order of the terms. Describe why this makes the process more complicated. Then perform the division again after putting the terms in the dividend in descending order of exponents.

$$\frac{4x^2 - 12x - 12 + 3x^3}{x - 2}$$

76. Gateway is a leading direct marketer of personal computers. Gateway's annual net profit can be modeled by the polynomial function

$$P(x) = -54x^3 + 305x^2 - 363x + 245$$

where $P(x)$ is net profit in millions of dollars in the year x. Gateway's annual revenue can be modeled by the function

$R(x) = 1140x + 5295$, where $R(x)$ is revenue in millions of dollars in the year x. In both models, $x = 0$ represents the year 1996. (*Source:* Gateway, Inc., 1996–2000)

a. Suppose that a market analyst has found the model $P(x)$, and another analyst at the same firm has found the model $R(x)$. The analysts have been asked by their manager to work together to find a model for Gateway's net profit margin. The analysts know that a company's net profit margin is the ratio of its net profit to its revenue. Describe how these two analysts could collaborate to find a function $m(x)$ that models Gateway's net profit margin based on the work they have done independently.

b. Without actually finding $m(x)$, give a general description of what you would expect the form of the result to be.

6.5   SYNTHETIC DIVISION AND THE REMAINDER THEOREM

Objectives

1   Use synthetic division to divide a polynomial by a binomial.

2   Use the remainder theorem to evaluate polynomials.

1   When a polynomial is to be divided by a binomial of the form $x - c$, a shortcut process called **synthetic division** may be used. On the left is an example of long division, and on the right, the same example showing the coefficients of the variables only.

$$
\begin{array}{r}
2x^2 + 5x + 2 \\
x - 3\overline{)2x^3 - x^2 - 13x + 1} \\
\underline{2x^3 - 6x^2} \\
5x^2 - 13x \\
\underline{5x^2 - 15x} \\
2x + 1 \\
\underline{2x - 6} \\
7
\end{array}
\qquad
\begin{array}{r}
2 \quad 5 \quad 2 \\
1 - 3\overline{)2 - 1 - 13 + 1} \\
\underline{2 - 6} \\
5 - 13 \\
\underline{5 - 15} \\
2 + 1 \\
\underline{2 - 6} \\
7
\end{array}
$$

Notice that as long as we keep coefficients of powers of x in the same column, we can perform division of polynomials by performing algebraic operations on the coefficients only. This shortcut process of dividing with coefficients only in a special format is called synthetic division. To find $(2x^3 - x^2 - 13x + 1) \div (x - 3)$ by synthetic division, follow the next example.

EXAMPLE 1

Use synthetic division to divide $2x^3 - x^2 - 13x + 1$ by $x - 3$.

EXAMPLE 6

Solve: $\dfrac{z}{2z^2 + 3z - 2} - \dfrac{1}{2z} = \dfrac{3}{z^2 + 2z}$

Solution Factor the denominators to find that the LCD is $2z(z + 2)(2z - 1)$. Multiply both sides by the LCD. Remember, by using the distributive property, this is the same as multiplying each term by $2z(z + 2)(2z - 1)$.

$$\frac{z}{2z^2 + 3z - 2} - \frac{1}{2z} = \frac{3}{z^2 + 2z}$$

$$\frac{z}{(2z - 1)(z + 2)} - \frac{1}{2z} = \frac{3}{z(z + 2)}$$

$$2z(z + 2)(2z - 1) \cdot \frac{z}{(2z - 1)(z + 2)} - 2z(z + 2)(2z - 1) \cdot \frac{1}{2z}$$

$$= 2z(z + 2)(2z - 1) \cdot \frac{3}{z(z + 2)} \quad \text{Apply the distributive property.}$$

$$2z(z) - (z + 2)(2z - 1) = 3 \cdot 2(2z - 1) \qquad \text{Simplify.}$$

$$2z^2 - (2z^2 + 3z - 2) = 12z - 6$$

$$2z^2 - 2z^2 - 3z + 2 = 12z - 6$$

$$-3z + 2 = 12z - 6$$

$$-15z = -8$$

$$z = \frac{8}{15} \qquad\qquad\qquad \text{Solve.}$$

The proposed solution $\dfrac{8}{15}$ does not make any denominator 0; the solution is $\dfrac{8}{15}$.

A graph can be helpful in visualizing solutions of equations. For example, to visualize the solution of the equation $\dfrac{3}{x} - \dfrac{x + 21}{3x} = \dfrac{5}{3}$ in Example 2, the graph of the related rational function $f(x) = \dfrac{3}{x} - \dfrac{x + 21}{3x}$ is shown. A solution of the equation is an x-value that corresponds to a y-value of $\dfrac{5}{3}$.

Notice that an x-value of -2 corresponds to a y-value of $\dfrac{5}{3}$. The solution of the equation is indeed -2 as shown in Example 2.

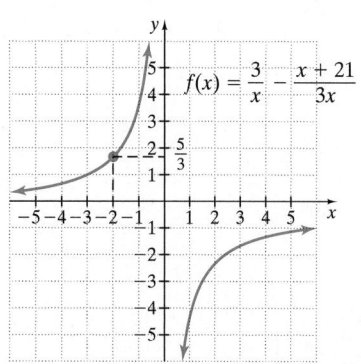

EXERCISE SET 6.6

STUDY GUIDE/SSM   CD/VIDEO   PH MATH TUTOR CENTER   MathXL®Tutorials ON CD   MathXL®   MyMathLab®

Solve each equation. See Examples 1 and 2.

1. $\dfrac{x}{2} - \dfrac{x}{3} = 12$

2. $x = \dfrac{x}{2} - 4$

3. $\dfrac{x}{3} = \dfrac{1}{6} + \dfrac{x}{4}$

4. $\dfrac{x}{2} = \dfrac{21}{10} - \dfrac{x}{5}$

5. $\dfrac{2}{x} + \dfrac{1}{2} = \dfrac{5}{x}$

6. $\dfrac{5}{3x} + 1 = \dfrac{7}{6}$

7. $\dfrac{x^2 + 1}{x} = \dfrac{5}{x}$

8. $\dfrac{x^2 - 14}{2x} = -\dfrac{5}{2x}$

Solve each equation. See Examples 3 through 6.

9. $\dfrac{x + 5}{x + 3} = \dfrac{2}{x + 3}$

10. $\dfrac{x - 7}{x - 1} = \dfrac{11}{x - 1}$

11. $\dfrac{5}{x - 2} - \dfrac{2}{x + 4} = -\dfrac{4}{x^2 + 2x - 8}$

12. $\dfrac{1}{x - 1} + \dfrac{1}{x + 1} = \dfrac{2}{x^2 - 1}$

13. $\dfrac{1}{x - 1} = \dfrac{2}{x + 1}$

14. $\dfrac{6}{x + 3} = \dfrac{4}{x - 3}$

15. $\dfrac{x^2 - 23}{2x^2 - 5x - 3} + \dfrac{2}{x - 3} = \dfrac{-1}{2x + 1}$

16. $\dfrac{4x^2 - 24x}{3x^2 - x - 2} + \dfrac{3}{3x + 2} = \dfrac{-4}{x - 1}$

17. $\dfrac{1}{x - 4} - \dfrac{3x}{x^2 - 16} = \dfrac{2}{x + 4}$

18. $\dfrac{3}{2x + 3} - \dfrac{1}{2x - 3} = \dfrac{4}{4x^2 - 9}$

19. $\dfrac{1}{x - 4} = \dfrac{8}{x^2 - 16}$

20. $\dfrac{2}{x^2 - 4} = \dfrac{1}{2x - 4}$

21. $\dfrac{1}{x - 2} - \dfrac{2}{x^2 - 2x} = 1$

22. $\dfrac{12}{3x^2 + 12x} = 1 - \dfrac{1}{x + 4}$

MIXED PRACTICE

Solve each equation.

23. $\dfrac{5}{x} = \dfrac{20}{12}$

24. $\dfrac{2}{x} = \dfrac{10}{5}$

25. $1 - \dfrac{4}{a} = 5$

26. $7 + \dfrac{6}{a} = 5$

27. $\dfrac{x^2 + 5}{x} - 1 = \dfrac{5(x + 1)}{x}$

28. $\dfrac{x^2 + 6}{x} + 5 = \dfrac{2(x + 3)}{x}$

29. $\dfrac{1}{2x} - \dfrac{1}{x + 1} = \dfrac{1}{3x^2 + 3x}$

30. $\dfrac{2}{x - 5} + \dfrac{1}{2x} = \dfrac{5}{3x^2 - 15x}$

31. $\dfrac{1}{x} - \dfrac{x}{25} = 0$

32. $\dfrac{x}{4} + \dfrac{5}{x} = 3$

33. $5 - \dfrac{2}{2y - 5} = \dfrac{3}{2y - 5}$

34. $1 - \dfrac{5}{y + 7} = \dfrac{4}{y + 7}$

35. $\dfrac{x - 1}{x + 2} = \dfrac{2}{3}$

36. $\dfrac{6x + 7}{2x + 9} = \dfrac{5}{3}$

37. $\dfrac{x + 3}{x + 2} = \dfrac{1}{x + 2}$

38. $\dfrac{2x + 1}{4 - x} = \dfrac{9}{4 - x}$

39. $\dfrac{1}{a - 3} + \dfrac{2}{a + 3} = \dfrac{1}{a^2 - 9}$

40. $\dfrac{12}{9 - a^2} + \dfrac{3}{3 + a} = \dfrac{2}{3 - a}$

41. $\dfrac{64}{x^2 - 16} + 1 = \dfrac{2x}{x - 4}$

42. $2 + \dfrac{3}{x} = \dfrac{2x}{x + 3}$

43. $\dfrac{-15}{4y + 1} + 4 = y$

44. $\dfrac{36}{x^2 - 9} + 1 = \dfrac{2x}{x + 3}$

45. $\dfrac{28}{x^2 - 9} + \dfrac{2x}{x - 3} + \dfrac{6}{x + 3} = 0$

46. $\dfrac{x^2 - 20}{x^2 - 7x + 12} = \dfrac{3}{x - 3} + \dfrac{5}{x - 4}$

47. $\dfrac{x + 2}{x^2 + 7x + 10} = \dfrac{1}{3x + 6} - \dfrac{1}{x + 5}$

48. $\dfrac{3}{2x - 5} + \dfrac{2}{2x + 3} = 0$

REVIEW AND PREVIEW

Write each sentence as an equation and solve. See Section 2.2.

49. Four more than 3 times a number is 19.

50. The sum of two consecutive integers is 147.

51. The length of a rectangle is 5 inches more than the width. I[t] perimeter is 50 inches. Find the length and width.

52. The sum of a number and its reciprocal is $\dfrac{5}{2}$.

The following graph is from a survey of state and federal prison[s]. Use this histogram to answer Exercises 53–56.

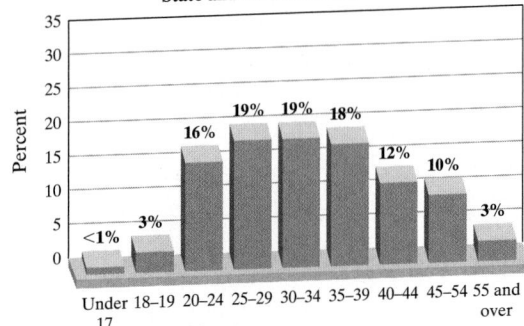

State and Federal Prison Inmates

Source: Bureau of Justice Statistics, U.S. Department of Justice

53. What percent of state and federal prison inmates are age 4[5] to 54?

4. What percent of state and federal prison inmates are 55 years old or older?

5. What age category shows the highest percent of prison inmates?

6. What percent of state and federal prison inmates are 20 to 34 years old?

7. At the end of 2001, there were 35,710 inmates under the jurisdiction of state and federal correctional authorities in the state of Louisiana. Approximately how many 25- to 29-year-old inmates would you expect to have been held in Louisiana at the end of 2001? Round to the nearest whole. (*Source:* Bureau of Justice Statistics)

Concept Extensions

8. The average cost of producing x game disks for a computer is given by the function $f(x) = 3.3 + \dfrac{5400}{x}$. Find the number of game disks that must be produced for the average cost to be $5.10.

9. The average cost of producing x electric pencil sharpeners is given by the function $f(x) = 20 + \dfrac{4000}{x}$. Find the number of electric pencil sharpeners that must be produced for the average cost to be $25.

Solve each equation. Begin by writing each equation with positive exponents only.

60. $x^{-2} - 19x^{-1} + 48 = 0$ **61.** $x^{-2} - 5x^{-1} - 36 = 0$

62. $p^{-2} + 4p^{-1} - 5 = 0$ **63.** $6p^{-2} - 5p^{-1} + 1 = 0$

Solve each equation. Round solutions to two decimal places.

64. $\dfrac{1.4}{x - 2.6} = \dfrac{-3.5}{x + 7.1}$ **65.** $\dfrac{-8.5}{x + 1.9} = \dfrac{5.7}{x - 3.6}$

66. $\dfrac{10.6}{y} - 14.7 = \dfrac{9.92}{3.2} + 7.6$ **67.** $\dfrac{12.2}{x} + 17.3 = \dfrac{9.6}{x} - 14.7$

Solve each equation by substitution.

For example, to solve Exercise 68, first let $u = x - 1$. After substituting, we have $u^2 + 3u + 2 = 0$. Solve for u and then substitute back to solve for x.

68. $(x - 1)^2 + 3(x - 1) + 2 = 0$

69. $(4 - x)^2 - 5(4 - x) + 6 = 0$

70. $\left(\dfrac{3}{x - 1}\right)^2 + 2\left(\dfrac{3}{x - 1}\right) + 1 = 0$

71. $\left(\dfrac{5}{2 + x}\right)^2 + \left(\dfrac{5}{2 + x}\right) - 20 = 0$

Use a graphing calculator to verify the solution of each given exercise.

72. Exercise 23   **73.** Exercise 24

74. Exercise 35   **75.** Exercise 36

EXPRESSIONS AND EQUATIONS CONTAINING RATIONAL EXPRESSIONS

INTEGRATED REVIEW

It is very important that you understand the difference between an expression and an equation containing rational expressions. An equation contains an equal sign; an expression does not.

Expression to be Simplified

$\dfrac{x}{2} + \dfrac{x}{6}$

Write both rational expressions with the LCD, 6, as the denominator.

$\dfrac{x}{2} + \dfrac{x}{6} = \dfrac{x \cdot 3}{2 \cdot 3} + \dfrac{x}{6}$

$= \dfrac{3x}{6} + \dfrac{x}{6}$

$= \dfrac{4x}{6} = \dfrac{2x}{3}$

Equation to be Solved

$\dfrac{x}{2} + \dfrac{x}{6} = \dfrac{2}{3}$

Multiply both sides by the LCD, 6.

$6\left(\dfrac{1}{2} + \dfrac{x}{6}\right) = 6\left(\dfrac{2}{3}\right)$

$3 + x = 4$

$x = 1$

Check to see that the solution is 1.

> **Helpful Hint**
>   Remember: Equations can be cleared
> of fractions; expressions cannot.

Perform each indicated operation and simplify, or solve the equation for the variable.

1. $\dfrac{x}{2} = \dfrac{1}{8} + \dfrac{x}{4}$

2. $\dfrac{x}{4} = \dfrac{3}{2} + \dfrac{x}{10}$

3. $\dfrac{1}{8} + \dfrac{x}{4}$

4. $\dfrac{3}{2} + \dfrac{x}{10}$

5. $\dfrac{4}{x + 2} - \dfrac{2}{x - 1}$

6. $\dfrac{5}{x - 2} - \dfrac{10}{x + 4}$

7. $\dfrac{4}{x + 2} = \dfrac{2}{x - 1}$

8. $\dfrac{5}{x - 2} = \dfrac{10}{x + 4}$

9. $\dfrac{2}{x^2 - 4} = \dfrac{1}{x + 2} - \dfrac{3}{x - 2}$

10. $\dfrac{3}{x^2 - 25} = \dfrac{1}{x + 5} + \dfrac{2}{x - 5}$

11. $\dfrac{5}{x^2 - 3x} + \dfrac{4}{2x - 6}$

12. $\dfrac{5}{x^2 - 3x} \div \dfrac{4}{2x - 6}$

13. $\dfrac{x - 1}{x + 1} + \dfrac{x + 7}{x - 1} = \dfrac{4}{x^2 - 1}$

14. $\left(1 - \dfrac{y}{x}\right) \div \left(1 - \dfrac{x}{y}\right)$

15. $\dfrac{a^2 - 9}{a - 6} \cdot \dfrac{a^2 - 5a - 6}{a^2 - a - 6}$

16. $\dfrac{2}{a - 6} + \dfrac{3a}{a^2 - 5a - 6} - \dfrac{a}{5a + 5}$

17. $\dfrac{2x + 3}{3x - 2} = \dfrac{4x + 1}{6x + 1}$

18. $\dfrac{5x - 3}{2x} = \dfrac{10x + 3}{4x + 1}$

19. $\dfrac{a}{9a^2 - 1} + \dfrac{2}{6a - 2}$

20. $\dfrac{3}{4a - 8} - \dfrac{a + 2}{a^2 - 2a}$

21. $-\dfrac{3}{x^2} - \dfrac{1}{x} + 2 = 0$

22. $\dfrac{x}{2x + 6} + \dfrac{5}{x^2 - 9}$

23. $\dfrac{x - 8}{x^2 - x - 2} + \dfrac{2}{x - 2}$

24. $\dfrac{x - 8}{x^2 - x - 2} + \dfrac{2}{x - 2} = \dfrac{3}{x + 1}$

25. $\dfrac{3}{a} - 5 = \dfrac{7}{a} - 1$

26. $\dfrac{7}{3z - 9} + \dfrac{5}{z}$

Use $\dfrac{x}{5} - \dfrac{x}{4} = \dfrac{1}{10}$ *and* $\dfrac{x}{5} - \dfrac{x}{4} + \dfrac{1}{10}$ *for Exercises 27 and 28.*

27. a. Which one above is an expression?

   b. Describe the first step to simplify this expression.

   c. Simplify the expression.

28. a. Which one above is an equation?

   b. Describe the first step to solve this equation.

   c. Solve the equation.

For each exercise, choose the correct statement.* Each figure represents a real number and no denominators are 0.

29. a. $\dfrac{\triangle + \square}{\triangle} = \square$

   b. $\dfrac{\triangle + \square}{\triangle} = 1 + \dfrac{\square}{\triangle}$

   c. $\dfrac{\triangle + \square}{\triangle} = \dfrac{\square}{\triangle}$

   d. $\dfrac{\triangle + \square}{\triangle} = 1 + \square$

   e. $\dfrac{\triangle + \square}{\triangle - \square} = -1$

30. a. $\dfrac{\triangle}{\square} + \dfrac{\square}{\triangle} = \dfrac{\triangle + \square}{\square + \triangle} = 1$

   b. $\dfrac{\triangle}{\square} + \dfrac{\square}{\triangle} = \dfrac{\triangle + \square}{\triangle\square}$

   c. $\dfrac{\triangle}{\square} + \dfrac{\square}{\triangle} = \triangle\triangle + \square\square$

   d. $\dfrac{\triangle}{\square} + \dfrac{\square}{\triangle} = \dfrac{\triangle\triangle + \square\square}{\square\triangle}$

   e. $\dfrac{\triangle}{\square} + \dfrac{\square}{\triangle} = \dfrac{\triangle\square}{\square\triangle} = 1$

31. a. $\dfrac{\triangle}{\square} \cdot \dfrac{\bigcirc}{\square} = \dfrac{\triangle\bigcirc}{\square}$

   b. $\dfrac{\triangle}{\square} \cdot \dfrac{\bigcirc}{\square} = \triangle\bigcirc$

   c. $\dfrac{\triangle}{\square} \cdot \dfrac{\bigcirc}{\square} = \dfrac{\triangle + \bigcirc}{\square + \square}$

   d. $\dfrac{\triangle}{\square} \cdot \dfrac{\bigcirc}{\square} = \dfrac{\triangle\bigcirc}{\square\square}$

32. a. $\dfrac{\triangle}{\square} \div \dfrac{\bigcirc}{\triangle} = \dfrac{\triangle\triangle}{\square\bigcirc}$

   b. $\dfrac{\triangle}{\square} \div \dfrac{\bigcirc}{\triangle} = \dfrac{\bigcirc\square}{\triangle\triangle}$

   c. $\dfrac{\triangle}{\square} \div \dfrac{\bigcirc}{\triangle} = \dfrac{\bigcirc}{\square}$

   d. $\dfrac{\triangle}{\square} \div \dfrac{\bigcirc}{\triangle} = \dfrac{\triangle + \triangle}{\square + \bigcirc}$

33. a. $\dfrac{\dfrac{\triangle + \square}{\bigcirc}}{\dfrac{\triangle}{\bigcirc}} = \square$

   b. $\dfrac{\dfrac{\triangle + \square}{\bigcirc}}{\dfrac{\triangle}{\bigcirc}} = \dfrac{\triangle\triangle + \triangle\square}{\bigcirc\bigcirc}$

   c. $\dfrac{\dfrac{\triangle + \square}{\bigcirc}}{\dfrac{\triangle}{\bigcirc}} = 1 + \square$

   d. $\dfrac{\dfrac{\triangle + \square}{\bigcirc}}{\dfrac{\triangle}{\bigcirc}} = \dfrac{\triangle + \square}{\triangle}$

*My thanks to Kelly Champagne for permission to use her exercises for 29 through 33.

6.7 RATIONAL EQUATIONS AND PROBLEM SOLVING

Objectives

1. Solve an equation containing rational expressions for a specified variable.
2. Solve problems by writing equations containing rational expressions.

1 In Section 2.3 we solved equations for a specified variable. In this section, we continue practicing this skill by solving equations containing rational expressions for a specified variable. The steps given in Section 2.3 for solving equations for a specified variable are repeated here.

Solving Equations for a Specified Variable

Step 1: Clear the equation of fractions or rational expressions by multiplying each side of the equation by the least common denominator (LCD) of all denominators in the equation.

Step 2: Use the distributive property to remove grouping symbols such as parentheses.

Step 3: Combine like terms on each side of the equation.

Step 4: Use the addition property of equality to rewrite the equation as an equivalent equation with terms containing the specified variable on one side and all other terms on the other side.

Step 5: Use the distributive property and the multiplication property of equality to get the specified variable alone.

EXAMPLE 1

Solve $\dfrac{1}{x} + \dfrac{1}{y} = \dfrac{1}{z}$ for x.

Solution To clear this equation of fractions, we multiply both sides of the equation by xyz, the LCD of $\dfrac{1}{x}, \dfrac{1}{y}$, and $\dfrac{1}{z}$.

$$\frac{1}{x} + \frac{1}{y} = \frac{1}{z}$$

$$xyz\left(\frac{1}{x} + \frac{1}{y}\right) = xyz\left(\frac{1}{z}\right) \quad \text{Multiply both sides by } xyz.$$

$$xyz\left(\frac{1}{x}\right) + xyz\left(\frac{1}{y}\right) = xyz\left(\frac{1}{z}\right) \quad \text{Use the distributive property.}$$

$$yz + xz = xy \quad \text{Simplify.}$$

Notice the two terms that contain the specified variable x.

Next, we subtract xz from both sides so that all terms containing the specified variable x are on one side of the equation and all other terms are on the other side.

$$yz = xy - xz$$

Now we use the distributive property to factor x from $xy - xz$ and then the multiplication property of equality to solve for x.

$$yz = x(y - z)$$

$$\frac{yz}{y - z} = x \quad \text{or} \quad x = \frac{yz}{y - z} \qquad \text{Divide both sides by } y - z.$$

2   Problem solving sometimes involves modeling a described situation with an equation containing rational expressions. In Examples 2 through 5, we practice solving such problems and use the problem-solving steps first introduced in Section 2.2.

EXAMPLE 2

FINDING AN UNKNOWN NUMBER

If a certain number is subtracted from the numerator and added to the denominator of $\frac{9}{19}$, the new fraction is equivalent to $\frac{1}{3}$. Find the number.

Solution   **1.** UNDERSTAND the problem.   Read and reread the problem and try guessing the solution. For example, if the unknown number is 3, we have

$$\frac{9 - 3}{19 + 3} = \frac{1}{3}$$

To see if this is a true statement, we simplify the fraction on the left side.

$$\frac{6}{22} = \frac{1}{3} \quad \text{or} \quad \frac{3}{11} = \frac{1}{3} \qquad \text{False.}$$

Since this is not a true statement, 3 is not the correct number. Remember that the purpose of this step is not to guess the correct solution but to gain an understanding of the problem posed.

We will let n = the number to be subtracted from the numerator and added to the denominator.

2. TRANSLATE the problem.

In words:	when the number is subtracted from the numerator and added to the denominator of the fraction $\frac{9}{19}$	this is equivalent to	$\frac{1}{3}$
	↓	↓	↓
Translate:	$\dfrac{9 - n}{19 + n}$	$=$	$\dfrac{1}{3}$

3. SOLVE the equation for n.

$$\frac{9 - n}{19 + n} = \frac{1}{3}$$

To solve for n, we begin by multiplying both sides by the LCD of $3(19 + n)$.

$$3(19 + n) \cdot \frac{9 - n}{19 + n} = 3(19 + n) \cdot \frac{1}{3} \qquad \text{Multiply both sides by the LC}$$

$$3(9 - n) = 19 + n \qquad \text{Simplify.}$$

$$27 - 3n = 19 + n$$

$$8 = 4n$$

$$2 = n \qquad \text{Solve.}$$

4. INTERPRET the results.

Check: If we subtract 2 from the numerator and add 2 to the denominator of $\frac{9}{19}$, w

have $\frac{9 - 2}{19 + 2} = \frac{7}{21} = \frac{1}{3}$, and the problem checks.

State: The unknown number is 2.

A **ratio** is the quotient of two number or two quantities. Since rational expressions ar quotients of quantities, rational expressions are ratios, also. A **proportion** is a mathe matical statement that two ratios are equal.

EXAMPLE 3

CALCULATING HOMES HEAT BY ELECTRICITY

In the United States, 7 out of every 25 homes are heated by electricity. At this rate, ho many homes in a community of 36,000 homes would you predict are heated by elec tricity? (*Source:* 2000 Census Survey)

Solution

1. UNDERSTAND. Read and reread the problem. Try to estimate a reasonable solutio For example, since 7 is less than $\frac{1}{3}$ of 25, we might reason that the solutio would be less than $\frac{1}{3}$ of 36,000 or 12,000.

Let's let x = number of homes in the community heated by electricity.

2. TRANSLATE.

$$\begin{array}{l} \text{homes heated by electricity} \to \\ \text{total homes} \to \end{array} \quad \frac{7}{25} = \frac{x}{36,000} \quad \begin{array}{l} \leftarrow \text{homes heated by electricity} \\ \leftarrow \text{total homes} \end{array}$$

3. SOLVE. To solve this proportion we can multiply both sides by the LCD, 36,000, c we can set cross products equal. We will set cross products equal.

$$\frac{7}{25} = \frac{x}{36,000}$$

$$25x = 7 \cdot 36,000$$

$$x = \frac{252,000}{25}$$

$$x = 10,080$$

4. INTERPRET.

Check: To check, replace x with 10,080 in the proportion and see that a true statement results. Notice that our answer is reasonable since it is less than 12,000 as we stated above.

State: We predict that 10,080 homes are heated by electricity.

The following work example leads to an equation containing rational expressions.

EXAMPLE 4

CALCULATING WORK HOURS

Melissa Scarlatti can clean the house in 4 hours, whereas her husband, Zack, can do the same job in 5 hours. They have agreed to clean together so that they can finish in time to watch a movie on TV that starts in 2 hours. How long will it take them to clean the house together? Can they finish before the movie starts?

Solution

1. UNDERSTAND. Read and reread the problem. The key idea here is the relationship between the *time* (in hours) it takes to complete the job and the *part of the job* completed in 1 unit of time (1 hour). For example, if the *time* it takes Melissa to complete the job is 4 hours, the part of the job she can complete in 1 hour is $\frac{1}{4}$. Similarly, Zack can complete $\frac{1}{5}$ of the job in 1 hour.

We will let $t = $ *the time* in hours it takes Melissa and Zack to clean the house together. Then $\frac{1}{t}$ represents the *part of the job* they complete in 1 hour. We summarize the given information in a chart.

	Hours to Complete the Job	Part of Job Completed in 1 Hour
MELISSA ALONE	4	$\frac{1}{4}$
ZACK ALONE	5	$\frac{1}{5}$
TOGETHER	t	$\frac{1}{t}$

2. TRANSLATE.

In words:

part of job Melissa can complete in 1 hour	added to	part of job Zack can complete in 1 hour	is equal to	part of job they can complete together in 1 hour
↓	↓	↓	↓	↓

Translate:

$$\frac{1}{4} \quad + \quad \frac{1}{5} \quad = \quad \frac{1}{t}$$

3. SOLVE.

$$\frac{1}{4} + \frac{1}{5} = \frac{1}{t}$$

$$20t\left(\frac{1}{4} + \frac{1}{5}\right) = 20t\left(\frac{1}{t}\right) \qquad \text{Multiply both sides by the LCD, } 20t.$$

$$5t + 4t = 20$$

$$9t = 20$$

$$t = \frac{20}{9} \quad \text{or} \quad 2\frac{2}{9} \qquad \text{Solve.}$$

4. INTERPRET.

Check: The proposed solution is $2\frac{2}{9}$. That is, Melissa and Zack would take $2\frac{2}{9}$ hour

to clean the house together. This proposed solution is reasonable since $2\frac{2}{9}$ hours

more than half of Melissa's time and less than half of Zack's time. Check this sol
tion in the originally stated problem.

State: Melissa and Zack can clean the house together in $2\frac{2}{9}$ hours. They cannot com

plete the job before the movie starts.

EXAMPLE 5

FINDING THE SPEED OF A CURRENT

Steve Deitmer takes $1\frac{1}{2}$ times as long to go 72 miles upstream in his boat as he does
return. If the boat cruises at 30 mph in still water, what is the speed of the current?

Solution   **1.** UNDERSTAND.   Read and reread the problem. Guess a solution. Suppose that th
current is 4 mph. The speed of the boat upstream is slowed down by the curren
$30 - 4$, or 26 mph, and the speed of the boat downstream is speeded up by the curren
$30 + 4$, or 34 mph. Next let's find out how long it takes to travel 72 miles upstrean
and 72 miles downstream. To do so, we use the formula $d = rt$, or $\frac{d}{r} = t$.

Upstream	*Downstream*
$\frac{d}{r} = t$	$\frac{d}{r} = t$
$\frac{72}{26} = t$	$\frac{72}{34} = t$
$2\frac{10}{13} = t$	$2\frac{2}{17} = t$

Since the time upstream $\left(2\dfrac{10}{13}\text{hours}\right)$ is not $1\dfrac{1}{2}$ times the time downstream $\left(2\dfrac{2}{17}\text{hours}\right)$, our guess is not correct. We do, however, have a better understanding of the problem.

We will let

$$x = \text{the speed of the current}$$
$$30 + x = \text{the speed of the boat downstream}$$
$$30 - x = \text{the speed of the boat upstream}$$

This information is summarized in the following chart, where we use the formula $\dfrac{d}{r} = t$.

	Distance	Rate	Time $\left(\dfrac{d}{r}\right)$
UPSTREAM	72	$30 - x$	$\dfrac{72}{30 - x}$
DOWNSTREAM	72	$30 + x$	$\dfrac{72}{30 + x}$

2. **TRANSLATE.** Since the time spent traveling upstream is $1\dfrac{1}{2}$ times the time spent traveling downstream, we have

In words:

time upstream	is	$1\dfrac{1}{2}$	times	time downstream
↓	↓	↓	↓	↓

Translate:
$$\dfrac{72}{30 - x} = \dfrac{3}{2} \quad \cdot \quad \dfrac{72}{30 + x}$$

3. **SOLVE.** $\dfrac{72}{30 - x} = \dfrac{3}{2} \cdot \dfrac{72}{30 + x}$

First we multiply both sides by the LCD, $2(30 + x)(30 - x)$.

$$2(30 + x)(30 - x) \cdot \dfrac{72}{30 - x} = 2(30 + x)(30 - x)\left(\dfrac{3}{2} \cdot \dfrac{72}{30 + x}\right)$$

$$72 \cdot 2(30 + x) = 3 \cdot 72 \cdot (30 - x) \quad \text{Simplify.}$$

$$2(30 + x) = 3(30 - x) \quad \text{Divide both sides by 72.}$$

$$60 + 2x = 90 - 3x \quad \text{Use the distributive property.}$$

$$5x = 30$$

$$x = 6 \quad \text{Solve.}$$

4. **INTERPRET.**

Check: Check the proposed solution of 6 mph in the originally stated problem.

State: The current's speed is 6 mph.

Spotlight on

DECISION
✈MAKING

Suppose you are an aviation safety inspector. You are testing the accuracy of the radioaltimeter on an airplane. To be acceptable, the altitude reading given by the altimeter must be within 3% of the actual altitude. You know that you can check the altimeter's altitude reading with the equation $t = \dfrac{2a}{c}$, where t is the time it takes a radar pulse aimed downward from the airplane to bounce off Earth's surface and return to the radioaltimeter, a is the altitude, and c is the speed of light, 3×10^8 meters per second.

During your test, you find that it takes 5×10^{-5} second for the radar pulse emitted by the altimeter to be returned. The altimeter reads an altitude of 7420 meters. Is the altimeter reading acceptable? Explain.

EXERCISE SET 6.7

| STUDY
GUIDE/SSM | CD/
VIDEO | PH MATH
TUTOR CENTER | MathXL®Tutorials
ON CD | MathXL® | MyMathLab® |

Solve each equation for the specified variable. See Example 1.

1. $F = \dfrac{9}{5}C + 32$ for C (Meteorology)

△ **2.** $V = \dfrac{1}{3}\pi r^2 h$ for h (Volume)

3. $Q = \dfrac{A - I}{L}$ for I (Finance)

4. $P = 1 - \dfrac{C}{S}$ for S (Finance)

5. $\dfrac{1}{R} = \dfrac{1}{R_1} + \dfrac{1}{R_2}$ for R (Electronics)

6. $\dfrac{1}{R} = \dfrac{1}{R_1} + \dfrac{1}{R_2}$ for R_1 (Electronics)

7. $S = \dfrac{n(a + L)}{2}$ for n (Sequences)

8. $S = \dfrac{n(a + L)}{2}$ for a (Sequences)

△ **9.** $A = \dfrac{h(a + b)}{2}$ for b (Geometry)

△ **10.** $A = \dfrac{h(a + b)}{2}$ for h (Geometry)

11. $\dfrac{P_1 V_1}{T_1} = \dfrac{P_2 V_2}{T_2}$ for T_2 (Chemistry)

12. $H = \dfrac{kA(T_1 - T_2)}{L}$ for T_2 (Physics)

13. $f = \dfrac{f_1 f_2}{f_1 + f_2}$ for f_2 (Optics)

14. $I = \dfrac{E}{R + r}$ for r (Electronics)

15. $\lambda = \dfrac{2L}{n}$ for L (Physics)

16. $S = \dfrac{a_1 - a_n r}{1 - r}$ for a_1 (Sequences)

17. $\dfrac{\theta}{\omega} = \dfrac{2L}{c}$ for c

18. $F = \dfrac{-GMm}{r^2}$ for M (Physics)

Solve. See Example 2.

19. The sum of a number and 5 times its reciprocal is 6. Find the number(s).

20. The quotient of a number and 9 times its reciprocal is 1. Find the number(s).

21. If a number is added to the numerator of $\frac{12}{41}$ and twice the number is added to the denominator of $\frac{12}{41}$, the resulting fraction is equivalent to $\frac{1}{3}$. Find the number.

22. If a number is subtracted from the numerator of $\frac{13}{8}$ and added to the denominator of $\frac{13}{8}$, the resulting fraction is equivalent to $\frac{2}{5}$. Find the number.

Solve. See Example 3.

23. An Arabian camel can drink 15 gallons of water in 10 minutes. At this rate, how much water can the camel drink in 3 minutes? (*Source:* Grolier, Inc.)

24. An Arabian camel can travel 20 miles in 8 hours, carrying a 300-pound load on its back. At this rate, how far can the camel travel in 10 hours? (*Source:* Grolier, Inc.)

25. In 2000, 10.2 out of every 100 Coast Guard personnel were women. If there are 35,712 total Coast Guard personnel on active duty, estimate the number of women. Round to the nearest whole. (*Source: The World Almanac,* 2003)

26. In 2000, 43 out of every 50 Navy personnel were men. If there are 375,618 total Navy personnel on active duty, estimate the number of men. Round to the nearest whole. (*Source: The World Almanac,* 2003)

Solve. See Example 4.

27. An experienced roofer can roof a house in 26 hours. A beginning roofer needs 39 hours to complete the same job. Find how long it takes for the two to do the job together.

28. Alan Cantrell can word process a research paper in 6 hours. With Steve Isaac's help, the paper can be processed in 4 hours. Find how long it takes Steve to word process the paper alone.

29. Three postal workers can sort a stack of mail in 20 minutes, 30 minutes, and 60 minutes, respectively. Find how long it takes them to sort the mail if all three work together.

30. A new printing press can print newspapers twice as fast as the old one can. The old one can print the afternoon edition in 4 hours. Find how long it takes to print the afternoon edition if both printers are operating.

Solve. See Example 5.

31. Mattie Evans drove 150 miles in the same amount of time that it took a turbopropeller plane to travel 600 miles. The speed of the plane was 150 mph faster than the speed of the car. Find the speed of the plane.

32. An F-100 plane and a Toyota truck leave the same town at sunrise and head for a town 450 miles away. The speed of the plane is three times the speed of the truck, and the plane arrives 6 hours ahead of the truck. Find the speed of the truck.

33. The speed of Lazy River's current is 5 mph. If a boat travels 20 miles downstream in the same time that it takes to travel 10 miles upstream, find the speed of the boat in still water.

34. The speed of a boat in still water is 24 mph. If the boat travels 54 miles upstream in the same time that it takes to travel 90 miles downstream, find the speed of the current.

MIXED PRACTICE

Solve.

35. The sum of the reciprocals of two consecutive integers is $-\frac{15}{56}$. Find the two integers.

36. The sum of the reciprocals of two consecutive odd integers is $\frac{20}{99}$. Find the two integers.

37. One hose can fill a goldfish pond in 45 minutes, and two hoses can fill the same pond in 20 minutes. Find how long it takes the second hose alone to fill the pond.

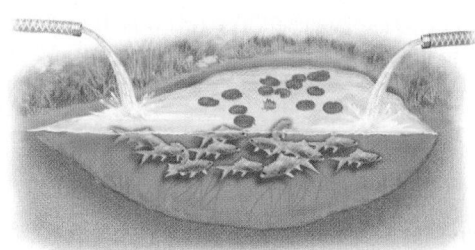

38. If Sarah Clark can do a job in 5 hours and Dick Belli and Sarah working together can do the same job in 2 hours, find how long it takes Dick to do the job alone.

39. Two trains going in opposite directions leave at the same time. One train travels 15 mph faster than the other. In 6 hours the trains are 630 miles apart. Find the speed of each.

40. The speed of a bicyclist is 10 mph faster than the speed of a walker. If the bicyclist travels 26 miles in the same amount of time that the walker travels 6 miles, find the speed of the bicyclist.

41. A giant tortoise can travel 0.17 miles in 1 hour. At this rate, how long would it take the tortoise to travel 1 mile? Round to the nearest tenth of an hour. (*Source: The World Almanac*, 2003)

42. A black mamba snake can travel 88 feet in 3 seconds. At this rate, how long does it take to travel 300 feet (the length of a football field)? Round to the nearest tenth of a second. (*Source: The World Almanac*, 2003)

43. Moo Dairy has three machines to fill half-gallon milk cartons. The machines can fill the daily quota in 5 hours, 6 hours, and 7.5 hours, respectively. Find how long it takes to fill the daily quota if all three machines are running.

44. The inlet pipe of an oil tank can fill the tank in 1 hour, 30 minutes. The outlet pipe can empty the tank in 1 hour. Find how long it takes to empty a full tank if both pipes are open.

45. A plane flies 465 miles with the wind and 345 miles against the wind in the same length of time. If the speed of the wind is 20 mph, find the speed of the plane in still air.

46. Two rockets are launched. The first travels at 9000 mph. Fifteen minutes later the second is launched at 10,000 mph. Find the distance at which both rockets are an equal distance from Earth.

47. Two joggers, one averaging 8 mph and one averaging 6 mph, start from a designated initial point. The slower jogger arrives at the end of the run a half-hour after the other jogger. Find the distance of the run.

48. A semi truck travels 300 miles through the flatland in the same amount of time that it travels 180 miles through the Great Smoky Mountains. The rate of the truck is 20 miles per hour slower in the mountains than in the flatland. Find both the flatland rate and mountain rate.

49. Smith Engineering is in the process of reviewing the salaries of their surveyors. During this review, the company found that an experienced surveyor can survey a roadbed in 4 hours. An apprentice surveyor needs 5 hours to survey the same stretch of road. If the two work together, find how long it takes them to complete the job.

50. The numerator of a fraction is 4 less than the denominator. If both the numerator and the denominator are increased by 2, the resulting fraction is equivalent to $\frac{2}{3}$. Find the fraction.

51. The denominator of a fraction is 1 more than the numerator. If both the numerator and the denominator are decreased by 3, the resulting fraction is equivalent to $\frac{4}{5}$. Find the fraction.

52. Cyclist Lance Armstrong of the United States won the 2003 Tour de France. This inspired an amateur cyclist to train for a local road race. He rode the first 20-mile portion of his workout at a constant rate. For the 16-mile cooldown portion of his workout, he reduced his speed by 2 miles per hour. Each portion of the workout took equal time. Find the cyclist's rate during the first portion and his rate during the cooldown portion.

53. In 2 minutes, a conveyor belt can move 300 pounds of recyclable aluminum from the delivery truck to a storage area. A smaller belt can move the same quantity of cans the same distance in 6 minutes. If both belts are used, find how long it takes to move the cans to the storage area.

54. Gary Marcus and Tony Alva work at Lombardo's Pipe and Concrete. Mr. Lombardo is preparing an estimate for a customer. He knows that Gary can lay a slab of concrete in 6 hours. Tony can lay the same size slab in 4 hours. If both work on the job and the cost of labor is $45.00 per hour, determine what the labor estimate should be.

55. While road testing a new make of car, the editor of a consumer magazine finds that she can go 10 miles into a 3-mile-per-hour wind in the same amount of time that she can go 11 miles with a 3-mile-per-hour wind behind her. Find the speed of the car in still air.

56. Mr. Dodson can paint his house by himself in four days. His son will need an additional day to complete the job if he works by himself. If they work together, find how long it takes to paint the house.

57. The world record for the largest white bass caught is held by Ronald Sprouse of Virginia. The bass weighed 6 pounds 13 ounces. If Ronald rows to his favorite fishing spot 9 miles downstream in the same amount of time that he rows 3 miles upstream and if the current is 6 mph, find how long it takes him to cover the 12 miles.

58. A marketing manager travels 1080 miles in a corporate jet and then an additional 240 miles by car. If the car ride takes 1 hour longer, and if the rate of the jet is 6 times the rate of the car, find the time the manager travels by jet and find the time she travels by car.

59. An experienced bricklayer can construct a small wall in 3 hours. An apprentice can complete the job in 6 hours. Find how long it takes if they work together.

REVIEW AND PREVIEW

Solve each equation for x. See Section 2.1.

60. $\dfrac{x}{5} = \dfrac{x+2}{3}$

61. $\dfrac{x}{4} = \dfrac{x+3}{6}$

62. $\dfrac{x-3}{2} = \dfrac{x-5}{6}$

63. $\dfrac{x-6}{4} = \dfrac{x-2}{5}$

Concept Extensions

Calculating body-mass index (BMI) is a way to gauge whether a person should lose weight. Doctors recommend that body-mass index values fall between 19 and 25. The formula for body-mass index B is $B = \dfrac{705w}{h^2}$, *where w is weight in pounds and h is height in inches. Use this formula to answer Exercises 64 and 65.*

64. A patient is 5 ft 8 in. tall. What should his or her weight be to have a body-mass index of 25? Round to the nearest whole pound.

65. A doctor recorded a body-mass index of 47 on a patient's chart. Later, a nurse notices that the doctor recorded the patient's weight as 240 pounds but neglected to record the patient's height. Explain how the nurse can use the information from the chart to find the patient's height. Then find the height.

In physics, when the source of a sound is traveling toward an observer, the relationship between the actual pitch a of the sound and the pitch h that the observer hears due to the Doppler effect is described by the formula $h = \dfrac{a}{1 - \dfrac{s}{770}}$, *where s is the speed of the sound source in miles per hour. Use this formula to answer Exercise 66.*

66. An emergency vehicle has a single-tone siren with the pitch of the musical note E. As it approaches an observer standing by the road, the vehicle is traveling 50 mph. Is the pitch that the observer hears due to the Doppler effect lower or higher than the actual pitch? To which musical note is the pitch that the observer hears closest?

Pitch of an Octave of Musical Notes in Hertz (HZ)

Note	Pitch
Middle C	261.63
D	293.66
E	329.63
F	349.23
G	392.00
A	440.00
B	493.88

Note: Greater numbers indicate higher pitches (acoustically).
(*Source*: American Standards Association)

In electronics, the relationship among the resistances R_1 and R_2 of two resistors wired in a parallel circuit and their combined resistance R is described by the formula $\dfrac{1}{R} = \dfrac{1}{R_1} + \dfrac{1}{R_2}$. *Use this formula to solve Exercises 67 through 69.*

67. If the combined resistance is 2 ohms and one of the two resistances is 3 ohms, find the other resistance.

68. Find the combined resistance of two resistors of 12 ohms each when they are wired in a parallel circuit.

69. The relationship among resistance of two resistors wired in a parallel circuit and their combined resistance may be extended to three resistors of resistances R_1, R_2, and R_3. Write an equation you believe may describe the relationship, and use it to find the combined resistance if R_1 is 5, R_2 is 6, and R_3 is 2.

6.8   VARIATION AND PROBLEM SOLVING

Objectives

1   Solve problems involving direct variation.

2   Solve problems involving inverse variation.

3   Solve problems involving joint variation.

4   Solve problems involving combined variation.

$C = 2\pi r$
⤓
constant

1   A very familiar example of direct variation is the relationship of the circumference C of a circle to its radius r. The formula $C = 2\pi r$ expresses that the circumference is always 2π times the radius. In other words, C is always a constant multiple (2π) of r. Because it is, we say that **C varies directly as r**, that **C varies directly with r**, or that **C is directly proportional to r**.

> ## Direct Variation
>
> **y varies directly as x**, or **y is directly proportional to x**, if there is a nonzero constant k such that
>
> $$y = kx$$
>
> The number k is called the **constant of variation** or the **constant of proportionality**.

In the above definition, the relationship described between x and y is a linear one. In other words, the graph of $y = kx$ is a line. The slope of the line is k, and the line passes through the origin.

For example, the graph of the direct variation equation $C = 2\pi r$ is shown. The horizontal axis represents the radius r, and the vertical axis is the circumference C. From the graph we can read that when the radius is 6 units, the circumference is approximately 38 units. Also, when the circumference is 45 units, the radius is between 7 and 8 units. Notice that as the radius increases, the circumference increases.

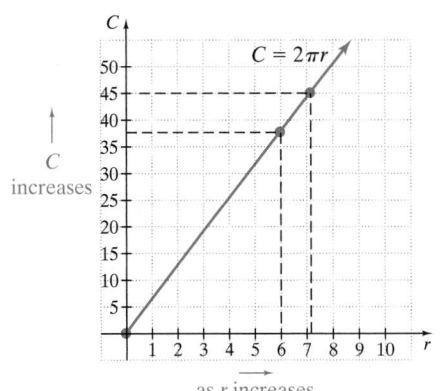

EXAMPLE 1

Suppose that y varies directly as x. If y is 5 when x is 30, find the constant of variation and the direct variation equation.

Solution   Since y varies directly as x, we write $y = kx$. If $y = 5$ when $x = 30$, we have that

$$y = kx$$
$$5 = k(30) \quad \text{Replace } y \text{ with 5 and } x \text{ with 30.}$$
$$\frac{1}{6} = k \quad \text{Solve for } k.$$

The constant of variation is $\frac{1}{6}$.

After finding the constant of variation k, the direct variation equation can be written as

$$y = \frac{1}{6}x.$$

EXAMPLE 2

USING DIRECT VARIATION AND HOOKE'S LAW

Hooke's law states that the distance a spring stretches is directly proportional to the weight attached to the spring. If a 40-pound weight attached to the spring stretches the spring 5 inches, find the distance that a 65-pound weight attached to the spring stretches the spring.

Solution   1. UNDERSTAND.   Read and reread the problem. Notice that we are given that the distance a spring stretches is **directly proportional** to the weight attached. We let

$$d = \text{the distance stretched}$$
$$w = \text{the weight attached}$$

The constant of variation is represented by k.

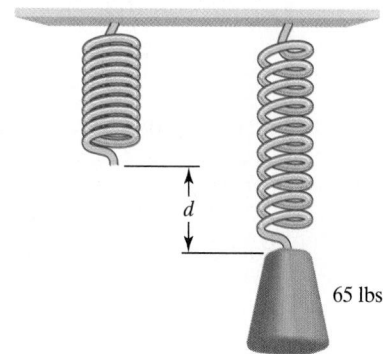

2. TRANSLATE.   Because d is directly proportional to w, we write

$$d = kw$$

3. SOLVE.   When a weight of 40 pounds is attached, the spring stretches 5 inches. That is, when $w = 40$, $d = 5$.

$$d = kw$$
$$5 = k(40) \quad \text{Replace } d \text{ with 5 and } w \text{ with 40.}$$
$$\frac{1}{8} = k \qquad \text{Solve for } k.$$

Now when we replace k with $\frac{1}{8}$ in the equation

$$d = kw, \text{ we have}$$

$$d = \frac{1}{8}w$$

To find the stretch when a weight of 65 pounds is attached, we replace w with 65 to find d.

$$d = \frac{1}{8}(65)$$

$$= \frac{65}{8} = 8\frac{1}{8} \quad \text{or} \quad 8.125$$

4. INTERPRET.

Check: Check the proposed solution of 8.125 inches in the original problem.
State: The spring stetches 8.125 inches when a 65-pound weight is attached.

2 When y is proportional to the **reciprocal** of another variable x, we say that y **varies inversely as x**, or that y **is inversely proportional to x**. An example of the inverse variation relationship is the relationship between the pressure that a gas exerts and the volume of its container. As the volume of a container decreases, the pressure of the gas it contains increases.

Inverse Variation

y **varies inversely as x**, or y **is inversely proportional to x**, if there is a nonzero constant k such that

$$y = \frac{k}{x}$$

The number k is called the **constant of variation** or the **constant of proportionality.**

Notice that $y = \dfrac{k}{x}$ is a rational equation. Its graph for $k > 0$ and $x > 0$ is shown.

From the graph, we can see that as x increases, y decreases.

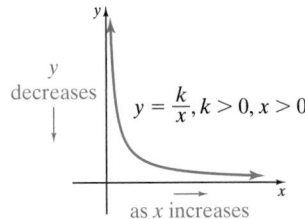

EXAMPLE 3

Suppose that u varies inversely as w. If u is 3 when w is 5, find the constant of variation and the inverse variation equation.

Solution Since u varies inversely as w, we have $u = \dfrac{k}{w}$. We let $u = 3$ and $w = 5$, and we solve for k.

$$u = \frac{k}{w}$$

$$3 = \frac{k}{5} \quad \text{Let } u = 3 \text{ and } w = 5.$$

$$15 = k \quad \text{Multiply both sides by 5.}$$

The constant of variation k is 15. This gives the inverse variation equation

$$u = \frac{15}{w}$$

EXAMPLE 4

USING INVERSE VARIATION AND BOYLE'S LAW

Boyle's law says that if the temperature stays the same, the pressure P of a gas is inversely proportional to the volume V. If a cylinder in a steam engine has a pressure of 960 kilopascals when the volume is 1.4 cubic meters, find the pressure when the volume increases to 2.5 cubic meters.

Solution   **1.** UNDERSTAND.   Read and reread the problem. Notice that we are given that the pressure of a gas is *inversely proportional* to the volume. We will let P = the pressure and V = the volume. The constant of variation is represented by k.

2. TRANSLATE.   Because P is inversely proportional to V, we write

$$P = \frac{k}{V}$$

When P = 960 kilopascals, the volume V = 1.4 cubic meters. We use this information to find k.

$$960 = \frac{k}{1.4} \qquad \text{Let } P = 960 \text{ and } V = 1.4.$$
$$1344 = k \qquad \text{Multiply both sides by } 1.4.$$

Thus, the value of k is 1344. Replacing k with 1344 in the variation equation, we have

$$P = \frac{1344}{V}$$

Next we find P when V is 2.5 cubic meters.

3. SOLVE.

$$P = \frac{1344}{2.5} \qquad \text{Let } V = 2.5.$$
$$= 537.6$$

4. INTERPRET.

Check: Check the proposed solution in the original problem.
State: When the volume is 2.5 cubic meters, the pressure is 537.6 kilopascals.

3 Sometimes the ratio of a variable to the product of many other variables is constant. For example, the ratio of distance traveled to the product of speed and time traveled is always 1.

$$\frac{d}{rt} = 1 \quad \text{or} \quad d = rt$$

Such a relationship is called **joint variation.**

Joint Variation

If the ratio of a variable y to the product of two or more variables is constant, then **y varies jointly as,** or **is jointly proportional to,** the other variables. If

$$y = kxz$$

then the number k is the **constant of variation** or the **constant of proportionality.**

✔ **CONCEPT CHECK**

Which type of variation is represented by the equation $xy = 8$? Explain.

   a. Direct variation

   b. Inverse variation

   c. Joint variation

△ (**EXAMPLE 5**)

EXPRESSING SURFACE AREA

The lateral surface area of a cylinder varies jointly as its radius and height. Express this surface area S in terms of radius r and height h.

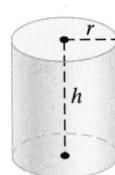

Solution   Because the surface area varies jointly as the radius r and the height h, we equate S to a constant multiple of r and h.

$$S = krh$$

In the equation, $S = krh$, it can be determined that the constant k is 2π, and we then have the formula $S = 2\pi rh$. (The lateral surface area formula does not include the areas of the two circular bases.)

4 Some examples of variation involve combinations of direct, inverse, and joint variation. We will call these variations **combined variation.**

△ **EXAMPLE 6**

FINDING COLUMN WEIGHT

The maximum weight that a circular column can support is directly proportional to the fourth power of its diameter and is inversely proportional to the square of its height. A 2-meter-diameter column that is 8 meters in height can support 1 ton. Find the weight that a 1-meter-diameter column that is 4 meters in height can support.

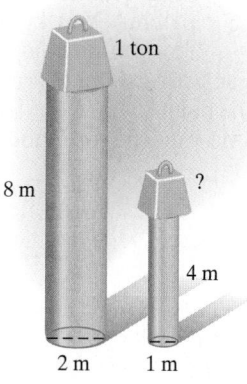

Solution 1. **UNDERSTAND.** Read and reread the problem. Let w = weight, d = diameter, h = height, and k = the constant of variation.

2. **TRANSLATE.** Since w is directly proportional to d^4 and inversely proportional to h^2, we have

$$w = \frac{kd^4}{h^2}$$

3. **SOLVE.** To find k, we are given that a 2-meter-diameter column that is 8 meters in height can support 1 ton. That is, $w = 1$ when $d = 2$ and $h = 8$, or

$$1 = \frac{k \cdot 2^4}{8^2} \qquad \text{Let } w = 1, d = 2, \text{ and } h = 8.$$

$$1 = \frac{k \cdot 16}{64}$$

$$4 = k \qquad \text{Solve for } k.$$

Now replace k with 4 in the equation $w = \frac{kd^4}{h^2}$ and we have

$$w = \frac{4d^4}{h^2}$$

To find weight w for a 1-meter-diameter column that is 4 meters in height, let $d = 1$ and $h = 4$.

$$w = \frac{4 \cdot 1^4}{4^2}$$

$$w = \frac{4}{16} = \frac{1}{4}$$

4. **INTERPRET.** **Check:** Check the proposed solution in the original problem.

State: The 1-meter-diameter column that is 4 meters in height can hold $\frac{1}{4}$ ton of weight.

Spotlight on
DECISION
✐ MAKING

Suppose you are a painting contractor. You have been hired to paint the ceilings of a one-story home, whose layout is shown in the figure. The amount of paint you need is directly proportional to the area that is to be painted. You know that 450 square feet can be painted with 4 quarts of paint. Quarts of paint cost $5.95 each and gallons of paint cost $21.50 each. You have estimated the cost of the paint to be about $50. Is your estimate correct? If so, explain why. If not, how much more should the estimate be?

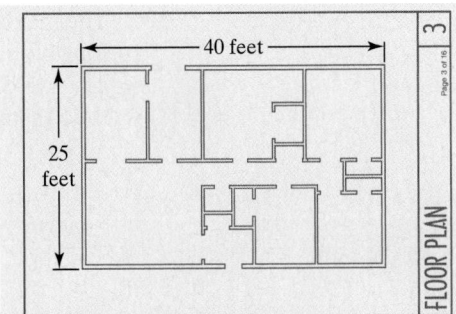

MENTAL MATH

State whether each equation represents direct, inverse, or joint variation.

1. $y = 5x$

2. $y = \dfrac{700}{x}$

3. $y = 5xz$

4. $y = \dfrac{1}{2}abc$

5. $y = \dfrac{9.1}{x}$

6. $y = 2.3x$

7. $y = \dfrac{2}{3}x$

8. $y = 3.1\,st$

EXERCISE SET 6.8

    *Math XP*

STUDY   CD/   PH MATH   MathXL®Tutorials   MathXL®   MyMathLab®
GUIDE/SSM   VIDEO   TUTOR CENTER   ON CD

MIXED PRACTICE

Write an equation to describe each variation. Use k for the constant of proportionality. See Examples 1 through 6.

1. y varies directly as x

2. p varies directly as q

3. a varies inversely as b

4. y varies inversely as x

5. y varies jointly as x and z

6. y varies jointly as q, r, and t

7. y varies inversely as x^3

8. y varies inversely as a^4

9. y varies directly as x and inversely as p^2

10. y varies directly as a^5 and inversely as b

If y varies directly as x, find the constant of variation k and the direct variation equation for each situation. See Example 1.

11. $y = 4$ when $x = 20$

12. $y = 5$ when $x = 30$

13. $y = 6$ when $x = 4$

14. $y = 12$ when $x = 8$

15. $y = 7$ when $x = \dfrac{1}{2}$

16. $y = 11$ when $x = \dfrac{1}{3}$

17. $y = 0.2$ when $x = 0.8$

18. $y = 0.4$ when $x = 2.5$

Solve. See Example 2.

19. The weight of a synthetic ball varies directly with the cube of its radius. A ball with a radius of 2 inches weighs 1.20 pounds. Find the weight of a ball of the same material with a 3-inch radius.

20. At sea, the distance to the horizon is directly proportional to the square root of the elevation of the observer. If a person who is 36 feet above the water can see 7.4 miles, find how far a person 64 feet above the water can see. Round answer to one decimal place.

21. The amount P of pollution varies directly with the population N of people. Kansas City has a population of 450,000 and produces 260,000 tons of pollutants. Find how many tons of pollution we should expect St. Louis to produce, if we know that its population is 980,000. Round answer to the nearest whole ton.

22. Charles' law states that if the pressure P stays the same, the volume V of a gas is directly proportional to its temperature T. If a balloon is filled with 20 cubic meters of a gas at a temperature of 300 K, find the new volume if the temperature rises to 360 K while the pressure stays the same.

If y varies inversely as x, find the constant of variation k and the inverse variation equation for each situation. See Example 3.

23. $y = 6$ when $x = 5$

24. $y = 20$ when $x = 9$

25. $y = 100$ when $x = 7$

26. $y = 63$ when $x = 3$

27. $y = \dfrac{1}{8}$ when $x = 16$

28. $y = \dfrac{1}{10}$ when $x = 40$

29. $y = 0.2$ when $x = 0.7$

30. $y = 0.6$ when $x = 0.3$

Solve. See Example 4.

31. Pairs of markings a set distance apart are made on highways so that police can detect drivers exceeding the speed limit. Over a fixed distance, the speed R varies inversely with the time T. In one particular pair of markings, R is 45 mph when T is 6 seconds. Find the speed of a car that travels the given distance in 5 seconds.

32. The weight of an object on or above the surface of Earth varies inversely as the square of the distance between the object and Earth's center. If a person weighs 160 pounds on Earth's surface, find the individual's weight if he moves 200 miles above Earth. Round answer to the nearest pound. (Assume that Earth's radius is 4000 miles.)

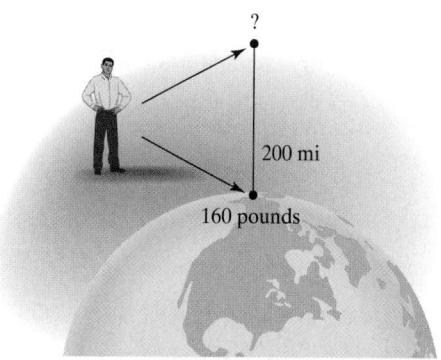

33. If the voltage V in an electric circuit is held constant, the current I is inversely proportional to the resistance R. If the current is 40 amperes when the resistance is 270 ohms, find the current when the resistance is 150 ohms.

34. Because it is more efficient to produce larger numbers of items, the cost of producing recordable disks is inversely proportional to the number produced. If 4000 can be produced at a cost of $0.45 each, find the cost per disk when 6000 are produced.

35. The intensity I of light varies inversely as the square of the distance d from the light source. If the distance from the light source is doubled (see the figure at the top of the next page and the figure directly below it), determine what happens to the intensity of light at the new location.

△ **36.** The maximum weight that a circular column can hold is inversely proportional to the square of its height. If an 8-foot column can hold 2 tons, find how much weight a 10-foot column can hold.

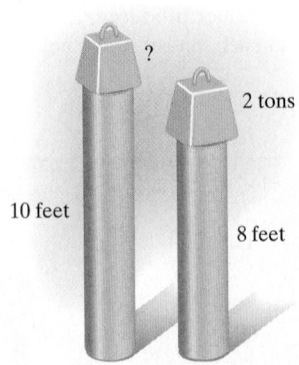

Write each statement as an equation. See Example 5.

37. x varies jointly as y and z.

38. P varies jointly as R and the square of S.

39. r varies jointly as s and the cube of t.

40. a varies jointly as b and c.

For each statement, find the constant of variation and the variation equation. See Examples 5 and 6.

41. y varies directly as the cube of x; $y = 9$ when $x = 3$

42. y varies directly as the cube of x; $y = 32$ when $x = 4$

43. y varies directly as the square root of x; $y = 0.4$ when $x = 4$

44. y varies directly as the square root of x; $y = 2.1$ when $x = 9$

45. y varies inversely as the square of x; $y = 0.052$ when $x = 5$

46. y varies inversely as the square of x; $y = 0.011$ when $x = 10$

47. y varies jointly as x and the cube of z; $y = 120$ when $x = 5$ and $z = 2$

48. y varies jointly as x and the square of z; $y = 360$ when $x = 4$ and $z = 3$

Solve. See Examples 5 and 6.

△ **49.** The maximum weight that a rectangular beam can support varies jointly as its width and the square of its height and inversely as its length. If a beam $\frac{1}{2}$ foot wide, $\frac{1}{3}$ foot high, and 10 feet long can support 12 tons, find how much a similar beam can support if the beam is $\frac{2}{3}$ foot wide, $\frac{1}{2}$ foot high, and 16 feet long.

50. The number of cars manufactured on an assembly line at a General Motors plant varies jointly as the number of workers and the time they work. If 200 workers can produce 60 cars in 2 hours, find how many cars 240 workers should be able to make in 3 hours.

△ **51.** The volume of a cone varies jointly as the square of its radius and its height. If the volume of a cone is 32π cubic inches when the radius is 4 inches and the height is 6 inches, find the volume of a cone when the radius is 3 inches and the height is 5 inches.

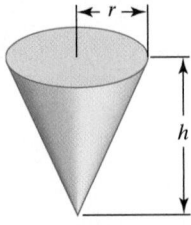

52. When a wind blows perpendicularly against a flat surface, its force is jointly proportional to the surface area and the speed of the wind. A sail whose surface area is 12 square feet experiences a 20-pound force when the wind speed is 10 miles per hour. Find the force on an 8-square-foot sail if the wind speed is 12 miles per hour.

53. The horsepower that can be safely transmitted to a shaft varies jointly as the shaft's angular speed of rotation (in revolutions per minute) and the cube of its diameter. A 2-inch shaft making 120 revolutions per minute safely transmits 40 horsepower. Find how much horsepower can be safely transmitted by a 3-inch shaft making 80 revolutions per minute.

54. The maximum weight that a rectangular beam can support varies jointly as its width and the square of its height and inversely as its length. If a beam $\frac{1}{3}$ foot wide, 1 foot high, and 10 feet long can support 3 tons, find how much weight a similar beam can support if it is 1 foot wide, $\frac{1}{3}$ foot high, and 9 feet long.

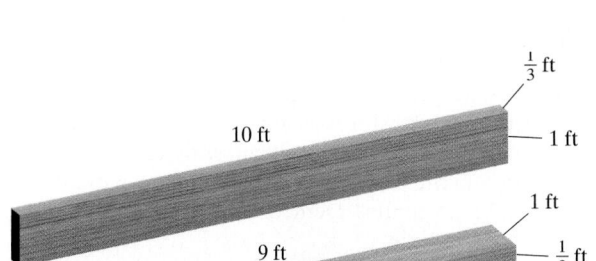
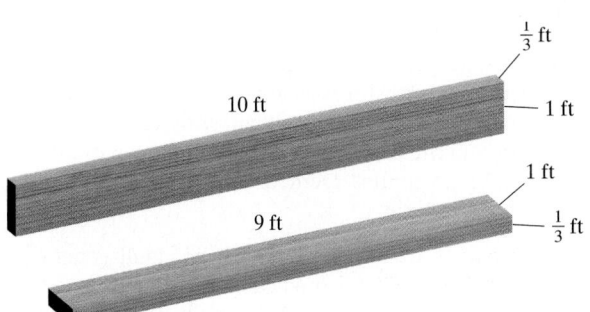

55. The atmospheric pressure y (in millibars) is inversely proportional to the altitude x (in kilometers). If the atmospheric pressure is 400 millibars at an altitude of 8 kilometers, find the atmospheric pressure at an altitude of 4 kilometers.

REVIEW AND PREVIEW

Find the exact circumference and area of each circle. See the inside cover for a list of geometric formulas.

56.

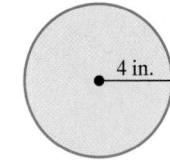

4 in.

57.

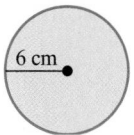

6 cm

58.

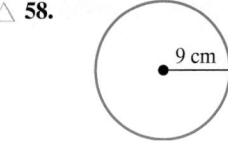

9 cm

59.

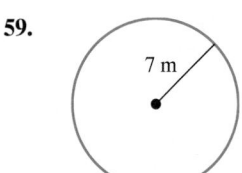

7 m

Find each square root. See Section 1.2.

60. $\sqrt{81}$ **61.** $\sqrt{36}$

62. $\sqrt{1}$ **63.** $\sqrt{4}$

64. $\sqrt{\dfrac{1}{4}}$ **65.** $\sqrt{\dfrac{1}{25}}$

66. $\sqrt{\dfrac{4}{9}}$ **67.** $\sqrt{\dfrac{25}{121}}$

Concept Extensions

68. The horsepower to drive a boat varies directly as the cube of the speed of the boat. If the speed of the boat is to double, determine the corresponding increase in horsepower required.

69. The volume of a cylinder varies jointly as the height and the square of the radius. If the height is halved and the radius is doubled, determine what happens to the volume.

70. Suppose that y varies directly as x. If x is doubled, what is the effect on y?

71. Suppose that y varies directly as x^2. If x is doubled, what is the effect on y?

Complete the following table for the inverse variation $y = \dfrac{k}{x}$ over each given value of k. Plot the points on a rectangular coordinate system.

x	$\dfrac{1}{4}$	$\dfrac{1}{2}$	1	2	4
$y = \dfrac{k}{x}$					

72. $k = 1$

73. $k = 3$

74. $k = 5$

75. $k = \dfrac{1}{2}$

CHAPTER 6 PROJECT

Modeling Electricity Production

According to the U.S. Department of Energy, energy produced by renewable sources (including hydroelectric, geothermal, wind, and solar powers) accounted for nearly 8% of the United States' total production of energy in 2004. Wind energy can be harnessed by windmills to produce electricity, but it is the least utilized of these renewable energy sources. However, progressive communities are experimenting with fields of windmills for communal electricity needs, examining exactly how wind speed affects the amount of electricity produced.

A community in California is experimenting with electricity generated by windmills. City engineers are analyzing data they have gathered about their field of windmills. The engineers are familiar with other research demonstrating that the amount of electricity that a windmill generates hourly (in watt-hours) is directly proportional to the cube of the wind speed (in miles per hour). In this project, you will use this fact to help the engineers analyze the amount of electricity generated by the windmill field. This project may be completed by working in groups or individually.

1. The city engineers have documented that when the wind speed is exactly 10 miles per hour, a windmill generates electricity at a rate of 15 watt-hours. Find a formula that models the relationship between the wind speed and the amount of electricity generated hourly by a windmill.

2. Complete the following table for the given wind speeds. Then use the table to estimate the wind speed required to obtain: **a.** 100 watt-hours, and **b.** 400 watt-hours.

3. Plot the ordered pairs from the table. Describe the trend shown by the graph.

Wind Speed (miles per hour)	Electricity Generated (watt-hours)
15	
17	
19	
21	
23	
25	
27	
29	
31	
33	
35	

4. The engineers' data show that for several days the wind speed was more or less steady at 20 miles per hour, and the windmills generated the expected 120 watt-hours. According to the weather forecast for the coming few days, wind speed will fluctuate wildly, but will still average 20 miles per hour. Should the engineers still expect the windmills to generate 120 watt-hours? Demonstrate your reasoning with a numerical example.

5. During one three-day period, each windmill generated 15 watt-hours. The forecast predicts that the wind speed for the coming few days will drop by half. How many watt-hours should the engineers now expect each windmill to generate? In general, if the wind speed yields c watt-hours, how many watt-hours does half the wind speed yield?

STUDY SKILLS REMINDER

Are You Preparing for a Test on Chapter 6?

Below I have listed some common trouble areas for students in Chapter 6. After studying for your test—but before taking your test—read these.

▶ Make sure you know the difference in the following:

Simplify: $\dfrac{\dfrac{3}{x}}{\dfrac{1}{x}-\dfrac{5}{y}}$ Solve: $\dfrac{5x}{6}-\dfrac{1}{2}=\dfrac{5x}{12}$ Subtract: $\dfrac{1}{2x}-\dfrac{7}{x-3}$

Multiply numerator and denominator by the LCD.

$$\dfrac{\dfrac{3}{x}\cdot xy}{\dfrac{1}{x}\cdot xy-\dfrac{5}{y}\cdot xy}$$

$$=\dfrac{3y}{y-5x}$$

Multiply both sides by the LCD.

$$12\cdot\dfrac{5x}{6}-12\cdot\dfrac{1}{2}=12\cdot\dfrac{5x}{12}$$
$$2\cdot5x-6=5x$$
$$10x-6=5x$$
$$5x=6$$
$$x=\dfrac{6}{5}$$

Write each expression as an equivalent expression with the LCD.

$$\dfrac{1\cdot(x-3)}{2x\cdot(x-3)}-\dfrac{7\cdot2x}{(x-3)\cdot2x}$$
$$=\dfrac{x-3}{2x(x-3)}-\dfrac{14x}{2x(x-3)}$$
$$=\dfrac{-13x-3}{2x(x-3)}$$

Remember: This is simply a checklist of common trouble areas. For a review of Chapter 6, see the Highlights and Chapter Review at the end of this chapter.

CHAPTER VOCABULARY CHECK

Fill in each blank with one of the words or phrases listed below.

rational expression   equation   complex fraction   opposites   synthetic division
least common denominator   expression   long division   jointly   directly   inversely

1. A rational expression whose numerator, denominator, or both contain one or more rational expressions is called a _____.

2. To divide a polynomial by a polynomial other than a monomial, we use _____.

3. In the equation $y = kx$, y varies _____ as x.

4. In the equation $y = \dfrac{k}{x}$, y varies _____ as x.

5. The _____ of a list of rational expressions is a polynomial of least degree whose factors include the denominator factors in the list.

6. When a polynomial is to be divided by a binomial of the form $x - c$, a shortcut process called _____ may be used.

7. In the equation $y = kxz$, y varies _____ as x and z.

8. The expressions $(x - 5)$ and $(5 - x)$ are called _____.

9. A _____ is an expression that can be written as the quotient $\dfrac{P}{Q}$ of two polynomials P and Q as long as Q is not 0.

10. Which is an expression and which is an equation? An example of an _____ is $\dfrac{2}{x} + \dfrac{2}{x^2} = 7$ and an example of an _____ is $\dfrac{2}{x} + \dfrac{5}{x^2}$.

CHAPTER 6 HIGHLIGHTS

Definitions and Concepts	**Examples**

Section 6.1 Rational Functions and Multiplying and Dividing Rational Expressions

A **rational expression** is the quotient $\frac{P}{Q}$ of two polynomials P and Q, as long as Q is not 0.

$$\frac{2x-6}{7}, \qquad \frac{t^2-3t+5}{t-1}$$

To Simplify a Rational Expression

Step 1: Completely factor the numerator and the denominator.

Step 2: Apply the fundamental principle of rational expressions.

Simplify.

$$\frac{2x^2+9x-5}{x^2-25} = \frac{(2x-1)(x+5)}{(x-5)(x+5)}$$
$$= \frac{2x-1}{x-5}$$

To Multiply Rational Expressions

Step 1: Completely factor numerators and denominators.

Step 2: Multiply the numerators and multiply the denominators.

Step 3: Apply the fundamental principle of rational expressions.

Multiply $\frac{x^3+8}{12x-18} \cdot \frac{14x^2-21x}{x^2+2x}$.

$$= \frac{(x+2)(x^2-2x+4)}{6(2x-3)} \cdot \frac{7x(2x-3)}{x(x+2)}$$
$$= \frac{7(x^2-2x+4)}{6}$$

To Divide Rational Expressions

Multiply the first rational expression by the reciprocal of the second rational expression.

Divide $\frac{x^2+6x+9}{5xy-5y} \div \frac{x+3}{10y}$.

$$= \frac{(x+3)(x+3)}{5y(x-1)} \cdot \frac{2 \cdot 5y}{x+3}$$
$$= \frac{2(x+3)}{x-1}$$

A **rational function** is a function described by a rational expression.

$$f(x) = \frac{2x-6}{7}, \qquad h(t) = \frac{t^2-3t+5}{t-1}$$

Section 6.2 Adding and Subtracting Rational Expressions

To Add or Subtract Rational Expressions

Step 1: Find the LCD.

Step 2: Write each rational expression as an equivalent rational expression whose denominator is the LCD.

Step 3: Add or subtract numerators and write the result over the common denominator.

Step 4: Simplify the resulting rational expression.

Subtract $\frac{3}{x+2} - \frac{x+1}{x-3}$.

$$= \frac{3 \cdot (x-3)}{(x+2) \cdot (x-3)} - \frac{(x+1) \cdot (x+2)}{(x-3) \cdot (x+2)}$$
$$= \frac{3(x-3) - (x+1)(x+2)}{(x+2)(x-3)}$$
$$= \frac{3x-9 - (x^2+3x+2)}{(x+2)(x-3)}$$
$$= \frac{3x-9 - x^2-3x-2}{(x+2)(x-3)}$$
$$= \frac{-x^2-11}{(x+2)(x-3)}$$

Definitions and Concepts	**Examples**

Section 6.3 Simplifying Complex Fractions

Method 1: Simplify the numerator and the denominator so that each is a single fraction. Then perform the indicated division and simplify if possible.

Simplify $\dfrac{\dfrac{x+2}{x}}{x - \dfrac{4}{x}}$.

Method 1: $\dfrac{\dfrac{x+2}{x}}{\dfrac{x \cdot x}{1 \cdot x} - \dfrac{4}{x}} = \dfrac{\dfrac{x+2}{x}}{\dfrac{x^2-4}{x}}$

$= \dfrac{x+2}{x} \cdot \dfrac{x}{(x+2)(x-2)} = \dfrac{1}{x-2}$

Method 2: Multiply the numerator and the denominator of the complex fraction by the LCD of the fractions in both the numerator and the denominator. Then simplify if possible.

Method 2: $\dfrac{\left(\dfrac{x+2}{x}\right) \cdot x}{\left(x - \dfrac{4}{x}\right) \cdot x} = \dfrac{x+2}{x \cdot x - \dfrac{4}{x} \cdot x}$

$= \dfrac{x+2}{x^2-4} = \dfrac{x+2}{(x+2)(x-2)} = \dfrac{1}{x-2}$

Section 6.4 Dividing Polynomials

To divide a polynomial by a monomial: Divide each term in the polynomial by the monomial.

Divide $\dfrac{12a^5b^3 - 6a^2b^2 + ab}{6a^2b^2}$

$= \dfrac{12a^5b^3}{6a^2b^2} - \dfrac{6a^2b^2}{6a^2b^2} + \dfrac{ab}{6a^2b^2}$

$= 2a^3b - 1 + \dfrac{1}{6ab}$

To divide a polynomial by a polynomial, other than a monomial:

Use **long division.**

Divide $2x^3 - x^2 - 8x - 1$ by $x - 2$.

$$
\begin{array}{r}
2x^2 + 3x - 2 \\
x - 2 \overline{)\,2x^3 - x^2 - 8x - 1} \\
\underline{2x^3 - 4x^2} \\
3x^2 - 8x \\
\underline{3x^2 - 6x} \\
-2x - 1 \\
\underline{-2x + 4} \\
-5
\end{array}
$$

The quotient is $2x^2 + 3x - 2 - \dfrac{5}{x-2}$.

Section 6.5 Synthetic Division and the Remainder Theorem

A shortcut method called **synthetic division** may be used to divide a polynomial by a binomial of the form $x - c$.

Use synthetic division to divide $2x^3 - x^2 - 8x - 1$ by $x - 2$.

$$
\begin{array}{r|rrrr}
2 & 2 & -1 & -8 & -1 \\
  & \downarrow & 4 & 6 & -4 \\
\hline
  & 2 & 3 & -2 & -5
\end{array}
$$

The quotient is $2x^2 + 3x - 2 - \dfrac{5}{x-2}$.

Definitions and Concepts	**Examples**

Section 6.6 Solving Equations Containing Rational Expressions

To solve an equation containing rational expressions: Multiply both sides of the equation by the LCD of all rational expressions. Then apply the distributive property and simplify. Solve the resulting equation and then check each proposed solution to see whether it makes the denominator 0. If so, it is an **extraneous solution**.

Solve $x - \dfrac{3}{x} = \dfrac{1}{2}$.

$$2x\left(x - \frac{3}{x}\right) = 2x\left(\frac{1}{2}\right) \quad \text{The LCD is } 2x.$$

$$2x \cdot x - 2x\left(\frac{3}{x}\right) = 2x\left(\frac{1}{2}\right) \quad \text{Distribute.}$$

$$2x^2 - 6 = x$$
$$2x^2 - x - 6 = 0 \quad \text{Subtract } x.$$
$$(2x + 3)(x - 2) = 0 \quad \text{Factor.}$$
$$x = -\frac{3}{2} \quad \text{or} \quad x = 2 \quad \text{Solve.}$$

Both $-\dfrac{3}{2}$ and 2 check. The solutions are 2 and $-\dfrac{3}{2}$.

Section 6.7 Rational Equations and Problem Solving

Solving an Equation for a Specified Variable

Treat the specified variable as the only variable of the equation and solve as usual.

Problem-Solving Steps to Follow

1. UNDERSTAND.

Solve for x.

$$A = \frac{2x + 3y}{5}$$
$$5A = 2x + 3y \quad \text{Multiply both sides by 5.}$$
$$5A - 3y = 2x \quad \text{Subtract } 3y \text{ from both sides.}$$
$$\frac{5A - 3y}{2} = x \quad \text{Divide both sides by 2.}$$

Jeanee and David Dillon volunteer every year to clean a strip of Lake Ponchartrain Beach. Jeanee can clean all the trash in this area of beach in 6 hours; David takes 5 hours. Find how long it will take them to clean the area of beach together.

1. Read and reread the problem.
   Let x = time in hours that it takes Jeanee and David to clean the beach together.

	Hours to Complete	*Part Completed in 1 Hour*
Jeanee Alone	6	$\dfrac{1}{6}$
David Alone	5	$\dfrac{1}{5}$
Together	x	$\dfrac{1}{x}$

(continued)

Definitions and Concepts	**Examples**

Section 6.7 Rational Equations and Problem Solving

2. TRANSLATE.

2. In words:

		part Jeanee can complete in 1 hour	+	part David can complete in 1 hour	=	part they can complete together in 1 hour
		↓		↓		↓

Translate:

$$\frac{1}{6} \quad + \quad \frac{1}{5} \quad = \quad \frac{1}{x}$$

3. SOLVE.

3. $\dfrac{1}{6} + \dfrac{1}{5} = \dfrac{1}{x}$ Multiply both sides by $30x$.

$$5x + 6x = 30$$

$$11x = 30$$

$$x = \frac{30}{11} \quad \text{or} \quad 2\frac{8}{11}$$

4. INTERPRET.

4. *Check* and then *state*. Together, they can clean the beach in $2\dfrac{8}{11}$ hours.

Section 6.8 Variation and Problem Solving

y **varies directly as** x, or *y* is **directly proportional to** x, if there is a nonzero constant k such that

$$y = kx$$

y **varies inversely as** x, or *y* is **inversely proportional to** x, if there is a nonzero constant k such that

$$y = \frac{k}{x}$$

y **varies jointly as** x and z or *y* is **jointly proportional to** x and z if there is a nonzero constant k such that

$$y = kxz$$

The circumference of a circle C varies directly as its radius r.

$$C = 2\pi r \atop k$$

Pressure P varies inversely with volume V.

$$P = \frac{k}{V}$$

The lateral surface area S of a cylinder varies jointly as its radius r and height h.

$$S = 2\pi rh \atop k$$

CHAPTER REVIEW

Find the domain for each rational function.

1. $f(x) = \dfrac{3 - 5x}{7}$

2. $g(x) = \dfrac{2x + 4}{11}$

3. $F(x) = \dfrac{-3x^2}{x - 5}$

4. $h(x) = \dfrac{4x}{3x - 12}$

5. $f(x) = \dfrac{x^3 + 2}{x^2 + 8x}$

6. $G(x) = \dfrac{20}{3x^2 - 48}$

Write each rational expression in lowest terms.

7. $\dfrac{15x^4}{45x^2}$

8. $\dfrac{x + 2}{2 + x}$

9. $\dfrac{18m^6 p^2}{10m^4 p}$

10. $\dfrac{x - 12}{12 - x}$

11. $\dfrac{5x - 15}{25x - 75}$

12. $\dfrac{22x + 8}{11x + 4}$

13. $\dfrac{2x}{2x^2 - 2x}$

14. $\dfrac{x + 7}{x^2 - 49}$

15. $\dfrac{2x^2 + 4x - 30}{x^2 + x - 20}$

16. $\dfrac{xy - 3x + 2y - 6}{x^2 + 4x + 4}$

17. The average cost of manufacturing x bookcases is given by the rational function

$$C(x) = \dfrac{35x + 4200}{x}$$

a. Find the average cost per bookcase of manufacturing 50 bookcases.

b. Find the average cost per bookcase of manufacturing 100 bookcases.

c. As the number of bookcases increases, does the average cost per bookcase increase or decrease? (See parts **a** and **b**.)

Perform the indicated operation. If possible, simplify your answer.

18. $\dfrac{5}{x^3} \cdot \dfrac{x^2}{15}$

19. $\dfrac{3x^4 yz^3}{15x^2 y^2} \cdot \dfrac{10xy}{z^6}$

20. $\dfrac{4 - x}{5} \cdot \dfrac{15}{2x - 8}$

21. $\dfrac{x^2 - 6x + 9}{2x^2 - 18} \cdot \dfrac{4x + 12}{5x - 15}$

22. $\dfrac{a - 4b}{a^2 + ab} \cdot \dfrac{b^2 - a^2}{8b - 2a}$

23. $\dfrac{x^2 - x - 12}{2x^2 - 32} \cdot \dfrac{x^2 + 8x + 16}{3x^2 + 21x + 36}$

24. $\dfrac{2x^3 + 54}{5x^2 + 5x - 30} \cdot \dfrac{6x + 12}{3x^2 - 9x + 27}$

25. $\dfrac{3}{4x} \div \dfrac{8}{2x^2}$

26. $\dfrac{4x + 8y}{3} \div \dfrac{5x + 10y}{9}$

27. $\dfrac{5ab}{14c^3} \div \dfrac{10a^4 b^2}{6ac^5}$

28. $\dfrac{2}{5x} \div \dfrac{4 - 18x}{6 - 27x}$

29. $\dfrac{x^2 - 25}{3} \div \dfrac{x^2 - 10x + 25}{x^2 - x - 20}$

30. $\dfrac{a - 4b}{a^2 + ab} \div \dfrac{20b - 5a}{b^2 - a^2}$

31. $\dfrac{7x + 28}{2x + 4} \div \dfrac{x^2 + 2x - 8}{x^2 - 2x - 8}$

32. $\dfrac{3x + 3}{x - 1} \div \dfrac{x^2 - 6x - 7}{x^2 - 1}$

33. $\dfrac{2x - x^2}{x^3 - 8} \div \dfrac{x^2}{x^2 + 2x + 4}$

34. $\dfrac{5a^2 - 20}{a^3 + 2a^2 + a + 2} \div \dfrac{7a}{a^3 + a}$

35. $\dfrac{2a}{21} \div \dfrac{3a^2}{7} \cdot \dfrac{4}{a}$

36. $\dfrac{5x - 15}{3 - x} \cdot \dfrac{x + 2}{10x + 20} \cdot \dfrac{x^2 - 9}{x^2 - x - 6}$

37. $\dfrac{4a + 8}{5a^2 - 20} \cdot \dfrac{3a^2 - 6a}{a + 3} \div \dfrac{2a^2}{5a + 15}$

(6.2) *Find the LCD of the rational expressions in the list.*

38. $\dfrac{4}{9}, \dfrac{5}{2}$

39. $\dfrac{5}{4x^2 y^5}, \dfrac{3}{10x^2 y^4}, \dfrac{x}{6y^4}$

40. $\dfrac{5}{2x}, \dfrac{7}{x - 2}$

41. $\dfrac{3}{5x}, \dfrac{2}{x - 5}$

42. $\dfrac{1}{5x^3}, \dfrac{4}{x^2 + 3x - 28}, \dfrac{11}{10x^2 - 30x}$

Perform the indicated operation. If possible, simplify your answer.

43. $\dfrac{2}{15} + \dfrac{4}{15}$

44. $\dfrac{4}{x - 4} + \dfrac{x}{x - 4}$

45. $\dfrac{4}{3x^2} + \dfrac{2}{3x^2}$

46. $\dfrac{1}{x-2} - \dfrac{1}{4-2x}$

47. $\dfrac{2x+1}{x^2+x-6} + \dfrac{2-x}{x^2+x-6}$

48. $\dfrac{7}{2x} + \dfrac{5}{6x}$

49. $\dfrac{1}{3x^2y^3} - \dfrac{1}{5x^4y}$

50. $\dfrac{1}{10-x} + \dfrac{x-1}{x-10}$

51. $\dfrac{x-2}{x+1} - \dfrac{x-3}{x-1}$

52. $\dfrac{x}{9-x^2} - \dfrac{2}{5x-15}$

53. $2x+1 - \dfrac{1}{x-3}$

54. $\dfrac{2}{a^2-2a+1} + \dfrac{3}{a^2-1}$

55. $\dfrac{x}{9x^2+12x+16} - \dfrac{3x+4}{27x^3-64}$

Perform the indicated operation. If possible, simplify your answer.

56. $\dfrac{2}{x-1} - \dfrac{3x}{3x-3} + \dfrac{1}{2x-2}$

57. $\dfrac{3}{2x} \cdot \left(\dfrac{2}{x+1} - \dfrac{2}{x-3} \right)$

58. $\left(\dfrac{2}{x} - \dfrac{1}{5} \right) \cdot \left(\dfrac{2}{x} + \dfrac{1}{3} \right)$

59. $\dfrac{2}{x^2-16} - \dfrac{3x}{x^2+8x+16} + \dfrac{3}{x+4}$

60. Find the perimeter of the heptagon (polygon with 7 sides).

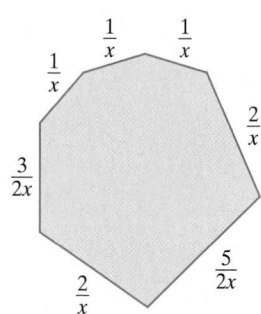

(6.3) *Simplify each complex fraction.*

61. $\dfrac{\frac{2}{5}}{\frac{3}{5}}$

62. $\dfrac{1 - \frac{3}{4}}{2 + \frac{1}{4}}$

63. $\dfrac{\frac{1}{x} - \frac{2}{3x}}{\frac{5}{2x} - \frac{1}{3}}$

64. $\dfrac{\frac{x^2}{15}}{\frac{x+1}{5x}}$

65. $\dfrac{\frac{3}{y^2}}{\frac{6}{y^3}}$

66. $\dfrac{\frac{x+2}{3}}{\frac{5}{x-2}}$

67. $\dfrac{2 - \frac{3}{2x}}{x - \frac{2}{5x}}$

68. $\dfrac{1 + \frac{x}{y}}{\frac{x^2}{y^2} - 1}$

69. $\dfrac{\frac{5}{x} + \frac{1}{xy}}{\frac{3}{x^2}}$

70. $\dfrac{\frac{x}{3} - \frac{3}{x}}{1 + \frac{3}{x}}$

71. $\dfrac{\frac{1}{x-1} + 1}{\frac{1}{x+1} - 1}$

72. $\dfrac{2}{1 - \frac{2}{x}}$

73. $\dfrac{1}{1 + \frac{2}{1 - \frac{1}{x}}}$

74. $\dfrac{\frac{x^2+5x-6}{4x+3}}{\frac{(x+6)^2}{8x+6}}$

75. $\dfrac{\frac{x-3}{x+3} + \frac{x+3}{x-3}}{\frac{x-3}{x+3} - \frac{x+3}{x-3}}$

76. $\dfrac{\frac{3}{x-1} - \frac{2}{1-x}}{\frac{2}{x-1} - \frac{2}{x}}$

77. If $f(x) = \dfrac{3}{x}$, find each of the following:

   a. $f(a+h)$

   b. $f(a)$

   c. Use parts **a** and **b** to find $\dfrac{f(a+h) - f(a)}{h}$.

   d. Simplify the results of part **c.**

(6.4) Divide.

78. Divide $3x^5yb^9$ by $9xy^7$.

79. Divide $-9xb^4z^3$ by $-4axb^2$.

80. $(4xy + 2x^2 - 9) \div 4xy$

81. Divide $12xb^2 + 16xb^4$ by $4xb^3$.

82. $(3x^4 - 25x^2 - 20) \div (x - 3)$

83. $(-x^2 + 2x^4 + 5x - 12) \div (x + 2)$

84. $(2x^4 - x^3 + 2x^2 - 3x + 1) \div (2x - 1)$

85. $(2x^3 + 3x^2 - 2x + 2) \div (2x + 3)$

86. $(3x^4 + 5x^3 + 7x^2 + 3x - 2) \div (x^2 + x + 2)$

87. $(9x^4 - 6x^3 + 3x^2 - 12x - 30) \div (3x^2 - 2x - 5)$

(6.5) Use synthetic division to find each quotient.

88. $(3x^3 + 12x - 4) \div (x - 2)$

89. $(3x^3 + 2x^2 - 4x - 1) \div \left(x + \dfrac{3}{2}\right)$

90. $(x^5 - 1) \div (x + 1)$

91. $(x^3 - 81) \div (x - 3)$

92. $(x^3 - x^2 + 3x^4 - 2) \div (x - 4)$

93. $(3x^4 - 2x^2 + 10) \div (x + 2)$

If $P(x) = 3x^5 - 9x + 7$, use the remainder theorem to find the following.

94. $P(4)$

95. $P(-5)$

96. $P\left(\dfrac{2}{3}\right)$

△ **97.** $P\left(-\dfrac{1}{2}\right)$

98. If the area of the rectangle is $(x^4 - x^3 - 6x^2 - 6x + 18)$ square miles and its width is $(x - 3)$ miles, find the length.

$$
\boxed{\begin{array}{c} x^4 - x^3 - 6x^2 - 6x + 18 \\ \text{square miles} \end{array}} \quad \begin{array}{c} x - 3 \\ \text{miles} \end{array}
$$

(6.6) Solve each equation for x.

99. $\dfrac{2}{5} = \dfrac{x}{15}$

100. $\dfrac{3}{x} + \dfrac{1}{3} = \dfrac{5}{x}$

101. $4 + \dfrac{8}{x} = 8$

102. $\dfrac{2x + 3}{5x - 9} = \dfrac{3}{2}$

103. $\dfrac{1}{x - 2} - \dfrac{3x}{x^2 - 4} = \dfrac{2}{x + 2}$

104. $\dfrac{7}{x} - \dfrac{x}{7} = 0$

105. $\dfrac{x - 2}{x^2 - 7x + 10} = \dfrac{1}{5x - 10} - \dfrac{1}{x - 5}$

Solve the equations for x or perform the indicated operation. Simplify.

106. $\dfrac{5}{x^2 - 7x} + \dfrac{4}{2x - 14}$

107. $3 - \dfrac{5}{x} - \dfrac{2}{x^2} = 0$

108. $\dfrac{4}{3 - x} - \dfrac{7}{2x - 6} + \dfrac{5}{x}$

Solution   **a.** $\sqrt{36} = 6$ because $6^2 = 36$ and 6 is not negative.

b. $\sqrt{0} = 0$ because $0^2 = 0$ and 0 is not negative.

c. $\sqrt{\dfrac{4}{49}} = \dfrac{2}{7}$ because $\left(\dfrac{2}{7}\right)^2 = \dfrac{4}{49}$ and $\dfrac{2}{7}$ is not negative.

d. $\sqrt{0.25} = 0.5$ because $(0.5)^2 = 0.25$.

e. $\sqrt{x^6} = x^3$ because $(x^3)^2 = x^6$.

f. $\sqrt{9x^{12}} = 3x^6$ because $(3x^6)^2 = 9x^{12}$.

g. $-\sqrt{81} = -9$. The negative in front of the radical indicates the negative square root of 81.

Can we find the square root of a negative number, say $\sqrt{-4}$? That is, can we find a real number whose square is -4? No, there is no real number whose square is -4, and we say that $\sqrt{-4}$ is not a real number. In general:

The square root of a negative number is not a real number.

> ### Helpful Hint
>
> * Remember: $\sqrt{0} = 0$
> * Don't forget, the square root of a negative number, such as $\sqrt{-9}$, is not a real number. In Section 7.7, we will see what kind of a number $\sqrt{-9}$ is.

2   Recall that numbers such as 1, 4, 9, and 25 are called **perfect squares**, since $1 = 1^2, 4 = 2^2, 9 = 3^2$, and $25 = 5^2$. Square roots of perfect square radicands simplify to rational numbers. What happens when we try to simplify a root such as $\sqrt{3}$? Since there is no rational number whose square is 3, then $\sqrt{3}$ is not a rational number. It is called an **irrational number**, and we can find a decimal **approximation** of it. To find decimal approximations, use a calculator. For example, an approximation for $\sqrt{3}$ is

$$\sqrt{3} \approx 1.732$$
$$\uparrow$$
approximation symbol

To see if the approximation is reasonable, notice that since

$$1 < 3 < 4, \text{ then}$$
$$\sqrt{1} < \sqrt{3} < \sqrt{4}, \text{ or}$$
$$1 < \sqrt{3} < 2.$$

We found $\sqrt{3} \approx 1.732$, a number between 1 and 2, so our result is reasonable.

EXAMPLE 2

Use a calculator to approximate $\sqrt{20}$. Round the approximation to 3 decimal places and check to see that your approximation is reasonable.

$$\sqrt{20} \approx 4.472$$

Solution   Is this reasonable? Since $16 < 20 < 25$, then $\sqrt{16} < \sqrt{20} < \sqrt{25}$, or $4 < \sqrt{20} < 5$. The approximation is between 4 and 5 and thus is reasonable.

3 Finding roots can be extended to other roots such as cube roots. For example, since $2^3 = 8$, we call 2 the **cube root** of 8. In symbols, we write

$$\sqrt[3]{8} = 2$$

Cube Root

The **cube root** of a real number a is written as $\sqrt[3]{a}$, and

$$\sqrt[3]{a} = b \text{ only if } b^3 = a$$

From this definition, we have

$$\sqrt[3]{64} = 4 \text{ since } 4^3 = 64$$
$$\sqrt[3]{-27} = -3 \text{ since } (-3)^3 = -27$$
$$\sqrt[3]{x^3} = x \text{ since } x^3 = x^3$$

Notice that, unlike with square roots, *it is possible to have a negative radicand when finding a cube root.* This is so because the *cube* of a negative number is a negative number. Therefore, the *cube root* of a negative number is a negative number.

EXAMPLE 3

Find the cube roots.

a. $\sqrt[3]{1}$ b. $\sqrt[3]{-64}$ c. $\sqrt[3]{\dfrac{8}{125}}$

d. $\sqrt[3]{x^6}$ e. $\sqrt[3]{-27x^9}$

Solution   a. $\sqrt[3]{1} = 1$ because $1^3 = 1$.

b. $\sqrt[3]{-64} = -4$ because $(-4)^3 = -64$.

c. $\sqrt[3]{\dfrac{8}{125}} = \dfrac{2}{5}$ because $\left(\dfrac{2}{5}\right)^3 = \dfrac{8}{125}$.

d. $\sqrt[3]{x^6} = x^2$ because $(x^2)^3 = x^6$.

e. $\sqrt[3]{-27x^9} = -3x^3$ because $(-3x^3)^3 = -27x^9$.

4 Just as we can raise a real number to powers other than 2 or 3, we can find roots other than square roots and cube roots. In fact, we can find the **nth root** of a number, where n is any natural number. In symbols, the *n*th root of a is written as $\sqrt[n]{a}$, where n is called the **index**. The index 2 is usually omitted for square roots.

> **Helpful Hint**
>
> If the index is even, such as $\sqrt{}$, $\sqrt[4]{}$, $\sqrt[6]{}$, and so on, the radicand must be non-negative for the root to be a real number. For example,
>
> $$\sqrt[4]{16} = 2, \text{ but } \sqrt[4]{-16} \text{ is not a real number.}$$
> $$\sqrt[6]{64} = 2, \text{ but } \sqrt[6]{-64} \text{ is not a real number.}$$
>
> If the index is odd, such as $\sqrt[3]{}$, $\sqrt[5]{}$, and so on, the radicand may be any real number. For example,
>
> $$\sqrt[3]{64} = 4 \text{ and } \sqrt[3]{-64} = -4$$
> $$\sqrt[5]{32} = 2 \text{ and } \sqrt[5]{-32} = -2$$

✔ **CONCEPT CHECK**

Which one is not a real number?

a. $\sqrt[3]{-15}$ **b.** $\sqrt[4]{-15}$ **c.** $\sqrt[5]{-15}$ **d.** $\sqrt{(-15)^2}$

EXAMPLE 4

Simplify the following expressions.

a. $\sqrt[4]{81}$ **b.** $\sqrt[5]{-243}$ **c.** $-\sqrt{25}$

d. $\sqrt[4]{-81}$ **e.** $\sqrt[3]{64x^3}$

Solution   **a.** $\sqrt[4]{81} = 3$ because $3^4 = 81$ and 3 is positive.
b. $\sqrt[5]{-243} = -3$ because $(-3)^5 = -243$.
c. $-\sqrt{25} = -5$ because -5 is the opposite of $\sqrt{25}$.
d. $\sqrt[4]{-81}$ is not a real number. There is no real number that, when raised to the fourth power, is -81.
e. $\sqrt[3]{64x^3} = 4x$ because $(4x)^3 = 64x^3$.

5 Recall that the notation $\sqrt{a^2}$ indicates the positive square root of a^2 only. For example,

$$\sqrt{(-5)^2} = \sqrt{25} = 5$$

When variables are present in the radicand and it is unclear whether the variable represents a positive number or a negative number, absolute value bars are sometimes needed to ensure that the result is a positive number. For example,

$$\sqrt{x^2} = |x|$$

This ensures that the result is positive. This same situation may occur when the index is any *even* positive integer. When the index is any *odd* positive integer, absolute value bars are not necessary.

> **Finding $\sqrt[n]{a^n}$**
>
> If n is an *even* positive integer, then $\sqrt[n]{a^n} = |a|$.
>
> If n is an *odd* positive integer, then $\sqrt[n]{a^n} = a$.

EXAMPLE 5

Simplify.

a. $\sqrt{(-3)^2}$ **b.** $\sqrt{x^2}$ **c.** $\sqrt[4]{(x-2)^4}$ **d.** $\sqrt[3]{(-5)^3}$

e. $\sqrt[5]{(2x-7)^5}$ **f.** $\sqrt{25x^2}$ **g.** $\sqrt{x^2 + 2x + 1}$

Solution

a. $\sqrt{(-3)^2} = |-3| = 3$ When the index is even, the absolute value bars ensure us that our result is not negative.

b. $\sqrt{x^2} = |x|$

c. $\sqrt[4]{(x-2)^4} = |x - 2|$

d. $\sqrt[3]{(-5)^3} = -5$

e. $\sqrt[5]{(2x-7)^5} = 2x - 7$ Absolute value bars are not needed when the index is odd.

f. $\sqrt{25x^2} = 5|x|$

g. $\sqrt{x^2 + 2x + 1} = \sqrt{(x+1)^2} = |x + 1|$

6   Recall that an equation in x and y describes a function if each x-value is paired with exactly one y-value. With this in mind, does the equation

$$y = \sqrt{x}$$

describe a function? First, notice that replacement values for x must be nonnegative real numbers, since $\sqrt{x}$ is not a real number if $x < 0$. The notation $\sqrt{x}$ denotes the principal square root of x, so for every nonnegative number x, there is exactly one number, $\sqrt{x}$. Therefore, $y = \sqrt{x}$ describes a function, and we may write it as

$$f(x) = \sqrt{x}$$

In general, radical functions are functions of the form

$$f(x) = \sqrt[n]{x}.$$

Recall that the domain of a function in x is the set of all possible replacement values of x. This means that if n is even, the domain is the set of all nonnegative numbers or $\{x | x \geq 0\}$. If n is odd, the domain is the set of all real numbers. Keep this in mind as we find function values.

EXAMPLE 6

If $f(x) = \sqrt{x - 4}$ and $g(x) = \sqrt[3]{x + 2}$, find each function value.

a. $f(8)$ **b.** $f(6)$

c. $g(-1)$ **d.** $g(1)$

Solution   **a.** $f(8) = \sqrt{8 - 4} = \sqrt{4} = 2$
b. $f(6) = \sqrt{6 - 4} = \sqrt{2}$
c. $g(-1) = \sqrt[3]{-1 + 2} = \sqrt[3]{1} = 1$
d. $g(1) = \sqrt[3]{1 + 2} = \sqrt[3]{3}$

> ### Helpful Hint
>
> Notice that for the function $f(x) = \sqrt{x - 4}$, the domain includes all real numbers that make the radicand ≥ 0. To see what numbers these are, solve $x - 4 \geq 0$ and find that $x \geq 4$. The domain is $\{x \mid x \geq 4\}$.
> The domain of the cube root function $g(x) = \sqrt[3]{x + 2}$ is the set of real numbers.

EXAMPLE 7

Graph the square root function $f(x) = \sqrt{x}$.

Solution   To graph, we identify the domain, evaluate the function for several values of x, plot the resulting points, and connect the points with a smooth curve. Since $\sqrt{x}$ represents the nonnegative square root of x, the domain of this function is the set of all nonnegative numbers, $\{x \mid x \geq 0\}$, or $[0, \infty)$. We have approximated $\sqrt{3}$ below to help us locate the point corresponding to $(3, \sqrt{3})$.

x	$f(x) = \sqrt{x}$
0	0
1	1
3	$\sqrt{3} \approx 1.7$
4	2
9	3

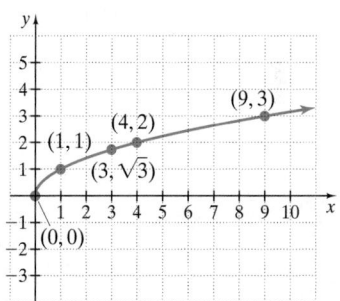

Notice that the graph of this function passes the vertical line test, as expected.

The equation $f(x) = \sqrt[3]{x}$ also describes a function. Here x may be any real number, so the domain of this function is the set of all real numbers, or $(-\infty, \infty)$. A few function values are given next.

$$f(0) = \sqrt[3]{0} = 0$$
$$f(1) = \sqrt[3]{1} = 1$$
$$f(-1) = \sqrt[3]{-1} = -1$$
$$f(6) = \sqrt[3]{6}$$
$$f(-6) = \sqrt[3]{-6}$$

Here, there is no rational number whose cube is 6. Thus, the radicals do not simplify to rational numbers.

$$f(8) = \sqrt[3]{8} = 2$$
$$f(-8) = \sqrt[3]{-8} = -2$$

EXAMPLE 8

Graph the function $f(x) = \sqrt[3]{x}$.

Solution   To graph, we identify the domain, plot points, and connect the points with a smooth curve. The domain of this function is the set of all real numbers. The table comes from the function values obtained earlier. We have approximated $\sqrt[3]{6}$ and $\sqrt[3]{-6}$ for graphing purposes.

x	$f(x) = \sqrt[3]{x}$
0	0
1	1
−1	−1
6	$\sqrt[3]{6} \approx 1.8$
−6	$\sqrt[3]{-6} \approx -1.8$
8	2
−8	−2

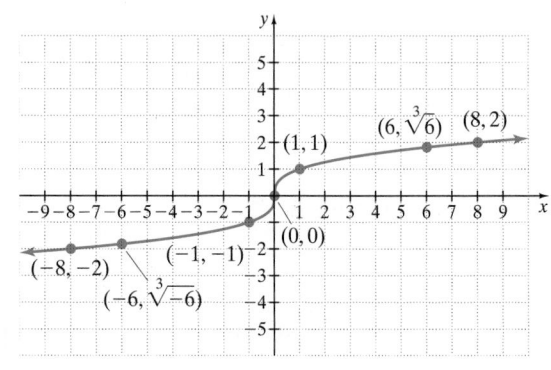

The graph of this function passes the vertical line test, as expected.

Spotlight on

DECISION
MAKING

Suppose you are a scientist working for NASA. A new moon, S/2001U1, has been discovered orbiting the planet Uranus in our outer solar system. You have been asked to check whether it is possible for this moon to have an oxygen atmosphere. You can do so by comparing the average speed of an oxygen molecule (480 meters per second) to the moon's **escape velocity**, the speed an object must travel to permanently leave the moon's gravitational pull. If the moon's escape velocity is greater than the average speed of oxygen molecules, then it is possible for the moon to retain oxygen in its atmosphere—that is, if oxygen exists on the moon at all.

Data about the new moon are listed in the table. Use that along with the escape velocity formula given to the right to decide whether it is possible for S/2001U1 to have an oxygen atmosphere.

S/2001U1 Parameters	
Mass	9.07×10^{20} kg
Radius	620,000 m
Visual geometric albedo	0.07
Orbital period	7.2 days

$$v = \sqrt{\frac{2GM}{r}}, \text{ where}$$

v is the escape velocity (in meters per second, m/s),

M is the mass of the moon (in kilograms, kg),

r is the radius of the moon (in meters, m), and

G is the universal constant of gravitation where

$$\left(G = 6.67 \times 10^{-11} \frac{m^3}{kg \cdot s^2} \right).$$

MENTAL MATH

Choose the correct letter. No pencil is needed, just think your way through these.

1. Which radical is not a real number?

 a. $\sqrt{3}$ **b.** $-\sqrt{11}$ **c.** $\sqrt[3]{-10}$ **d.** $\sqrt{-10}$

2. Which radical(s) simplify to 3?

 a. $\sqrt{9}$ **b.** $\sqrt{-9}$ **c.** $\sqrt[3]{27}$ **d.** $\sqrt[3]{-27}$

3. Which radical(s) simplify to -3?

 a. $\sqrt{9}$ **b.** $\sqrt{-9}$ **c.** $\sqrt[3]{27}$ **d.** $\sqrt[3]{-27}$

4. Which radical does not simplify to a whole number?

 a. $\sqrt{64}$ **b.** $\sqrt[3]{64}$ **c.** $\sqrt{8}$ **d.** $\sqrt[3]{8}$

EXERCISE SET 7.1

STUDY GUIDE/SSM   CD/VIDEO   PH MATH TUTOR CENTER   MathXL®Tutorials ON CD   MathXL®   MyMathLab®

Simplify. Assume that variables represent positive real numbers. See Example 1.

1. $\sqrt{100}$ **2.** $\sqrt{400}$

3. $\sqrt{\dfrac{1}{4}}$ **4.** $\sqrt{\dfrac{9}{25}}$

5. $\sqrt{0.0001}$ **6.** $\sqrt{0.04}$

7. $-\sqrt{36}$ **8.** $-\sqrt{9}$

9. $\sqrt{x^{10}}$ **10.** $\sqrt{x^{16}}$

11. $\sqrt{16y^6}$ **12.** $\sqrt{64y^{20}}$

Use a calculator to approximate each square root to 3 decimal places. Check to see that each approximation is reasonable. See Example 2.

13. $\sqrt{7}$ **14.** $\sqrt{11}$

15. $\sqrt{38}$ **16.** $\sqrt{56}$

17. $\sqrt{200}$ **18.** $\sqrt{300}$

Find each cube root. See Example 3.

19. $\sqrt[3]{64}$ **20.** $\sqrt[3]{27}$

21. $\sqrt[3]{\dfrac{1}{8}}$ **22.** $\sqrt[3]{\dfrac{27}{64}}$

23. $\sqrt[3]{-1}$ **24.** $\sqrt[3]{-125}$

25. $\sqrt[3]{x^{12}}$ **26.** $\sqrt[3]{x^{15}}$

27. $\sqrt[3]{-27x^9}$ **28.** $\sqrt[3]{-64x^6}$

Find each root. Assume that all variables represent nonnegative real numbers. See Example 4.

29. $-\sqrt[4]{16}$ **30.** $\sqrt[5]{-243}$

31. $\sqrt[4]{16}$ **32.** $\sqrt{-16}$

33. $\sqrt[5]{-32}$ **34.** $\sqrt[5]{-1}$

35. $\sqrt[5]{x^{20}}$ **36.** $\sqrt[4]{x^{20}}$

37. $\sqrt[6]{64x^{12}}$ **38.** $\sqrt[5]{-32x^{15}}$

39. $\sqrt{81x^4}$ **40.** $\sqrt[4]{81x^4}$

41. $\sqrt[4]{256x^8}$ **42.** $\sqrt{256x^8}$

Simplify. Assume that the variables represent any real number. See Example 5.

43. $\sqrt{(-8)^2}$ **44.** $\sqrt{(-7)^2}$

45. $\sqrt[3]{(-8)^3}$ **46.** $\sqrt[5]{(-7)^5}$

47. $\sqrt{4x^2}$ **48.** $\sqrt[4]{16x^4}$

49. $\sqrt[3]{x^3}$ **50.** $\sqrt[5]{x^5}$

 **51.** $\sqrt{(x-5)^2}$ **52.** $\sqrt{(y-6)^2}$

53. $\sqrt{x^2+4x+4}$

 (*Hint:* Factor the polynomial first.)

54. $\sqrt{x^2-8x+16}$

 (*Hint:* Factor the polynomial first.)

MIXED PRACTICE

Simplify each radical. Assume that all variables represent positive real numbers.

55. $-\sqrt{121}$

56. $-\sqrt[3]{125}$

57. $\sqrt[3]{8x^3}$

58. $\sqrt{16x^8}$

59. $\sqrt{y^{12}}$

60. $\sqrt[3]{y^{12}}$

61. $\sqrt{25a^2b^{20}}$

62. $\sqrt{9x^4y^6}$

63. $\sqrt[3]{-27x^{12}y^9}$

64. $\sqrt[3]{-8a^{21}b^6}$

65. $\sqrt[4]{a^{16}b^4}$

66. $\sqrt[4]{x^8y^{12}}$

67. $\sqrt[5]{-32x^{10}y^5}$

68. $\sqrt[5]{-243z^{15}}$

69. $\sqrt{\dfrac{25}{49}}$

70. $\sqrt{\dfrac{4}{81}}$

71. $\sqrt{\dfrac{x^2}{4y^2}}$

72. $\sqrt{\dfrac{y^{10}}{9x^6}}$

73. $-\sqrt[3]{\dfrac{z^{21}}{27x^3}}$

74. $-\sqrt[3]{\dfrac{64a^3}{b^9}}$

75. $\sqrt[4]{\dfrac{x^4}{16}}$

76. $\sqrt[4]{\dfrac{y^4}{81x^4}}$

If $f(x) = \sqrt{2x + 3}$ and $g(x) = \sqrt[3]{x - 8}$, find the following function values. See Example 6.

77. $f(0)$

78. $g(0)$

79. $g(7)$

80. $f(-1)$

81. $g(-19)$

82. $f(3)$

83. $f(2)$

84. $g(1)$

Identify the domain and then graph each function. See Example 7.

85. $f(x) = \sqrt{x} + 2$

86. $f(x) = \sqrt{x} - 2$

87. $f(x) = \sqrt{x - 3}$; use the following table.

x	f(x)
3	
4	
7	
12	

88. $f(x) = \sqrt{x + 1}$; use the following table.

x	f(x)
-1	
0	
3	
8	

Identify the domain and then graph each function. See Example 8

89. $f(x) = \sqrt[3]{x} + 1$

90. $f(x) = \sqrt[3]{x} - 2$

91. $g(x) = \sqrt[3]{x - 1}$; use the following table.

x	g(x)
1	
2	
0	
9	
-7	

92. $g(x) = \sqrt[3]{x + 1}$; use the following table.

x	g(x)
-1	
0	
-2	
7	
-9	

REVIEW AND PREVIEW

Simplify each exponential expression. See Sections 5.1 and 5.2.

93. $(-2x^3y^2)^5$

94. $(4y^6z^7)^3$

95. $(-3x^2y^3z^5)(20x^5y^7)$

96. $(-14a^5bc^2)(2abc^4)$

97. $\dfrac{7x^{-1}y}{14(x^5y^2)^{-2}}$

98. $\dfrac{(2a^{-1}b^2)^3}{(8a^2b)^{-2}}$

Concept Extensions

99. Explain why $\sqrt{-64}$ is not a real number.

100. Explain why $\sqrt[3]{-64}$ is a real number.

For Exercises 101 through 104, do not use a calculator.

101. $\sqrt{160}$ is closest to

　　a. 10　　**b.** 13　　**c.** 20　　**d.** 40

102. $\sqrt{1000}$ is closest to

　　a. 10　　**b.** 30　　**c.** 100　　**d.** 500

△ **103.** The perimeter of the triangle is closest to

　　a. 12　　**b.** 18　　**c.** 66　　**d.** 132

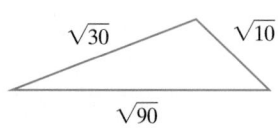

104. The length of the bent wire is closest to

a. 5   **b.** $\sqrt{28}$ **c.** 7   **d.** 14

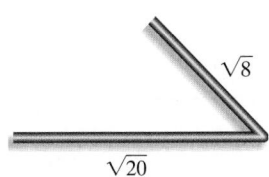

The Mosteller formula for calculating adult body surface area is

$B = \sqrt{\dfrac{hw}{3131}}$, *where B is an individual's body surface area in square meters, h is the individual's height in inches, and w is the individual's weight in pounds. Use this information to answer Exercises 105 and 106. Round answers to 2 decimal places.*

105. Find the body surface area of an individual who is 66 inches tall and who weighs 135 pounds.

106. Find the body surface area of an individual who is 74 inches tall and who weighs 225 pounds.

107. Suppose that a friend tells you that $\sqrt{13} \approx 5.7$. Without a calculator, how can you convince your friend that he or she must have made an error?

108. Escape velocity is the minimum speed that an object must reach to escape a planet's pull of gravity. Escape velocity v is given by the equation $v = \sqrt{\dfrac{2Gm}{r}}$, where m is the mass of the planet, r is its radius, and G is the universal gravitational constant, which has a value of $G = 6.67 \times 10^{-11}$ m³/kg·s². The mass of Earth is 5.97×10^{24} kg and its radius is 6.37×10^{6} m. Use this information to find the escape velocity for Earth. Round to the nearest whole number. (Source: National Space Science Data Center)

Use a graphing calculator to verify the domain of each function and its graph.

109. Exercise 85

110. Exercise 86

111. Exercise 89

112. Exercise 90

RATIONAL EXPONENTS

Objectives

1 Understand the meaning of $a^{1/n}$.

2 Understand the meaning of $a^{m/n}$.

3 Understand the meaning of $a^{-m/n}$.

4 Use rules for exponents to simplify expressions that contain rational exponents.

5 Use rational exponents to simplify radical expressions.

1   So far in this text, we have not defined expressions with rational exponents such as $3^{1/2}$, $x^{2/3}$, and $-9^{-1/4}$. We will define these expressions so that the rules for exponents will apply to these rational exponents as well.

Suppose that $x = 5^{1/3}$. Then

$$x^3 = (5^{1/3})^3 = 5^{1/3 \cdot 3} = 5^1 \text{ or } 5$$

L using rules ↑
for exponents

Since $x^3 = 5$, then x is the number whose cube is 5, or $= \sqrt[3]{5}$. Notice that we also know that $x = 5^{1/3}$. This means

$$5^{1/3} = \sqrt[3]{5}$$

> **Definition of $a^{1/n}$**
>
> If n is a positive integer greater than 1 and $\sqrt[n]{a}$ is a real number, then
>
> $$a^{1/n} = \sqrt[n]{a}$$

Notice that the denominator of the rational exponent corresponds to the index o
the radical.

EXAMPLE 1

Use radical notation to write the following. Simplify if possible.

a. $4^{1/2}$ **b.** $64^{1/3}$

c. $x^{1/4}$ **d.** $0^{1/6}$

e. $-9^{1/2}$ **f.** $(81x^8)^{1/4}$

g. $(5y)^{1/3}$

Solution
     a. $4^{1/2} = \sqrt{4} = 2$ **b.** $64^{1/3} = \sqrt[3]{64} = 4$

     c. $x^{1/4} = \sqrt[4]{x}$ **d.** $0^{1/6} = \sqrt[6]{0} = 0$

     e. $-9^{1/2} = -\sqrt{9} = -3$ **f.** $(81x^8)^{1/4} = \sqrt[4]{81x^8} = 3x^2$

     g. $(5y)^{1/3} = \sqrt[3]{5y}$

2   As we expand our use of exponents to include $\dfrac{m}{n}$, we define their meaning s
that rules for exponents still hold true. For example, by properties of exponents,

$$8^{2/3} = (8^{1/3})^2 = \left(\sqrt[3]{8}\right)^2 \qquad \text{or}$$
$$8^{2/3} = (8^2)^{1/3} = \sqrt[3]{8^2}$$

> **Definition of $a^{m/n}$**
>
> If m and n are positive integers greater than 1 with $\dfrac{m}{n}$ in lowest terms, then
>
> $$a^{m/n} = \sqrt[n]{a^m} = \left(\sqrt[n]{a}\right)^m$$
>
> as long as $\sqrt[n]{a}$ is a real number.

Notice that the denominator n of the rational exponent corresponds to the index of the
radical. The numerator m of the rational exponent indicates that the base is to be
raised to the mth power. This means

$$8^{2/3} = \sqrt[3]{8^2} = \sqrt[3]{64} = 4 \qquad \text{or}$$
$$8^{2/3} = \left(\sqrt[3]{8}\right)^2 = 2^2 = 4$$

From simplifying $8^{2/3}$, can you see that it doesn't matter whether you raise to a power first and then take the nth root or you take the nth root first and then raise to a power?

> **Helpful Hint**
> Most of the time, $\left(\sqrt[n]{a}\right)^m$ will be easier to calculate than $\sqrt[n]{a^m}$.

EXAMPLE 2

Use radical notation to write the following. Then simplify if possible.

a. $4^{3/2}$ **b.** $-16^{3/4}$ **c.** $(-27)^{2/3}$

d. $\left(\dfrac{1}{9}\right)^{3/2}$ **e.** $(4x - 1)^{3/5}$

Solution **a.** $4^{3/2} = \left(\sqrt{4}\right)^3 = 2^3 = 8$

b. $-16^{3/4} = -\left(\sqrt[4]{16}\right)^3 = -(2)^3 = -8$

c. $(-27)^{2/3} = \left(\sqrt[3]{-27}\right)^2 = (-3)^2 = 9$

d. $\left(\dfrac{1}{9}\right)^{3/2} = \left(\sqrt{\dfrac{1}{9}}\right)^3 = \left(\dfrac{1}{3}\right)^3 = \dfrac{1}{27}$

e. $(4x - 1)^{3/5} = \sqrt[5]{(4x - 1)^3}$

> **Helpful Hint**
> The *denominator* of a rational exponent is the index of the corresponding radical. For example, $x^{1/5} = \sqrt[5]{x}$ and $z^{2/3} = \sqrt[3]{z^2}$, or $z^{2/3} = \left(\sqrt[3]{z}\right)^2$.

3   The rational exponents we have given meaning to exclude negative rational numbers. To complete the set of definitions, we define $a^{-m/n}$.

Definition of $a^{-m/n}$

$$a^{-m/n} = \frac{1}{a^{m/n}}$$

as long as $a^{m/n}$ is a nonzero real number.

EXAMPLE 3

Write each expression with a positive exponent, and then simplify.

a. $16^{-3/4}$ **b.** $(-27)^{-2/3}$

Solution **a.** $16^{-3/4} = \dfrac{1}{16^{3/4}} = \dfrac{1}{\left(\sqrt[4]{16}\right)^3} = \dfrac{1}{2^3} = \dfrac{1}{8}$

b. $(-27)^{-2/3} = \dfrac{1}{(-27)^{2/3}} = \dfrac{1}{\left(\sqrt[3]{-27}\right)^2} = \dfrac{1}{(-3)^2} = \dfrac{1}{9}$

> **Helpful Hint**
>
> If an expression contains a negative rational exponent, such as $9^{-3/2}$, you may want to first write the expression with a positive exponent and then interpret the rational exponent. Notice that the sign of the base is not affected by the sign of its exponent. For example,
>
> $$9^{-3/2} = \dfrac{1}{9^{3/2}} = \dfrac{1}{\left(\sqrt{9}\right)^3} = \dfrac{1}{27}$$
>
> Also,
>
> $$(-27)^{-1/3} = \dfrac{1}{(-27)^{1/3}} = -\dfrac{1}{3}$$

✔ **CONCEPT CHECK**

Which one is correct?

a. $-8^{2/3} = \dfrac{1}{4}$

b. $8^{-2/3} = -\dfrac{1}{4}$

c. $8^{-2/3} = -4$

d. $-8^{-2/3} = -\dfrac{1}{4}$

4   It can be shown that the properties of integer exponents hold for rational exponents. By using these properties and definitions, we can now simplify expressions that contain rational exponents.

These rules are repeated here for review.

Note: For the remainder of this chapter, we will assume that variables represent positive real numbers. Since this is so, we need not insert absolute value bars when we simplify even roots.

Summary of Exponent Rules

If m and n are rational numbers, and a, b, and c are numbers for which the expressions below exist, then

Product rule for exponents:	$a^m \cdot a^n = a^{m+n}$
Power rule for exponents:	$(a^m)^n = a^{m \cdot n}$
Power rules for products and quotients:	$(ab)^n = a^n b^n$ and

$$\left(\frac{a}{c}\right)^n = \frac{a^n}{c^n}, c \neq 0$$

Quotient rule for exponents:	$\dfrac{a^m}{a^n} = a^{m-n}, a \neq 0$
Zero exponent:	$a^0 = 1, a \neq 0$
Negative exponent:	$a^{-n} = \dfrac{1}{a^n}, a \neq 0$

EXAMPLE 4

Use properties of exponents to simplify. Write results with only positive exponents.

a. $b^{1/3} \cdot b^{5/3}$ **b.** $x^{1/2}x^{1/3}$ **c.** $\dfrac{7^{1/3}}{7^{4/3}}$

d. $y^{-4/7} \cdot y^{6/7}$ **e.** $\dfrac{(2x^{2/5}y^{-1/3})^5}{x^2 y}$

Solution

a. $b^{1/3} \cdot b^{5/3} = b^{(1/3+5/3)} = b^{6/3} = b^2$

b. $x^{1/2}x^{1/3} = x^{(1/2+1/3)} = x^{3/6+2/6} = x^{5/6}$ *Use the product rule.*

c. $\dfrac{7^{1/3}}{7^{4/3}} = 7^{1/3-4/3} = 7^{-3/3} = 7^{-1} = \dfrac{1}{7}$ *Use the quotient rule.*

d. $y^{-4/7} \cdot y^{6/7} = y^{-4/7+6/7} = y^{2/7}$ *Use the product rule.*

e. We begin by using the power rule $(ab)^m = a^m b^m$ to simplify the numerator.

$$\frac{(2x^{2/5}y^{-1/3})^5}{x^2 y} = \frac{2^5(x^{2/5})^5(y^{-1/3})^5}{x^2 y} = \frac{32x^2 y^{-5/3}}{x^2 y} \quad \text{\small Use the power rule and simplify}$$

$$= 32x^{2-2}y^{-5/3-3/3} \quad \text{\small Apply the quotient rule.}$$

$$= 32x^0 y^{-8/3}$$

$$= \frac{32}{y^{8/3}}$$

EXAMPLE 5

Multiply.

a. $z^{2/3}(z^{1/3} - z^5)$

b. $(x^{1/3} - 5)(x^{1/3} + 2)$

Solution   **a.** $z^{2/3}(z^{1/3} - z^5) = z^{2/3}z^{1/3} - z^{2/3}z^5$ Apply the distributive property.

$$= z^{(2/3+1/3)} - z^{(2/3+5)}$$ Use the product rule.

$$= z^{3/3} - z^{(2/3+15/3)}$$

$$= z - z^{17/3}$$

b. $(x^{1/3} - 5)(x^{1/3} + 2) = x^{2/3} + 2x^{1/3} - 5x^{1/3} - 10$ Think of $(x^{1/3} - 5)$ and $(x^{1/3} + 2)$ as 2 binomials, and FOIL.

$$= x^{2/3} - 3x^{1/3} - 10$$

EXAMPLE 6

Factor $x^{-1/2}$ from the expression $3x^{-1/2} - 7x^{5/2}$. Assume that all variables represent positive numbers.

Solution

$$3x^{-1/2} - 7x^{5/2} = (x^{-1/2})(3) - (x^{-1/2})(7x^{6/2})$$

$$= x^{-1/2}(3 - 7x^3)$$

To check, multiply $x^{-1/2}(3 - 7x^3)$ to see that the product is $3x^{-1/2} - 7x^{5/2}$.

5   Some radical expressions are easier to simplify when we first write them with rational exponents. We can simplify some radical expressions by first writing the expression with rational exponents. Use properties of exponents to simplify, and then convert back to radical notation.

EXAMPLE 7

Use rational exponents to simplify. Assume that variables represent positive numbers.

a. $\sqrt[8]{x^4}$ **b.** $\sqrt[6]{25}$ **c.** $\sqrt[4]{r^2s^6}$

Solution   **a.** $\sqrt[8]{x^4} = x^{4/8} = x^{1/2} = \sqrt{x}$

b. $\sqrt[6]{25} = 25^{1/6} = (5^2)^{1/6} = 5^{2/6} = 5^{1/3} = \sqrt[3]{5}$

c. $\sqrt[4]{r^2s^6} = (r^2s^6)^{1/4} = r^{2/4}s^{6/4} = r^{1/2}s^{3/2} = (rs^3)^{1/2} = \sqrt{rs^3}$

EXAMPLE 8

Use rational exponents to write as a single radical.

a. $\sqrt{x} \cdot \sqrt[4]{x}$

b. $\dfrac{\sqrt{x}}{\sqrt[3]{x}}$

c. $\sqrt[3]{3} \cdot \sqrt{2}$

Solution

a. $\sqrt{x} \cdot \sqrt[4]{x} = x^{1/2} \cdot x^{1/4} = x^{1/2+1/4}$
$$= x^{3/4} = \sqrt[4]{x^3}$$

b. $\dfrac{\sqrt{x}}{\sqrt[3]{x}} = \dfrac{x^{1/2}}{x^{1/3}} = x^{1/2-1/3} = x^{3/6-2/6}$
$$= x^{1/6} = \sqrt[6]{x}$$

c. $\sqrt[3]{3} \cdot \sqrt{2} = 3^{1/3} \cdot 2^{1/2}$ Write with rational exponents.
$$= 3^{2/6} \cdot 2^{3/6}$$ Write the exponents so that they have the same denominator.
$$= (3^2 \cdot 2^3)^{1/6}$$ Use $a^n b^n = (ab)^n$
$$= \sqrt[6]{3^2 \cdot 2^3}$$ Write with radical notation.
$$= \sqrt[6]{72}$$ Multiply $3^2 \cdot 2^3$.

Spotlight on
DECISION
MAKING

Suppose you are a telecommunications industry analyst. A colleague has just formulated a mathematical model for the number of cellular telephone subscriptions in the United States from 1985 to 2002. The model is $y = 0.162x^{22/5}$ where y is the number of cellular telephone subscriptions x years after 1980. The actual data from 1985 to 2002 are listed in the table.

Your colleague has asked your help in evaluating whether this model represents the actual data well. By comparing the numbers of subscriptions given by the model to the actual data given in the table, decide whether this mathematical model is acceptable. Explain your reasoning.

U.S. Cellular Telephone Subscriptions, 1985–2002

Year	Subscriptions (in thousands)	Year	Subscriptions (in thousands)
1985	204	1994	19,283
1986	500	1995	28,154
1987	884	1996	38,195
1988	1607	1997	48,706
1989	2692	1998	60,831
1990	4367	1999	76,285
1991	6380	2000	97,036
1992	8893	2001	118,398
1993	13,067	2002	134,561

(*Source:* The CTIA Semi-Annual Wireless Survey)

MENTAL MATH

Choose the correct letter for each exercise. Letters will be used more than once. No pencil is needed. Just think about the meaning of each expression.

A = 2, B = −2, C = not a real number

1. $4^{1/2}$

2. $-4^{1/2}$

3. $(-4)^{1/2}$

4. $8^{1/3}$

5. $-8^{1/3}$

6. $(-8)^{1/3}$

7. $(-32)^{1/5}$

8. $(-16)^{1/4}$

9. $-16^{1/4}$

10. $-32^{1/5}$

EXERCISE SET 7.2

STUDY GUIDE/SSM   CD/VIDEO   PH MATH TUTOR CENTER   MathXL®Tutorials ON CD   MathXL®   MyMathLab®

Use radical notation to write each expression. Simplify if possible. See Example 1.

 1. $49^{1/2}$

2. $64^{1/3}$

3. $27^{1/3}$

4. $8^{1/3}$

5. $\left(\dfrac{1}{16}\right)^{1/4}$

6. $\left(\dfrac{1}{64}\right)^{1/2}$

7. $169^{1/2}$

8. $81^{1/4}$

9. $2m^{1/3}$

10. $(2m)^{1/3}$

11. $(9x^4)^{1/2}$

12. $(16x^8)^{1/2}$

13. $(-27)^{1/3}$

14. $-64^{1/2}$

15. $-16^{1/4}$

16. $(-32)^{1/5}$

Use radical notation to write each expression. Simplify if possible. See Example 2.

 17. $16^{3/4}$

18. $4^{5/2}$

19. $(-64)^{2/3}$

20. $(-8)^{4/3}$

21. $(-16)^{3/4}$

22. $(-9)^{3/2}$

23. $(2x)^{3/5}$

24. $2x^{3/5}$

25. $(7x+2)^{2/3}$

26. $(x-4)^{3/4}$

27. $\left(\dfrac{16}{9}\right)^{3/2}$

28. $\left(\dfrac{49}{25}\right)^{3/2}$

Write with positive exponents. Simplify if possible. See Example 3.

 29. $8^{-4/3}$

30. $64^{-2/3}$

31. $(-64)^{-2/3}$

32. $(-8)^{-4/3}$

33. $(-4)^{-3/2}$

34. $(-16)^{-5/4}$

35. $x^{-1/4}$

36. $y^{-1/6}$

37. $\dfrac{1}{a^{-2/3}}$

38. $\dfrac{1}{n^{-8/9}}$

39. $\dfrac{5}{7x^{-3/4}}$

40. $\dfrac{2}{3y^{-5/7}}$

41. Explain how writing x^{-7} with positive exponents is similar to writing $x^{-1/4}$ with positive exponents.

42. Explain how writing $2x^{-5}$ with positive exponents is similar to writing $2x^{-3/4}$ with positive exponents.

Use the properties of exponents to simplify each expression. Write with positive exponents. See Example 4.

43. $a^{2/3}a^{5/3}$

44. $b^{9/5}b^{8/5}$

45. $x^{-2/5} \cdot x^{7/5}$

46. $y^{4/3} \cdot y^{-1/3}$

47. $3^{1/4} \cdot 3^{3/8}$

48. $5^{1/2} \cdot 5^{1/6}$

49. $\dfrac{y^{1/3}}{y^{1/6}}$

50. $\dfrac{x^{3/4}}{x^{1/8}}$

51. $(4u^2)^{3/2}$

52. $(32^{1/5}x^{2/3})^3$

53. $\dfrac{b^{1/2}b^{3/4}}{-b^{1/4}}$

54. $\dfrac{a^{1/4}a^{-1/2}}{a^{2/3}}$

55. $\dfrac{(3x^{1/4})^3}{x^{1/12}}$

56. $\dfrac{(2x^{1/5})^4}{x^{3/10}}$

Multiply. See Example 5.

57. $y^{1/2}(y^{1/2} - y^{2/3})$

58. $x^{1/2}(x^{1/2} + x^{3/2})$

59. $x^{2/3}(2x - 2)$

60. $3x^{1/2}(x + y)$

61. $(2x^{1/3} + 3)(2x^{1/3} - 3)$

62. $(y^{1/2} + 5)(y^{1/2} + 5)$

Factor the common factor from the given expression. See Example 6.

63. $x^{8/3}; x^{8/3} + x^{10/3}$

64. $x^{3/2}; x^{5/2} - x^{3/2}$

65. $x^{1/5}; x^{2/5} - 3x^{1/5}$

66. $x^{2/7}; x^{3/7} - 2x^{2/7}$

67. $x^{-1/3}; 5x^{-1/3} + x^{2/3}$

68. $x^{-3/4}; x^{-3/4} + 3x^{1/4}$

Use rational exponents to simplify each radical. Assume that all variables represent positive numbers. See Example 7.

69. $\sqrt[6]{x^3}$

70. $\sqrt[9]{a^3}$

71. $\sqrt[6]{4}$

72. $\sqrt[4]{36}$

73. $\sqrt[4]{16x^2}$

74. $\sqrt[8]{4y^2}$

75. $\sqrt[8]{x^4y^4}$

76. $\sqrt[9]{y^6z^3}$

Use rational expressions to write as a single radical expression. See Example 8.

77. $\sqrt[3]{y} \cdot \sqrt[5]{y^2}$

78. $\sqrt[3]{y^2} \cdot \sqrt[6]{y}$

79. $\dfrac{\sqrt[3]{b^2}}{\sqrt[4]{b}}$

80. $\dfrac{\sqrt[4]{a}}{\sqrt[5]{a}}$

81. $\dfrac{\sqrt[3]{a^2}}{\sqrt[6]{a}}$

82. $\dfrac{\sqrt[5]{b^2}}{\sqrt[10]{b^3}}$

83. $\sqrt[3]{3} \cdot \sqrt[4]{4}$

84. $\sqrt[3]{5} \cdot \sqrt{2}$

85. $\sqrt[5]{7} \cdot \sqrt[3]{y}$

86. $\sqrt[4]{5} \cdot \sqrt[3]{x}$

REVIEW AND PREVIEW

Write each integer as a product of two integers such that one of the factors is a perfect square. For example, write 18 as $9 \cdot 2$, because 9 is a perfect square.

87. 75

88. 20

89. 48

90. 45

Write each integer as a product of two integers such that one of the factors is a perfect cube. For example, write 24 as $8 \cdot 3$, because 8 is a perfect cube.

91. 16

92. 56

93. 54

94. 80

Concept Extensions

Basal metabolic rate (BMR) is the number of calories per day a person needs to maintain life. A person's basal metabolic rate $B(w)$ in calories per day can be estimated with the function $B(w) = 70w^{3/4}$, where w is the person's weight in kilograms. Use this information to answer Exercises 95 and 96.

95. Estimate the BMR for a person who weighs 60 kilograms. Round to the nearest calorie. (*Note:* 60 kilograms is approximately 132 pounds.)

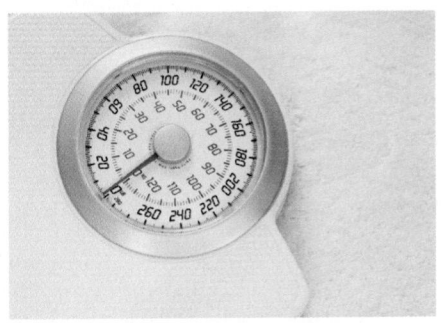

96. Estimate the BMR for a person who weighs 90 kilograms. Round to the nearest calorie. (*Note:* 90 kilograms is approximately 198 pounds.)

The number of cellular telephone subscriptions in the United States from 1994 through 2002 can be modeled by the function $f(x) = 1.54x^{9/5}$, where y is the number of cellular telephone subscriptions in millions, x years after 1990. (Source: Based on data from the Cellular Telecommunications & Internet Association, 1994–2000) Use this information to answer Exercises 97 and 98.

97. Use this model to estimate the number of cellular telephone subscriptions in the United States in 2000. Round to the nearest tenth of a million.

98. Predict the number of cellular telephone subscriptions in the United States in 2007. Round to the nearest tenth of a million.

Fill in each box with the correct expression.

99. $\square \cdot a^{2/3} = a^{3/3}$, or a

100. $\square \cdot x^{1/8} = x^{4/8}$, or $x^{1/2}$

101. $\dfrac{\square}{x^{-2/5}} = x^{3/5}$

102. $\dfrac{\square}{y^{-3/4}} = y^{4/4}$, or y

Use a calculator to write a four-decimal-place approximation of each number.

103. $8^{1/4}$

104. $20^{1/5}$

105. $18^{3/5}$

106. $76^{5/7}$

107. In physics, the speed of a wave traveling over a stretched string with tension t and density u is given by the expression $\dfrac{\sqrt{t}}{\sqrt{u}}$. Write this expression with rational exponents.

108. In electronics, the angular frequency of oscillations in a certain type of circuit is given by the expression $(LC)^{-1/2}$. Use radical notation to write this expression.

7.3 SIMPLIFYING RADICAL EXPRESSIONS

Objectives

1 Use the product rule for radicals.

2 Use the quotient rule for radicals.

3 Simplify radicals.

1 It is possible to simplify some radicals that do not evaluate to rational numbers. To do so, we use a product rule and a quotient rule for radicals. To discover the product rule, notice the following pattern.

$$\sqrt{9} \cdot \sqrt{4} = 3 \cdot 2 = 6$$
$$\sqrt{9 \cdot 4} = \sqrt{36} = 6$$

Since both expressions simplify to 6, it is true that

$$\sqrt{9} \cdot \sqrt{4} = \sqrt{9 \cdot 4}$$

This pattern suggests the following product rule for radicals.

> **Product Rule for Radicals**
>
> If $\sqrt[n]{a}$ and $\sqrt[n]{b}$ are real numbers, then
>
> $$\sqrt[n]{a} \cdot \sqrt[n]{b} = \sqrt[n]{ab}$$

Notice that the product rule is the relationship $a^{1/n} \cdot b^{1/n} = (ab)^{1/n}$ stated in radical notation.

EXAMPLE 1

Multiply.

a. $\sqrt{3} \cdot \sqrt{5}$ **b.** $\sqrt{21} \cdot \sqrt{x}$ **c.** $\sqrt[3]{4} \cdot \sqrt[3]{2}$

d. $\sqrt[4]{5y^2} \cdot \sqrt[4]{2x^3}$ **e.** $\sqrt{\dfrac{2}{a}} \cdot \sqrt{\dfrac{b}{3}}$

Solution   **a.** $\sqrt{3} \cdot \sqrt{5} = \sqrt{3 \cdot 5} = \sqrt{15}$

b. $\sqrt{21} \cdot \sqrt{x} = \sqrt{21x}$

c. $\sqrt[3]{4} \cdot \sqrt[3]{2} = \sqrt[3]{4 \cdot 2} = \sqrt[3]{8} = 2$

d. $\sqrt[4]{5y^2} \cdot \sqrt[4]{2x^3} = \sqrt[4]{5y^2 \cdot 2x^3} = \sqrt[4]{10y^2x^3}$

e. $\sqrt{\dfrac{2}{a}} \cdot \sqrt{\dfrac{b}{3}} = \sqrt{\dfrac{2}{a} \cdot \dfrac{b}{3}} = \sqrt{\dfrac{2b}{3a}}$

2   To discover a quotient rule for radicals, notice the following pattern.

$$\sqrt{\frac{4}{9}} = \frac{2}{3}$$

$$\frac{\sqrt{4}}{\sqrt{9}} = \frac{2}{3}$$

Since both expressions simplify to $\frac{2}{3}$, it is true that

$$\sqrt{\frac{4}{9}} = \frac{\sqrt{4}}{\sqrt{9}}$$

This pattern suggests the following quotient rule for radicals.

Quotient Rule for Radicals

If $\sqrt[n]{a}$ and $\sqrt[n]{b}$ are real numbers and $\sqrt[n]{b}$ is not zero, then

$$\sqrt[n]{\frac{a}{b}} = \frac{\sqrt[n]{a}}{\sqrt[n]{b}}$$

Notice that the quotient rule is the relationship $\left(\frac{a}{b}\right)^{1/n} = \frac{a^{1/n}}{b^{1/n}}$ stated in radical notation. We can use the quotient rule to simplify radical expressions by reading the rule from left to right, or to divide radicals by reading the rule from right to left.

For example,

$$\sqrt{\frac{x}{16}} = \frac{\sqrt{x}}{\sqrt{16}} = \frac{\sqrt{x}}{4} \qquad \text{Using } \sqrt[n]{\frac{a}{b}} = \frac{\sqrt[n]{a}}{\sqrt[n]{b}}$$

$$\frac{\sqrt{75}}{\sqrt{3}} = \sqrt{\frac{75}{3}} = \sqrt{25} = 5 \qquad \text{Using } \frac{\sqrt[n]{a}}{\sqrt[n]{b}} = \sqrt[n]{\frac{a}{b}}$$

Note: *Recall that from Section 7.2 on, we assume that variables represent positive real numbers. Since this is so, we need not insert absolute value bars when we simplify even roots.*

EXAMPLE 2

Use the quotient rule to simplify.

a. $\sqrt{\frac{25}{49}}$ **b.** $\sqrt{\frac{x}{9}}$

c. $\sqrt[3]{\frac{8}{27}}$ **d.** $\sqrt[4]{\frac{3}{16y^4}}$

Solution

a. $\sqrt{\dfrac{25}{49}} = \dfrac{\sqrt{25}}{\sqrt{49}} = \dfrac{5}{7}$

b. $\sqrt{\dfrac{x}{9}} = \dfrac{\sqrt{x}}{\sqrt{9}} = \dfrac{\sqrt{x}}{3}$

c. $\sqrt[3]{\dfrac{8}{27}} = \dfrac{\sqrt[3]{8}}{\sqrt[3]{27}} = \dfrac{2}{3}$

d. $\sqrt[4]{\dfrac{3}{16y^4}} = \dfrac{\sqrt[4]{3}}{\sqrt[4]{16y^4}} = \dfrac{\sqrt[4]{3}}{2y}$

3   Both the product and quotient rules can be used to simplify a radical. If the product rule is read from right to left, we have that $\sqrt[n]{ab} = \sqrt[n]{a} \cdot \sqrt[n]{b}$. This is used to simplify the following radicals.

EXAMPLE 3

Simplify the following.

a. $\sqrt{50}$ b. $\sqrt[3]{24}$ c. $\sqrt{26}$ d. $\sqrt[4]{32}$

Solution

a. Factor 50 such that one factor is the largest perfect square that divides 50. The largest perfect square factor of 50 is 25, so we write 50 as $25 \cdot 2$ and use the product rule for radicals to simplify.

$$\sqrt{50} = \sqrt{25 \cdot 2} = \sqrt{25} \cdot \sqrt{2} = 5\sqrt{2}$$

         ↑   The largest perfect square factor of 50.

> **Helpful Hint**
>
> Don't forget that, for example, $5\sqrt{2}$ means $5 \cdot \sqrt{2}$.

b. $\sqrt[3]{24} = \sqrt[3]{8 \cdot 3} = \sqrt[3]{8} \cdot \sqrt[3]{3} = 2\sqrt[3]{3}$

      ↑   The largest perfect cube factor of 24.

c. $\sqrt{26}$ The largest perfect square factor of 26 is 1, so $\sqrt{26}$ cannot be simplified further.

d. $\sqrt[4]{32} = \sqrt[4]{16 \cdot 2} = \sqrt[4]{16} \cdot \sqrt[4]{2} = 2\sqrt[4]{2}$

      ↑   The largest fourth power factor of 32.

After simplifying a radical such as a square root, always check the radicand to see that it contains no other perfect square factors. It may, if the largest perfect square factor of the radicand was not originally recognized. For example,

$$\sqrt{200} = \sqrt{4 \cdot 50} = \sqrt{4} \cdot \sqrt{50} = 2\sqrt{50}$$

Notice that the radicand 50 still contains the perfect square factor 25. This is because 4 is not the largest perfect square factor of 200. We continue as follows.

$$2\sqrt{50} = 2\sqrt{25 \cdot 2} = 2 \cdot \sqrt{25} \cdot \sqrt{2} = 2 \cdot 5 \cdot \sqrt{2} = 10\sqrt{2}$$

The radical is now simplified since 2 contains no perfect square factors (other than 1).

> **Helpful Hint**
>
> To help you recognize largest perfect power factors of a radicand, it will help if you are familiar with some perfect powers. A few are listed below.
>
> | Perfect Squares | 1, | 4, | 9, | 16, | 25, | 36, | 49, | 64, | 81, | 100, | 121, | 144 |
> |---|---|---|---|---|---|---|---|---|---|---|---|---|
> | | 1^2 | 2^2 | 3^2 | 4^2 | 5^2 | 6^2 | 7^2 | 8^2 | 9^2 | 10^2 | 11^2 | 12^2 |
>
> | Perfect Cubes | 1, | 8, | 27, | 64, | 125 |
> |---|---|---|---|---|---|
> | | 1^3 | 2^3 | 3^3 | 4^3 | 5^3 |
>
> | Perfect Fourth Powers | 1, | 16, | 81, | 256 |
> |---|---|---|---|---|
> | | 1^4 | 2^4 | 3^4 | 4^4 |

In general, we say that a radicand of the form $\sqrt[n]{a}$ is simplified when the radicand a contains no factors that are perfect nth powers (other than 1 or -1).

EXAMPLE 4

Use the product rule to simplify.

a. $\sqrt{25x^3}$ **b.** $\sqrt[3]{54x^6y^8}$ **c.** $\sqrt[4]{81z^{11}}$

Solution   **a.** $\sqrt{25x^3} = \sqrt{25x^2 \cdot x}$ Find the largest perfect square factor.

$\qquad = \sqrt{25x^2} \cdot \sqrt{x}$ Apply the product rule.

$\qquad = 5x\sqrt{x}$ Simplify.

b. $\sqrt[3]{54x^6y^8} = \sqrt[3]{27 \cdot 2 \cdot x^6 \cdot y^6 \cdot y^2}$ Factor the radicand and identify perfect cube factors.

$\qquad = \sqrt[3]{27x^6y^6 \cdot 2y^2}$

$\qquad = \sqrt[3]{27x^6y^6} \cdot \sqrt[3]{2y^2}$ Apply the product rule.

$\qquad = 3x^2y^2\sqrt[3]{2y^2}$ Simplify.

c. $\sqrt[4]{81z^{11}} = \sqrt[4]{81 \cdot z^8 \cdot z^3}$ Factor the radicand and identify perfect fourth power factors.

$\qquad = \sqrt[4]{81z^8} \cdot \sqrt[4]{z^3}$ Apply the product rule.

$\qquad = 3z^2\sqrt[4]{z^3}$ Simplify.

EXAMPLE 5

Use the quotient rule to divide, and simplify if possible.

a. $\dfrac{\sqrt{20}}{\sqrt{5}}$

b. $\dfrac{\sqrt{50x}}{2\sqrt{2}}$

c. $\dfrac{7\sqrt[3]{48x^4y^8}}{\sqrt[3]{6y^2}}$

d. $\dfrac{2\sqrt[4]{32a^8b^6}}{\sqrt[4]{a^{-1}b^2}}$

Solution

a. $\dfrac{\sqrt{20}}{\sqrt{5}} = \sqrt{\dfrac{20}{5}}$ Apply the quotient rule.

$= \sqrt{4}$ Simplify.

$= 2$ Simplify.

b. $\dfrac{\sqrt{50x}}{2\sqrt{2}} = \dfrac{1}{2} \cdot \sqrt{\dfrac{50x}{2}}$ Apply the quotient rule.

$= \dfrac{1}{2} \cdot \sqrt{25x}$ Simplify.

$= \dfrac{1}{2} \cdot \sqrt{25} \cdot \sqrt{x}$ Factor $25x$.

$= \dfrac{1}{2} \cdot 5 \cdot \sqrt{x}$ Simplify.

$= \dfrac{5}{2}\sqrt{x}$

c. $\dfrac{7\sqrt[3]{48x^4y^8}}{\sqrt[3]{6y^2}} = 7 \cdot \sqrt[3]{\dfrac{48x^4y^8}{6y^2}}$ Apply the quotient rule.

$= 7 \cdot \sqrt[3]{8x^4y^6}$ Simplify.

$= 7\sqrt[3]{8x^3y^6 \cdot x}$ Factor.

$= 7 \cdot \sqrt[3]{8x^3y^6} \cdot \sqrt[3]{x}$ Apply the product rule.

$= 7 \cdot 2xy^2 \cdot \sqrt[3]{x}$ Simplify.

$= 14xy^2\sqrt[3]{x}$

d. $\dfrac{2\sqrt[4]{32a^8b^6}}{\sqrt[4]{a^{-1}b^2}} = 2\sqrt[4]{\dfrac{32a^8b^6}{a^{-1}b^2}} = 2\sqrt[4]{32a^9b^4} = 2\sqrt[4]{16 \cdot a^8 \cdot b^4 \cdot 2 \cdot a}$

$= 2\sqrt[4]{16a^8b^4} \cdot \sqrt[4]{2a} = 2 \cdot 2a^2b \cdot \sqrt[4]{2a} = 4a^2b\sqrt[4]{2a}$

✔ **CONCEPT CHECK**

Find and correct the error:

$$\dfrac{\sqrt[3]{27}}{\sqrt{9}} = \sqrt[3]{\dfrac{27}{9}} = \sqrt[3]{3}$$

Concept Check Answer:

$\dfrac{\sqrt[3]{27}}{\sqrt{9}} = \dfrac{3}{3} = 1$

EXERCISE SET 7.3

STUDY GUIDE/SSM   CD/VIDEO   PH MATH TUTOR CENTER   MathXL®Tutorials ON CD   MathXL®   MyMathLab®

Use the product rule to multiply. See Example 1.

1. $\sqrt{7} \cdot \sqrt{2}$

2. $\sqrt{11} \cdot \sqrt{10}$

3. $\sqrt[4]{8} \cdot \sqrt[4]{2}$

4. $\sqrt[4]{27} \cdot \sqrt[4]{3}$

5. $\sqrt[3]{4} \cdot \sqrt[3]{9}$

6. $\sqrt[3]{10} \cdot \sqrt[3]{5}$

7. $\sqrt{2} \cdot \sqrt{3x}$

8. $\sqrt{3y} \cdot \sqrt{5x}$

9. $\sqrt{\dfrac{7}{x}} \cdot \sqrt{\dfrac{2}{y}}$

10. $\sqrt{\dfrac{6}{m}} \cdot \sqrt{\dfrac{n}{5}}$

11. $\sqrt[4]{4x^3} \cdot \sqrt[4]{5}$

12. $\sqrt[4]{ab^2} \cdot \sqrt[4]{27ab}$

Use the quotient rule to simplify. See Examples 2 and 3.

13. $\sqrt{\dfrac{6}{49}}$

14. $\sqrt{\dfrac{8}{81}}$

15. $\sqrt{\dfrac{2}{49}}$

16. $\sqrt{\dfrac{5}{121}}$

17. $\sqrt[4]{\dfrac{x^3}{16}}$

18. $\sqrt[4]{\dfrac{y}{81x^4}}$

19. $\sqrt[3]{\dfrac{4}{27}}$

20. $\sqrt[3]{\dfrac{3}{64}}$

21. $\sqrt[4]{\dfrac{8}{x^8}}$

22. $\sqrt[4]{\dfrac{a^3}{81}}$

23. $\sqrt[3]{\dfrac{2x}{81y^{12}}}$

24. $\sqrt[3]{\dfrac{3}{8x^6}}$

25. $\sqrt{\dfrac{x^2y}{100}}$

26. $\sqrt{\dfrac{y^2z}{36}}$

27. $\sqrt{\dfrac{5x^2}{4y^2}}$

28. $\sqrt{\dfrac{y^{10}}{9x^6}}$

29. $-\sqrt[3]{\dfrac{z^7}{27x^3}}$

30. $-\sqrt[3]{\dfrac{64a}{b^9}}$

Simplify. See Examples 3 and 4.

31. $\sqrt{32}$

32. $\sqrt{27}$

33. $\sqrt[3]{192}$

34. $\sqrt[3]{108}$

35. $5\sqrt{75}$

36. $3\sqrt{8}$

37. $\sqrt{24}$

38. $\sqrt{20}$

39. $\sqrt{100x^5}$

40. $\sqrt{64y^9}$

41. $\sqrt[3]{16y^7}$

42. $\sqrt[3]{64y^9}$

43. $\sqrt[4]{a^8b^7}$

44. $\sqrt[5]{32z^{12}}$

45. $\sqrt{y^5}$

46. $\sqrt[3]{y^5}$

47. $\sqrt{25a^2b^3}$

48. $\sqrt{9x^5y^7}$

49. $\sqrt[5]{-32x^{10}y}$

50. $\sqrt[5]{-243z^9}$

51. $\sqrt[3]{50x^{14}}$

52. $\sqrt[3]{40y^{10}}$

53. $-\sqrt{32a^8b^7}$

54. $-\sqrt{20ab^6}$

55. $\sqrt{9x^7y^9}$

56. $\sqrt{12r^9s^{12}}$

57. $\sqrt[3]{125r^9s^{12}}$

58. $\sqrt[3]{8a^6b^9}$

Use the quotient rule to divide. Then simplify if possible. See Example 5.

59. $\dfrac{\sqrt{14}}{\sqrt{7}}$

60. $\dfrac{\sqrt{45}}{\sqrt{9}}$

61. $\dfrac{\sqrt[3]{24}}{\sqrt[3]{3}}$

62. $\dfrac{\sqrt[3]{10}}{\sqrt[3]{2}}$

63. $\dfrac{5\sqrt[4]{48}}{\sqrt[4]{3}}$

64. $\dfrac{7\sqrt[4]{162}}{\sqrt[4]{2}}$

65. $\dfrac{\sqrt{x^5y^3}}{\sqrt{xy}}$

66. $\dfrac{\sqrt{a^7b^6}}{\sqrt{a^3b^2}}$

67. $\dfrac{8\sqrt[3]{54m^7}}{\sqrt[3]{2m}}$

68. $\dfrac{\sqrt[3]{128x^3}}{-3\sqrt[3]{2x}}$

69. $\dfrac{3\sqrt{100x^2}}{2\sqrt{2x^{-1}}}$

70. $\dfrac{\sqrt{270y^2}}{5\sqrt{3y^{-4}}}$

71. $\dfrac{\sqrt[4]{96a^{10}b^3}}{\sqrt[4]{3a^2b^3}}$

72. $\dfrac{\sqrt[5]{64x^{10}y^3}}{\sqrt[5]{2x^3y^{-7}}}$

REVIEW AND PREVIEW

Perform each indicated operation. See Sections 1.4 and 5.4.

73. $6x + 8x$

74. $(6x)(8x)$

75. $(2x + 3)(x - 5)$

76. $(2x + 3) + (x - 5)$

77. $9y^2 - 8y^2$

78. $(9y^2)(-8y^2)$

79. $-3(x + 5)$

80. $-3 + x + 5$

81. $(x - 4)^2$

82. $(2x + 1)^2$

Concept Extensions

△ **83.** The formula for the surface area A of a cone with height h and radius r is given by

$$A = \pi r \sqrt{r^2 + h^2}$$

a. Find the surface area of a cone whose height is 3 centimeters and whose radius is 4 centimeters.

b. Approximate to two decimal places the surface area of a cone whose height is 7.2 feet and whose radius is 6.8 feet.

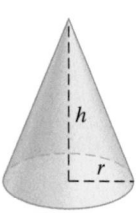

△ **84.** Before Mount Vesuvius, a volcano in Italy, erupted violently in 79 A.D., its height was 4190 feet. Vesuvius was roughly cone-shaped, and its base had a radius of approximately 25,200 feet. Use the formula for the surface area of a cone, given in Exercise 83, to approximate the surface area this volcano had before it erupted. (*Source:* Global Volcanism Network)

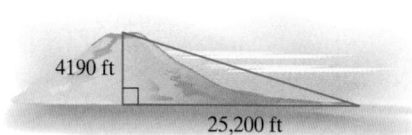

4190 ft

25,200 ft

85. The owner of Knightime Video has determined that the demand equation for renting older releases is given by the equation $F(x) = 0.6\sqrt{49 - x^2}$, where x is the price in dollars per two-day rental and $F(x)$ is the number of times the video is demanded per week.

a. Approximate to one decimal place the demand per week of an older release if the rental price is $3 per two-day rental.

b. Approximate to one decimal place the demand per week of an older release if the rental price is $5 per two-day rental.

c. Explain how the owner of the video store can use this equation to predict the number of copies of each tape that should be in stock.

7.4 ADDING, SUBTRACTING, AND MULTIPLYING RADICAL EXPRESSIONS

Objectives

1 Add or subtract radical expressions.

2 Multiply radical expressions.

1 We have learned that sums or differences of like terms can be simplified. To simplify these sums or differences, we use the distributive property. For example,

$$2x + 3x = (2 + 3)x = 5x \quad \text{and} \quad 7x^2y - 4x^2y = (7 - 4)x^2y = 3x^2y$$

The distributive property can also be used to add **like radicals**.

> **Like Radicals**
>
> Radicals with the same index and the same radicand are like radicals.

For example, $2\sqrt{7} + 3\sqrt{7} = (2 + 3)\sqrt{7} = 5\sqrt{7}$. Also,

$$5\sqrt{3x} - 7\sqrt{3x} = (5 - 7)\sqrt{3x} = -2\sqrt{3x}$$

The expression $2\sqrt{7} + 2\sqrt[3]{7}$ cannot be simplified further since $2\sqrt{7}$ and $2\sqrt[3]{7}$ are not like radicals.

EXAMPLE 1

Add or subtract as indicated.

a. $4\sqrt{11} + 8\sqrt{11}$ **b.** $5\sqrt[3]{3x} - 7\sqrt[3]{3x}$ **c.** $2\sqrt{7} + 2\sqrt[3]{7}$

Solution   **a.** $4\sqrt{11} + 8\sqrt{11} = (4 + 8)\sqrt{11} = 12\sqrt{11}$

b. $5\sqrt[3]{3x} - 7\sqrt[3]{3x} = (5 - 7)\sqrt[3]{3x} = -2\sqrt[3]{3x}$

c. $2\sqrt{7} + 2\sqrt[3]{7}$

This expression cannot be simplified since $2\sqrt{7}$ and $2\sqrt[3]{7}$ do not contain like radicals.

When adding or subtracting radicals, always check first to see whether any radicals can be simplified.

✔ **CONCEPT CHECK**

True or false:

$$\sqrt{a} + \sqrt{b} = \sqrt{a + b}?$$

Explain.

EXAMPLE 2

Add or subtract. Assume that variables represent positive real numbers.

a. $\sqrt{20} + 2\sqrt{45}$ **b.** $\sqrt[3]{54} - 5\sqrt[3]{16} + \sqrt[3]{2}$ **c.** $\sqrt{27x} - 2\sqrt{9x} + \sqrt{72x}$

d. $\sqrt[3]{98} + \sqrt{98}$ **e.** $\sqrt[3]{48y^4} + \sqrt[3]{6y^4}$

Solution   First, simplify each radical. Then add or subtract any like radicals.

a. $\sqrt{20} + 2\sqrt{45} = \sqrt{4 \cdot 5} + 2\sqrt{9 \cdot 5}$ *Factor 20 and 45.*

$\qquad\qquad\qquad = \sqrt{4} \cdot \sqrt{5} + 2 \cdot \sqrt{9} \cdot \sqrt{5}$ *Use the product rule.*

$\qquad\qquad\qquad = 2 \cdot \sqrt{5} + 2 \cdot 3 \cdot \sqrt{5}$ *Simplify $\sqrt{4}$ and $\sqrt{9}$.*

$\qquad\qquad\qquad = 2\sqrt{5} + 6\sqrt{5}$ *Add like radicals.*

$\qquad\qquad\qquad = 8\sqrt{5}$

b. $\sqrt[3]{54} - 5\sqrt[3]{16} + \sqrt[3]{2}$

$\qquad = \sqrt[3]{27} \cdot \sqrt[3]{2} - 5 \cdot \sqrt[3]{8} \cdot \sqrt[3]{2} + \sqrt[3]{2}$ *Factor and use the product rule.*

$\qquad = 3 \cdot \sqrt[3]{2} - 5 \cdot 2 \cdot \sqrt[3]{2} + \sqrt[3]{2}$ *Simplify $\sqrt[3]{27}$ and $\sqrt[3]{8}$.*

$\qquad = 3\sqrt[3]{2} - 10\sqrt[3]{2} + \sqrt[3]{2}$ *Write $5 \cdot 2$ as 10.*

$\qquad = -6\sqrt[3]{2}$ *Combine like radicals.*

c. $\sqrt{27x} - 2\sqrt{9x} + \sqrt{72x}$

$= \sqrt{9} \cdot \sqrt{3x} - 2 \cdot \sqrt{9} \cdot \sqrt{x} + \sqrt{36} \cdot \sqrt{2x}$ Factor and use the product rule.

$= 3 \cdot \sqrt{3x} - 2 \cdot 3 \cdot \sqrt{x} + 6 \cdot \sqrt{2x}$ Simplify $\sqrt{9}$ and $\sqrt{36}$.

$= 3\sqrt{3x} - 6\sqrt{x} + 6\sqrt{2x}$ Write $2 \cdot 3$ as 6.

> **Helpful Hint**
> None of these terms contain like radicals. We can simplify no further.

d. $\sqrt[3]{98} + \sqrt{98} = \sqrt[3]{98} + \sqrt{49} \cdot \sqrt{2}$ Factor and use the product rule.

$= \sqrt[3]{98} + 7\sqrt{2}$ No further simplification is possible.

e. $\sqrt[3]{48y^4} + \sqrt[3]{6y^4} = \sqrt[3]{8y^3} \cdot \sqrt[3]{6y} + \sqrt[3]{y^3} \cdot \sqrt[3]{6y}$ Factor and use the product rule.

$= 2y\sqrt[3]{6y} + y\sqrt[3]{6y}$ Simplify $\sqrt[3]{8y^3}$ and $\sqrt[3]{y^3}$.

$= 3y\sqrt[3]{6y}$ Combine like radicals.

EXAMPLE 3

Add or subtract as indicated.

a. $\dfrac{\sqrt{45}}{4} - \dfrac{\sqrt{5}}{3}$ **b.** $\sqrt[3]{\dfrac{7x}{8}} + 2\sqrt[3]{7x}$

Solution   **a.** $\dfrac{\sqrt{45}}{4} - \dfrac{\sqrt{5}}{3} = \dfrac{3\sqrt{5}}{4} - \dfrac{\sqrt{5}}{3}$ To subtract, notice that the LCD is 12.

$= \dfrac{3\sqrt{5} \cdot 3}{4 \cdot 3} - \dfrac{\sqrt{5} \cdot 4}{3 \cdot 4}$ Write each expression as an equivalent expression with a denominator of 12.

$= \dfrac{9\sqrt{5}}{12} - \dfrac{4\sqrt{5}}{12}$ Multiply factors in the numerator and the denominator.

$= \dfrac{5\sqrt{5}}{12}$ Subtract.

b. $\sqrt[3]{\dfrac{7x}{8}} + 2\sqrt[3]{7x} = \dfrac{\sqrt[3]{7x}}{\sqrt[3]{8}} + 2\sqrt[3]{7x}$ Apply the quotient rule for radicals.

$= \dfrac{\sqrt[3]{7x}}{2} + 2\sqrt[3]{7x}$ Simplify.

$= \dfrac{\sqrt[3]{7x}}{2} + \dfrac{2\sqrt[3]{7x} \cdot 2}{2}$ Write each expression as an equivalent expression with a denominator of 2.

$= \dfrac{\sqrt[3]{7x}}{2} + \dfrac{4\sqrt[3]{7x}}{2}$

$= \dfrac{5\sqrt[3]{7x}}{2}$ Add.

2   We can multiply radical expressions by using many of the same properties used to multiply polynomial expressions. For instance, to multiply $\sqrt{2}\left(\sqrt{6} - 3\sqrt{2}\right)$, we use the distributive property and multiply $\sqrt{2}$ by each term inside the parentheses.

$$\sqrt{2}\left(\sqrt{6} - 3\sqrt{2}\right) = \sqrt{2}\left(\sqrt{6}\right) - \sqrt{2}\left(3\sqrt{2}\right) \quad \text{Use the distributive property.}$$
$$= \sqrt{2 \cdot 6} - 3\sqrt{2 \cdot 2}$$
$$= \sqrt{2 \cdot 2 \cdot 3} - 3 \cdot 2 \quad \text{Use the product rule for radicals.}$$
$$= 2\sqrt{3} - 6$$

EXAMPLE 4

Multiply.

a. $\sqrt{3}\left(5 + \sqrt{30}\right)$ **b.** $\left(\sqrt{5} - \sqrt{6}\right)\left(\sqrt{7} + 1\right)$ **c.** $\left(7\sqrt{x} + 5\right)\left(3\sqrt{x} - \sqrt{5}\right)$

d. $\left(4\sqrt{3} - 1\right)^2$ **e.** $\left(\sqrt{2x} - 5\right)\left(\sqrt{2x} + 5\right)$ **f.** $\left(\sqrt{x - 3} + 5\right)^2$

Solution   **a.** $\sqrt{3}\left(5 + \sqrt{30}\right) = \sqrt{3}(5) + \sqrt{3}\left(\sqrt{30}\right)$
$$= 5\sqrt{3} + \sqrt{3 \cdot 30}$$
$$= 5\sqrt{3} + \sqrt{3 \cdot 3 \cdot 10}$$
$$= 5\sqrt{3} + 3\sqrt{10}$$

b. To multiply, we can use the FOIL method.

$$\left(\sqrt{5} - \sqrt{6}\right)\left(\sqrt{7} + 1\right) = \overset{\text{First}}{\sqrt{5} \cdot \sqrt{7}} + \overset{\text{Outer}}{\sqrt{5} \cdot 1} - \overset{\text{Inner}}{\sqrt{6} \cdot \sqrt{7}} - \overset{\text{Last}}{\sqrt{6} \cdot 1}$$
$$= \sqrt{35} + \sqrt{5} - \sqrt{42} - \sqrt{6}$$

c. $\left(7\sqrt{x} + 5\right)\left(3\sqrt{x} - \sqrt{5}\right) = 7\sqrt{x}\left(3\sqrt{x}\right) - 7\sqrt{x}\left(\sqrt{5}\right) + 5\left(3\sqrt{x}\right) - 5\left(\sqrt{5}\right)$
$$= 21x - 7\sqrt{5x} + 15\sqrt{x} - 5\sqrt{5}$$

d. $\left(4\sqrt{3} - 1\right)^2 = \left(4\sqrt{3} - 1\right)\left(4\sqrt{3} - 1\right)$
$$= 4\sqrt{3}\left(4\sqrt{3}\right) - 4\sqrt{3}(1) - 1\left(4\sqrt{3}\right) - 1(-1)$$
$$= 16 \cdot 3 - 4\sqrt{3} - 4\sqrt{3} + 1$$
$$= 48 - 8\sqrt{3} + 1$$
$$= 49 - 8\sqrt{3}$$

e. $\left(\sqrt{2x} - 5\right)\left(\sqrt{2x} + 5\right) = \sqrt{2x} \cdot \sqrt{2x} + 5\sqrt{2x} - 5\sqrt{2x} - 5 \cdot 5$
$$= 2x - 25$$

f. $\left(\underbrace{\sqrt{x - 3}}_{a} + \underbrace{5}_{b}\right)^2 = \underbrace{\left(\sqrt{x - 3}\right)^2}_{a^2} + \underbrace{2 \cdot}_{+\ 2 \cdot} \cdot \underbrace{\sqrt{x - 3}}_{a} \cdot \underbrace{5}_{\cdot b} + \underbrace{5^2}_{+\ b^2}$

$$= x - 3 + 10\sqrt{x - 3} + 25 \quad \text{Simplify.}$$
$$= x + 22 + 10\sqrt{x - 3} \quad \text{Combine like terms.}$$

MENTAL MATH

Simplify. Assume that all variables represent positive real numbers.

1. $2\sqrt{3} + 4\sqrt{3}$ **2.** $5\sqrt{7} + 3\sqrt{7}$ **3.** $8\sqrt{x} - 5\sqrt{x}$

4. $3\sqrt{y} + 10\sqrt{y}$ **5.** $7\sqrt[3]{x} + 5\sqrt[3]{x}$ **6.** $8\sqrt[3]{z} - 2\sqrt[3]{z}$

Add or Subtract if possible.

7. $\sqrt{11} + \sqrt{11}$ **8.** $\sqrt{11} + \sqrt[3]{11}$ **9.** $9\sqrt{13} - \sqrt{13}$

10. $9\sqrt{13} - \sqrt[4]{13}$ **11.** $8\sqrt[3]{2x} + 3\sqrt[3]{2x} - \sqrt[3]{2x}$ **12.** $8\sqrt[3]{2x} + 3\sqrt[3]{2x^2} - \sqrt[3]{2x}$

EXERCISE SET 7.4

STUDY   CD/   PH MATH   MathXL®Tutorials   MathXL®   MyMathLab®
GUIDE/SSM   VIDEO   TUTOR CENTER   ON CD

Add or subtract. See Examples 1 through 3.

1. $\sqrt{8} - \sqrt{32}$ **2.** $\sqrt{27} - \sqrt{75}$

3. $2\sqrt{2x^3} + 4x\sqrt{8x}$ **4.** $3\sqrt{45x^3} + x\sqrt{5x}$

 5. $2\sqrt{50} - 3\sqrt{125} + \sqrt{98}$

6. $4\sqrt{32} - \sqrt{18} + 2\sqrt{128}$

7. $\sqrt[3]{16x} - \sqrt[3]{54x}$ **8.** $2\sqrt[3]{3a^4} - 3a\sqrt[3]{81a}$

9. $\sqrt{9b^3} - \sqrt{25b^3} + \sqrt{49b^3}$

10. $\sqrt{4x^7} + 9x^2\sqrt{x^3} - 5x\sqrt{x^5}$

11. $\dfrac{5\sqrt{2}}{3} + \dfrac{2\sqrt{2}}{5}$ **12.** $\dfrac{\sqrt{3}}{2} + \dfrac{4\sqrt{3}}{3}$

 13. $\sqrt[3]{\dfrac{11}{8}} - \dfrac{\sqrt[3]{11}}{6}$ **14.** $\dfrac{2\sqrt[3]{4}}{7} - \dfrac{\sqrt[3]{4}}{14}$

15. $\dfrac{\sqrt{20x}}{9} + \sqrt{\dfrac{5x}{9}}$ **16.** $\dfrac{3x\sqrt{7}}{5} + \sqrt{\dfrac{7x^2}{100}}$

17. $7\sqrt{9} - 7 + \sqrt{3}$ **18.** $\sqrt{16} - 5\sqrt{10} + 7$

19. $2 + 3\sqrt{y^2} - 6\sqrt{y^2} + 5$

20. $3\sqrt{7} - \sqrt[3]{x} + 4\sqrt{7} - 3\sqrt[3]{x}$

21. $3\sqrt{108} - 2\sqrt{18} - 3\sqrt{48}$

22. $-\sqrt{75} + \sqrt{12} - 3\sqrt{3}$

23. $-5\sqrt[3]{625} + \sqrt[3]{40}$ **24.** $-2\sqrt[3]{108} - \sqrt[3]{32}$

25. $\sqrt{9b^3} - \sqrt{25b^3} + \sqrt{16b^3}$

26. $\sqrt{4x^7y^5} + 9x^2\sqrt{x^3y^5} - 5xy\sqrt{x^5y^3}$

27. $5y\sqrt{8y} + 2\sqrt{50y^3}$ **28.** $3\sqrt{8x^2y^3} - 2x\sqrt{32y^3}$

29. $\sqrt[3]{54xy^3} - 5\sqrt[3]{2xy^3} + y\sqrt[3]{128x}$

30. $2\sqrt[3]{24x^3y^4} + 4x\sqrt[3]{81y^4}$

31. $6\sqrt[3]{11} + 8\sqrt{11} - 12\sqrt{11}$ **32.** $3\sqrt[3]{5} + 4\sqrt{5}$

33. $-2\sqrt[4]{x^7} + 3\sqrt[4]{16x^7}$

34. $6\sqrt[3]{24x^3} - 2\sqrt[3]{81x^3} - x\sqrt[3]{3}$

35. $\dfrac{4\sqrt{3}}{3} - \dfrac{\sqrt{12}}{3}$ **36.** $\dfrac{\sqrt{45}}{10} + \dfrac{7\sqrt{5}}{10}$

37. $\dfrac{\sqrt[3]{8x^4}}{7} + \dfrac{3x\sqrt[3]{x}}{7}$ **38.** $\dfrac{\sqrt[4]{48}}{5x} - \dfrac{2\sqrt[4]{3}}{10x}$

39. $\sqrt{\dfrac{28}{x^2}} + \sqrt{\dfrac{7}{4x^2}}$ **40.** $\dfrac{\sqrt{99}}{5x} - \sqrt{\dfrac{44}{x^2}}$

41. $\sqrt[3]{\dfrac{16}{27}} - \dfrac{\sqrt[3]{54}}{6}$ **42.** $\dfrac{\sqrt[3]{3}}{10} + \sqrt[3]{\dfrac{24}{125}}$

43. $-\dfrac{\sqrt[3]{2x^4}}{9} + \sqrt[3]{\dfrac{250x^4}{27}}$ **44.** $\dfrac{\sqrt[3]{y^5}}{8} + \dfrac{5y\sqrt[3]{y^2}}{4}$

△ **45.** Find the perimeter of the trapezoid.

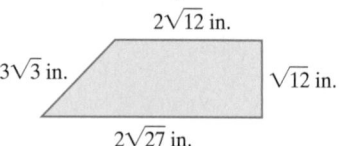

△ **46.** Find the perimeter of the triangle.

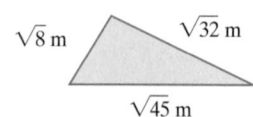

Multiply, and then simplify if possible. See Example 4.

47. $\sqrt{7}(\sqrt{5} + \sqrt{3})$

48. $\sqrt{5}(\sqrt{15} - \sqrt{35})$

49. $(\sqrt{5} - \sqrt{2})^2$

50. $(3x - \sqrt{2})(3x - \sqrt{2})$

51. $\sqrt{3x}(\sqrt{3} - \sqrt{x})$

52. $\sqrt{5y}(\sqrt{y} + \sqrt{5})$

53. $(2\sqrt{x} - 5)(3\sqrt{x} + 1)$

54. $(8\sqrt{y} + z)(4\sqrt{y} - 1)$

55. $(\sqrt[3]{a} - 4)(\sqrt[3]{a} + 5)$

56. $(\sqrt[3]{a} + 2)(\sqrt[3]{a} + 7)$

57. $6(\sqrt{2} - 2)$

58. $\sqrt{5}(6 - \sqrt{5})$

59. $\sqrt{2}(\sqrt{2} + x\sqrt{6})$

60. $\sqrt{3}(\sqrt{3} - 2\sqrt{5x})$

61. $(2\sqrt{7} + 3\sqrt{5})(\sqrt{7} - 2\sqrt{5})$

62. $(\sqrt{6} - 4\sqrt{2})(3\sqrt{6} + 1)$

63. $(\sqrt{x} - y)(\sqrt{x} + y)$

64. $(3\sqrt{x} + 2)(\sqrt{3x} - 2)$

65. $(\sqrt{3} + x)^2$

66. $(\sqrt{y} - 3x)^2$

67. $(\sqrt{5x} - 3\sqrt{2})(\sqrt{5x} - 3\sqrt{3})$

68. $(5\sqrt{3x} - \sqrt{y})(4\sqrt{x} + 1)$

69. $(\sqrt[3]{4} + 2)(\sqrt[3]{2} - 1)$

70. $(\sqrt[3]{3} + \sqrt[3]{2})(\sqrt[3]{9} - \sqrt[3]{4})$

71. $(\sqrt[3]{x} + 1)(\sqrt[3]{x} - 4\sqrt{x} + 7)$

72. $(\sqrt[3]{3x} + 3)(\sqrt[3]{2x} - 3x - 1)$

73. $(\sqrt{x - 1} + 5)^2$

74. $(\sqrt{3x + 1} + 2)^2$

75. $(\sqrt{2x + 5} - 1)^2$

76. $(\sqrt{x - 6} - 7)^2$

REVIEW AND PREVIEW

Factor each numerator and denominator. Then simplify if possible. See Section 6.1.

77. $\dfrac{2x - 14}{2}$

78. $\dfrac{8x - 24y}{4}$

79. $\dfrac{7x - 7y}{x^2 - y^2}$

80. $\dfrac{x^3 - 8}{4x - 8}$

81. $\dfrac{6a^2b - 9ab}{3ab}$

82. $\dfrac{14r - 28r^2s^2}{7rs}$

83. $\dfrac{-4 + 2\sqrt{3}}{6}$

84. $\dfrac{-5 + 10\sqrt{7}}{5}$

Concept Extensions

△ **85.** Find the perimeter and area of the rectangle.

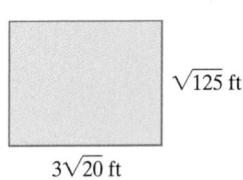

$\sqrt{125}$ ft

$3\sqrt{20}$ ft

△ **86.** Find the area and perimeter of the trapezoid. (*Hint:* The area of a trapezoid is the product of half the height $6\sqrt{3}$ meters and the sum of the bases $2\sqrt{63}$ and $7\sqrt{7}$ meters.)

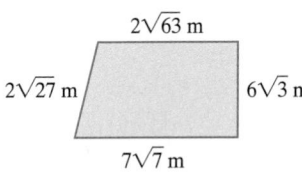

$2\sqrt{63}$ m

$2\sqrt{27}$ m

$6\sqrt{3}$ m

$7\sqrt{7}$ m

87. a. Add: $\sqrt{3} + \sqrt{3}$

b. Multiply: $\sqrt{3} \cdot \sqrt{3}$

c. Describe the differences in parts **a** and **b**.

88. Multiply: $(\sqrt{2} + \sqrt{3} - 1)^2$

89. Explain how simplifying $2x + 3x$ is similar to simplifying $2\sqrt{x} + 3\sqrt{x}$.

90. Explain how multiplying $(x - 2)(x + 3)$ is similar to multiplying $(\sqrt{x} - \sqrt{2})(\sqrt{x} + 3)$.

7.5 *RATIONALIZING DENOMINATORS AND NUMERATORS OF RADICAL EXPRESSIONS*

Objectives

1 Rationalize denominators.

2 Rationalize denominators having two terms.

3 Rationalize numerators.

1   Often in mathematics, it is helpful to write a radical expression such as $\dfrac{\sqrt{3}}{\sqrt{2}}$ either without a radical in the denominator or without a radical in the numerator. The process of writing this expression as an equivalent expression but without a radical in the denominator is called **rationalizing the denominator**. To rationalize the denominator of $\dfrac{\sqrt{3}}{\sqrt{2}}$, we use the fundamental principle of fractions and multiply the numerator and the denominator by $\sqrt{2}$. Recall that this is the same as multiplying by $\dfrac{\sqrt{2}}{\sqrt{2}}$, which simplifies to 1.

$$\frac{\sqrt{3}}{\sqrt{2}} = \frac{\sqrt{3} \cdot \sqrt{2}}{\sqrt{2} \cdot \sqrt{2}} = \frac{\sqrt{6}}{\sqrt{4}} = \frac{\sqrt{6}}{2}$$

EXAMPLE 1

Rationalize the denominator of each expression.

a. $\dfrac{2}{\sqrt{5}}$ **b.** $\dfrac{2\sqrt{16}}{\sqrt{9x}}$ **c.** $\sqrt[3]{\dfrac{1}{2}}$

Solution   **a.** To rationalize the denominator, we multiply the numerator and denominator by a factor that makes the radicand in the denominator a perfect square.

$$\frac{2}{\sqrt{5}} = \frac{2 \cdot \sqrt{5}}{\sqrt{5} \cdot \sqrt{5}} = \frac{2\sqrt{5}}{5} \qquad \text{\textit{The denominator is now rationalized}}$$

b. First, we simplify the radicals and then rationalize the denominator.

$$\frac{2\sqrt{16}}{\sqrt{9x}} = \frac{2(4)}{3\sqrt{x}} = \frac{8}{3\sqrt{x}}$$

To rationalize the denominator, multiply the numerator and denominator by $\sqrt{x}$. Then

$$\frac{8}{3\sqrt{x}} = \frac{8 \cdot \sqrt{x}}{3\sqrt{x} \cdot \sqrt{x}} = \frac{8\sqrt{x}}{3x}$$

c. $\sqrt[3]{\dfrac{1}{2}} = \dfrac{\sqrt[3]{1}}{\sqrt[3]{2}} = \dfrac{1}{\sqrt[3]{2}}$. Now we rationalize the denominator. Since $\sqrt[3]{2}$ is a cube root, we want to multiply by a value that will make the radicand 2 a perfect cube. If we multiply $\sqrt[3]{2}$ by $\sqrt[3]{2^2}$, we get $\sqrt[3]{2^3} = \sqrt[3]{8} = 2$.

$$\frac{1 \cdot \sqrt[3]{2^2}}{\sqrt[3]{2} \cdot \sqrt[3]{2^2}} = \frac{\sqrt[3]{4}}{\sqrt[3]{2^3}} = \frac{\sqrt[3]{4}}{2} \qquad \text{\textit{Multiply the numerator and denominator by }} \sqrt[3]{2^2} \text{ \textit{and then simplify.}}$$

✔ **CONCEPT CHECK**

Determine by which number both the numerator and denominator can be multiplied to rationalize the denominator of the radical expression.

a. $\dfrac{1}{\sqrt[3]{7}}$ b. $\dfrac{1}{\sqrt[4]{8}}$

EXAMPLE 2

Rationalize the denominator of $\sqrt{\dfrac{7x}{3y}}$.

Solution $\sqrt{\dfrac{7x}{3y}} = \dfrac{\sqrt{7x}}{\sqrt{3y}}$ Use the quotient rule. No radical may be simplified further.

$= \dfrac{\sqrt{7x} \cdot \sqrt{3y}}{\sqrt{3y} \cdot \sqrt{3y}}$ Multiply numerator and denominator by $\sqrt{3y}$ so that the radicand in the denominator is a perfect square.

$= \dfrac{\sqrt{21xy}}{3y}$ Use the product rule in the numerator and denominator. Remember that $\sqrt{3y} \cdot \sqrt{3y} = 3y$.

EXAMPLE 3

Rationalize the denominator of $\dfrac{\sqrt[4]{x}}{\sqrt[4]{81y^5}}$.

Solution   First, simplify each radical if possible.

$\dfrac{\sqrt[4]{x}}{\sqrt[4]{81y^5}} = \dfrac{\sqrt[4]{x}}{\sqrt[4]{81y^4} \cdot \sqrt[4]{y}}$ Use the product rule in the denominator.

$= \dfrac{\sqrt[4]{x}}{3y\sqrt[4]{y}}$ Write $\sqrt[4]{81y^4}$ as $3y$.

$= \dfrac{\sqrt[4]{x} \cdot \sqrt[4]{y^3}}{3y\sqrt[4]{y} \cdot \sqrt[4]{y^3}}$ Multiply numerator and denominator by $\sqrt[4]{y^3}$ so that the radicand in the denominator is a perfect fourth power.

$= \dfrac{\sqrt[4]{xy^3}}{3y\sqrt[4]{y^4}}$ Use the product rule in the numerator and denominator.

$= \dfrac{\sqrt[4]{xy^3}}{3y^2}$ In the denominator, $\sqrt[4]{y^4} = y$ and $3y \cdot y = 3y^2$.

---

2   Remember the product of the sum and difference of two terms?

$$(a + b)(a - b) = a^2 - b^2$$

These two expressions are called conjugates of each other.

To rationalize a numerator or denominator that is a sum or difference of two terms, we use conjugates. To see how and why this works, let's rationalize the denominator of the expression $\dfrac{5}{\sqrt{3} - 2}$. To do so, we multiply both the numerator and the denominator by $\sqrt{3} + 2$, the **conjugate** of the denominator $\sqrt{3} - 2$, and see what happens.

$$\dfrac{5}{\sqrt{3} - 2} = \dfrac{5\left(\sqrt{3} + 2\right)}{\left(\sqrt{3} - 2\right)\left(\sqrt{3} + 2\right)}$$

$$= \dfrac{5\left(\sqrt{3} + 2\right)}{\left(\sqrt{3}\right)^2 - 2^2} \qquad \text{Multiply the sum and difference of two terms: } (a + b)(a - b) = a^2 - b^2.$$

$$= \dfrac{5\left(\sqrt{3} + 2\right)}{3 - 4}$$

$$= \dfrac{5\left(\sqrt{3} + 2\right)}{-1}$$

$$= -5\left(\sqrt{3} + 2\right) \quad \text{or} \quad -5\sqrt{3} - 10$$

Notice in the denominator that the product of $\left(\sqrt{3} - 2\right)$ and its conjugate $\left(\sqrt{3} + 2\right)$, is -1. In general, the product of an expression and its conjugate will contain no radical terms. This is why, when rationalizing a denominator or a numerator containing two terms, we multiply by its conjugate. Examples of conjugates are

$$\sqrt{a} - \sqrt{b} \quad \text{and} \quad \sqrt{a} + \sqrt{b}$$
$$x + \sqrt{y} \quad \text{and} \quad x - \sqrt{y}$$

EXAMPLE 4

Rationalize each denominator.

a. $\dfrac{2}{3\sqrt{2} + 4}$ **b.** $\dfrac{\sqrt{6} + 2}{\sqrt{5} - \sqrt{3}}$ **c.** $\dfrac{2\sqrt{m}}{3\sqrt{x} + \sqrt{m}}$

Solution   **a.** Multiply the numerator and denominator by the conjugate of the denominator $3\sqrt{2} + 4$.

$$\dfrac{2}{3\sqrt{2} + 4} = \dfrac{2\left(3\sqrt{2} - 4\right)}{\left(3\sqrt{2} + 4\right)\left(3\sqrt{2} - 4\right)}$$

$$= \dfrac{2\left(3\sqrt{2} - 4\right)}{\left(3\sqrt{2}\right)^2 - 4^2}$$

$$= \dfrac{2\left(3\sqrt{2} - 4\right)}{18 - 16}$$

$$= \dfrac{2\left(3\sqrt{2} - 4\right)}{2}, \quad \text{or} \quad 3\sqrt{2} - 4$$

It is often helpful to leave a numerator in factored form to help determine whether the expression can be simplified.

b. Multiply the numerator and denominator by the conjugate of $\sqrt{5} - \sqrt{3}$.

$$\frac{\sqrt{6} + 2}{\sqrt{5} - \sqrt{3}} = \frac{\left(\sqrt{6} + 2\right)\left(\sqrt{5} + \sqrt{3}\right)}{\left(\sqrt{5} - \sqrt{3}\right)\left(\sqrt{5} + \sqrt{3}\right)}$$

$$= \frac{\sqrt{6}\sqrt{5} + \sqrt{6}\sqrt{3} + 2\sqrt{5} + 2\sqrt{3}}{\left(\sqrt{5}\right)^2 - \left(\sqrt{3}\right)^2}$$

$$= \frac{\sqrt{30} + \sqrt{18} + 2\sqrt{5} + 2\sqrt{3}}{5 - 3}$$

$$= \frac{\sqrt{30} + 3\sqrt{2} + 2\sqrt{5} + 2\sqrt{3}}{2}$$

c. Multiply by the conjugate of $3\sqrt{x} + \sqrt{m}$ to eliminate the radicals from the denominator.

$$\frac{2\sqrt{m}}{3\sqrt{x} + \sqrt{m}} = \frac{2\sqrt{m}\left(3\sqrt{x} - \sqrt{m}\right)}{\left(3\sqrt{x} + \sqrt{m}\right)\left(3\sqrt{x} - \sqrt{m}\right)} = \frac{6\sqrt{mx} - 2m}{\left(3\sqrt{x}\right)^2 - \left(\sqrt{m}\right)^2}$$

$$= \frac{6\sqrt{mx} - 2m}{9x - m}$$

3   As mentioned earlier, it is also often helpful to write an expression such as $\dfrac{\sqrt{3}}{\sqrt{2}}$ as an equivalent expression without a radical in the numerator. This process is called **rationalizing the numerator**. To rationalize the numerator of $\dfrac{\sqrt{3}}{\sqrt{2}}$, we multiply the numerator and the denominator by $\sqrt{3}$.

$$\frac{\sqrt{3}}{\sqrt{2}} = \frac{\sqrt{3} \cdot \sqrt{3}}{\sqrt{2} \cdot \sqrt{3}} = \frac{\sqrt{9}}{\sqrt{6}} = \frac{3}{\sqrt{6}}$$

EXAMPLE 5

Rationalize the numerator of $\dfrac{\sqrt{7}}{\sqrt{45}}$.

Solution   First we simplify $\sqrt{45}$.

$$\frac{\sqrt{7}}{\sqrt{45}} = \frac{\sqrt{7}}{\sqrt{9 \cdot 5}} = \frac{\sqrt{7}}{3\sqrt{5}}$$

Next we rationalize the numerator by multiplying the numerator and the denominator by $\sqrt{7}$.

$$\frac{\sqrt{7}}{3\sqrt{5}} = \frac{\sqrt{7} \cdot \sqrt{7}}{3\sqrt{5} \cdot \sqrt{7}} = \frac{7}{3\sqrt{5 \cdot 7}} = \frac{7}{3\sqrt{35}}$$

EXAMPLE 6

Rationalize the numerator of $\dfrac{\sqrt[3]{2x^2}}{\sqrt[3]{5y}}$.

Solution The numerator and the denominator of this expression are already simplified. To rationalize the numerator, $\sqrt[3]{2x^2}$, we multiply the numerator and denominator by a facto that will make the radicand a perfect cube. If we multiply $\sqrt[3]{2x^2}$ by $\sqrt[3]{4x}$, we g $\sqrt[3]{8x^3} = 2x$.

$$\frac{\sqrt[3]{2x^2}}{\sqrt[3]{5y}} = \frac{\sqrt[3]{2x^2} \cdot \sqrt[3]{4x}}{\sqrt[3]{5y} \cdot \sqrt[3]{4x}} = \frac{\sqrt[3]{8x^3}}{\sqrt[3]{20xy}} = \frac{2x}{\sqrt[3]{20xy}}$$

EXAMPLE 7

Rationalize the numerator of $\dfrac{\sqrt{x} + 2}{5}$.

Solution We multiply the numerator and the denominator by the conjugate of the numerato $\sqrt{x} + 2$.

$$\frac{\sqrt{x} + 2}{5} = \frac{\left(\sqrt{x} + 2\right)\left(\sqrt{x} - 2\right)}{5\left(\sqrt{x} - 2\right)} \quad \text{Multiply by } \sqrt{x} - 2, \text{ the conjugate of } \sqrt{x} + 2.$$

$$= \frac{\left(\sqrt{x}\right)^2 - 2^2}{5\left(\sqrt{x} - 2\right)} \quad (a+b)(a-b) = a^2 - b^2.$$

$$= \frac{x - 4}{5\left(\sqrt{x} - 2\right)}$$

STUDY SKILLS REMINDER

How Are Your Homework Assignments Going?

By now, you should have good homework habits. If not, it's never too late to begin. Why is it so important in mathematics to keep up with homework? You probably now know the answer to that question. You have probably realized by now that many concepts in mathematics build on each other. Your understanding of one chapter in mathematics usually depends on your understanding of the previous chapter's material.

Don't forget that completing your homework assignment involves a lot more than attempting a few of the problems assigned.

To complete a homework assignment, remember these four things:

1. Attempt all of it.
2. Check it.
3. Correct it.
4. If needed, ask questions about it.

MENTAL MATH

Find the conjugate of each expression.

1. $\sqrt{2} + x$ **2.** $\sqrt{3} + y$ **3.** $5 - \sqrt{a}$

4. $6 - \sqrt{b}$ **5.** $7\sqrt{5} + 8\sqrt{x}$ **6.** $9\sqrt{2} - 6\sqrt{y}$

EXERCISE SET 7.5

STUDY GUIDE/SSM   CD/VIDEO   PH MATH TUTOR CENTER   MathXL®Tutorials ON CD   MathXL®   MyMathLab®

Rationalize each denominator. See Examples 1 through 3.

1. $\dfrac{\sqrt{2}}{\sqrt{7}}$ **2.** $\dfrac{\sqrt{3}}{\sqrt{2}}$

3. $\sqrt{\dfrac{1}{5}}$ **4.** $\sqrt{\dfrac{1}{2}}$

5. $\sqrt[3]{\dfrac{3}{4}}$ **6.** $\sqrt[3]{\dfrac{2}{9}}$

7. $\dfrac{4}{\sqrt[3]{3}}$ **8.** $\dfrac{6}{\sqrt[3]{9}}$

9. $\dfrac{3}{\sqrt{8x}}$ **10.** $\dfrac{5}{\sqrt{27a}}$

11. $\dfrac{3}{\sqrt[3]{4x^2}}$ **12.** $\dfrac{5}{\sqrt[3]{3y}}$

13. $\sqrt{\dfrac{4}{x}}$ **14.** $\sqrt{\dfrac{25}{y}}$

15. $\dfrac{9}{\sqrt{3a}}$ **16.** $\dfrac{x}{\sqrt{5}}$

17. $\dfrac{3}{\sqrt[3]{2}}$ **18.** $\dfrac{5}{\sqrt[3]{9}}$

19. $\dfrac{2\sqrt{3}}{\sqrt{7}}$ **20.** $\dfrac{-5\sqrt{2}}{\sqrt{11}}$

21. $\sqrt{\dfrac{2x}{5y}}$ **22.** $\sqrt{\dfrac{13a}{2b}}$

23. $\sqrt[4]{\dfrac{81}{8}}$ **24.** $\sqrt[4]{\dfrac{1}{9}}$

25. $\sqrt[4]{\dfrac{16}{9x^7}}$ **26.** $\sqrt[5]{\dfrac{32}{m^6 n^{13}}}$

27. $\dfrac{5a}{\sqrt[5]{8a^9 b^{11}}}$ **28.** $\dfrac{9y}{\sqrt[4]{4y^9}}$

Rationalize each denominator. See Example 4.

29. $\dfrac{6}{2 - \sqrt{7}}$ **30.** $\dfrac{3}{\sqrt{7} - 4}$

31. $\dfrac{-7}{\sqrt{x} - 3}$ **32.** $\dfrac{-8}{\sqrt{y} + 4}$

33. $\dfrac{\sqrt{2} - \sqrt{3}}{\sqrt{2} + \sqrt{3}}$ **34.** $\dfrac{\sqrt{3} + \sqrt{4}}{\sqrt{2} + \sqrt{3}}$

35. $\dfrac{\sqrt{a} + 1}{2\sqrt{a} - \sqrt{b}}$ **36.** $\dfrac{2\sqrt{a} - 3}{2\sqrt{a} - \sqrt{b}}$

37. $\dfrac{8}{1 + \sqrt{10}}$ **38.** $\dfrac{-3}{\sqrt{6} - 2}$

39. $\dfrac{\sqrt{x}}{\sqrt{x} + \sqrt{y}}$ **40.** $\dfrac{2\sqrt{a}}{2\sqrt{x} - \sqrt{y}}$

41. $\dfrac{2\sqrt{3} + \sqrt{6}}{4\sqrt{3} - \sqrt{6}}$ **42.** $\dfrac{4\sqrt{5} + \sqrt{2}}{2\sqrt{5} - \sqrt{2}}$

Rationalize each numerator. See Examples 5 and 6.

43. $\sqrt{\dfrac{5}{3}}$ **44.** $\sqrt{\dfrac{3}{2}}$

45. $\sqrt{\dfrac{18}{5}}$ **46.** $\sqrt{\dfrac{12}{7}}$

47. $\dfrac{\sqrt{4x}}{7}$

48. $\dfrac{\sqrt{3x^5}}{6}$

49. $\dfrac{\sqrt[3]{5y^2}}{\sqrt[3]{4x}}$

50. $\dfrac{\sqrt[3]{4x}}{\sqrt[3]{z^4}}$

51. $\sqrt{\dfrac{2}{5}}$

52. $\sqrt{\dfrac{3}{7}}$

53. $\dfrac{\sqrt{2x}}{11}$

54. $\dfrac{\sqrt{y}}{7}$

55. $\sqrt[3]{\dfrac{7}{8}}$

56. $\sqrt[3]{\dfrac{25}{2}}$

57. $\dfrac{\sqrt[3]{3x^5}}{10}$

58. $\sqrt[3]{\dfrac{9y}{7}}$

59. $\sqrt{\dfrac{18x^4y^6}{3z}}$

60. $\sqrt{\dfrac{8x^5y}{2z}}$

61. When rationalizing the denominator of $\dfrac{\sqrt{5}}{\sqrt{7}}$, explain why both the numerator and the denominator must be multiplied by $\sqrt{7}$.

62. When rationalizing the numerator of $\dfrac{\sqrt{5}}{\sqrt{7}}$, explain why both the numerator and the denominator must be multiplied by $\sqrt{5}$.

Rationalize each numerator. See Example 7.

63. $\dfrac{2 - \sqrt{11}}{6}$

64. $\dfrac{\sqrt{15} + 1}{2}$

65. $\dfrac{2 - \sqrt{7}}{-5}$

66. $\dfrac{\sqrt{5} + 2}{\sqrt{2}}$

67. $\dfrac{\sqrt{x} + 3}{\sqrt{x}}$

68. $\dfrac{5 + \sqrt{2}}{\sqrt{2x}}$

69. $\dfrac{\sqrt{2} - 1}{\sqrt{2} + 1}$

70. $\dfrac{\sqrt{8} - \sqrt{3}}{\sqrt{2} + \sqrt{3}}$

71. $\dfrac{\sqrt{x} + 1}{\sqrt{x} - 1}$

72. $\dfrac{\sqrt{x} + \sqrt{y}}{\sqrt{x} - \sqrt{y}}$

REVIEW AND PREVIEW

Solve each equation. See Sections 2.1 and 5.7.

73. $2x - 7 = 3(x - 4)$

74. $9x - 4 = 7(x - 2)$

75. $(x - 6)(2x + 1) = 0$

76. $(y + 2)(5y + 4) = 0$

77. $x^2 - 8x = -12$

78. $x^3 = x$

Concepts Extensions

79. The formula of the radius r of a sphere with surface area A i

$$r = \sqrt{\dfrac{A}{4\pi}}$$

Rationalize the denominator of the radical expression in thi formula.

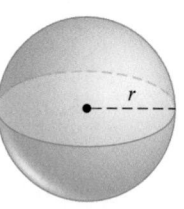

80. The formula for the radius r of a cone with height 7 centime ters and volume V is

$$r = \sqrt{\dfrac{3V}{7\pi}}$$

Rationalize the numerator of the radical expression in thi formula.

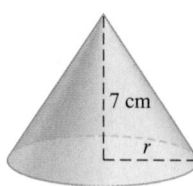

81. Explain why rationalizing the denominator does not chang the value of the original expression.

82. Explain why rationalizing the numerator does not chang the value of the original expression.

RADICALS AND RATIONAL EXPONENTS   INTEGRATED REVIEW

Throughout this review, assume that all variables represent positive real numbers. Find each root.

1. $\sqrt{81}$

2. $\sqrt[3]{-8}$

3. $\sqrt[4]{\dfrac{1}{16}}$

4. $\sqrt{x^6}$

5. $\sqrt[3]{y^9}$

6. $\sqrt{4y^{10}}$

7. $\sqrt[5]{-32y^5}$

8. $\sqrt[4]{81b^{12}}$

Use radical notation to rewrite each expression. Simplify if possible.

9. $36^{1/2}$

10. $(3y)^{1/4}$

11. $64^{-2/3}$

12. $(x+1)^{3/5}$

Use the properties of exponents to simplify each expression. Write with positive exponents.

13. $y^{-1/6} \cdot y^{7/6}$

14. $\dfrac{(2x^{1/3})^4}{x^{5/6}}$

15. $\dfrac{x^{1/4}x^{3/4}}{x^{-1/4}}$

16. $4^{1/3} \cdot 4^{2/5}$

Use rational exponents to simplify each radical.

17. $\sqrt[3]{8x^6}$

18. $\sqrt[12]{a^9b^6}$

Use rational exponents to write each as a single radical expression.

19. $\sqrt[4]{x} \cdot \sqrt{x}$

20. $\sqrt{5} \cdot \sqrt[3]{2}$

Simplify.

21. $\sqrt{40}$

22. $\sqrt[4]{16x^7y^{10}}$

23. $\sqrt[3]{54x^4}$

24. $\sqrt[5]{-64b^{10}}$

Multiply or divide. Then simplify if possible.

25. $\sqrt{5} \cdot \sqrt{x}$

26. $\sqrt[3]{8x} \cdot \sqrt[3]{8x^2}$

27. $\dfrac{\sqrt{98y^6}}{\sqrt{2y}}$

28. $\dfrac{\sqrt[4]{48a^9b^3}}{\sqrt[4]{ab^3}}$

Perform each indicated operation.

29. $\sqrt{20} - \sqrt{75} + 5\sqrt{7}$

30. $\sqrt[3]{54y^4} - y\sqrt[3]{16y}$

31. $\sqrt{3}\left(\sqrt{5} - \sqrt{2}\right)$

32. $\left(\sqrt{7} + \sqrt{3}\right)^2$

33. $\left(2x - \sqrt{5}\right)\left(2x + \sqrt{5}\right)$

34. $\left(\sqrt{x+1} - 1\right)^2$

Rationalize each denominator.

35. $\sqrt{\dfrac{7}{3}}$

36. $\dfrac{5}{\sqrt[3]{2x^2}}$

37. $\dfrac{\sqrt{3} - \sqrt{7}}{2\sqrt{3} + \sqrt{7}}$

Rationalize each numerator.

38. $\sqrt{\dfrac{7}{3}}$

39. $\sqrt[3]{\dfrac{9y}{11}}$

40. $\dfrac{\sqrt{x} - 2}{\sqrt{x}}$

7.6   RADICAL EQUATIONS AND PROBLEM SOLVING

Objectives

1   Solve equations that contain radical expressions.

2   Use the Pythagorean theorem to model problems.

1   In this section, we present techniques to solve equations containing radical expressions such as

$$\sqrt{2x - 3} = 9$$

We use the power rule to help us solve these radical equations.

> **Power Rule**
>
> If both sides of an equation are raised to the same power, **all** solutions of the original equation are **among** the solutions of the new equation.

This property *does not* say that raising both sides of an equation to a power yields an equivalent equation. A solution of the new equation *may or may not* be a solution of the original equation. For example, $(-2)^2 = 2^2$, but $-2 \neq 2$. Thus, *each solution of the new equation must be checked* to make sure it is a solution of the original equation. Recall that a proposed solution that is not a solution of the original equation is called an **extraneous solution**.

EXAMPLE 1

Solve $\sqrt{2x - 3} = 9$.

Solution   We use the power rule to square both sides of the equation to eliminate the radical.

$$\sqrt{2x - 3} = 9$$
$$\left(\sqrt{2x - 3}\right)^2 = 9^2$$
$$2x - 3 = 81$$
$$2x = 84$$
$$x = 42$$

Now we, check the solution in the original equation.

Check:
$$\sqrt{2x - 3} = 9$$
$$\sqrt{2(42) - 3} \stackrel{?}{=} 9 \qquad \text{Let } x = 42.$$
$$\sqrt{84 - 3} \stackrel{?}{=} 9$$
$$\sqrt{81} \stackrel{?}{=} 9$$
$$9 = 9 \qquad \text{True.}$$

The solution checks, so we conclude that the solution is 42 or the solution set is $\{42\}$.

To solve a radical equation, first isolate a radical on one side of the equation.

EXAMPLE 2

Solve $\sqrt{-10x - 1} + 3x = 0$.

Solution   First, isolate the radical on one side of the equation. To do this, we subtract $3x$ from both sides.

$$\sqrt{-10x - 1} + 3x = 0$$
$$\sqrt{-10x - 1} + 3x - 3x = 0 - 3x$$
$$\sqrt{-10x - 1} = -3x$$

Next we use the power rule to eliminate the radical.

$$\left(\sqrt{-10x - 1}\right)^2 = (-3x)^2$$
$$-10x - 1 = 9x^2$$

Since this is a quadratic equation, we can set the equation equal to 0 and try to solve by factoring.

$$9x^2 + 10x + 1 = 0$$
$$(9x + 1)(x + 1) = 0 \qquad \text{Factor.}$$
$$9x + 1 = 0 \quad \text{or} \quad x + 1 = 0 \qquad \text{Set each factor equal to } 0.$$
$$x = -\frac{1}{9} \quad \text{or} \quad x = -1$$

Check: Let $x = -\dfrac{1}{9}$.   Let $x = -1$.

$$\sqrt{-10x - 1} + 3x = 0$$ $$\sqrt{-10x - 1} + 3x = 0$$

$$\sqrt{-10\left(-\dfrac{1}{9}\right) - 1} + 3\left(-\dfrac{1}{9}\right) \stackrel{?}{=} 0$$ $$\sqrt{-10(-1) - 1} + 3(-1) \stackrel{?}{=} 0$$

$$\sqrt{\dfrac{10}{9} - \dfrac{9}{9}} - \dfrac{3}{9} \stackrel{?}{=} 0$$ $$\sqrt{10 - 1} - 3 \stackrel{?}{=} 0$$

$$\sqrt{\dfrac{1}{9}} - \dfrac{1}{3} \stackrel{?}{=} 0$$ $$\sqrt{9} - 3 \stackrel{?}{=} 0$$

$$\dfrac{1}{3} - \dfrac{1}{3} = 0 \quad \text{True.}$$ $$3 - 3 = 0 \quad \text{True.}$$

Both solutions check. The solutions are $-\dfrac{1}{9}$ and -1 or the solution set is $\left\{-\dfrac{1}{9}, -1\right\}$

The following steps may be used to solve a radical equation.

Solving a Radical Equation

Step 1: Isolate one radical on one side of the equation.

Step 2: Raise each side of the equation to a power equal to the index of the radical and simplify.

Step 3: If the equation still contains a radical term, repeat Steps 1 and 2. If not, solve the equation.

Step 4: Check all proposed solutions in the original equation.

EXAMPLE 3

Solve $\sqrt[3]{x + 1} + 5 = 3$.

Solution   First we isolate the radical by subtracting 5 from both sides of the equation.

$$\sqrt[3]{x + 1} + 5 = 3$$
$$\sqrt[3]{x + 1} = -2$$

Next we raise both sides of the equation to the third power to eliminate the radical.

$$\left(\sqrt[3]{x + 1}\right)^3 = (-2)^3$$
$$x + 1 = -8$$
$$x = -9$$

The solution checks in the original equation, so the solution is -9.

EXAMPLE 4

Solve $\sqrt{4 - x} = x - 2$.

Solution

$$\sqrt{4 - x} = x - 2$$
$$\left(\sqrt{4 - x}\right)^2 = (x - 2)^2$$
$$4 - x = x^2 - 4x + 4$$
$$x^2 - 3x = 0 \qquad \text{Write the quadratic equation in standard form.}$$
$$x(x - 3) = 0 \qquad \text{Factor.}$$
$$x = 0 \quad \text{or} \quad x - 3 = 0 \qquad \text{Set each factor equal to } 0.$$
$$x = 3$$

Check:

$$\sqrt{4 - x} = x - 2$$
$$\sqrt{4 - 0} \stackrel{?}{=} 0 - 2 \quad \text{Let } x = 0.$$
$$2 = -2 \qquad \text{False.}$$

$$\sqrt{4 - x} = x - 2$$
$$\sqrt{4 - 3} \stackrel{?}{=} 3 - 2 \quad \text{Let } x = 3.$$
$$1 = 1 \qquad \text{True.}$$

The proposed solution 3 checks, but 0 does not. Since 0 is an extraneous solution, the only solution is 3.

> **Helpful Hint**
> In Example 4, notice that $(x - 2)^2 = x^2 - 4x + 4$. Make sure binomials are squared correctly.

✔ **CONCEPT CHECK**

How can you immediately tell that the equation $\sqrt{2y + 3} = -4$ has no real solution?

EXAMPLE 5

Solve $\sqrt{2x + 5} + \sqrt{2x} = 3$.

Solution   We get one radical alone by subtracting $\sqrt{2x}$ from both sides.

$$\sqrt{2x + 5} + \sqrt{2x} = 3$$
$$\sqrt{2x + 5} = 3 - \sqrt{2x}$$

Now we use the power rule to begin eliminating the radicals. First we square both sides.

$$\left(\sqrt{2x + 5}\right)^2 = \left(3 - \sqrt{2x}\right)^2$$
$$2x + 5 = 9 - 6\sqrt{2x} + 2x \quad \text{Multiply } \left(3 - \sqrt{2x}\right)\left(3 - \sqrt{2x}\right).$$

Concept Check Answer:
answers may vary

There is still a radical in the equation, so we get a radical alone again. Then we square both sides.

$$2x + 5 = 9 - 6\sqrt{2x} + 2x \qquad \textit{Get the radical alone.}$$

$$6\sqrt{2x} = 4$$

$$36(2x) = 16 \qquad \textit{Square both sides of the equation to}$$
$$\textit{eliminate the radical.}$$

$$72x = 16 \qquad \textit{Multiply.}$$

$$x = \frac{16}{72} \qquad \textit{Solve.}$$

$$x = \frac{2}{9} \qquad \textit{Simplify.}$$

The proposed solution, $\frac{2}{9}$, checks in the original equation. The solution is $\frac{2}{9}$.

Helpful Hint

Make sure expressions are squared correctly. In Example 5, we squared $\left(3 - \sqrt{2x}\right)$ as

$$\left(3 - \sqrt{2x}\right)^2 = \left(3 - \sqrt{2x}\right)\left(3 - \sqrt{2x}\right)$$
$$= 3 \cdot 3 - 3\sqrt{2x} - 3\sqrt{2x} + \sqrt{2x} \cdot \sqrt{2x}$$
$$= 9 - 6\sqrt{2x} + 2x$$

✔ **CONCEPT CHECK**

What is wrong with the following solution?

$$\sqrt{2x + 5} + \sqrt{4 - x} = 8$$
$$\left(\sqrt{2x + 5} + \sqrt{4 - x}\right)^2 = 8^2$$
$$(2x + 5) + (4 - x) = 64$$
$$x + 9 = 64$$
$$x = 55$$

---

2   Recall that the Pythagorean theorem states that in a right triangle, the length of the hypotenuse squared equals the sum of the lengths of each of the legs squared.

Pythagorean Theorem

If a and b are the lengths of the legs of a right triangle and c is the length of the hypotenuse, then $a^2 + b^2 = c^2$.

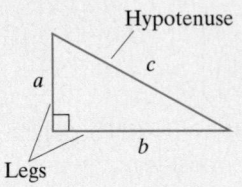

Concept Check Answer:

$\left(\sqrt{2x + 5} + \sqrt{4 - x}\right)^2$ is not $(2x + 5) + (4 - x)$.

2   Two complex numbers $a + bi$ and $c + di$ are equal if and only if $a = c$ and $b = d$. Complex numbers can be added or subtracted by adding or subtracting their real parts and then adding or subtracting their imaginary parts.

Sum or Difference of Complex Numbers

If $a + bi$ and $c + di$ are complex numbers, then their sum is

$$(a + bi) + (c + di) = (a + c) + (b + d)i$$

Their difference is

$$(a + bi) - (c + di) = a + bi - c - di = (a - c) + (b - d)i$$

EXAMPLE 3

Add or subtract the complex numbers. Write the sum or difference in the form $a + bi$.

a. $(2 + 3i) + (-3 + 2i)$ **b.** $5i - (1 - i)$ **c.** $(-3 - 7i) - (-6)$

Solution   **a.** $(2 + 3i) + (-3 + 2i) = (2 - 3) + (3 + 2)i = -1 + 5i$

b. $5i - (1 - i) = 5i - 1 + i$

$$= -1 + (5 + 1)i$$

$$= -1 + 6i$$

c. $(-3 - 7i) - (-6) = -3 - 7i + 6$

$$= (-3 + 6) - 7i$$

$$= 3 - 7i$$

3   To multiply two complex numbers of the form $a + bi$, we multiply as though they are binomials. Then we use the relationship $i^2 = -1$ to simplify.

EXAMPLE 4

Multiply the complex numbers. Write the product in the form $a + bi$.

a. $-7i \cdot 3i$ **b.** $3i(2 - i)$ **c.** $(2 - 5i)(4 + i)$

d. $(2 - i)^2$ **e.** $(7 + 3i)(7 - 3i)$

Solution   **a.** $-7i \cdot 3i = -21i^2$

$= -21(-1)$ Replace i^2 with -1.

$= 21$

b. $3i(2 - i) = 3i \cdot 2 - 3i \cdot i$ Use the distributive property.

$= 6i - 3i^2$ Multiply.

$= 6i - 3(-1)$ Replace i^2 with -1.

$= 6i + 3$

$= 3 + 6i$

Use the FOIL order below. (First, Outer, Inner, Last)

c. $(2 - 5i)(4 + i) = 2(4) + 2(i) - 5i(4) - 5i(i)$

 FOIL

$= 8 + 2i - 20i - 5i^2$

$= 8 - 18i - 5(-1)$ $i^2 = -1$.

$= 8 - 18i + 5$

$= 13 - 18i$

d. $(2 - i)^2 = (2 - i)(2 - i)$

$= 2(2) - 2(i) - 2(i) + i^2$

$= 4 - 4i + (-1)$ $i^2 = -1$.

$= 3 - 4i$

e. $(7 + 3i)(7 - 3i) = 7(7) - 7(3i) + 3i(7) - 3i(3i)$

$= 49 - 21i + 21i - 9i^2$

$= 49 - 9(-1)$ $i^2 = -1$.

$= 49 + 9$

$= 58$

Notice that if you add, subtract, or multiply two complex numbers, just like real numbers, the result is a complex number.

4   From Example 4e, notice that the product of $7 + 3i$ and $7 - 3i$ is a real number. These two complex numbers are called **complex conjugates** of one another. In general, we have the following definition.

Complex Conjugates

The complex numbers $(a + bi)$ and $(a - bi)$ are called **complex conjugates** of each other, and $(a + bi)(a - bi) = a^2 + b^2$.

To see that the product of a complex number $a + bi$ and its conjugate $a - bi$ is the real number $a^2 + b^2$ we multiply.

$$(a + bi)(a - bi) = a^2 - abi + abi - b^2i^2$$

$$= a^2 - b^2(-1)$$

$$= a^2 + b^2$$

We use complex conjugates to divide by a complex number.

EXAMPLE 5

Divide. Write in the form $a + bi$.

a. $\dfrac{2 + i}{1 - i}$ **b.** $\dfrac{7}{3i}$

Solution   **a.** Multiply the numerator and denominator by the complex conjugate of $1 - i$ to eliminate the imaginary number in the denominator.

$$\frac{2 + i}{1 - i} = \frac{(2 + i)(1 + i)}{(1 - i)(1 + i)}$$

$$= \frac{2(1) + 2(i) + 1(i) + i^2}{1^2 - i^2}$$

$$= \frac{2 + 3i - 1}{1 + 1} \qquad \text{Here, } i^2 = -1.$$

$$= \frac{1 + 3i}{2} \quad \text{or} \quad \frac{1}{2} + \frac{3}{2}i$$

> **Helpful Hint**
>
> Recall that division can be checked by multiplication.
>
> To check that $\dfrac{2 + i}{1 - i} = \dfrac{1}{2} + \dfrac{3}{2}i$, in Example 5a, multiply $\left(\dfrac{1}{2} + \dfrac{3}{2}i\right)(1 - i)$ to verify that the product is $2 + i$.

b. Multiply the numerator and denominator by the conjugate of $3i$. Note that $3i = 0 + 3i$, so its conjugate is $0 - 3i$ or $-3i$.

$$\frac{7}{3i} = \frac{7(-3i)}{(3i)(-3i)} = \frac{-21i}{-9i^2} = \frac{-21i}{-9(-1)} = \frac{-21i}{9} = \frac{-7i}{3} \quad \text{or} \quad 0 - \frac{7}{3}i$$

5 We can use the fact that $i^2 = -1$ to find higher powers of i. To find i^3, we rewrite it as the product of i^2 and i.

$$i^3 = i^2 \cdot i = (-1)i = -i$$
$$i^4 = i^2 \cdot i^2 = (-1) \cdot (-1) = 1$$

We continue this process and use the fact that $i^4 = 1$ and $i^2 = -1$ to simplify i^5 and i^6.

$$i^5 = i^4 \cdot i = 1 \cdot i = i$$
$$i^6 = i^4 \cdot i^2 = 1 \cdot (-1) = -1$$

If we continue finding powers of i, we generate the following pattern. Notice that the values i, -1, $-i$, and 1 repeat as i is raised to higher and higher powers.

$$
\begin{array}{lll}
i^1 = i & i^5 = i & i^9 = i \\
i^2 = -1 & i^6 = -1 & i^{10} = -1 \\
i^3 = -i & i^7 = -i & i^{11} = -i \\
i^4 = 1 & i^8 = 1 & i^{12} = 1
\end{array}
$$

This pattern allows us to find other powers of i. To do so, we will use the fact that $i^4 = 1$ and rewrite a power of i in terms of i^4.

For example, $i^{22} = i^{20} \cdot i^2 = (i^4)^5 \cdot i^2 = 1^5 \cdot (-1) = 1 \cdot (-1) = -1$.

EXAMPLE 6

Find the following powers of i.

a. i^7 **b.** i^{20} **c.** i^{46} **d.** i^{-12}

Solution   **a.** $i^7 = i^4 \cdot i^3 = 1(-i) = -i$

b. $i^{20} = (i^4)^5 = 1^5 = 1$

c. $i^{46} = i^{44} \cdot i^2 = (i^4)^{11} \cdot i^2 = 1^{11}(-1) = -1$

d. $i^{-12} = \dfrac{1}{i^{12}} = \dfrac{1}{(i^4)^3} = \dfrac{1}{(1)^3} = \dfrac{1}{1} = 1$

MENTAL MATH

Simplify. See Example 1.

 **1.** $\sqrt{-81}$ **2.** $\sqrt{-49}$ **3.** $\sqrt{-7}$ **4.** $\sqrt{-3}$

5. $-\sqrt{16}$ **6.** $-\sqrt{4}$ **7.** $\sqrt{-64}$ **8.** $\sqrt{-100}$

EXERCISE SET 7.7

    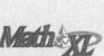

STUDY   CD/   PH MATH   MathXL®Tutorials   MathXL®   MyMathLab®
GUIDE/SSM   VIDEO   TUTOR CENTER   ON CD

Write in terms of i. See Example 1.

1. $\sqrt{-24}$ **2.** $\sqrt{-32}$

3. $-\sqrt{-36}$ **4.** $-\sqrt{-121}$

5. $8\sqrt{-63}$ **6.** $4\sqrt{-20}$

7. $-\sqrt{54}$ **8.** $\sqrt{-63}$

Multiply or divide. See Example 2.

9. $\sqrt{-2}\cdot\sqrt{-7}$ **10.** $\sqrt{-11}\cdot\sqrt{-3}$

11. $\sqrt{-5}\cdot\sqrt{-10}$ **12.** $\sqrt{-2}\cdot\sqrt{-6}$

13. $\sqrt{16}\cdot\sqrt{-1}$ **14.** $\sqrt{3}\cdot\sqrt{-27}$

15. $\dfrac{\sqrt{-9}}{\sqrt{3}}$ **16.** $\dfrac{\sqrt{49}}{\sqrt{-10}}$

17. $\dfrac{\sqrt{-80}}{\sqrt{-10}}$ **18.** $\dfrac{\sqrt{-40}}{\sqrt{-8}}$

Add or subtract. Write the sum or difference in the form a + bi. See Example 3.

19. $(4 - 7i) + (2 + 3i)$ **20.** $(2 - 4i) - (2 - i)$

21. $(6 + 5i) - (8 - i)$ **22.** $(8 - 3i) + (-8 + 3i)$

23. $6 - (8 + 4i)$

24. $(9 - 4i) - 9$

Multiply. Write the product in the form a + bi. See Example 4.

25. $6i(2 - 3i)$ **26.** $5i(4 - 7i)$

27. $(\sqrt{3} + 2i)(\sqrt{3} - 2i)$ **28.** $(\sqrt{5} - 5i)(\sqrt{5} + 5i)$

29. $(4 - 2i)^2$ **30.** $(6 - 3i)^2$

Write each quotient in the form a + bi. See Example 5.

31. $\dfrac{4}{i}$ **32.** $\dfrac{5}{6i}$

33. $\dfrac{7}{4 + 3i}$ **34.** $\dfrac{9}{1 - 2i}$

35. $\dfrac{3 + 5i}{1 + i}$ **36.** $\dfrac{6 + 2i}{4 - 3i}$

37. $\dfrac{5 - i}{3 - 2i}$ **38.** $\dfrac{6 - i}{2 + i}$

MIXED PRACTICE

Perform the indicated operation. Write the result in the form a + bi.

39. $(7i)(-9i)$ **40.** $(-6i)(-4i)$

41. $(6 - 3i) - (4 - 2i)$ **42.** $(-2 - 4i) - (6 - 8i)$

43. $(6 - 2i)(3 + i)$ **44.** $(2 - 4i)(2 - i)$

45. $(8 - 3i) + (2 + 3i)$

46. $(7 + 4i) + (4 - 4i)$

47. $(1 - i)(1 + i)$ **48.** $(6 + 2i)(6 - 2i)$

49. $\dfrac{16 + 15i}{-3i}$ **50.** $\dfrac{2 - 3i}{-7i}$

51. $(9 + 8i)^2$ **52.** $(4 - 7i)^2$

53. $\dfrac{2}{3 + i}$ **54.** $\dfrac{5}{3 - 2i}$

55. $(5 - 6i) - 4i$ **56.** $(6 - 2i) + 7i$

57. $\dfrac{2 - 3i}{2 + i}$ **58.** $\dfrac{6 + 5i}{6 - 5i}$

59. $(2 + 4i) + (6 - 5i)$ **60.** $(5 - 3i) + (7 - 8i)$

Find each power of i. See Example 6.

61. i^8 **62.** i^{10}

63. i^{21} **64.** i^{15}

65. i^{11} **66.** i^{40}

67. i^{-6} **68.** i^{-9}

69. $(2i)^6$ **70.** $(5i)^4$

71. $(-3i)^5$ **72.** $(-2i)^7$

REVIEW AND PREVIEW

Recall that the sum of the measures of the angles of a triangle is 180°. Find the unknown angle in each triangle. See Section 4.3.

 73.

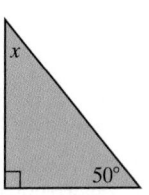

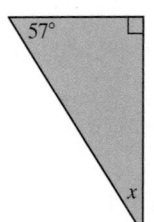 **74.**

Use synthetic division to divide the following. See Section 6.5.

75. $(x^3 - 6x^2 + 3x - 4) \div (x - 1)$

76. $(5x^4 - 3x^2 + 2) \div (x + 2)$

Thirty people were recently polled about their average monthly balance in their checking accounts. The results of this poll are shown in the following histogram. Use this graph to answer Exercises 77 through 82. See Section 1.2.

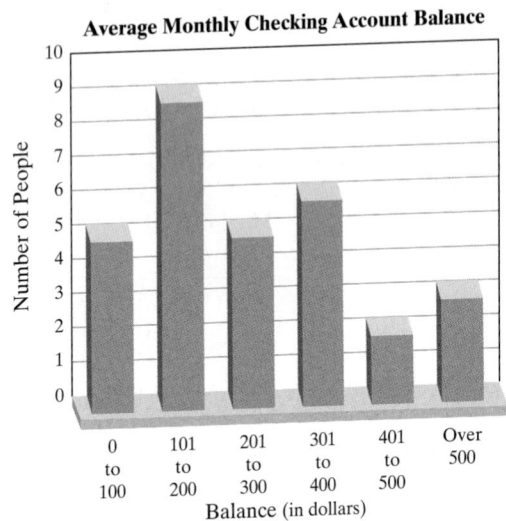

Average Monthly Checking Account Balance

80. How many people polled reported an average checking balance of $301 or more?

81. What percent of people polled reported an average checking balance of $201 to $300?

82. What percent of people polled reported an average checking balance of $0 to $100?

Concept Extensions

Write in the form $a + bi$.

83. $i^3 + i^4$

84. $i^8 - i^7$

85. $i^6 + i^8$

86. $i^4 + i^{12}$

87. $2 + \sqrt{-9}$

88. $5 - \sqrt{-16}$

89. $\dfrac{6 + \sqrt{-18}}{3}$

90. $\dfrac{4 - \sqrt{-8}}{2}$

91. $\dfrac{5 - \sqrt{-75}}{10}$

92. Describe how to find the conjugate of a complex number

93. Explain why the product of a complex number and its complex conjugate is a real number.

77. How many people polled reported an average checking balance of $201 to $300?

78. How many people polled reported an average checking balance of $0 to $100?

79. How many people polled reported an average checking balance of $200 or less?

Simplify.

94. $\left(8 - \sqrt{-3}\right) - \left(2 + \sqrt{-12}\right)$

95. $\left(8 - \sqrt{-4}\right) - \left(2 + \sqrt{-16}\right)$

96. Determine whether $2i$ is a solution of $x^2 + 4 = 0$.

97. Determine whether $-1 + i$ is a solution of $x^2 + 2x = -2$.

CHAPTER 7 PROJECT

Calculating the Length and Period of a Pendulum

Materials:

- string (at least 1 meter long)
- weight
- meter stick
- stopwatch
- calculator

This activity may be completed by working in groups or individually. Make a simple pendulum by securely tying the string to a weight.

The formula relating a pendulum's period T (in seconds) to its length l (in centimeters) is

$$T = 2\pi\sqrt{\frac{l}{980}}$$

The **period** of a pendulum is defined as the time it takes the pendulum to complete one full back-and-forth swing. In this activity, you will be measuring your simple pendulum's period with a stopwatch. Because the periods will be only a few seconds long, it will be more accurate for you to time a total of five complete swings and then find the average time of one complete swing.

1. For each of the pendulum (string) lengths given in Table 1, measure the time required for 5 complete swings and record it in the appropriate column. Next, divide this value by 5 to find the measured period of the pendulum for the given length and record it in the Measured Period T_m column in the table. Use the given formula to calculate the theoretical period T for the same pendulum length and record it in the appropriate column. (Round to two decimal places.) Find and record in the last column the difference between the measured period and the theoretical period.

2. For each of the periods T given in Table 2, use the given formula and calculate the theoretical pendulum length l required

to yield the given period. Record l in the appropriate column; round to one decimal place. Next, use this length l and measure and record the time for 5 complete swings. Divide this value by 5 to find the measured period T_m, and record it. Then find and record in the last column the difference between the theoretical period and the measured period.

3. Use the general trends you find in the tables to describe the relationship between a pendulum's period and its length.

4. Discuss the differences you found between the values of the theoretical period and the measured period. What factors contributed to these differences?

Table 1

Length l (centimeters)	Time for 5 Swings (seconds)	Measured Period T_m (seconds)	Theoretical Period T (seconds)	Difference $\|T - T_m\|$
30				
55				
70				

Table 2

Period T (seconds)	Theoretical Length l (centimeters)	Time for 5 Swings (seconds)	Measured Period T_m (seconds)	Difference $\|T - T_m\|$
1				
1.25				
2				

STUDY SKILLS REMINDER

Are You Preparing for a Test on Chapter 7?

Below I have listed some common trouble areas for students in Chapter 7. After studying for your test, but before taking your test, read these.

▶ Remember how to convert an expression with rational expressions to one with radicals and one with radicals to one with rational expressions.

$$7^{2/3} = \sqrt[3]{7^2} \text{ or } \left(\sqrt[3]{7}\right)^2$$
$$\sqrt[5]{4^3} = 4^{3/5}$$

▶ Remember the difference between $\sqrt{x} + \sqrt{x}$ and $\sqrt{x} \cdot \sqrt{x}, x > 0$.

$$\sqrt{x} + \sqrt{x} = 2\sqrt{x}$$
$$\sqrt{x} \cdot \sqrt{x} = x$$

▶ Don't forget the difference between rationalizing the denominator of $\sqrt{\dfrac{2}{x}}$ and rationalizing the denominator of

$$\dfrac{\sqrt{2}}{\sqrt{x} + 1}, x > 0.$$

$$\sqrt{\dfrac{2}{x}} = \dfrac{\sqrt{2}}{\sqrt{x}} = \dfrac{\sqrt{2} \cdot \sqrt{x}}{\sqrt{x} \cdot \sqrt{x}} = \dfrac{\sqrt{2x}}{x}$$

$$\dfrac{\sqrt{2}}{\sqrt{x} + 1} = \dfrac{\sqrt{2}\left(\sqrt{x} - 1\right)}{\left(\sqrt{x} + 1\right)\left(\sqrt{x} - 1\right)} = \dfrac{\sqrt{2}\left(\sqrt{x} - 1\right)}{x - 1}$$

Remember: This is simply a checklist of common trouble areas. For a review of Chapter 7, see the Highlights and Chapter Review at the end of this chapter.

CHAPTER VOCABULARY CHECK

Fill in each blank with one of the words or phrases listed below.

index	rationalizing	conjugate	principal square root	cube root
complex number	like radicals	radicand	imaginary unit	

1. The _____ of $\sqrt{3} + 2$ is $\sqrt{3} - 2$.

2. The _____ of a nonnegative number a is written as $\sqrt{a}$.

3. The process of writing a radical expression as an equivalent expression but without a radical in the denominator is called _____ the denominator.

4. The _____, written i, is the number whose square is -1.

5. The _____ of a number is written as $\sqrt[3]{a}$.

6. In the notation $\sqrt[n]{a}$, n is called the _____ and a is called the _____ .

7. Radicals with the same index and the same radicand are called _____ .

8. A _____ is a number that can be written in the form $a + bi$ where a and b are real numbers.

CHAPTER 7 HIGHLIGHTS

Definitions and Concepts	**Examples**

Section 7.1 Radicals and Radical Functions

The **positive**, or **principal**, **square root** of a nonnegative number a is written as $\sqrt{a}$.

$$\sqrt{a} = b \text{ only if } b^2 = a \text{ and } b \geq 0$$

The **negative square root of** a is written as $-\sqrt{a}$.

The **cube root** of a real number a is written as $\sqrt[3]{a}$.

$$\sqrt[3]{a} = b \text{ only if } b^3 = a$$

If n is an even positive integer, then $\sqrt[n]{a^n} = |a|$.

If n is an odd positive integer, then $\sqrt[n]{a^n} = a$.

A **radical function** in x is a function defined by an expression containing a root of x.

Examples:

$$\sqrt{36} = 6 \qquad \sqrt{\frac{9}{100}} = \frac{3}{10}$$

$$-\sqrt{36} = -6 \qquad \sqrt{0.04} = 0.2$$

$$\sqrt[3]{27} = 3 \qquad \sqrt[9]{-\frac{1}{8}} = -\frac{1}{2}$$

$$\sqrt[3]{y^6} = y^2 \qquad \sqrt[3]{64x^9} = 4x^3$$

$$\sqrt{(-3)^2} = |-3| = 3$$

$$\sqrt[3]{(-7)^3} = -7$$

If $\quad f(x) = \sqrt{x} + 2$,

$$f(1) = \sqrt{(1)} + 2 = 1 + 2 = 3$$

$$f(3) = \sqrt{(3)} + 2 \approx 3.73$$

Section 7.2 Rational Exponents

$a^{1/n} = \sqrt[n]{a}$ if $\sqrt[n]{a}$ is a real number.

If m and n are positive integers greater than 1 with $\dfrac{m}{n}$ in lowest terms and $\sqrt[n]{a}$ is a real number, then

$$a^{m/n} = (a^{1/n})^m = \left(\sqrt[n]{a}\right)^m$$

$a^{-m/n} = \dfrac{1}{a^{m/n}}$ as long as $a^{m/n}$ is a nonzero number.

Exponent rules are true for rational exponents.

Examples:

$$81^{1/2} = \sqrt{81} = 9$$

$$(-8x^3)^{1/3} = \sqrt[3]{-8x^3} = -2x$$

$$4^{5/2} = \left(\sqrt{4}\right)^5 = 2^5 = 32$$

$$27^{2/3} = \left(\sqrt[3]{27}\right)^2 = 3^2 = 9$$

$$16^{-3/4} = \frac{1}{16^{3/4}} = \frac{1}{\left(\sqrt[4]{16}\right)^3} = \frac{1}{2^3} = \frac{1}{8}$$

$$x^{2/3} \cdot x^{-5/6} = x^{2/3-5/6} = x^{-1/6} = \frac{1}{x^{1/6}}$$

$$(8^4)^{1/2} = 8^2 = 64$$

$$\frac{a^{4/5}}{a^{-2/5}} = a^{4/5-(-2/5)} = a^{6/5}$$

(continued)

Definitions and Concepts	**Examples**

Section 7.3 Simplifying Radical Expressions

Product and Quotient Rules

If $\sqrt[n]{a}$ and $\sqrt[n]{b}$ are real numbers,

$$\sqrt[n]{a} \cdot \sqrt[n]{b} = \sqrt[n]{a \cdot b}$$

$$\frac{\sqrt[n]{a}}{\sqrt[n]{b}} = \sqrt[n]{\frac{a}{b}}, \text{ provided } \sqrt[n]{b} \neq 0$$

A radical of the form $\sqrt[n]{a}$ is **simplified** when a contains no factors that are perfect nth powers.

Multiply or divide as indicated:

$$\sqrt{11} \cdot \sqrt{3} = \sqrt{33}$$

$$\frac{\sqrt[3]{40x}}{\sqrt[3]{5x}} = \sqrt[3]{8} = 2$$

$$\sqrt{40} = \sqrt{4 \cdot 10} = 2\sqrt{10}$$

$$\sqrt{36x^5} = \sqrt{36x^4 \cdot x} = 6x^2\sqrt{x}$$

$$\sqrt[3]{24x^7y^3} = \sqrt[3]{8x^6y^3 \cdot 3x} = 2x^2y\sqrt[3]{3x}$$

$$\sqrt{36x^4 \cdot x} = 6x^2\sqrt{x}$$

Section 7.4 Adding, Subtracting, and Multiplying Radical Expressions

Radicals with the same index and the same radicand are **like radicals**.

The distributive property can be used to add like radicals.

Radical expressions are multiplied by using many of the same properties used to multiply polynomials.

$$5\sqrt{6} + 2\sqrt{6} = (5 + 2)\sqrt{6} = 7\sqrt{6}$$
$$= \sqrt[3]{3x} - 10\sqrt[3]{3x} + 3\sqrt[3]{10x}$$
$$= (-1 - 10)\sqrt[3]{3x} + 3\sqrt[3]{10x}$$
$$= -11\sqrt[3]{3x} + 3\sqrt[3]{10x}$$

Multiply.

$$\left(\sqrt{5} - \sqrt{2x}\right)\left(\sqrt{2} + \sqrt{2x}\right)$$
$$= \sqrt{10} + \sqrt{10x} - \sqrt{4x} - 2x$$
$$= \sqrt{10} + \sqrt{10x} - 2\sqrt{x} - 2x$$
$$\left(2\sqrt{3} - \sqrt{8x}\right)\left(2\sqrt{3} + \sqrt{8x}\right)$$
$$= 4(3) - 8x = 12 - 8x$$

Section 7.5 Rationalizing Denominators and Numerators of Radical Expressions

The **conjugate** of $a + b$ is $a - b$.

The process of writing the denominator of a radical expression without a radical is called **rationalizing the denominator**.

The conjugate of $\sqrt{7} + \sqrt{3}$ is $\sqrt{7} - \sqrt{3}$

Rationalize each denominator.

$$\frac{\sqrt{5}}{\sqrt{3}} = \frac{\sqrt{5} \cdot \sqrt{3}}{\sqrt{3} \cdot \sqrt{3}} = \frac{\sqrt{15}}{3}$$

$$\frac{6}{\sqrt{7} + \sqrt{3}} = \frac{6(\sqrt{7} - \sqrt{3})}{(\sqrt{7} + \sqrt{3})(\sqrt{7} - \sqrt{3})}$$

$$= \frac{6(\sqrt{7} - \sqrt{3})}{7 - 3}$$

$$= \frac{6(\sqrt{7} - \sqrt{3})}{4} = \frac{3(\sqrt{7} - \sqrt{3})}{2}$$

(continued)

Definitions and Concepts	**Examples**

Section 7.5 Rationalizing Denominators and Numerators of Radical Expressions

The process of writing the numerator of a radical expression without a radical is called **rationalizing the numerator.**

Rationalize each numerator.

$$\frac{\sqrt[3]{9}}{\sqrt[3]{5}} = \frac{\sqrt[3]{9} \cdot \sqrt[3]{3}}{\sqrt[3]{5} \cdot \sqrt[3]{3}} = \frac{\sqrt[3]{27}}{\sqrt[3]{15}} = \frac{3}{\sqrt[3]{15}}$$

$$\frac{\sqrt{9} + \sqrt{3x}}{12} = \frac{\left(\sqrt{9} + \sqrt{3x}\right)\left(\sqrt{9} - \sqrt{3x}\right)}{12\left(\sqrt{9} - \sqrt{3x}\right)}$$

$$= \frac{9 - 3x}{12\left(\sqrt{9} - \sqrt{3x}\right)}$$

$$= \frac{3(3 - x)}{3 \cdot 4\left(3 - \sqrt{3x}\right)} = \frac{3 - x}{4\left(3 - \sqrt{3x}\right)}$$

Section 7.6 Radical Equations and Problem Solving

To Solve a Radical Equation

Step 1: Write the equation so that one radical is by itself on one side of the equation.

Step 2: Raise each side of the equation to a power equal to the index of the radical and simplify.

Step 3: If the equation still contains a radical, repeat Steps 1 and 2. If not, solve the equation.

Step 4: Check all proposed solutions in the original equation.

Solve $x = \sqrt{4x + 9} + 3$.

1. $x - 3 = \sqrt{4x + 9}$

2. $(x - 3)^2 = \left(\sqrt{4x + 9}\right)^2$
$x^2 - 6x + 9 = 4x + 9$

3. $x^2 - 10x = 0$
$x(x - 10) = 0$
$x = 0 \quad \text{or} \quad x = 10$

4. The proposed solution 10 checks, but 0 does not. The solution is 10.

Section 7.7 Complex Numbers

$$i^2 = -1 \text{ and } i = \sqrt{-1}$$

A **complex number** is a number that can be written in the form $a + bi$, where a and b are real numbers.

Simplify $\sqrt{-9}$.

$$\sqrt{-9} = \sqrt{-1 \cdot 9} = \sqrt{-1} \cdot \sqrt{9} = i \cdot 3 \text{ or } 3i$$

Complex Numbers	*Written in form $a + bi$*
12	$12 + 0i$
$-5i$	$0 + (-5)i$
$-2 - 3i$	$-2 + (-3)i$

Multiply,

$$\sqrt{-3} \cdot \sqrt{-7} = i\sqrt{3} \cdot i\sqrt{7}$$

$$= i^2\sqrt{21}$$

$$= -\sqrt{21}$$

(continued)

Definitions and Concepts	**Examples**

Section 7.7 Complex Numbers

To add or subtract complex numbers, add or subtract their real parts and then add or subtract their imaginary parts.

Perform each indicated operation.

$$(-3 + 2i) - (7 - 4i) = -3 + 2i - 7 + 4i$$
$$= -10 + 6i$$

To multiply complex numbers, multiply as though they are binomials.

$$(-7 - 2i)(6 + i) = -42 - 7i - 12i - 2i^2$$
$$= -42 - 19i - 2(-1)$$
$$= -42 - 19i + 2$$
$$= -40 - 19i$$

The complex numbers $(a + bi)$ and $(a - bi)$ are called **complex conjugates.**

The complex conjugate of
$$(3 + 6i) \text{ is } (3 - 6i).$$
Their product is a real number.
$$(3 - 6i)(3 + 6i) = 9 - 36i^2$$
$$= 9 - 36(-1) = 9 + 36 = 45$$

To divide complex numbers, multiply the numerator and the denominator by the conjugate of the denominator.

Divide.

$$\frac{4}{2 - i} = \frac{4(2 + i)}{(2 - i)(2 + i)}$$
$$= \frac{4(2 + i)}{4 - i^2}$$
$$= \frac{4(2 + i)}{5}$$
$$= \frac{8 + 4i}{5} = \frac{8}{5} + \frac{4}{5}i$$

CHAPTER REVIEW

(7.1) Find the root. Assume that all variables represent positive numbers.

1. $\sqrt{81}$

2. $\sqrt[4]{81}$

3. $\sqrt[3]{-8}$

4. $\sqrt[4]{-16}$

5. $-\sqrt{\dfrac{1}{49}}$

6. $\sqrt{x^{64}}$

7. $-\sqrt{36}$

8. $\sqrt[3]{64}$

9. $\sqrt[3]{-a^6 b^9}$

10. $\sqrt{16a^4 b^{12}}$

11. $\sqrt[5]{32a^5 b^{10}}$

12. $\sqrt[5]{-32x^{15}y^{20}}$

13. $\sqrt{\dfrac{x^{12}}{36y^2}}$

14. $\sqrt[3]{\dfrac{27y^3}{z^{12}}}$

Simplify. Use absolute value bars when necessary.

15. $\sqrt{(-x)^2}$

16. $\sqrt[4]{(x^2 - 4)^4}$

17. $\sqrt[3]{(-27)^3}$

18. $\sqrt[5]{(-5)^5}$

19. $-\sqrt[5]{x^5}$

20. $\sqrt[4]{16(2y + z)^{12}}$

21. $\sqrt{25(x - y)^{10}}$

22. $\sqrt[5]{-y^5}$

23. $\sqrt[9]{-x^9}$

Identify the domain and then graph each function.

24. $f(x) = \sqrt{x} + 3$

25. $g(x) = \sqrt[3]{x} - 3$; use the accompanying table.

x	-5	2	3	4	11
$g(x)$					

(7.2) *Evaluate the following.*

26. $\left(\dfrac{1}{81}\right)^{1/4}$

27. $\left(-\dfrac{1}{27}\right)^{1/3}$

28. $(-27)^{-1/3}$

29. $(-64)^{-1/3}$

30. $-9^{3/2}$

31. $64^{-1/3}$

32. $(-25)^{5/2}$

33. $\left(\dfrac{25}{49}\right)^{-3/2}$

34. $\left(\dfrac{8}{27}\right)^{-2/3}$

35. $\left(-\dfrac{1}{36}\right)^{-1/4}$

Write with rational exponents.

36. $\sqrt[3]{x^2}$

37. $\sqrt[5]{5x^2y^3}$

Write with radical notation.

38. $y^{4/5}$

39. $5(xy^2z^5)^{1/3}$

40. $(x + 2y)^{-1/2}$

Simplify each expression. Assume that all variables represent positive numbers. Write with only positive exponents.

41. $a^{1/3}a^{4/3}a^{1/2}$

42. $\dfrac{b^{1/3}}{b^{4/3}}$

43. $(a^{1/2}a^{-2})^3$

44. $(x^{-3}y^6)^{1/3}$

45. $\left(\dfrac{b^{3/4}}{a^{-1/2}}\right)^8$

46. $\dfrac{x^{1/4}x^{-1/2}}{x^{2/3}}$

47. $\left(\dfrac{49c^{5/3}}{a^{-1/4}b^{5/6}}\right)^{-1}$

48. $a^{-1/4}(a^{5/4} - a^{9/4})$

Use a calculator and write a three-decimal-place approximation.

49. $\sqrt{20}$

50. $\sqrt[3]{-39}$

51. $\sqrt[4]{726}$

52. $56^{1/3}$

53. $-78^{3/4}$

54. $105^{-2/3}$

Use rational exponents to write each radical with the same index. Then multiply.

55. $\sqrt[3]{2} \cdot \sqrt{7}$

56. $\sqrt[3]{3} \cdot \sqrt[4]{x}$

(7.3) *Perform the indicated operations and then simplify if possible. For the remainder of this review, assume that variables represent positive numbers only.*

57. $\sqrt{3} \cdot \sqrt{8}$

58. $\sqrt[3]{7y} \cdot \sqrt[3]{x^2z}$

59. $\dfrac{\sqrt{44x^3}}{\sqrt{11x}}$

60. $\dfrac{\sqrt[4]{a^6b^{13}}}{\sqrt[4]{a^2b}}$

Simplify.

61. $\sqrt{60}$

62. $-\sqrt{75}$

63. $\sqrt[3]{162}$

64. $\sqrt[3]{-32}$

65. $\sqrt{36x^7}$

66. $\sqrt[3]{24a^5b^7}$

67. $\sqrt{\dfrac{p^{17}}{121}}$

68. $\sqrt[3]{\dfrac{y^5}{27x^6}}$

69. $\sqrt[4]{\dfrac{xy^6}{81}}$

70. $\sqrt{\dfrac{2x^3}{49y^4}}$

△ **71.** The formula for the radius r of a circle of area A is

$$r = \sqrt{\dfrac{A}{\pi}}$$

a. Find the exact radius of a circle whose area is 25 square meters.

b. Approximate to two decimal places the radius of a circle whose area is 104 square inches.

(7.4) *Perform the indicated operation.*

72. $x\sqrt{75xy} - \sqrt{27x^3y}$

73. $2\sqrt{32x^2y^3} - xy\sqrt{98y}$

74. $\sqrt[3]{128} + \sqrt[3]{250}$

75. $3\sqrt[4]{32a^5} - a\sqrt[4]{162a}$

76. $\dfrac{5}{\sqrt{4}} + \dfrac{\sqrt{3}}{3}$

77. $\sqrt{\dfrac{8}{x^2}} - \sqrt{\dfrac{50}{16x^2}}$

78. $2\sqrt{50} - 3\sqrt{125} + \sqrt{98}$

79. $2a\sqrt[4]{32b^5} - 3b\sqrt[4]{162a^4b} + \sqrt[4]{2a^4b^5}$

Multiply and then simplify if possible.

80. $\sqrt{3}(\sqrt{27} - \sqrt{3})$

81. $(\sqrt{x} - 3)^2$

82. $(\sqrt{5} - 5)(2\sqrt{5} + 2)$

83. $(2\sqrt{x} - 3\sqrt{y})(2\sqrt{x} + 3\sqrt{y})$

84. $(\sqrt{a} + 3)(\sqrt{a} - 3)$

85. $(\sqrt[3]{a} + 2)^2$

86. $(\sqrt[3]{5x} + 9)(\sqrt[3]{5x} - 9)$

87. $(\sqrt[3]{a} + 4)(\sqrt[3]{a^2} - 4\sqrt[3]{a} + 16)$

(7.5) *Rationalize each denominator.*

88. $\dfrac{3}{\sqrt{7}}$

89. $\sqrt{\dfrac{x}{12}}$

90. $\dfrac{5}{\sqrt[3]{4}}$

91. $\sqrt{\dfrac{24x^5}{3y^2}}$

92. $\sqrt[3]{\dfrac{15x^6y^7}{z^2}}$

93. $\dfrac{5}{2 - \sqrt{7}}$

94. $\dfrac{3}{\sqrt{y} - 2}$

95. $\dfrac{\sqrt{2} - \sqrt{3}}{\sqrt{2} + \sqrt{3}}$

Rationalize each numerator.

96. $\dfrac{\sqrt{11}}{3}$

97. $\sqrt{\dfrac{18}{y}}$

98. $\dfrac{\sqrt[3]{9}}{7}$

99. $\sqrt{\dfrac{24x^5}{3y^2}}$

100. $\sqrt[3]{\dfrac{xy^2}{10z}}$

101. $\dfrac{\sqrt{x}+5}{-3}$

(7.6) *Solve each equation for the variable.*

102. $\sqrt{y-7}=5$

103. $\sqrt{2x}+10=4$

104. $\sqrt[3]{2x-6}=4$

105. $\sqrt{x+6}=\sqrt{x+2}$

106. $2x-5\sqrt{x}=3$

107. $\sqrt{x+9}=2+\sqrt{x-7}$

Find each unknown length.

 108.

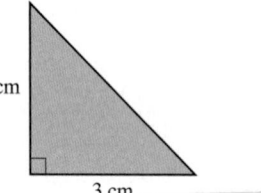

3 cm

3 cm

 **109.**

7 ft

$8\sqrt{3}$ ft

110. Beverly Hillis wants to determine the distance x across a pond on her property. She is able to measure the distances shown on the following diagram. Find how wide the lake is at the crossing point, indicated by the triangle, to the nearest tenth of a foot.

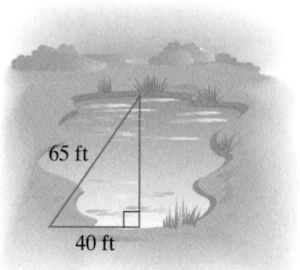

65 ft

40 ft

△ **111.** A pipe fitter needs to connect two underground pipelines that are offset by 3 feet, as pictured in the diagram. Neglecting the joints needed to join the pipes, find the length of the shortest possible connecting pipe rounded to the nearest hundredth of a foot.

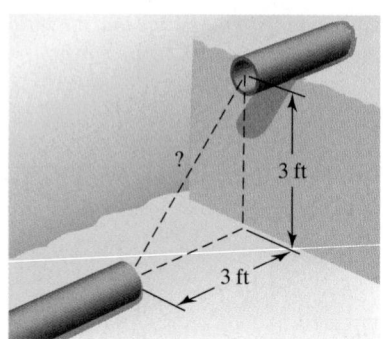

?

3 ft

3 ft

(7.7) *Perform the indicated operation and simplify. Write the result in the form $a+bi$.*

112. $\sqrt{-8}$

113. $-\sqrt{-6}$

114. $\sqrt{-4}+\sqrt{-16}$

115. $\sqrt{-2}\cdot\sqrt{-5}$

116. $(12-6i)+(3+2i)$

117. $(-8-7i)-(5-4i)$

118. $\left(\sqrt{3}+\sqrt{2}\right)+\left(3\sqrt{2}-\sqrt{-8}\right)$

119. $2i(2-5i)$

120. $-3i(6-4i)$

121. $(3+2i)(1+i)$

122. $(2-3i)^2$

123. $\left(\sqrt{6}-9i\right)\left(\sqrt{6}+9i\right)$

124. $\dfrac{2+3i}{2i}$

125. $\dfrac{1+i}{-3i}$

CHAPTER 7 TEST

Remember to use your Chapter Test Prep Video CD to help you study and view solutions to the test questions you need help with.

Raise to the power or find the root. Assume that all variables represent positive numbers. Write with only positive exponents.

1. $\sqrt{216}$

2. $-\sqrt[4]{x^{64}}$

3. $\left(\dfrac{1}{125}\right)^{1/3}$

4. $\left(\dfrac{1}{125}\right)^{-1/3}$

5. $\left(\dfrac{8x^3}{27}\right)^{2/3}$

6. $\sqrt[3]{-a^{18}b^9}$

7. $\left(\dfrac{64c^{4/3}}{a^{-2/3}b^{5/6}}\right)^{1/2}$

8. $a^{-2/3}(a^{5/4} - a^3)$

Find the root. Use absolute value bars when necessary.

9. $\sqrt[4]{(4xy)^4}$

10. $\sqrt[3]{(-27)^3}$

Rationalize the denominator. Assume that all variables represent positive numbers.

11. $\sqrt{\dfrac{9}{y}}$

12. $\dfrac{4 - \sqrt{x}}{4 + 2\sqrt{x}}$

13. $\dfrac{\sqrt[3]{ab}}{\sqrt[3]{ab^2}}$

14. Rationalize the numerator of $\dfrac{\sqrt{6} + x}{8}$ and simplify.

Perform the indicated operations. Assume that all variables represent positive numbers.

15. $\sqrt{125x^3} - 3\sqrt{20x^3}$

16. $\sqrt{3}(\sqrt{16} - \sqrt{2})$

17. $(\sqrt{x} + 1)^2$

18. $(\sqrt{2} - 4)(\sqrt{3} + 1)$

19. $(\sqrt{5} + 5)(\sqrt{5} - 5)$

Use a calculator to approximate each to three decimal places.

20. $\sqrt{561}$

21. $386^{-2/3}$

Solve.

22. $x = \sqrt{x - 2} + 2$

23. $\sqrt{x^2 - 7} + 3 = 0$

24. $\sqrt[3]{x + 5} = \sqrt[3]{2x - 1}$

Perform the indicated operation and simplify. Write the result in the form $a + bi$.

25. $\sqrt{-2}$

26. $-\sqrt{-8}$

27. $(12 - 6i) - (12 - 3i)$

28. $(6 - 2i)(6 + 2i)$

29. $(4 + 3i)^2$

30. $\dfrac{1 + 4i}{1 - i}$

△ **31.** Find x.

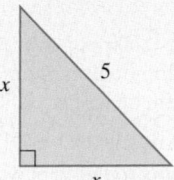

32. Identify the domain of $g(x)$. Then complete the accompanying table and graph $g(x)$.

$$g(x) = \sqrt{x + 2}$$

x	-2	-1	2	7
$g(x)$				

Solve.

33. The function $V(r) = \sqrt{2.5r}$ can be used to estimate the maximum safe velocity V in miles per hour at which a car can travel if it is driven along a curved road with a *radius of curvature r* in feet. To the nearest whole number, find the maximum safe speed if a cloverleaf exit on an expressway has a radius of curvature of 300 feet.

34. Use the formula from Exercise 33 to find the radius of curvature if the safe velocity is 30 mph.

CHAPTER CUMULATIVE REVIEW

1. Simplify each expression.

   a. $3xy - 2xy + 5 - 7 + xy$

   b. $7x^2 + 3 - 5(x^2 - 4)$

   c. $(2.1x - 5.6) - (-x - 5.3)$

   d. $\frac{1}{2}(4a - 6b) - \frac{1}{3}(9a + 12b - 1) + \frac{1}{4}$

2. Simplify each expression.

   a. $2(x - 3) + (5x + 3)$

   b. $4(3x + 2) - 3(5x - 1)$

   c. $7x + 2(x - 7) - 3x$

3. Solve for x: $\dfrac{x + 5}{2} + \dfrac{1}{2} = 2x - \dfrac{x - 3}{8}$

4. Solve $\dfrac{a - 1}{2} + a = 2 - \dfrac{2a + 7}{8}$

5. A salesperson earns $600 per month plus a commission of 20% of sales. Find the minimum amount of sales needed to receive a total income of at least $1500 per month.

6. The Smith family owns a lake house 121.5 miles from home. If it takes them $4\frac{1}{2}$ hours round-trip to drive from their house to their lake house, find their average speed.

7. Solve: $2|x| + 25 = 23$

8. Solve: $|3x - 2| + 5 = 5$

9. Solve: $\left|\dfrac{x}{3} - 1\right| - 7 \geq -5$

10. Solve: $\left|\dfrac{x}{2} - 1\right| \leq 0$.

11. Graph the equation $y = |x|$.

12. Graph $y = |x - 2|$.

13. Determine the domain and range of each relation.

    a. $\{(2, 3), (2, 4), (0, -1), (3, -1)\}$

    b.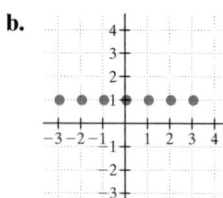

    c.   Input: Output:

    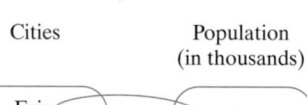

    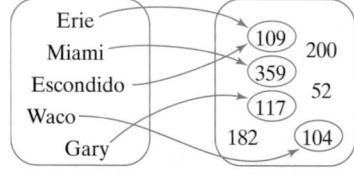

14. Find the domain and the range of each relation. Use the vertical line test to determine whether each graph is the graph of a function.

    a.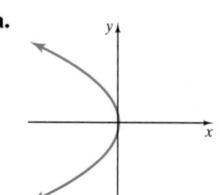

    b.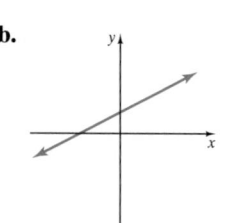

    c.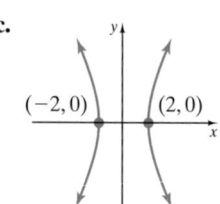

15. Graph $y = -3$.

16. Graph $f(x) = -2$.

17. Find the slope of the line $x = -5$.

18. Find the slope of $y = -3$.

19. Use the substitution method to solve the system.

$$\begin{cases} -\dfrac{x}{6} + \dfrac{y}{2} = \dfrac{1}{2} \\ \dfrac{x}{3} - \dfrac{y}{6} = -\dfrac{3}{4} \end{cases}$$

20. Use the substitution method to solve the system.

$$\begin{cases} \dfrac{x}{6} - \dfrac{y}{2} = 1 \\ \dfrac{x}{3} - \dfrac{y}{4} = 2 \end{cases}$$

21. Use the product rule to simplify.

    a. $2^2 \cdot 2^5$

    b. $x^7 x^3$

    c. $y \cdot y^2 \cdot y^4$

22. At a seasonal clearance sale, Nana Long spent $33.75. She paid $3.50 for tee-shirts and $4.25 for shorts. If she bought items, how many of each item did she buy?

23. Use scientific notation to simplify $\dfrac{2000 \times 0.000021}{700}$.

24. Use scientific notation to simplify and write the answer in scientific notation. $\dfrac{0.0000035 \times 4000}{0.28}$

25. If $P(x) = 3x^2 - 2x - 5$, find the following.

  a. $P(1)$

  b. $P(-2)$

26. Subtract $(2x - 5)$ from the sum of $(5x^2 - 3x + 6)$ and $(4x^2 + 5x - 3)$.

27. Multiply and simplify the product if possible.

  a. $(x + 3)(2x + 5)$

  b. $(2x - 3)(5x^2 - 6x + 7)$

28. Multiply and simplify the product if possible.

  a. $(y - 2)(3y + 4)$

  b. $(3y - 1)(2y^2 + 3y - 1)$

29. Find the GCF of $20x^3y$, $10x^2y^2$, and $35x^3$.

30. Factor $x^3 - x^2 + 4x - 4$

31. Simplify each rational expression.

  a. $\dfrac{x^3 + 8}{2 + x}$

  b. $\dfrac{2y^2 + 2}{y^3 - 5y^2 + y - 5}$

32. Simplify each rational expression.

  a. $\dfrac{a^3 - 8}{2 - a}$

  b. $\dfrac{3a^2 - 3}{a^3 + 5a^2 - a - 5}$

33. Perform the indicated operation.

  a. $\dfrac{2}{x^2y} + \dfrac{5}{3x^3y}$

  b. $\dfrac{3x}{x + 2} + \dfrac{2x}{x - 2}$

  c. $\dfrac{x}{x - 1} - \dfrac{4}{1 - x}$

34. Perform the indicated operations.

  a. $\dfrac{3}{xy^2} - \dfrac{2}{3x^2y}$

  b. $\dfrac{5x}{x + 3} - \dfrac{2x}{x - 3}$

  c. $\dfrac{x}{x - 2} - \dfrac{5}{2 - x}$

35. Simplify each complex fraction.

  a. $\dfrac{\dfrac{5x}{x + 2}}{\dfrac{10}{x - 2}}$

  b. $\dfrac{\dfrac{x}{y^2} + \dfrac{1}{y}}{\dfrac{y}{x^2} + \dfrac{1}{x}}$

36. Simplify each complex fraction.

  a. $\dfrac{\dfrac{y - 2}{16}}{\dfrac{2y + 3}{12}}$

  b. $\dfrac{\dfrac{x}{16} - \dfrac{1}{x}}{1 - \dfrac{4}{x}}$

37. Divide $10x^3 - 5x^2 + 20x$ by $5x$.

38. Divide $x^3 - 2x^2 + 3x - 6$ by $x - 2$.

39. Use synthetic division to divide $2x^3 - x^2 - 13x + 1$ by $x - 3$.

40. Use synthetic division to divide $4y^3 - 12y^2 - y + 12$ by $y - 3$.

41. Solve: $\dfrac{x + 6}{x - 2} = \dfrac{2(x + 2)}{x - 2}$

42. Solve: $\dfrac{28}{9 - a^2} = \dfrac{2a}{a - 3} + \dfrac{6}{a + 3}$

43. Solve $\dfrac{1}{x} + \dfrac{1}{y} = \dfrac{1}{z}$ for x.

44. Solve $A = \dfrac{h(a + b)}{2}$ for a.

45. Suppose that u varies inversely as w. If u is 3 when w is 5, find the constant of variation and the inverse variation equation.

46. Suppose that y varies directly as x. If $y = 0.51$ when $x = 3$, find the constant of variation and the direct variation equation.

47. Write each expression with a positive exponent, and then simplify.

  a. $16^{-3/4}$

  b. $(-27)^{-2/3}$

48. Write each expression with a positive exponent, and then simplify.

   a. $(81)^{-3/4}$

   b. $(-125)^{-2/3}$

49. Rationalize the numerator of $\dfrac{\sqrt{x}+2}{5}$.

50. Add or subtract.

   a. $\sqrt{36a^3} - \sqrt{144a^3} + \sqrt{4a^3}$

   b. $\sqrt[3]{128ab^3} - 3\sqrt[3]{2ab^3} + b\sqrt[3]{16a}$

   c. $\dfrac{\sqrt[3]{81}}{10} + \sqrt[3]{\dfrac{192}{125}}$

Add 1 to both sides of the original equation.

$$p^2 + 2p = 4$$

$$p^2 + 2p + 1 = 4 + 1 \qquad \text{Add 1 to both sides.}$$

$$(p + 1)^2 = 5 \qquad \text{Factor the trinomial; simplify the right side.}$$

We may now use the square root property and solve for p.

$$p + 1 = \pm\sqrt{5} \qquad \text{Use the square root property.}$$

$$p = -1 \pm \sqrt{5} \qquad \text{Subtract 1 from both sides.}$$

Notice that there are two solutions: $-1 + \sqrt{5}$ and $-1 - \sqrt{5}$.

EXAMPLE 6

Solve $m^2 - 7m - 1 = 0$ for m by completing the square.

Solution First, add 1 to both sides of the equation so that the left side has no constant term.

$$m^2 - 7m - 1 = 0$$

$$m^2 - 7m = 1$$

Now find the constant term that makes the left side a perfect square trinomial by squaring half the coefficient of m. Add this constant to both sides of the equation.

$$\frac{1}{2}(-7) = -\frac{7}{2} \quad \text{and} \quad \left(-\frac{7}{2}\right)^2 = \frac{49}{4}$$

$$m^2 - 7m + \frac{49}{4} = 1 + \frac{49}{4} \qquad \text{Add } \frac{49}{4} \text{ to both sides of the equation.}$$

$$\left(m - \frac{7}{2}\right)^2 = \frac{53}{4} \qquad \text{Factor the perfect square trinomial and simplify the right side.}$$

$$m - \frac{7}{2} = \pm\sqrt{\frac{53}{4}} \qquad \text{Apply the square root property.}$$

$$m = \frac{7}{2} \pm \frac{\sqrt{53}}{2} \qquad \text{Add } \frac{7}{2} \text{ to both sides and simplify } \sqrt{\frac{53}{4}}.$$

$$m = \frac{7 \pm \sqrt{53}}{2} \qquad \text{Simplify.}$$

The solutions are $\dfrac{7 + \sqrt{53}}{2}$ and $\dfrac{7 - \sqrt{53}}{2}$.

EXAMPLE 7

Solve $2x^2 - 8x + 3 = 0$.

Solution   Our procedure for finding the constant term to complete the square works only if the coefficient of the squared variable term is 1. Therefore, to solve this equation, the first step is to divide both sides by 2, the coefficient of x^2.

$$2x^2 - 8x + 3 = 0$$

$$x^2 - 4x + \frac{3}{2} = 0 \qquad \text{Divide both sides by 2.}$$

$$x^2 - 4x = -\frac{3}{2} \qquad \text{Subtract } \frac{3}{2} \text{ from both sides.}$$

Next find the square of half of -4.

$$\frac{1}{2}(-4) = -2 \quad \text{and} \quad (-2)^2 = 4$$

Add 4 to both sides of the equation to complete the square.

$$x^2 - 4x + 4 = -\frac{3}{2} + 4$$

$$(x - 2)^2 = \frac{5}{2} \qquad \text{Factor the perfect square and simplify the right side.}$$

$$x - 2 = \pm\sqrt{\frac{5}{2}} \qquad \text{Apply the square root property.}$$

$$x - 2 = \pm\frac{\sqrt{10}}{2} \qquad \text{Rationalize the denominator.}$$

$$x = 2 \pm \frac{\sqrt{10}}{2} \qquad \text{Add 2 to both sides.}$$

$$= \frac{4}{2} \pm \frac{\sqrt{10}}{2} \qquad \text{Find the common denominator.}$$

$$= \frac{4 \pm \sqrt{10}}{2} \qquad \text{Simplify.}$$

The solutions are $\dfrac{4 + \sqrt{10}}{2}$ and $\dfrac{4 - \sqrt{10}}{2}$.

The following steps may be used to solve a quadratic equation such as $ax^2 + bx + c = 0$ by completing the square. This method may be used whether or not the polynomial $ax^2 + bx + c$ is factorable.

> **Solving a Quadratic Equation in x By Completing the Square**
>
> **Step 1:** If the coefficient of x^2 is 1, go to Step 2. Otherwise, divide both sides of the equation by the coefficient of x^2.
>
> **Step 2:** Isolate all variable terms on one side of the equation.
>
> **Step 3:** Complete the square for the resulting binomial by adding the square of half of the coefficient of x to both sides of the equation.
>
> **Step 4:** Factor the resulting perfect square trinomial and write it as the square of a binomial.
>
> **Step 5:** Use the square root property to solve for x.

EXAMPLE 8

Solve $3x^2 - 9x + 8 = 0$ by completing the square.

Solution $3x^2 - 9x + 8 = 0$

Step 1: $x^2 - 3x + \dfrac{8}{3} = 0$ Divide both sides of the equation by 3.

Step 2: $x^2 - 3x = -\dfrac{8}{3}$ Subtract $\dfrac{8}{3}$ from both sides.

Since $\dfrac{1}{2}(-3) = -\dfrac{3}{2}$ and $\left(-\dfrac{3}{2}\right)^2 = \dfrac{9}{4}$, we add $\dfrac{9}{4}$ to both sides of the equation.

Step 3: $x^2 - 3x + \dfrac{9}{4} = -\dfrac{8}{3} + \dfrac{9}{4}$

Step 4: $\left(x - \dfrac{3}{2}\right)^2 = -\dfrac{5}{12}$ Factor the perfect square trinomial.

Step 5: $x - \dfrac{3}{2} = \pm\sqrt{-\dfrac{5}{12}}$ Apply the square root property.

$\qquad x - \dfrac{3}{2} = \pm\dfrac{i\sqrt{5}}{2\sqrt{3}}$ Simplify the radical.

$\qquad x - \dfrac{3}{2} = \pm\dfrac{i\sqrt{15}}{6}$ Rationalize the denominator.

$\qquad x = \dfrac{3}{2} \pm \dfrac{i\sqrt{15}}{6}$ Add $\dfrac{3}{2}$ to both sides.

$\qquad = \dfrac{9}{6} \pm \dfrac{i\sqrt{15}}{6}$ Find a common denominator.

$\qquad = \dfrac{9 \pm i\sqrt{15}}{6}$ Simplify.

The solutions are $\dfrac{9 + i\sqrt{15}}{6}$ and $\dfrac{9 - i\sqrt{15}}{6}$.

3   Recall the **simple interest** formula $I = Prt$, where I is the interest earned, P the principal, r is the rate of interest, and t is time. If $100 is invested at a simple interest rate of 5% annually, at the end of 3 years the total interest I earned is

$$I = P \cdot r \cdot t$$

or

$$I = 100 \cdot 0.05 \cdot 3 = \$15$$

and the new principal is

$$\$100 + \$15 = \$115$$

Most of the time, the interest computed on money borrowed or money deposited **compound interest.** Compound interest, unlike simple interest, is computed on origina principal *and* on interest already earned. To see the difference between simple interest an compound interest, suppose that $100 is invested at a rate of 5% compounded annually. T find the total amount of money at the end of 3 years, we calculate as follows.

$$I = P \cdot r \cdot t$$

First year: Interest $= \$100 \cdot 0.05 \cdot 1 = \$5.00$
              New principal $= \$100.00 + \$5.00 = \$105.00$
Second year: Interest $= \$105.00 \cdot 0.05 \cdot 1 = \$5.25$
              New principal $= \$105.00 + \$5.25 = \$110.25$
Third year: Interest $= \$110.25 \cdot 0.05 \cdot 1 \approx \$5.51$
              New principal $= \$110.25 + \$5.51 = \$115.76$

At the end of the third year, the total compound interest earned is $15.76, whereas th total simple interest earned is $15.

It is tedious to calculate compound interest as we did above, so we use a com pound interest formula. The formula for calculating the total amount of money whe interest is compounded annually is

$$A = P(1 + r)^t$$

where P is the original investment, r is the interest rate per compounding period, and is the number of periods. For example, the amount of money A at the end of 3 years $100 is invested at 5% compounded annually is

$$A = \$100(1 + 0.05)^3 \approx \$100(1.1576) = \$115.76$$

as we previously calculated.

EXAMPLE 9

FINDING INTEREST RATES

Find the interest rate r if $2000 compounded annually grows to $2420 in 2 years.

Solution   **1.** UNDERSTAND the problem. Since the $2000 is compounded annually, we use th compound interest formula. For this example, make sure that you understand th formula for compounding interest annually.

2. TRANSLATE. We substitute the given values into the formula.

$$A = P(1 + r)^t$$

$$2420 = 2000(1 + r)^2 \qquad \text{Let } A = 2420, P = 2000, \text{ and } t = 2.$$

3. SOLVE. Solve the equation for r.

$$2420 = 2000(1 + r)^2$$

$$\frac{2420}{2000} = (1 + r)^2 \qquad \text{Divide both sides by } 2000.$$

$$\frac{121}{100} = (1 + r)^2 \qquad \text{Simplify the fraction.}$$

$$\pm\sqrt{\frac{121}{100}} = 1 + r \qquad \text{Use the square root property.}$$

$$\pm\frac{11}{10} = 1 + r \qquad \text{Simplify.}$$

$$-1 \pm \frac{11}{10} = r$$

$$-\frac{10}{10} \pm \frac{11}{10} = r$$

$$\frac{1}{10} = r \quad \text{or} \quad -\frac{21}{10} = r$$

4. INTERPRET. The rate cannot be negative, so we reject $-\dfrac{21}{10}$.

Check: $\dfrac{1}{10} = 0.10 = 10\%$ per year. If we invest \$2000 at 10% compounded annually, in 2 years the amount in the account would be $2000(1 + 0.10)^2 = 2420$ dollars, the desired amount.

State: The interest rate is 10% compounded annually.

Graphing Calculator Explorations

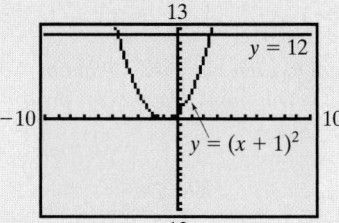

In Section 5.8, we showed how we can use a grapher to approximate real number solutions of a quadratic equation written in standard form. We can also use a grapher to solve a quadratic equation when it is not written in standard form. For example, to solve $(x + 1)^2 = 12$, the quadratic equation in Example 3, we graph the following on the same set of axes. Use $\text{Xmin} = -10$, $\text{Xmax} = 10$, $\text{Ymin} = -13$, and $\text{Ymax} = 13$.

$$Y_1 = (x + 1)^2 \quad \text{and} \quad Y_2 = 12$$

Use the Intersect feature or the Zoom and Trace features to locate the points of intersection of the graphs. (See your manuals for specific instructions.) The x-values of these points are the solutions of $(x + 1)^2 = 12$. The solutions, rounded to two decimal places, are 2.46 and -4.46.

Check to see that these numbers are approximations of the exact solutions $-1 \pm 2\sqrt{3}$.

(continued)

Use a graphing calculator to solve each quadratic equation. Round all solutions to the nearest hundredth.

1. $x(x - 5) = 8$

2. $x(x + 2) = 5$

3. $x^2 + 0.5x = 0.3x + 1$

4. $x^2 - 2.6x = -2.2x + 3$

5. Use a grapher and solve $(2x - 5)^2 = -16$, Example 4 in this section, using the window

$$\text{Xmin} = -20$$
$$\text{Xmax} = 20$$
$$\text{Xscl} = 1$$
$$\text{Ymin} = -20$$
$$\text{Ymax} = 20$$
$$\text{Yscl} = 1$$

Explain the results. Compare your results with the solution found in Example 4.

6. What are the advantages and disadvantages of using a grapher to solve quadratic equations?

EXERCISE SET 8.1

STUDY GUIDE/SSM | CD/ VIDEO | PH MATH TUTOR CENTER | MathXL®Tutorials ON CD | MathXL® | MyMathLab®

Use the square root property to solve each equation. These equations have real-number solutions. See Examples 1 through 3.

 1. $x^2 = 16$

2. $x^2 = 49$

3. $x^2 - 7 = 0$

4. $x^2 - 11 = 0$

5. $x^2 = 18$

6. $y^2 = 20$

7. $3z^2 - 30 = 0$

8. $2x^2 = 4$

9. $(x + 5)^2 = 9$

10. $(y - 3)^2 = 4$

11. $(z - 6)^2 = 18$

12. $(y + 4)^2 = 27$

13. $(2x - 3)^2 = 8$

14. $(4x + 9)^2 = 6$

Use the square root property to solve each equation. See Examples 1 through 4.

15. $x^2 + 9 = 0$

16. $x^2 + 4 = 0$

17. $x^2 - 6 = 0$

18. $y^2 - 10 = 0$

19. $2z^2 + 16 = 0$

20. $3p^2 + 36 = 0$

21. $(x - 1)^2 = -16$

22. $(y + 2)^2 = -25$

23. $(z + 7)^2 = 5$

24. $(x + 10)^2 = 11$

25. $(x + 3)^2 = -8$

26. $(y - 4)^2 = -18$

Add the proper constant to each binomial so that the resulting trinomial is a perfect square trinomial. Then factor the trinomial.

27. $x^2 + 16x +$ _____

28. $y^2 + 2y +$ _____

29. $z^2 - 12z +$ _____

30. $x^2 - 8x +$ _____

31. $p^2 + 9p +$ _____

32. $n^2 + 5n +$ _____

33. $x^2 + x +$ _____

34. $y^2 - y +$ _____

MIXED PRACTICE

Solve each equation by completing the square. These equations have real number solutions. See Examples 5 through 7.

35. $x^2 + 8x = -15$

36. $y^2 + 6y = -8$

37. $x^2 + 6x + 2 = 0$

38. $x^2 - 2x - 2 = 0$

39. $x^2 + x - 1 = 0$

40. $x^2 + 3x - 2 = 0$

41. $x^2 + 2x - 5 = 0$

42. $y^2 + y - 7 = 0$

43. $3p^2 - 12p + 2 = 0$

44. $2x^2 + 14x - 1 = 0$

45. $4y^2 - 12y - 2 = 0$

46. $6x^2 - 3 = 6x$

47. $2x^2 + 7x = 4$

48. $3x^2 - 4x = 4$

49. $x^2 - 4x - 5 = 0$

50. $y^2 + 6y - 8 = 0$

51. $x^2 + 8x + 1 = 0$

52. $x^2 - 10x + 2 = 0$

53. $3y^2 + 6y - 4 = 0$

54. $2y^2 + 12y + 3 = 0$

55. $2x^2 - 3x - 5 = 0$

56. $5x^2 + 3x - 2 = 0$

Solve each equation by completing the square. See Examples 5 through 8.

57. $y^2 + 2y + 2 = 0$

58. $x^2 + 4x + 6 = 0$

59. $x^2 - 6x + 3 = 0$

60. $x^2 - 7x - 1 = 0$

61. $2a^2 + 8a = -12$

62. $3x^2 + 12x = -14$

63. $5x^2 + 15x - 1 = 0$

64. $16y^2 + 16y - 1 = 0$

65. $2x^2 - x + 6 = 0$

66. $4x^2 - 2x + 5 = 0$

67. $x^2 + 10x + 28 = 0$

68. $y^2 + 8y + 18 = 0$

69. $z^2 + 3z - 4 = 0$

70. $y^2 + y - 2 = 0$

71. $2x^2 - 4x + 3 = 0$

72. $9x^2 - 36x = -40$

73. $3x^2 + 3x = 5$

74. $5y^2 - 15y = 1$

Use the formula $A = P(1 + r)^t$ to solve Exercises 75–78. See Example 9.

75. Find the rate r at which $3000 grows to $4320 in 2 years.

76. Find the rate r at which $800 grows to $882 in 2 years.

77. Find the rate at which $810 grows to $1000 in 2 years.

78. Find the rate at which $2000 grows to $2880 in 2 years.

79. In your own words, what is the difference between simple interest and compound interest?

80. If you are depositing money in an account that pays 4%, would you prefer the interest to be simple or compound? Explain why.

81. If you are borrowing money at a rate of 10%, would you prefer the interest to be simple or compound? Explain why.

REVIEW AND PREVIEW

Simplify each expression. See Section 7.1.

82. $\dfrac{3}{4} - \sqrt{\dfrac{25}{16}}$

83. $\dfrac{3}{5} + \sqrt{\dfrac{16}{25}}$

84. $\dfrac{1}{2} - \sqrt{\dfrac{9}{4}}$

85. $\dfrac{9}{10} - \sqrt{\dfrac{49}{100}}$

Simplify each expression. See Section 7.5.

86. $\dfrac{6 + 4\sqrt{5}}{2}$

87. $\dfrac{10 - 20\sqrt{3}}{2}$

88. $\dfrac{3 - 9\sqrt{5}}{6}$

89. $\dfrac{12 - 8\sqrt{7}}{16}$

Evaluate $\sqrt{b^2 - 4ac}$ for each set of values. See Section 7.3.

90. $a = 2, b = 4, c = -1$

91. $a = 1, b = 6, c = 2$

92. $a = 3, b = -1, c = -2$

93. $a = 1, b = -3, c = -1$

Concept Extensions

Find two possible missing terms so that each is a perfect square trinomial.

94. $x^2 + \quad + 16$

95. $y^2 + \quad + 9$

96. $z^2 + \quad + \dfrac{25}{4}$

97. $x^2 + \quad + \dfrac{1}{4}$

Neglecting air resistance, the distance $s(t)$ in feet traveled by a freely falling object is given by the function $s(t) = 16t^2$, where t is time in seconds. Use this formula to solve Exercises 98 through 101. Round answers to two decimal places.

98. The Petronas Towers in Kuala Lumpur, built in 1997, are the tallest buildings in Malaysia. Each tower is 1483 feet tall. How long would it take an object to fall to the ground from the top of one of the towers? (*Source:* Council on Tall Buildings and Urban Habitat, Lehigh University)

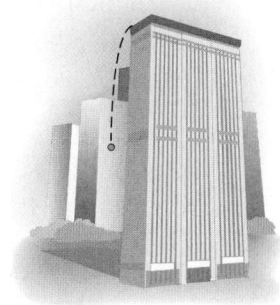

99. The height of the Chicago Beach Tower Hotel, built in 1998 in Dubai, United Arab Emirates, is 1053 feet. How long would it take an object to fall to the ground from the top of the building? (*Source:* Council on Tall Buildings and Urban Habitat, Lehigh University)

100. The height of the Nurek Dam in Tajikistan (part of the former USSR that borders Afghanistan) is 984 feet. How long would it take an object to fall from the top to the base of the dam? (*Source:* U.S. Committee on Large Dams of the International Commission on Large Dams)

101. The Hoover Dam, located on the Colorado River on the border of Nevada and Arizona near Las Vegas, is 725 feet tall. How long would it take an object to fall from the top to the base of the dam? (*Source:* U.S. Committee on Large Dams of the International Commission on Large Dams)

Solve.

△ **102.** The area of a square room is 225 square feet. Find the dimensions of the room.

△ **103.** The area of a circle is 36π square inches. Find the radius of the circle.

△ **104.** An isosceles right triangle has legs of equal length. If the hypotenuse is 20 centimeters long, find the length of each leg.

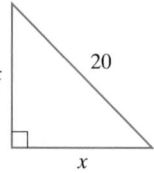

△ **105.** A 27-inch TV is advertised in the *Daily Sentry* newspaper. If 27 inches is the measure of the diagonal of the picture tube, find the measure of each side of the picture tube.

A common equation used in business is a demand equation. It expresses the relationship between the unit price of some commodity and the quantity demanded. For Exercises 106 and 107, p represents the unit price and x represents the quantity demanded in thousands.

106. A manufacturing company has found that the demand equation for a certain type of scissors is given by the equation $p = -x^2 + 47$. Find the demand for the scissors if the price is \$11 per pair.

107. Acme, Inc., sells desk lamps and has found that the demand equation for a certain style of desk lamp is given by the equation $p = -x^2 + 15$. Find the demand for the desk lamp if the price is \$7 per lamp.

8.2   **SOLVING QUADRATIC EQUATIONS BY THE QUADRATIC FORMULA**

Objectives

1   Solve quadratic equations by using the quadratic formula.

2   Determine the number and type of solutions of a quadratic equation by using the discriminant.

3   Solve geometric problems modeled by quadratic equations.

1   Any quadratic equation can be solved by completing the square. Since the same sequence of steps is repeated each time we complete the square, let's complete the square for a general quadratic equation, $ax^2 + bx + c = 0, a \neq 0$. By doing so, we find a pattern for the solutions of a quadratic equation known as the **quadratic formula.**

Recall that to complete the square for an equation such as $ax^2 + bx + c = 0$, we first divide both sides by the coefficient of x^2.

$$ax^2 + bx + c = 0$$

$$x^2 + \frac{b}{a}x + \frac{c}{a} = 0 \qquad \text{Divide both sides by } a, \text{ the coefficient of } x^2.$$

$$x^2 + \frac{b}{a}x = -\frac{c}{a} \qquad \text{Subtract the constant } \frac{c}{a} \text{ from both sides.}$$

Next, find the square of half $\frac{b}{a}$, the coefficient of x.

$$\frac{1}{2}\left(\frac{b}{a}\right) = \frac{b}{2a} \quad \text{and} \quad \left(\frac{b}{2a}\right)^2 = \frac{b^2}{4a^2}$$

Add this result to both sides of the equation.

$$x^2 + \frac{b}{a}x + \frac{b^2}{4a^2} = -\frac{c}{a} + \frac{b^2}{4a^2} \qquad \text{Add } \frac{b^2}{4a^2} \text{ to both sides.}$$

$$x^2 + \frac{b}{a}x + \frac{b^2}{4a^2} = \frac{-c \cdot 4a}{a \cdot 4a} + \frac{b^2}{4a^2} \qquad \text{Find a common denominator on the right side.}$$

$$x^2 + \frac{b}{a}x + \frac{b^2}{4a^2} = \frac{b^2 - 4ac}{4a^2} \qquad \text{Simplify the right side.}$$

$$\left(x + \frac{b}{2a}\right)^2 = \frac{b^2 - 4ac}{4a^2} \qquad \text{Factor the perfect square trinomial on the left side.}$$

$$x + \frac{b}{2a} = \pm\sqrt{\frac{b^2 - 4ac}{4a^2}} \qquad \text{Apply the square root property.}$$

$$x + \frac{b}{2a} = \pm\frac{\sqrt{b^2 - 4ac}}{2a} \qquad \text{Simplify the radical.}$$

$$x = -\frac{b}{2a} \pm \frac{\sqrt{b^2 - 4ac}}{2a} \qquad \text{Subtract } \frac{b}{2a} \text{ from both sides.}$$

$$x = \frac{-b \pm \sqrt{b^2 - 4ac}}{2a} \qquad \text{Simplify.}$$

This equation identifies the solutions of the general quadratic equation in standard form and is called the quadratic formula. It can be used to solve any equation written in standard form $ax^2 + bx + c = 0$ as long as a is not 0.

Quadratic Formula

A quadratic equation written in the form $ax^2 + bx + c = 0$ has the solutions

$$x = \frac{-b \pm \sqrt{b^2 - 4ac}}{2a}$$

EXAMPLE 1

Solve $3x^2 + 16x + 5 = 0$ for x.

Solution This equation is in standard form, so $a = 3$, $b = 16$, and $c = 5$. Substitute these values into the quadratic formula.

$$x = \frac{-b \pm \sqrt{b^2 - 4ac}}{2a} \qquad \text{Quadratic formula.}$$

$$= \frac{-16 \pm \sqrt{16^2 - 4(3)(5)}}{2 \cdot 3} \qquad \text{Use } a = 3, b = 16, \text{ and } c = 5.$$

$$= \frac{-16 \pm \sqrt{256 - 60}}{6}$$

$$= \frac{-16 \pm \sqrt{196}}{6} = \frac{-16 \pm 14}{6}$$

$$x = \frac{-16 + 14}{6} = -\frac{1}{3} \quad \text{or} \quad x = \frac{-16 - 14}{6} = -\frac{30}{6} = -5$$

The solutions are $-\dfrac{1}{3}$ and -5, or the solution set is $\{-\frac{1}{3}, -5\}$.

EXAMPLE 2

Solve $2x^2 - 4x = 3$.

Solution First write the equation in standard form by subtracting 3 from both sides.

$$2x^2 - 4x - 3 = 0$$

Helpful Hint

To replace a, b, and c correctly in the quadratic formula, write the quadratic equation in standard form $ax^2 + bx + c = 0$.

Now $a = 2$, $b = -4$, and $c = -3$. Substitute these values into the quadratic formula.

$$x = \frac{-b \pm \sqrt{b^2 - 4ac}}{2a}$$

$$= \frac{-(-4) \pm \sqrt{(-4)^2 - 4(2)(-3)}}{2 \cdot 2}$$

$$= \frac{4 \pm \sqrt{16 + 24}}{4}$$

$$= \frac{4 \pm \sqrt{40}}{4} = \frac{4 \pm 2\sqrt{10}}{4}$$

$$= \frac{2(2 \pm \sqrt{10})}{2 \cdot 2} = \frac{2 \pm \sqrt{10}}{2}$$

The solutions are $\dfrac{2 + \sqrt{10}}{2}$ and $\dfrac{2 - \sqrt{10}}{2}$, or the solution set is $\left\{ \dfrac{2 - \sqrt{10}}{2}, \dfrac{2 + \sqrt{10}}{2} \right\}$.

> **Helpful Hint**
>
> To simplify the expression $\dfrac{4 \pm 2\sqrt{10}}{4}$ in the preceding example, note that 2 is factored out of both terms of the numerator *before* simplifying.
>
> $$\frac{4 \pm 2\sqrt{10}}{4} = \frac{2(2 \pm \sqrt{10})}{2 \cdot 2} = \frac{2 \pm \sqrt{10}}{2}$$

✔ **CONCEPT CHECK**

For the quadratic equation $x^2 = 7$, which substitution is correct?

    a. $a = 1, b = 0$, and $c = -7$

    b. $a = 1, b = 0$, and $c = 7$

    c. $a = 0, b = 0$, and $c = 7$

    d. $a = 1, b = 1$, and $c = -7$

EXAMPLE 3

Solve $\dfrac{1}{4}m^2 - m + \dfrac{1}{2} = 0$.

Solution We could use the quadratic formula with $a = \dfrac{1}{4}, b = -1$, and $c = \dfrac{1}{2}$. Instead, we find a simpler, equivalent standard form equation whose coefficients are not fractions.

Multiply both sides of the equation by 4 to clear fractions.

$$4\left(\frac{1}{4}m^2 - m + \frac{1}{2} \right) = 4 \cdot 0$$

$$m^2 - 4m + 2 = 0 \qquad \text{Simplify.}$$

Substitute $a = 1, b = -4$, and $c = 2$ into the quadratic formula and simplify.

$$m = \frac{-(-4) \pm \sqrt{(-4)^2 - 4(1)(2)}}{2 \cdot 1} = \frac{4 \pm \sqrt{16 - 8}}{2}$$

$$= \frac{4 \pm \sqrt{8}}{2} = \frac{4 \pm 2\sqrt{2}}{2} = \frac{2(2 \pm \sqrt{2})}{2}$$

$$= 2 \pm \sqrt{2}$$

Concept Check Answer:

a

The solutions are $2 + \sqrt{2}$ and $2 - \sqrt{2}$.

EXAMPLE 4

Solve $x = -3x^2 - 3$.

Solution The equation in standard form is $3x^2 + x + 3 = 0$. Thus, let $a = 3, b = 1$, and $c = 3$ in the quadratic formula.

$$x = \frac{-1 \pm \sqrt{1^2 - 4(3)(3)}}{2 \cdot 3} = \frac{-1 \pm \sqrt{1 - 36}}{6} = \frac{-1 \pm \sqrt{-35}}{6} = \frac{-1 \pm i\sqrt{35}}{6}$$

The solutions are $\dfrac{-1 + i\sqrt{35}}{6}$ and $\dfrac{-1 - i\sqrt{35}}{6}$.

✔ **CONCEPT CHECK**

What is the first step in solving $-3x^2 = 5x - 4$ using the quadratic formula?

In Example 1, the equation $3x^2 + 16x + 5 = 0$ had 2 real roots, $-\dfrac{1}{3}$ and -5. In Example 4, the equation $3x^2 + x + 3 = 0$ (written in standard form) had no real roots. How do their related graphs compare? Recall that the x-intercepts of $f(x) = 3x^2 + 16x + 5$ occur where $f(x) = 0$ or where $3x^2 + 16x + 5 = 0$. Since this equation has 2 real roots, the graph has 2 x-intercepts. Similarly, since the equation $3x^2 + x + 3 = 0$ has no real roots, the graph of $f(x) = 3x^2 + x + 3$ has no x-intercepts.

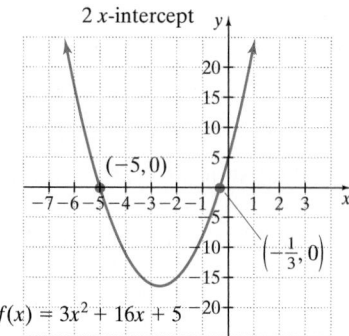

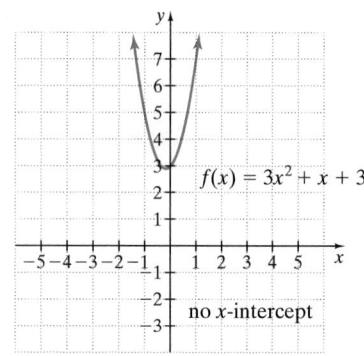

2 In the quadratic formula, $x = \dfrac{-b \pm \sqrt{b^2 - 4ac}}{2a}$, the radicand $b^2 - 4ac$ is called the **discriminant** because, by knowing its value, we can **discriminate** among the possible number and type of solutions of a quadratic equation. Possible values of the discriminant and their meanings are summarized next.

Discriminant

The following table corresponds the discriminant $b^2 - 4ac$ of a quadratic equation of the form $ax^2 + bx + c = 0$ with the number and type of solutions of the equation.

$b^2 - 4ac$	Number and Type of Solutions
Positive	Two real solutions
Zero	One real solution
Negative	Two complex but not real solutions

Concept Check Answer:
Write the equation in standard form.

EXAMPLE 5

Use the discriminant to determine the number and type of solutions of each quadratic equation.

a. $x^2 + 2x + 1 = 0$ **b.** $3x^2 + 2 = 0$ **c.** $2x^2 - 7x - 4 = 0$

Solution   **a.** In $x^2 + 2x + 1 = 0$, $a = 1$, $b = 2$, and $c = 1$. Thus,

$$b^2 - 4ac = 2^2 - 4(1)(1) = 0$$

Since $b^2 - 4ac = 0$, this quadratic equation has one real solution.

b. In this equation, $a = 3$, $b = 0$, $c = 2$. Then $b^2 - 4ac = 0 - 4(3)(2) = -24$. Since $b^2 - 4ac$ is negative, the quadratic equation has two complex but not real solutions.

c. In this equation, $a = 2$, $b = -7$, and $c = -4$. Then

$$b^2 - 4ac = (-7)^2 - 4(2)(-4) = 81$$

Since $b^2 - 4ac$ is positive, the quadratic equation has two real solutions.

The discriminant helps us determine the number and type of solutions of a quadratic equation, $ax^2 + bx + c = 0$. Recall that the solutions of this equation are the same as the x-intercepts of its related graph $f(x) = ax^2 + bx + c$. This means that the discriminant of $ax^2 + bx + c = 0$ also tells us the number of x-intercepts for the graph of $f(x) = ax^2 + bx + c$, or equivalently $y = ax^2 + bx + c$.

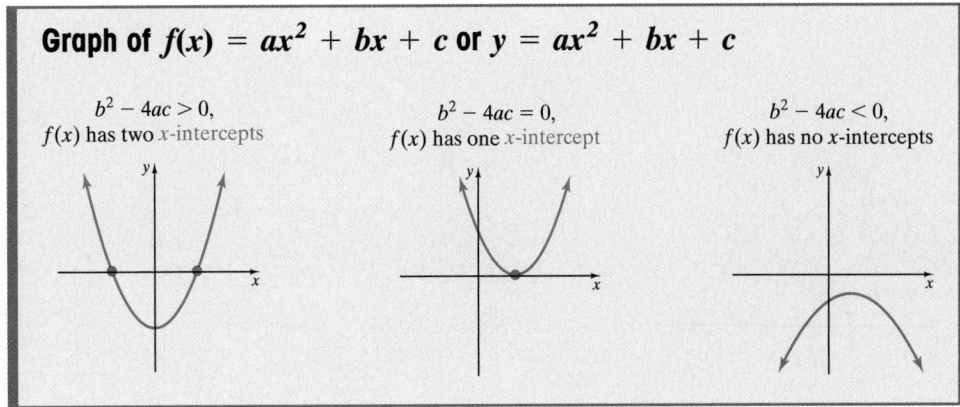

Graph of $f(x) = ax^2 + bx + c$ or $y = ax^2 + bx + c$

$b^2 - 4ac > 0$,
$f(x)$ has two x-intercepts

$b^2 - 4ac = 0$,
$f(x)$ has one x-intercept

$b^2 - 4ac < 0$,
$f(x)$ has no x-intercepts

3   The quadratic formula is useful in solving problems that are modeled by quadratic equations.

EXAMPLE 6

CALCULATING DISTANCE SAVED

At a local university, students often leave the sidewalk and cut across the lawn to save walking distance. Given the diagram below of a favorite place to cut across the lawn approximate how many feet of walking distance a student saves by cutting across the lawn instead of walking on the sidewalk.

Solution   1. UNDERSTAND. Read and reread the problem. In the diagram, notice that a triangle is formed. Since the corner of the block forms a right angle, we use the Pythagorean theorem for right triangles. You may want to review this theorem.

2. TRANSLATE. By the Pythagorean theorem, we have

In words: $(\text{leg})^2 + (\text{leg})^2 = (\text{hypotenuse})^2$

Translate: $x^2 + (x + 20)^2 = 50^2$

3. SOLVE. Use the quadratic formula to solve.

$$x^2 + x^2 + 40x + 400 = 2500 \qquad \text{Square } (x + 20) \text{ and } 50.$$

$$2x^2 + 40x - 2100 = 0 \qquad \text{Set the equation equal to } 0.$$

$$x^2 + 20x - 1050 = 0 \qquad \text{Divide by } 2.$$

Here, $a = 1, b = 20, c = -1050$. By the quadratic formula,

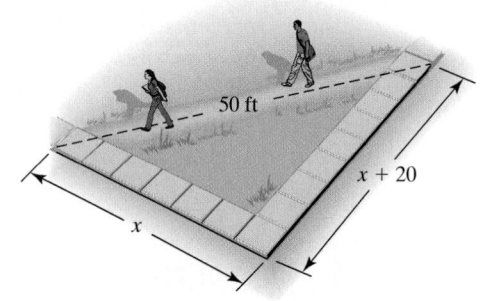

50 ft

$x + 20$

x

$$x = \frac{-20 \pm \sqrt{20^2 - 4(1)(-1050)}}{2 \cdot 1}$$

$$= \frac{-20 \pm \sqrt{400 + 4200}}{2} = \frac{-20 \pm \sqrt{4600}}{2}$$

$$= \frac{-20 \pm \sqrt{100 \cdot 46}}{2} = \frac{-20 \pm 10\sqrt{46}}{2}$$

$$= -10 \pm 5\sqrt{46} \qquad \text{Simplify.}$$

4. INTERPRET.

Check: Your calculations in the quadratic formula. The length of a side of a triangle can't be negative, so we reject $-10 - 5\sqrt{46}$. Since $-10 + 5\sqrt{46} \approx 24$ feet, the walking distance along the sidewalk is

$$x + (x + 20) \approx 24 + (24 + 20) = 68 \text{ feet.}$$

State: A student saves about $68 - 50$ or 18 feet of walking distance by cutting across the lawn.

EXAMPLE 7

CALCULATING LANDING TIME

An object is thrown upward from the top of a 200-foot cliff with a velocity of 12 feet per second. The height h in feet of the object after t seconds is

$$h = -16t^2 + 12t + 200$$

How long after the object is thrown will it strike the ground? Round to the nearest tenth of a second.

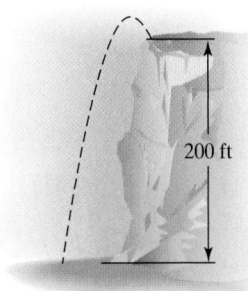

200 ft

Solution 1. UNDERSTAND. Read and reread the problem.

2. TRANSLATE. Since we want to know when the object strikes the ground, we want to know when the height $h = 0$, or

$$0 = -16t^2 + 12t + 200$$

3. SOLVE. First we divide both sides of the equation by -4.

$$0 = 4t^2 - 3t - 50 \qquad \text{Divide both sides by } -4.$$

Here, $a = 4$, $b = -3$, and $c = -50$. By the quadratic formula,

$$t = \frac{-(-3) \pm \sqrt{(-3)^2 - 4(4)(-50)}}{2 \cdot 4}$$

$$= \frac{3 \pm \sqrt{9 + 800}}{8}$$

$$= \frac{3 \pm \sqrt{809}}{8}$$

4. INTERPRET. **Check:** We check our calculations from the quadratic formula. Since the time won't be negative, we reject the proposed solution

$$\frac{3 - \sqrt{809}}{8}.$$

State: The time it takes for the object to strike the ground is exactly

$$\frac{3 + \sqrt{809}}{8} \text{ seconds} \approx 3.9 \text{ seconds.}$$

STUDY SKILLS REMINDER

Continue your outline started in Section 2.1. For this section, you only need to expand on your earlier section – **I.C.**– on solving quadratic equations. For example:

Solving Equations and Inequalities

I. Equations

   A. Linear equations (Sec. 2.1)

   B. Absolute value equations (Sec. 2.6)

   C. Quadratic and Higher Degree Equations—

   Solve: first write the equation in standard form (one side is 0.)

      1. If the polynomial on one side factors, solve by factoring.

      2. If the polynomial does not factor, solve by the quadratic formula.

   D. Equations with rational expressions (Sec. 6.6)

   E. Equations with radicals (Sec. 7.6)

II. Inequalities

   A. Linear inequalities (Sec. 2.4)

   B. Compound inequalities (Sec. 2.5)

   C. Absolute value inequalities (Sec. 2.7)

Spotlight on DECISION MAKING

Suppose you are a registered dietician. Recently, you read an article in a nutrition journal that described a relationship between weight and the Recommended Dietary Allowance (RDA) for vitamin A in children up to age 10. The relationship is $y = 0.149x^2 - 4.475x + 406.478$, where y is the RDA for vitamin A in micrograms for a child whose weight is x pounds. (*Source:* Food and Nutrition Board, National Academy of Sciences—Institute of Medicine, 1989)

You are working with a 4-year-old patient who weighs 40 pounds. After analyzing her diet, you are able to determine that she is currently getting an average of 400 micrograms of vitamin A daily. Decide whether her current vitamin A intake is adequate. If not, how much more is needed each day? In either case, determine how much weight she will need to gain before a daily intake of 500 micrograms of vitamin A is appropriate.

MENTAL MATH

Identify the values of a, b, and c in each quadratic equation.

1. $x^2 + 3x + 1 = 0$

2. $2x^2 - 5x - 7 = 0$

3. $7x^2 - 4 = 0$

4. $x^2 + 9 = 0$

5. $6x^2 - x = 0$

6. $5x^2 + 3x = 0$

EXERCISE SET 8.2

STUDY GUIDE/SSM   CD/VIDEO   PH MATH TUTOR CENTER   MathXL®Tutorials ON CD   MathXL®   MyMathLab®

Use the quadratic formula to solve each equation. These equations have real number solutions. See Examples 1 through 3.

1. $m^2 + 5m - 6 = 0$

2. $p^2 + 11p - 12 = 0$

3. $2y = 5y^2 - 3$

4. $5x^2 - 3 = 14x$

5. $x^2 - 6x + 9 = 0$

6. $y^2 + 10y + 25 = 0$

7. $x^2 + 7x + 4 = 0$

8. $y^2 + 5y + 3 = 0$

9. $8m^2 - 2m = 7$

10. $11n^2 - 9n = 1$

11. $3m^2 - 7m = 3$

12. $x^2 - 13 = 5x$

13. $\frac{1}{2}x^2 - x - 1 = 0$

14. $\frac{1}{6}x^2 + x + \frac{1}{3} = 0$

15. $\frac{2}{5}y^2 + \frac{1}{5}y = \frac{3}{5}$

16. $\frac{1}{8}x^2 + x = \frac{5}{2}$

17. $\frac{1}{3}y^2 - y - \frac{1}{6} = 0$

18. $\frac{1}{2}y^2 = y + \frac{1}{2}$

19. Solve Exercise 1 by factoring. Explain the result.

20. Solve Exercise 2 by factoring. Explain the result.

Use the quadratic formula to solve each equation. See Example 4.

21. $6 = -4x^2 + 3x$

22. $9x^2 + x + 2 = 0$

23. $(x + 5)(x - 1) = 2$

24. $x(x + 6) = 2$

25. $10y^2 + 10y + 3 = 0$

26. $3y^2 + 6y + 5 = 0$

The solutions of the quadratic equation $ax^2 + bx + c = 0$ are

$$\frac{-b + \sqrt{b^2 - 4ac}}{2a} \quad and \quad \frac{-b - \sqrt{b^2 - 4ac}}{2a}$$

Use the discriminant to determine the number and type of solutions of each equation. See Example 5.

27. $9x - 2x^2 + 5 = 0$

28. $5 - 4x + 12x^2 = 0$

29. $4x^2 + 12x = -9$

30. $9x^2 + 1 = 6x$

31. $3x = -2x^2 + 7$

32. $3x^2 = 5 - 7x$

33. $6 = 4x - 5x^2$

34. $8x = 3 - 9x^2$

MIXED PRACTICE

Use the quadratic formula to solve each equation. These equations have real number solutions.

35. $x^2 + 5x = -2$

36. $y^2 - 8 = 4y$

37. $(m + 2)(2m - 6) = 5(m - 1) - 12$

38. $7p(p - 2) + 2(p + 4) = 3$

39. $\frac{x^2}{3} - x = \frac{5}{3}$

40. $\frac{x^2}{2} - 3 = -\frac{9}{2}x$

41. $x(6x + 2) - 3 = 0$

42. $x(7x + 1) = 2$

Use the quadratic formula to solve each equation.

43. $x^2 + 6x + 13 = 0$

44. $x^2 + 2x + 2 = 0$

45. $\frac{2}{5}y^2 + \frac{1}{5}y + \frac{3}{5} = 0$

46. $\frac{1}{8}x^2 + x + \frac{5}{2} = 0$

47. $\frac{1}{2}y^2 = y - \frac{1}{2}$

48. $\frac{2}{3}x^2 - \frac{20}{3}x = -\frac{100}{6}$

49. $(n - 2)^2 = 15n$

50. $\left(p - \frac{1}{2}\right)^2 = \frac{p}{2}$

Solve. See Examples 6 and 7.

51. Nancy, Thelma, and John Varner live on a corner lot. Often, neighborhood children cut across their lot to save walking distance. Given the diagram below, approximate to the nearest foot how many feet of walking distance is saved by cutting across their property instead of walking around the lot.

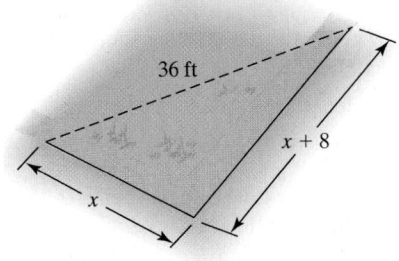

△ **52.** Given the diagram below, approximate to the nearest foot how many feet of walking distance a person saves by cutting across the lawn instead of walking on the sidewalk.

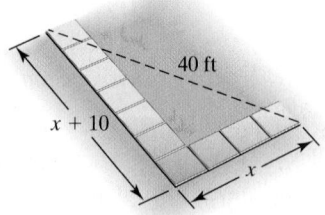

△ **53.** The hypotenuse of an isosceles right triangle is 2 centimeters longer than either of its legs. Find the exact length of each side. (*Hint:* An isosceles right triangle is a right triangle whose legs are the same length.)

△ **54.** The hypotenuse of an isosceles right triangle is one meter longer than either of its legs. Find the length of each side.

△ **55.** Uri Chechov's rectangular dog pen for his Irish setter must have an area of 400 square feet. Also, the length must be 10 feet longer than the width. Find the dimensions of the pen.

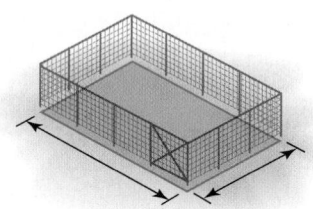

△ **56.** An entry in the Peach Festival Poster Contest must be rectangular and have an area of 1200 square inches. Furthermore, its length must be 20 inches longer than its width. Find the dimensions each entry must have.

△ **57.** A holding pen for cattle must be square and have a diagonal length of 100 meters.

   a. Find the length of a side of the pen.

   b. Find the area of the pen.

△ **58.** A rectangle is three times longer than it is wide. It has a diagonal of length 50 centimeters.

   a. Find the dimensions of the rectangle.

   b. Find the perimeter of the rectangle.

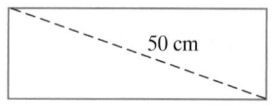

△ **59.** The heaviest reported door in the world is the 708.6 ton radiation shield door in the National Institute for Fusion Science at Toki, Japan. If the height of the door is 1.1 feet longer than its width, and its front area (neglecting depth) is 1439.9 square feet, find its width and height [Interesting note: the door is 6.6 feet thick.] (Source: Guiness World Records,)

△ **60.** Christi and Robbie Wegmann are constructing a rectangular stained glass window whose length is 7.3 inches longer than its width. If the area of the window is 569.9 square inches, find its width and length.

61. If a point B divides a line segment such that the smaller portion is to the larger portion as the larger is to the whole, the whole is the length of the *golden ratio*.

$$\overbrace{\underbrace{\bullet \quad 1 \quad \bullet \quad x-1 \quad \bullet}_{\substack{A \qquad\qquad B \qquad\qquad C}}}^{x(\text{whole})}$$

The golden ratio was thought by the Greeks to be the most pleasing to the eye, and many of their buildings contained numerous examples of the golden ratio. The value of the golden ratio is the positive solution of

$$\begin{array}{cc}(\text{smaller}) & \dfrac{x-1}{1} = \dfrac{1}{x} \quad (\text{larger})\\(\text{larger}) & \qquad\qquad (\text{whole})\end{array}$$

Find this value.

△ **62.** The base of a triangle is four more than twice its height. If the area of the triangle is 42 square centimeters, find its base and height.

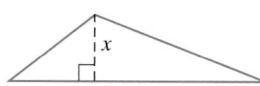

The Wollomombi Falls in Australia have a height of 1100 feet. A pebble is thrown upward from the top of the falls with an initial velocity of 20 feet per second. The height of the pebble h after t seconds is given by the equation $h = -16t^2 + 20t + 1100$. Use this equation for Exercises 63 and 64.

63. How long after the pebble is thrown will it hit the ground? Round to the nearest tenth of a second.

64. How long after the pebble is thrown will it be 550 feet from the ground? Round to the nearest tenth of a second.

A ball is thrown downward from the top of a 180-foot building with an initial velocity of 20 feet per second. The height of the ball h after t seconds is given by the equation $h = -16t^2 - 20t + 180$. *Use this equation to answer Exercises 65 and 66.*

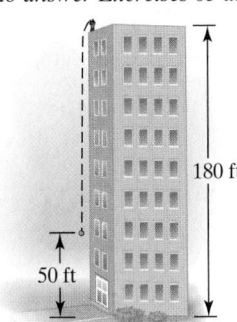

180 ft

50 ft

65. How long after the ball is thrown will it strike the ground? Round the result to the nearest tenth of a second.

66. How long after the ball is thrown will it be 50 feet from the ground? Round the result to the nearest tenth of a second.

REVIEW AND PREVIEW

Solve each equation. See Sections 6.6 and 7.6.

67. $\sqrt{5x - 2} = 3$

68. $\sqrt{y + 2} + 7 = 12$

69. $\dfrac{1}{x} + \dfrac{2}{5} = \dfrac{7}{x}$

70. $\dfrac{10}{z} = \dfrac{5}{z} - \dfrac{1}{3}$

Factor. See Section 5.7.

71. $x^4 + x^2 - 20$

72. $2y^4 + 11y^2 - 6$

73. $z^4 - 13z^2 + 36$

74. $x^4 - 1$

Concept Extensions

Use the quadratic formula and a calculator to approximate each solution to the nearest tenth.

75. $2x^2 - 6x + 3 = 0$

76. $3.6x^2 + 1.8x - 4.3 = 0$

The accompanying graph shows the daily low temperatures for one week in New Orleans, Louisiana.

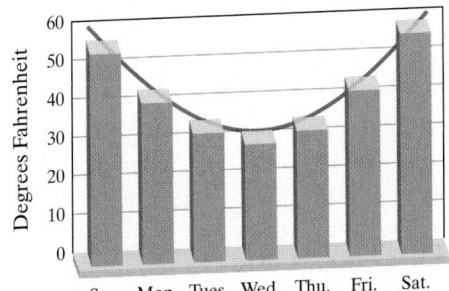

77. Which day of the week shows the greatest decrease in low temperature?

78. Which day of the week shows the greatest increase in low temperature?

79. Which day of the week had the lowest low temperature?

80. Use the graph to estimate the low temperature on Thursday.

Notice that the shape of the temperature graph is similar to the curve drawn. In fact, this graph can be modeled by the quadratic function $f(x) = 3x^2 - 18x + 56$, *where f(x) is the temperature in degrees Fahrenheit and x is the number of days from Sunday. (This graph is shown in red.) Use this function to answer Exercises 81 and 82.*

81. Use the quadratic function given to approximate the temperature on Thursday. Does your answer agree with the graph above?

82. Use the function given and the quadratic formula to find when the temperature was 35° F. [*Hint:* Let $f(x) = 35$ and solve for *x*.] Round your answer to one decimal place and interpret your result. Does your answer agree with the graph above?

83. Wal-Mart Stores' net income can be modeled by the quadratic function $f(x) = 112.5x^2 + 498.7x + 5454$, where *f(x)* is net income in millions of dollars and *x* is the number of years after 2000. (*Source:* Based on data from Wal-Mart Stores, Inc.)

   a. Find Wal-Mart's net income in 2002.

   b. If the trend described by the model continues, predict the year after 2000 in which Wal-Mart's net income will be $15,000 million. Round to the nearest whole year.

84. The number of inmates in custody in U.S. prisons and jails can be modeled by the quadratic function $p(x) = -3892.4x^2 + 91,152x + 1,576,254$ where *p(x)* is the number of inmates and *x* is the number of years after 1995. (*Source:* Based on data from the Bureau of Justice Statistics, U.S. Department of Justice, 1995–2002) Round **a** and **b** to the nearest ten thousand.

   a. Find the number of prison inmates in the United States in 2000.

   b. Find the number of prison inmates in the United States in 2002.

The solutions of the quadratic equation $ax^2 + bx + c = 0$ are $\dfrac{-b + \sqrt{b^2 - 4ac}}{2a}$ and $\dfrac{-b - \sqrt{b^2 - 4ac}}{2a}$.

85. Show that the sum of these solutions is $\dfrac{-b}{a}$.

86. Show that the product of these solutions is $\dfrac{c}{a}$.

Use the quadratic formula to solve each quadratic equation.

87. $3x^2 - \sqrt{12}x + 1 = 0$,

   (*Hint:* $a = 3, b = -\sqrt{12}, c = 1$)

88. $5x^2 + \sqrt{20}x + 1 = 0$

89. $x^2 + \sqrt{2}x + 1 = 0$

90. $x^2 - \sqrt{2}x + 1 = 0$

91. $2x^2 - \sqrt{3}x - 1 = 0$

92. $7x^2 + \sqrt{7}x - 2 = 0$

93. Use a graphing calculator to solve Exercises 63 and 65.

94. Use a graphing calculator to solve Exercises 64 and 66.

Recall that the discriminant also tells us the number of x-intercepts of the related function.

95. Check the results of Exercise 27 by graphing $y = 9x - 2x^2 + 5$.

96. Check the results of Exercise 28 by graphing $y = 5 - 4x + 12x^2$.

8.3   SOLVING EQUATIONS BY USING QUADRATIC METHODS

Objectives

1 Solve various equations that are quadratic in form.

2 Solve problems that lead to quadratic equations.

1   In this section, we discuss various types of equations that can be solved in part by using the methods for solving quadratic equations.

Once each equation is simplified, you may want to use these steps when deciding what method to use to solve the quadratic equation.

> ### Solving a Quadratic Equation
>
> **Step 1:** If the equation is in the form $(ax + b)^2 = c$, use the square root property and solve. If not, go to Step 2.
>
> **Step 2:** Write the equation in standard form: $ax^2 + bx + c = 0$.
>
> **Step 3:** Try to solve the equation by the factoring method. If not possible, go to Step 4.
>
> **Step 4:** Solve the equation by the quadratic formula.

The first example is a radical equation that becomes a quadratic equation once we square both sides.

EXAMPLE 1

Solve $x - \sqrt{x} - 6 = 0$.

Solution

Recall that to solve a radical equation, first get the radical alone on one side of the equation. Then square both sides.

$$x - 6 = \sqrt{x} \qquad \text{Add } \sqrt{x} \text{ to both sides.}$$

$$(x - 6)^2 = \left(\sqrt{x}\right)^2 \qquad \text{Square both sides.}$$

$$x^2 - 12x + 36 = x$$

Solving Equations and Inequalities—Study Skills Practice

Each set of exercises corresponds to the Study Skills Reminder in the section noted. After reviewing the outline in that section's Study Skills Reminder, solve each equation or inequality.

APPENDIX A EXERCISE SET

Section 2.1

Solve.

1. $3x - 4 = 3(2x - 1) + 7$

2. $\dfrac{7}{5} + \dfrac{y}{10} = 2$

3. $5 + 2x = 5(x + 1)$

4. $5 + 2x = 2(x + 1)$

Section 2.4

Solve. Write inequality solutions in interval notation.

1. $\dfrac{x + 3}{2} > 1$

2. $4(x - 2) + 3x \geq 9(x - 1) - 2$

3. $\dfrac{x - 2}{2} - \dfrac{x - 4}{3} = \dfrac{5}{6}$

4. $6(x + 1) - 2 = 6x + 4$

Section 2.5

Solve. Write inequality solutions in interval notation.

1. $x - 2 \leq 1$ and $3x - 1 \geq -4$

2. $-2 < x - 1 < 5$

3. $-2x + 2.5 = -7.7$

4. $-5x > 20$

5. $x \leq -3$ or $x \leq -5$

Section 2.6

Solve. Write inequality solutions in interval notation.

1. $|2 + 3x| = 7$

2. $5x < -10$ or $3x - 4 > 2$

3. $\dfrac{5t}{2} - \dfrac{3t}{4} = 7$

4. $|x - 2| = |x + 1|$

5. $5(x - 3) + x + 2 \geq 3(x + 2) + 2x$

Section 2.7

Solve. Write inequality solutions in interval notation.

1. $|x - 11| \geq 7$

2. $|x - 11| = 7$

3. $-5 < x - (2x + 3) < 0$

4. $|9x| - 8 = -1$

5. $\dfrac{4x}{5} - 1 = \dfrac{x}{2} + 2$

Section 5.8

Solve. Write inequality solutions in interval notation.

1. $2x^2 - 17x = 9$

2. $14x - 17x + 6 = 6(x + 1)$

3. $|4x + 7| = |-35|$

4. $\left|\dfrac{3x - 5}{4}\right| > 1$

5. $3(2x - 1) < 9$ and $-4x > -12$

6. $\frac{2}{3}x \leq \frac{5}{6}$

Section 6.6

Solve. Write inequality solutions in interval notation.

1. $\dfrac{x}{10} - \dfrac{1}{2} = \dfrac{7}{5x}$

2. $|1 - 5x| = 9$

3. $x + 2 \leq 0$ or $5x \leq 0$

4. $5(x - 3) + 2x = 7(x + 1) - 22$

5. $-8 + |2x - 4| \leq -2$

6. $x^3 = 25x$

Section 7.6

Solve. Write inequality solutions in interval notation.

1. $x(3x + 14) = 5$

2. $\dfrac{2}{x - 2} + \dfrac{3}{x + 2} = \dfrac{7}{x^2 - 4}$

3. $|5x - 4| = |4x + 1|$

4. $\sqrt{6x - 1} = 7$

5. $-2(x - 4) + 3x \leq -3(x + 2) - 2$

6. $|-x + 3| > 5$

Section 8.2

Solve. Write inequality solutions in interval notation.

1. $(x - 2)^2 = 17$

2. $x^2 - 5x + 2 = 0$

3. $x^2 - 5x + 6 = 0$

4. $\dfrac{x}{4} - \dfrac{3}{2} > 1$

5. $\sqrt{2x + 30} = x + 3$

6. $|3x + 11| - 12 = -1$

7. $\dfrac{3x^2 - 7}{3x^2 - 8x - 3} = \dfrac{1}{x - 3} + \dfrac{2}{3x + 1}$

8. $\left|\dfrac{x - 4}{3}\right| < 10$

Review of Volume and Surface Area

A **convex solid** is a set of points, S, not all in one plane, such that for any two points A and B in S, all points between A and B are also in S. In this appendix, we will find the volume and surface area of special types of solids called polyhedrons. A solid formed by the intersection of a finite number of planes is called a **polyhedron**. The box below is an example of a polyhedron.

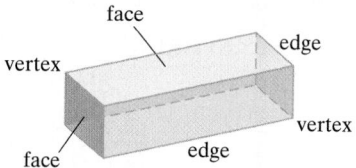

Each of the plane regions of the polyhedron is called a **face** of the polyhedron. If the intersection of two faces is a line segment, this line segment is an **edge** of the polyhedron. The intersections of the edges are the **vertices** of the polyhedron.

Volume is a measure of the space of a solid. The volume of a box or can, for example, is the amount of space inside. Volume can be used to describe the amount of juice in a pitcher or the amount of concrete needed to pour a foundation for a house.

The volume of a solid is the number of **cubic units** in the solid. A cubic centimeter and a cubic inch are illustrated.

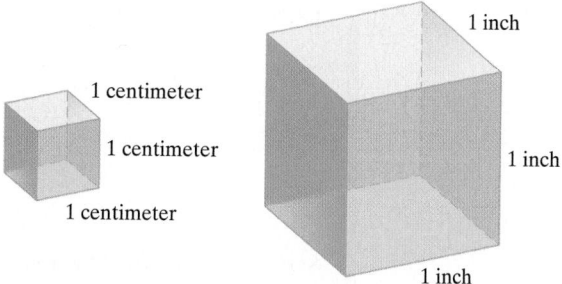

The **surface area** of a polyhedron is the sum of the areas of the faces of the polyhedron. For example, each face of the cube to the left above has an area of 1 square centimeter. Since there are 6 faces of the cube, the sum of the areas of the faces is 6 square centimeters. Surface area can be used to describe the amount of material needed to cover or form a solid. Surface area is measured in square units.

Formulas for finding the volumes, V, and surface areas, SA, of some common solids are given next.

Volume and Surface Area Formulas of Common Solids

| *Solid* | *Formulas* |

RECTANGULAR SOLID

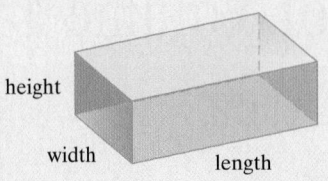

$V = lwh$
$SA = 2lh + 2wh + 2lw$
where h = height, w = width, l = length

CUBE

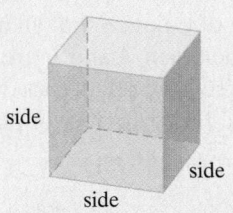

$V = s^3$
$SA = 6s^2$
where s = side

SPHERE

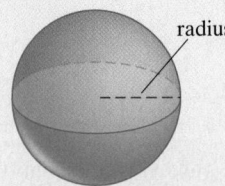

$V = \dfrac{4}{3}\pi r^3$

$SA = 4\pi r^2$
where r = radius

CIRCULAR CYLINDER

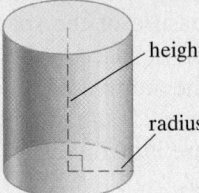

$V = \pi r^2 h$
$SA = 2\pi rh + 2\pi r^2$
where h = height, r = radius

CONE

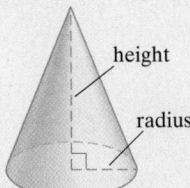

$V = \dfrac{1}{3}\pi r^2 h$

$SA = \pi r\sqrt{r^2 + h^2} + \pi r^2$
where h = height, r = radius

SQUARE-BASED PYRAMID

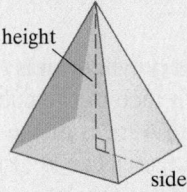

$V = \dfrac{1}{3}s^2 h$

$SA = B + \dfrac{1}{2}pl$

where B = area of base, p = perimeter of base, h = height, s = side, l = slant height

> **Helpful Hint**
> Volume is measured in cubic units. Surface area is measured in square units.

EXAMPLE 1

Find the volume and surface area of a rectangular box that is 12 inches long, 6 inches wide, and 3 inches high.

3 in.

6 in.   12 in.

Solution Let $h = 3$ in., $l = 12$ in., and $w = 6$ in.

$V = lwh$

$V = 12$ inches $\cdot$ 6 inches $\cdot$ 3 inches $= 216$ cubic inches

The volume of the rectangular box is 216 cubic inches.

$SA = 2lh + 2wh + 2lw$

$\quad = 2(12 \text{ in.})(3 \text{ in.}) + 2(6 \text{ in.})(3 \text{ in.}) + 2(12 \text{ in.})(6 \text{ in.})$

$\quad = 72 \text{ sq. in.} + 36 \text{ sq. in.} + 144 \text{ sq. in.}$

$\quad = 252 \text{ sq. in.}$

The surface area of the rectangular box is 252 square inches.

EXAMPLE 2

Find the volume and surface area of a ball of radius 2 inches. Give the exact volume and surface area and then use the approximation $\frac{22}{7}$ for π.

Solution

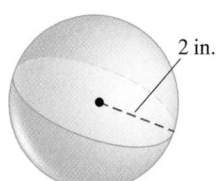

2 in.

$$V = \frac{4}{3}\pi r^3 \qquad \text{Formula for volume of a sphere.}$$

$$V = \frac{4}{3}\pi(2 \text{ in.})^3 \qquad \text{Let } r = 2 \text{ inches.}$$

$$= \frac{32}{3}\pi \text{ cu. in.} \qquad \text{Simplify.}$$

$$\approx \frac{32}{3} \cdot \frac{22}{7} \text{ cu. in.} \qquad \text{Approximate } \pi \text{ with } \frac{22}{7}.$$

$$= \frac{704}{21} \text{ or } 33\frac{11}{21} \text{ cu. in.}$$

The volume of the sphere is exactly $\frac{32}{3}\pi$ cubic inches or approximately $33\frac{11}{21}$ cubic inches.

$$SA = 4\pi r^2 \qquad \text{Formula for surface area.}$$

$$SA = 4\pi(2 \text{ in.})^2 \qquad \text{Let } r = 2 \text{ inches.}$$

$$= 16\pi \text{ sq. in.} \qquad \text{Simplify.}$$

$$\approx 16 \cdot \frac{22}{7} \text{ sq. in.} \qquad \text{Approximate } \pi \text{ with } \frac{22}{7}.$$

$$= \frac{352}{7} \text{ or } 50\frac{2}{7} \text{ sq. in.}$$

The surface area of the sphere is exactly 16π square inches or approximately $50\frac{2}{7}$ square inches.

APPENDIX C EXERCISE SET

Find the volume and surface area of each solid. See Examples 1 and 2. For formulas that contain π, give an exact answer and then approximate using $\dfrac{22}{7}$ for π.

1.

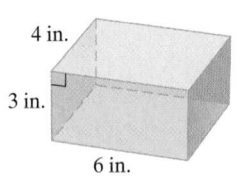

4 in.
3 in.
6 in.

2.

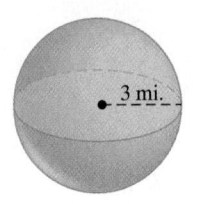

3 mi.

3.

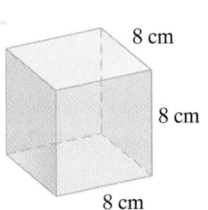

8 cm
8 cm
8 cm

4.

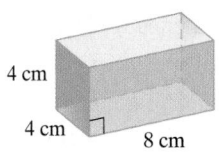

4 cm
4 cm
8 cm

5. (For surface area, use 3.14 for π and approximate to two decimal places.)

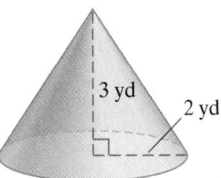

3 yd
2 yd

6.

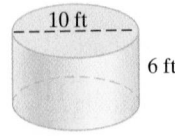

10 ft
6 ft

7.

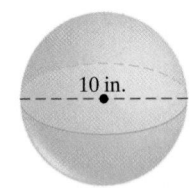

10 in.

8. Find the volume only.

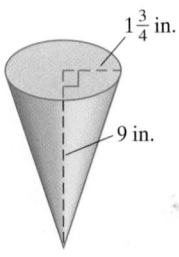

$1\frac{3}{4}$ in.
9 in.

9.

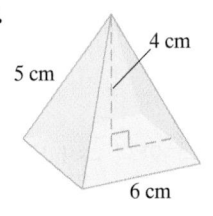

4 cm
5 cm
6 cm

10.

1 ft

Solve.

11. Find the volume of a cube with edges of $1\frac{1}{3}$ inches.

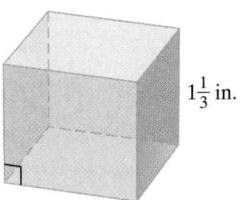

$1\frac{1}{3}$ in.

12. A water storage tank is in the shape of a cone with the pointed end down. If the radius is 14 ft and the depth of the tank is 15 ft, approximate the volume of the tank in cubic feet. Use $\dfrac{22}{7}$ for π.

14 ft
15 ft

13. Find the surface area of a rectangular box 2 ft by 1.4 ft by 3 ft.

14. Find the surface area of a box in the shape of a cube that is 5 ft on each side.

15. Find the volume of a pyramid with a square base 5 in. on a side and a height of 1.3 in.

16. Approximate to the nearest hundredth the volume of a sphere with a radius of 2 cm. Use 3.14 for π.

17. A paperweight is in the shape of a square-based pyramid 20 cm tall. If an edge of the base is 12 cm, find the volume of the paperweight.

18. A bird bath is made in the shape of a hemisphere (half-sphere). If its radius is 10 in., approximate the volume. Use $\frac{22}{7}$ for π.

10 in.

19. Find the exact surface area of a sphere with a radius of 7 in.

20. A tank is in the shape of a cylinder 8 ft tall and 3 ft in radius. Find the exact surface area of the tank.

21. Find the volume of a rectangular block of ice 2 ft by $2\frac{1}{2}$ ft by $1\frac{1}{2}$ ft.

22. Find the capacity (volume in cubic feet) of a rectangular ice chest with inside measurements of 3 ft by $1\frac{1}{2}$ ft by $1\frac{3}{4}$ ft.

23. An ice cream cone with a 4-cm diameter and 3-cm depth is filled exactly level with the top of the cone. Approximate how much ice cream (in cubic centimeters) is in the cone. Use $\frac{22}{7}$ for π.

24. A child's toy is in the shape of a square-based pyramid 10 in. tall. If an edge of the base is 7 in., find the volume of the toy.

An Introduction to Using a Graphing Utility

THE VIEWING WINDOW AND INTERPRETING WINDOW SETTINGS

In this appendix, we will use the term **graphing utility** to mean a graphing calculator or a computer software graphing package. All graphing utilities graph equations by plotting points on a screen. While plotting several points can be slow and sometimes tedious for us, a graphing utility can quickly and accurately plot hundreds of points. How does a graphing utility show plotted points? A computer or calculator screen is made up of a grid of small rectangular areas called **pixels**. If a pixel contains a point to be plotted, the pixel is turned "on"; otherwise, the pixel remains "off." The graph of an equation is then a collection of pixels turned "on." The graph of $y = 3x + 1$ from a graphing calculator is shown in Figure A–1. Notice the irregular shape of the line caused by the rectangular pixels.

The portion of the coordinate plane shown on the screen in Figure A-1 is called the **viewing window** or the **viewing rectangle**. Notice the x-axis and the y-axis on the graph. While tick marks are shown on the axes, they are not labeled. This means that from this screen alone, we do not know how many units each tick mark represents. To see what each tick mark represents and the minimum and maximum values on the axes, check the window setting of the graphing utility. It defines the viewing window. The window of the graph of $y = 3x + 1$ shown in Figure A-1 has the following settings (Figure A-2):

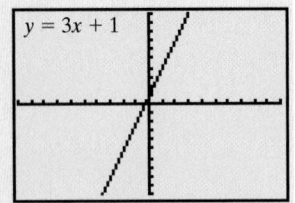

$y = 3x + 1$

Figure A-1

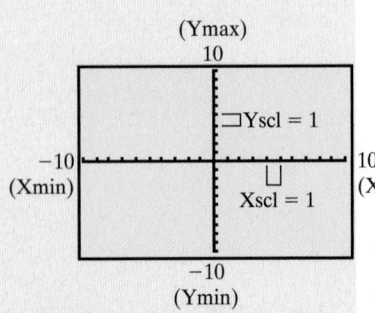

(Ymax)
10

Yscl = 1

−10
(Xmin)

10
(Xmax)

Xscl = 1

−10
(Ymin)

Figure A-2

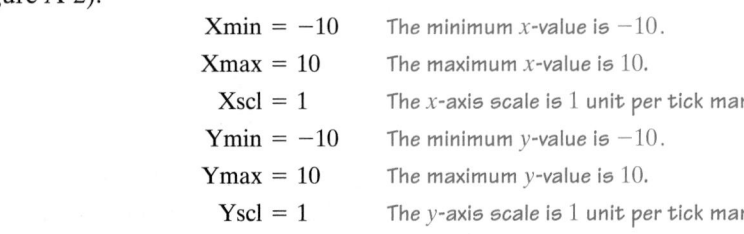

Xmin = −10	The minimum x-value is −10.
Xmax = 10	The maximum x-value is 10.
Xscl = 1	The x-axis scale is 1 unit per tick mark.
Ymin = −10	The minimum y-value is −10.
Ymax = 10	The maximum y-value is 10.
Yscl = 1	The y-axis scale is 1 unit per tick mark.

By knowing the scale, we can find the minimum and the maximum values on the axes simply by counting tick marks. For example, if both the Xscl (x-axis scale) and the

Yscl are 1 unit per tick mark on the graph in Figure A-3, we can count the tick marks and find that the minimum *x*-value is −10 and the maximum *x*-value is 10. Also, the minimum *y*-value is −10 and the maximum *y*-value is 10. If the Xscl (*x*-axis scale) changes to 2 units per tick mark (shown in Figure A-4), by counting tick marks, we see that the minimum *x*-value is now −20 and the maximum *x*-value is now 20.

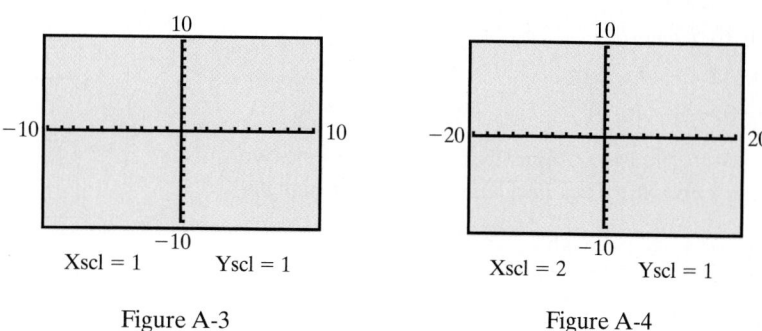

Figure A-3   Figure A-4

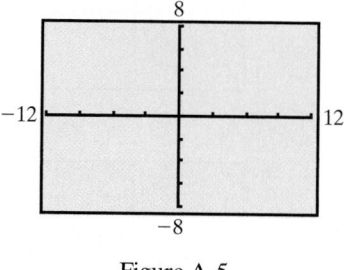

Figure A-5

It is also true that if we know the Xmin and the Xmax values, we can calculate the Xscl by the displayed axes. For example, the Xscl of the graph in Figure A-5 must be 3 units per tick mark for the maximum and minimum *x*-values to be as shown. Also, the Yscl of that graph must be 2 units per tick mark for the maximum and minimum *y*-values to be as shown.

We will call the viewing window in Figure A-3 a *standard* viewing window or rectangle. Although a standard viewing window is sufficient for much of this text, special care must be taken to ensure that all key features of a graph are shown. Figures A-6, A-7, and A-8 show the graph of $y = x^2 + 11x - 1$ on three different viewing windows. Note that certain viewing windows for this equation are misleading.

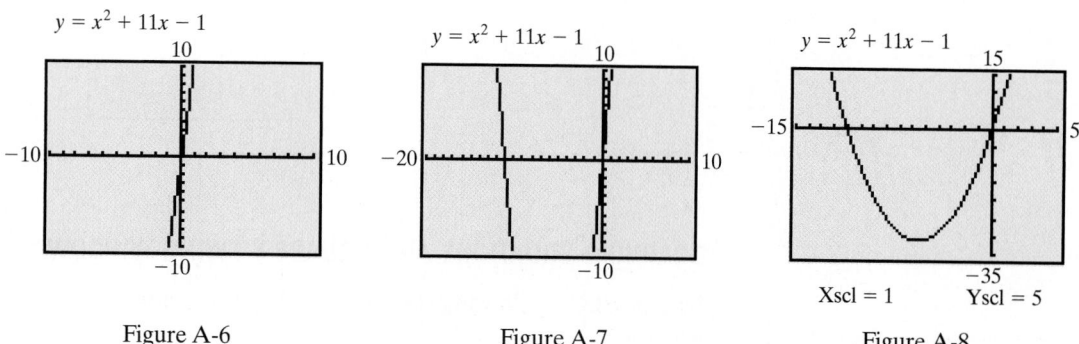

Figure A-6   Figure A-7   Figure A-8

How do we ensure that all distinguishing features of the graph of an equation are shown? It helps to know about the equation that is being graphed. For example, the equation $y = x^2 + 11x - 1$ is not a linear equation and its graph is not a line. This equation is a quadratic equation and, therefore, its graph is a parabola. By knowing this information, we know that the graph shown in Figure A-6, although correct, is misleading. Of the three viewing rectangles shown, the graph in Figure A-8 is best because it shows more of the distinguishing features of the parabola. Properties of equations needed for graphing will be studied in this text.

VIEWING WINDOW AND INTERPRETING WINDOW SETTINGS EXERCISE SET

In Exercises 1–4, determine whether all ordered pairs listed will lie within a standard viewing rectangle.

1. $(-9, 0), (5, 8), (1, -8)$

2. $(4, 7), (0, 0), (-8, 9)$

3. $(-11, 0), (2, 2), (7, -5)$

4. $(3, 5), (-3, -5), (15, 0)$

In Exercises 5–10, choose an Xmin, Xmax, Ymin, and Ymax so that all ordered pairs listed will lie within the viewing rectangle.

5. $(-90, 0), (55, 80), (0, -80)$

6. $(4, 70), (20, 20), (-18, 90)$

7. $(-11, 0), (2, 2), (7, -5)$

8. $(3, 5), (-3, -5), (15, 0)$

9. $(200, 200), (50, -50), (70, -50)$

10. $(40, 800), (-30, 500), (15, 0)$

Write the window setting for each viewing window shown. Use the following format:

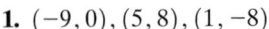

$$
\begin{array}{ll}
\text{Xmin} = & \text{Ymin} = \\
\text{Xmax} = & \text{Ymax} = \\
\text{Xscl} = & \text{Yscl} =
\end{array}
$$

11.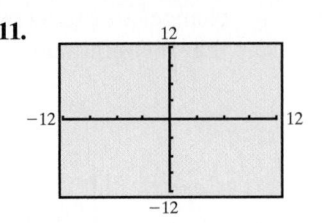

12.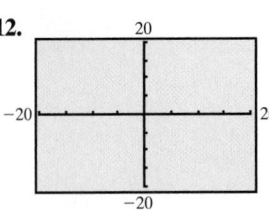

13.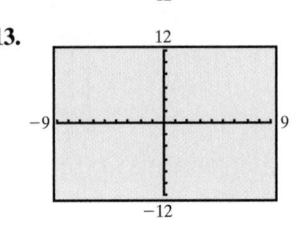

14.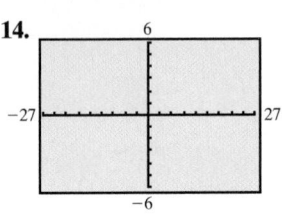

15.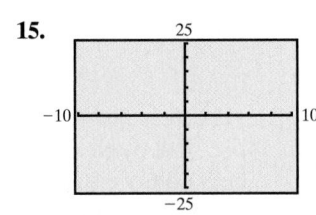

16.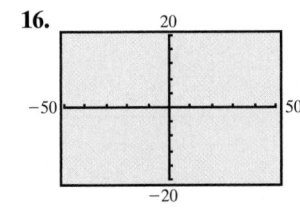

17.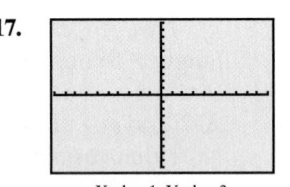
Xscl = 1, Yscl = 3

18.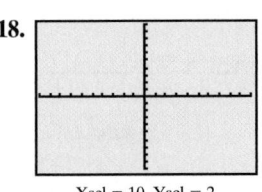
Xscl = 10, Yscl = 2

19.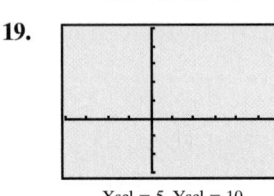
Xscl = 5, Yscl = 10

20.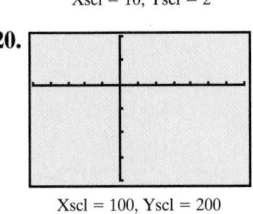
Xscl = 100, Yscl = 200

GRAPHING EQUATIONS AND SQUARE VIEWING WINDOW

In general, the following steps may be used to graph an equation on a standard viewing window.

Graphing an Equation in X and Y with a Graphing Utility on a Standard Viewing Window

Step 1: Solve the equation for y.

Step 2: Using your graphing utility and enter the equation in the form
$Y = $ *expression involving x.*

Step 3: Activate the graphing utility.

Special care must be taken when entering the *expression involving x* in Step 2. You must be sure that the graphing utility you are using interprets the expression as you want it to. For example, let's graph $3y = 4x$. To do so,

Step 1: Solve the equation for y.

$$3y = 4x$$

$$\frac{3y}{3} = \frac{4x}{3}$$

$$y = \frac{4}{3}x$$

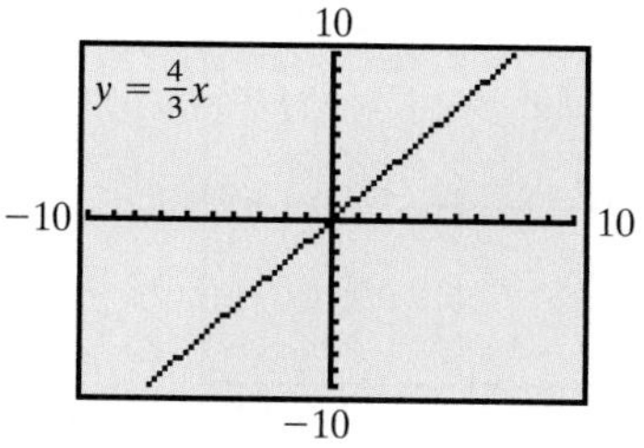

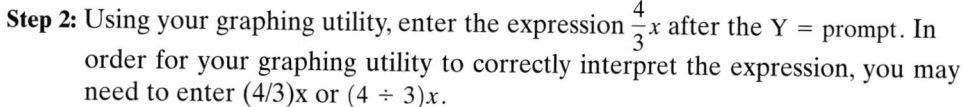

Step 2: Using your graphing utility, enter the expression $\frac{4}{3}x$ after the Y = prompt. In order for your graphing utility to correctly interpret the expression, you may need to enter (4/3)x or (4 ÷ 3)x.

Step 3: Activate the graphing utility. The graph should appear as in Figure A-9.

Figure A-9

Distinguishing features of the graph of a line include showing all the intercepts of the line. For example, the window of the graph of the line in Figure A-10 does not show both intercepts of the line, but the window of the graph of the same line in Figure A-11 does show both intercepts. Notice the notation below each graph. This is a shorthand notation of the range setting of the graph. This notation means [Xmin, Xmax] by [Ymin, Ymax].

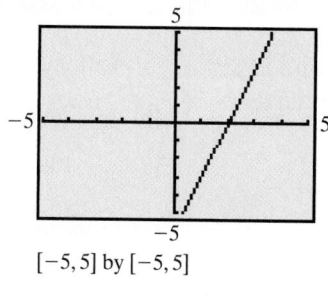

[−5, 5] by [−5, 5]

Figure A-10

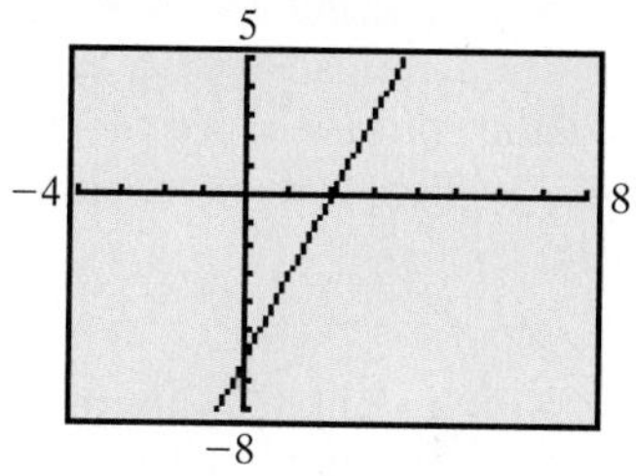

[−4, 8] by [−8, 5]

Figure A-11

On a standard viewing window, the tick marks on the y-axis are closer together than the tick marks on the x-axis. This happens because the viewing window is a rectangle, and so 10 equally spaced tick marks on the positive y-axis will be closer together than 10 equally spaced tick marks on the positive x-axis. This causes the appearance of graphs to be distorted.

For example, notice the different appearances of the same line graphed using different viewing windows. The line in Figure A-12 is distorted because the tick marks along the x-axis are farther apart than the tick marks along the y-axis. The graph of the same line in Figure A-13 is not distorted because the viewing rectangle has been selected so that there is equal spacing between tick marks on both axes.

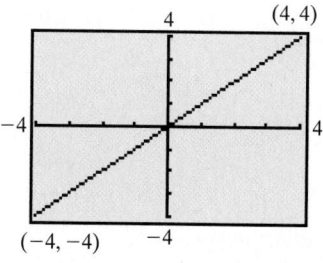

Figure A-12

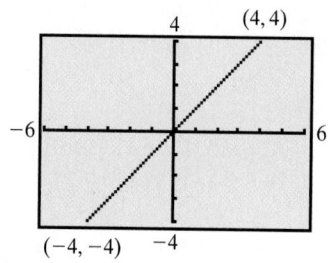

Figure A-13

We say that the line in Figure A-13 is graphed on a *square* setting. Some graphing utilities have a built-in program that, if activated, will automatically provide a square setting. A square setting is especially helpful when we are graphing perpendicular lines, circles, or when a true geometric perspective is desired. Some examples of square screens are shown in Figures A-14 and A-15.

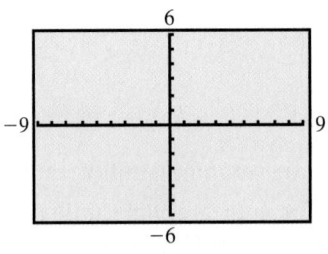

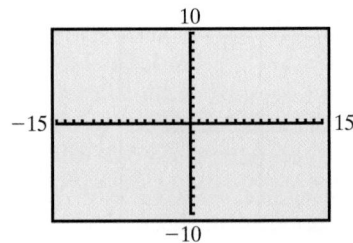

Figure A-14   Figure A-15

Other features of a graphing utility such as Trace, Zoom, Intersect, and Table are discussed in appropriate Graphing Calculator Explorations in this text.

GRAPHING EQUATIONS AND SQUARE VIEWING WINDOW EXERCISE SET

Graph each linear equation in two variables, using the two different range settings given. Determine which setting shows all intercepts of a line.

1. $y = 2x + 12$

   Setting A: $[-10, 10]$ by $[-10, 10]$
   Setting B: $[-10, 10]$ by $[-10, 15]$

2. $y = -3x + 25$

   Setting A: $[-5, 5]$ by $[-30, 10]$
   Setting B: $[-10, 10]$ by $[-10, 30]$

3. $y = -x - 41$

   Setting A: $[-50, 10]$ by $[-10, 10]$
   Setting B: $[-50, 10]$ by $[-50, 15]$

4. $y = 6x - 18$

   Setting A: $[-10, 10]$ by $[-20, 10]$
   Setting B: $[-10, 10]$ by $[-10, 10]$

5. $y = \dfrac{1}{2}x - 15$

   Setting A: $[-10, 10]$ by $[-20, 10]$
   Setting B: $[-10, 35]$ by $[-20, 15]$

6. $y = -\dfrac{2}{3}x - \dfrac{29}{3}$

   Setting A: $[-10, 10]$ by $[-10, 10]$
   Setting B: $[-15, 5]$ by $[-15, 5]$

The graph of each equation is a line. Use a graphing utility and a standard viewing window to graph each equation.

7. $3x = 5y$ **8.** $7y = -3x$ **9.** $9x - 5y = 30$

10. $4x + 6y = 20$ **11.** $y = -7$ **12.** $y = 2$

13. $x + 10y = -5$ **14.** $x - 5y = 9$

Graph the following equations using the square setting given. Some keystrokes that may be helpful are given.

15. $y = \sqrt{x}$ $[-12, 12]$ by $[-8, 8]$

   Suggested keystrokes: $\sqrt{}\, x$

16. $y = \sqrt{2x}$ $[-12, 12]$ by $[-8, 8]$

   Suggested keystrokes: $\sqrt{}\,(2x)$

17. $y = x^2 + 2x + 1$ $[-15, 15]$ by $[-10, 10]$

   Suggested keystrokes: $x^2 + 2x + 1$

18. $y = x^2 - 5$ $[-15, 15]$ by $[-10, 10]$

   Suggested keystrokes: $x^2 - 5$

19. $y = |x|$ $[-9, 9]$ by $[-6, 6]$

   Suggested keystrokes: $ABS\,(x)$

20. $y = |x - 2|$ $[-9, 9]$ by $[-6, 6]$

   Suggested keystrokes: $ABS(x - 2)$

Graph each line. Use a standard viewing window; then, if necessary, change the viewing window so that all intercepts of each line show.

21. $x + 2y = 30$ **22.** $1.5x - 3.7y = 40.3$

ANSWERS TO SELECTED EXERCISES

CHAPTER 1   REAL NUMBERS AND ALGEBRAIC EXPRESSIONS

Exercise Set 1.2   1. 35   **3.** 30.38   **5.** $\dfrac{3}{8}$ **7.** 22   **9.** 2000 mi   **11.** 20.4 sq. ft   **13.** \$10,612.80   **15.** $\{1, 2, 3, 4, 5\}$

17. $\{11, 12, 13, 14, 15, 16\}$ **19.** $\{0\}$ **21.** $\{0, 2, 4, 6, 8\}$ **23.**   **25.**

27.   **29.** Answers may vary.   **31.** $\{3, 0, \sqrt{36}\}$ **33.** $\{3, \sqrt{36}\}$

35. $\{\sqrt{7}\}$ **37.** $\in$ **39.** $\notin$ **41.** $\notin$ **43.** $\notin$ **45.** true   **47.** true   **49.** false   **51.** false   **53.** true   **55.** false   **57.** answers may vary   **59.** -2 **61.** 4   **63.** 0   **65.** -3 **67.** answers may vary   **69.** 6.2   **71.** $-\dfrac{4}{7}$ **73.** $\dfrac{2}{3}$ **75.** 0   **77.** $2x$

79. $2x + 5$ **81.** $x - 10$ **83.** $x + 2$ **85.** $\dfrac{x}{11}$ **87.** $3x + 12$ **89.** $x - 17$ **91.** $2(x + 3)$ **93.** $\dfrac{5}{4 - x}$ **95.** 137; 100; 91; 69; 56

97. answers may vary

Mental Math   1. B, C   **3.** B, D   **5.** B

Exercise Set 1.3   1. 5   **3.** -24 **5.** -11 **7.** -4 **9.** $\dfrac{4}{3}$ **11.** -2 **13.** -60 **15.** 80   **17.** 3   **19.** 0   **21.** -8 **23.** $-\dfrac{3}{7}$

25. $\dfrac{1}{21}$ **27.** -49 **29.** 36   **31.** -8 **33.** 7   **35.** $-\dfrac{1}{3}$ **37.** 4   **39.** 3   **41.** not a real number   **43.** 48   **45.** -1 **47.** -3

49. 14.4   **51.** -2.1 **53.** $-\dfrac{1}{3}$ **55.** 17   **57.** 40   **59.** 11   **61.** $-\dfrac{3}{4}$ **63.** 7   **65.** -11 **67.** $-\dfrac{4}{5}$ **69.** $-\dfrac{79}{15}$ **71.** $-\dfrac{5}{14}$

73. 13   **75.** 65   **77.** -2 **79.** $\dfrac{5}{2}$ **81. a.** 18; 22; 28; 208   **b.** increase   **83. a.** 600; 150; 105   **b.** decrease   **85.** $\dfrac{13}{35}$ **87.** 4205 m

89. 5.4; 2.1; 1.7; 2.6; 1.4; 0.7   **91.** $6 - (5 \cdot 2 + 2)$ **93.** answers may vary   **95.** 16.5227   **97.** 4.4272   **99.** 1.4187   **101.** 13.2%

103. 10.8%   **105.** b   **107.** d   **109.** Yes.   Two players have 6 points each (the third player has 0 points) or two players have 5 points each (the third has 2 points).

Integrated Review   1. 16   **2.** -16 **3.** 0   **4.** -11 **5.** -5 **6.** $-\dfrac{1}{60}$ **7.** undefined   **8.** -2.97 **9.** 4   **10.** -50

11. 35   **12.** 92   **13.** $-15 - 2x$ **14.** $3x + 5$ **15.** 0   **16.** true

Exercise Set 1.4   1. $>$ **3.** $=$ **5.** $<$ **7.** $2x + 5 = -14$ **9.** $3(x + 1) = 7$ **11.** $\dfrac{n}{5} = 4n$ **13.** $z - 2 = 2z$ **15.** $7x \leq -21$

17. $-2 + x \neq 10$ **19.** $2(x - 6) > \dfrac{1}{11}$ **21.** $5y - 7 = 6$ **23.** $2(x - 6) = -27$ **25.** $-5; \dfrac{1}{5}$ **27.** $8; -\dfrac{1}{8}$ **29.** $\dfrac{1}{7}; -7$ **31.** 0; unde-

fined   **33.** $\dfrac{7}{8}; -\dfrac{7}{8}$ **35.** Zero. For every real number $x, 0 \cdot x \neq 1$, so 0 has no reciprocal. It is the only real number that has no reciprocal because

if $x \neq 0$, then $x \cdot \dfrac{1}{x} = 1$ by definition.   **37.** $y + 7x$ **39.** $w \cdot z$ **41.** $\dfrac{x}{5} \cdot \dfrac{1}{3}$ **43.** no; answers may vary   **45.** $(5 \cdot 7)x$ **47.** $x + (1.2 + y)$

49. $14(z \cdot y)$ **51.** 10 and 4. Subtraction is not associative.   **53.** $3x + 15$ **55.** $-2a - b$ **57.** $12x + 10y + 4z$ **59.** $-4x + 8y - 28$

61. $3xy - 1.5x$ **63.** $6 + 3x$ **65.** 0   **67.** 7   **69.** $(10 \cdot 2)y$ **71.** $a(b + c) = ab + ac$ **73.** $0.1d$ **75.** $112 - x$ **77.** $90 - 5x$

79. $\$35.61y$ **81.** $2x + 2$ **83.** $-8y - 14$ **85.** $-9c - 4$ **87.** $4 - 8y$ **89.** $y^2 - 11yz - 11$ **91.** $3t - 14$ **93.** 0   **95.** $13n - 20$

97. $8.5y - 20.8$ **99.** $\dfrac{3}{8}a - \dfrac{1}{12}$ **101.** $20y + 48$ **103.** $-5x + \dfrac{5}{6}y - 1$ **105.** $-x - 6y - \dfrac{11}{24}$ **107.** $-180.96y - 74.33$

109. $6.5y - 7.92x + 25.47$ **111.** no   **113.** 80 million   **115.** 35 million   **117.** 20.25%

Chapter 1 Review   1. 21   **3.** 324,000   **5.** $\{-2, 0, 2, 4, 6\}$ **7.** $\varnothing$ **9.** $\{\ldots, -1, 0, 1, 2\}$ **11.** false   **13.** true   **15.** true

17. true   **19.** true   **21.** true   **23.** true   **25.** true   **27.** true   **29.** $\left\{5, \dfrac{8}{2}, \sqrt{9}\right\}$ **31.** $\{\sqrt{7}, \pi\}$ **33.** $\left\{5, \dfrac{8}{2}, \sqrt{9}, -1\right\}$ **35.** -0.6

37. -1 **39.** $\dfrac{1}{0.6}$ **41.** 1   **43.** -35 **45.** 0.31   **47.** 13.3   **49.** 0   **51.** 0   **53.** -5 **55.** 4   **57.** 9   **59.** 3   **61.** $-\dfrac{32}{135}$

63. $-\dfrac{5}{4}$ **65.** $\dfrac{5}{8}$ **67.** -1 **69.** 1   **71.** -4 **73.** $\dfrac{5}{7}$ **75.** $\dfrac{1}{5}$ **77.** -5 **79.** 5   **81. a.** 6.28; 62.8; 628   **b.** increase

83. $-5x - 9$ **85.** $-15x^2 + 6$ **87.** $5.7x + 1.1$ **89.** $n + 2n = -15$ **91.** $6(t - 5) = 4$ **93.** $9x - 10 = 5$ **95.** $-4 < 7y$

A1

97. $t + 6 \le -12$ **99.** distributive property   **101.** commutative property of addition   **103.** multiplicative inverse property

105. associative property of multiplication   **107.** multiplicative identity property   **109.** $(3 + x) + (7 + y)$ **111.** $2 \cdot \frac{1}{2}$, for example

113. $7 + 0$ **115.** $>$ **117.** $=$ **119.** $>$

Chapter 1 Test   **1.** true   **2.** false   **3.** false   **4.** false   **5.** true   **6.** false   **7.** -3 **8.** -56 **9.** -225 **10.** 3   **11.** 1

12. $-\frac{3}{2}$ **13.** 12   **14.** 1   **15. a.** 5.75; 17.25; 57.50; 115.00   **b.** increase   **16.** $2(x + 5) = 30$ **17.** $\frac{(6 - y)^2}{7} < -2$

18. $\frac{9z}{|-12|} \neq 10$ **19.** $3\left(\frac{n}{5}\right) = -n$ **20.** $20 = 2x - 6$ **21.** $-2 = \frac{x}{x + 5}$ **22.** distributive property   **23.** associative property of addition

24. additive inverse property   **25.** multiplication property of zero   **26.** $0.05n + 0.1d$ **27.** $-6x - 14$ **28.** $\frac{1}{2}a - \frac{9}{8}$ **29.** $2y - 10$
30. $-1.3x + 1.9$

CHAPTER 2   EQUATIONS, INEQUALITIES, AND PROBLEM SOLVING

Mental Math   **1.** $8x + 21$ **3.** $6n - 7$ **5.** $-4x - 1$ **7.** expression   **9.** equation   **11.** all real numbers   **13.** no solution

Exercise Set 2.1   **1.** -12 **3.** -0.9 **5.** 6   **7.** -5 **9.** -1.1 **11.** -5 **13.** 0   **15.** 2   **17.** -9 **19.** $-\frac{10}{7}$ **21. a.** $4x + 5$

b. -3 **c.** answers may vary   **23.** $\frac{1}{6}$ **25.** 4   **27.** 1   **29.** 5   **31.** all real numbers   **33.** Ø   **35.** answers may vary   **37.** 8

39. -5.9 **41.** 7   **43.** 4.2   **45.** 2   **47.** -2 **49.** 0   **51.** 5   **53.** Ø   **55.** $\frac{1}{8}$ **57.** 0   **59.** 29   **61.** -8 **63.** all real numbers

65. 4   **67.** -2 **69.** all real numbers   **71.** $\frac{40}{3}$ **73.** 17   **75.** $\frac{3}{5}$ **77.** $\frac{103}{5}$ or 20.6   **79.** $\frac{8}{x}$ **81.** $8x$ **83.** $3x + 2$ **85.** $K = -11$

87. $K = 24$ **89.** 1   **91.** 3   **93.** -4.86 **95.** 1.53   **97.** not a fair game

Exercise Set 2.2   **1.** $4y$ **3.** $3z + 3$ **5.** $(15x + 30)$ cents   **7.** $10x + 3$ **9.** -5 **11.** 45,225   **13.** 78   **15.** 1.92   **17.** 1612.41
million acres   **19.** 1991 earthquakes   **21.** 860 shoppers   **23.** 17%   **25.** 6750 users   **27.** Los Angeles: 61.6 million; Atlanta: 76.9 million;
Chicago: 67.4 million   **29.** $737 - 200$: 113 seats; $737 - 300$: 134 seats; $757 - 200$: 190 seats   **31.** $430.00   **33.** Mile High Stadium: 76,125
seats; Heinz Field Stadium: 64,450 seats   **35.** AOL: 23,700,000; Earthlink: 4,700,000; MSN: 4,000,000   **37.** 28.6 million   **39. a.** 214,866 operators
b. answers may vary   **41.** 75, 76, 77   **43.** $64°, 32°, 84°$ **45.** height: 48 in.; width: 108 in.   **47.** length: 14 cm; width: 6 cm   **49.** $80°, 100°$
51. $15°, 75°$ **53.** $40°, 140°$ **55.** width: 8.4 m; height: 47 m   **57.** incandescent: 1500 bulb hours; fluorescent: 100,000 bulb hours; halogen: 4000
bulb hours   **59.** 21.1 million returns   **61.** Thome: 49; Palmeiro: 47; Sexson: 45   **63.** 6   **65.** 208   **67.** -55 **69.** 3195   **71.** 11 million
trees   **73. a.** during the year 2033   **b.** 1828.75   **c.** 5; no: this is the average daily number of cigarettes for all American adults—smokers and
nonsmokers   **75.** no such odd integers exist   **77.** 500 boards; $30,000   **79.** company makes a profit

Mental Math   **1.** $y = 5 - 2x$ **3.** $a = 5b + 8$ **5.** $k = h - 5j + 6$

Exercise Set 2.3   **1.** $t = \frac{D}{r}$ **3.** $R = \frac{I}{PT}$ **5.** $y = \frac{9x - 16}{4}$ **7.** $W = \frac{P - 2L}{2}$ **9.** $A = \frac{J + 3}{C}$ **11.** $g = \frac{W}{h - 3t^2}$

13. $B = \frac{T - 2C}{AC}$ **15.** $r = \frac{C}{2\pi}$ **17.** $r = \frac{E - IR}{I}$ **19.** $L = \frac{2s - an}{n}$ **21.** $v = \frac{3st^4 - N}{5s}$ **23.** $H = \frac{S - 2LW}{2L + 2W}$ **25.** $4703.71;
$4713.99; $4719.22; $4722.74; $4724.45   **27. a.** $7313.97   **b.** $7321.14   **c.** $7325.98   **29.** $40°C$ **31.** 3.6 hr, or 3 hr and 36 min
33. 171 packages   **35.** 9 ft   **37.** 2 gal   **39. a.** 1174.86 cu. m   **b.** 310.34 cu. m   **c.** 1485.20 cu. m   **41.** 164,921 mi   **43.** 0.42 ft
45. 41.125π ft $\approx$ 129.1325 ft   **47.** $1831.96   **49.** $f = \frac{C - 4h - 4p}{9}$ **51.** 178 cal   **53.** 1.5 g   **55.** $\{-3, -2, -1\}$
57. $\{-3, -2, -1, 0, 1\}$ **59.** answers may vary   **61.** 0.388; 0.723; 1.00; 1.523; 5.202; 9.538; 19.193; 30.065; 39.505   **63.** $6.80 per person
65. answers may vary   **67.** 0.25 sec   **69.** $\frac{1}{4}$ **71.** $\frac{3}{8}$ **73.** $\frac{3}{8}$ **75.** $\frac{3}{4}$ **77.** 1   **79.** 1

Mental Math   **1.** $\{x | x < 6\}$ **3.** $\{x | x \ge 10\}$ **5.** $\{x | x > 4\}$ **7.** $\{x | x \le 2\}$

Exercise Set 2.4   **1.** $\longrightarrow$; $(-\infty, -3)$ **3.** $\longleftarrow$; $[0.3, \infty)$ **5.** $\longleftarrow$; $\left(\frac{5}{9}, \infty\right)$

7. $\longleftrightarrow$; $(-2, 5)$ **9.** $\longleftrightarrow$; $(-1, 5)$ **11.** answers may vary   **13.** D   **15.** B   **17.** $\longrightarrow$; $[-2, \infty)$

19. $\longrightarrow$; $(-\infty, 1)$ **21.** $\longrightarrow$; $(-\infty, 2]$ **23.** $\longrightarrow$; $(-\infty, -4)$ **25.** $\longleftarrow$; $\left[\frac{8}{3}, \infty\right)$

27. $\longrightarrow$ $;(-\infty,-4.7)$ **29.** $\longleftarrow$ $;(-\infty,-3]$ **31.** $\longleftarrow$ $;(4,\infty)$ **33.** $(-\infty,-1]$ **35.** $(-\infty,11]$

37. $(-13,\infty)$ **39.** $(-\infty,7]$ **41.** $(-\infty,\infty)$ **43.** $\varnothing$ **45.** $(0,\infty)$ **47.** $(-2,\infty)$ **49.** $\left[-\dfrac{3}{5},\infty\right)$ **51.** $[-9.6,\infty)$ **53.** $(38,\infty)$

55. answers may vary   **57.** $[0,\infty)$ **59.** $(-\infty,-5]$ **61.** $\left(-\infty,\dfrac{1}{4}\right)$ **63.** $(-\infty,-1]$ **65.** $\left[-\dfrac{79}{3},\infty\right)$ **67.** $(-\infty,-15)$ **69.** $[3,\infty)$

71. $\left[-\dfrac{37}{3},\infty\right)$ **73.** $(-\infty,5)$ **75.** 30   **77.** 1040 lb   **79.** 16 oz   **81.** more than 200 calls   **83.** $F \geq 932°$ **85. a.** the end of 2004
b. answers may vary   **87.** decreasing   **89.** 6.57 gal   **91.** 2004   **93.** answers may vary   **95.** 2, 3, 4   **97.** 2, 3, 4 ...

99. $\longleftrightarrow$ $;[0,5]$ **101.** $\longleftarrow$ $;\left(-\dfrac{1}{2},\dfrac{3}{2}\right)$ **103.** $(-\infty,\infty)$ **105.** $\varnothing$

Integrated Review **1.** -5 **2.** $(-5,\infty)$ **3.** $\left[\dfrac{8}{3},\infty\right)$ **4.** $[-1,\infty)$ **5.** 0 **6.** $\left[-\dfrac{1}{10},\infty\right)$ **7.** $\left(-\infty,-\dfrac{1}{6}\right]$ **8.** 0 **9.** $\varnothing$

10. $\left[-\dfrac{3}{5},\infty\right)$ **11.** 4.2   **12.** 6   **13.** -8 **14.** $(-\infty,-16)$ **15.** $\dfrac{20}{11}$ **16.** 1   **17.** $(38,\infty)$ **18.** $-5,5$ **19.** $\dfrac{3}{5}$ **20.** $(-\infty,\infty)$

21. 29   **22.** all real numbers   **23.** $(-\infty,5)$ **24.** $\dfrac{9}{13}$ **25.** $(23,\infty)$ **26.** $(-\infty,6]$ **27.** $\left(-\infty,\dfrac{3}{5}\right]$ **28.** $\left(-\infty,-\dfrac{19}{32}\right)$

Exercise Set 2.5 **1.** $\{2,3,4,5,6,7\}$ **3.** $\{4,6\}$ **5.** $\{\ldots,-2,-1,0,1,\ldots\}$ **7.** $\{5,7\}$ **9.** $\{x\,|\,x$ is an odd integer or $x=2$ or $x=4\}$

11. $\{2,4\}$ **13.** $\longleftrightarrow$ $;(-2,5)$ **15.** $\longleftarrow$ $;[6,\infty)$ **17.** $\longleftarrow$ $;(-\infty,-3]$ **19.** $\longleftrightarrow$ $;(11,17)$

21. $\longleftrightarrow$ $;[1,4]$ **23.** $\longleftrightarrow$ $;\left[-3,\dfrac{3}{2}\right]$ **25.** $\longleftrightarrow$ $;[-21,-9]$ **27.** $\longleftarrow$ $;(-\infty,-1)\cup(0,\infty)$

29. $\longleftarrow$ $;[2,\infty)$ **31.** $\longleftarrow$ $;(-\infty,\infty)$ **33.** answers may vary   **35.** $\longleftrightarrow$ $;(-1,2)$

37. $\longleftarrow$ $;(-\infty,\infty)$ **39.** $\longleftarrow$ $;[-1,\infty)$ **41.** $\longleftarrow$ $;[-5,\infty)$ **43.** $\longleftrightarrow$ $;\left[\dfrac{3}{2},6\right]$

45. $\longleftrightarrow$ $;\left(\dfrac{5}{4},\dfrac{11}{4}\right)$ **47.** $\longleftarrow$ $;\varnothing$ **49.** $\longleftarrow$ $;(-7,\infty)$ **51.** $\longleftrightarrow$ $;\left(-5,\dfrac{5}{2}\right)$

53. $\longleftrightarrow$ $;\left(0,\dfrac{14}{3}\right]$ **55.** $\longleftarrow$ $;(-\infty,-3]$ **57.** $\longleftarrow$ $;(-\infty,1]\cup\left(\dfrac{29}{7},\infty\right)$ **59.** $\longleftarrow$ $;\varnothing$

61. $\longleftrightarrow$ $;\left[-\dfrac{1}{2},\dfrac{3}{2}\right)$ **63.** $\longleftrightarrow$ $;\left(-\dfrac{4}{3},\dfrac{7}{3}\right)$ **65.** $\longleftrightarrow$ $;(6,12)$ **67.** -12 **69.** -4 **71.** $-7,7$ **73.** 0

75. $-20.2° \leq F \leq 95°$ **77.** $67 \leq$ final score ≤ 94 **79.** 1994–1995; 1998–1999   **81.** $\longleftarrow$ $;(6,\infty)$

83. $\longleftrightarrow$ $;[3,7]$ **85.** $\longleftarrow$ $;(-\infty,-1)$

Mental Math **1.** 7   **3.** -5 **5.** -6 **7.** 12

Exercise Set 2.6 **1.** $7,-7$ **3.** $4.2,-4.2$ **5.** $7,-2$ **7.** $8,4$ **9.** $5,-5$ **11.** $3,-3$ **13.** 0   **15.** $\varnothing$ **17.** $\dfrac{1}{5}$ **19.** $|x|=5$

21. $9,-\dfrac{1}{2}$ **23.** $-\dfrac{5}{2}$ **25.** answers may vary   **27.** $4,-4$ **29.** 0   **31.** $\varnothing$ **33.** $0,\dfrac{14}{3}$ **35.** $2,-2$ **37.** $\varnothing$ **39.** $7,-1$ **41.** $\varnothing$

43. $\varnothing$ **45.** $-\dfrac{1}{8}$ **47.** $\dfrac{1}{2},-\dfrac{5}{6}$ **49.** $2,-\dfrac{12}{5}$ **51.** $3,-2$ **53.** $-8,\dfrac{2}{3}$ **55.** $\varnothing$ **57.** 4   **59.** $13,-8$ **61.** $3,-3$ **63.** $8,-7$

65. $2,3$ **67.** $2,-\dfrac{10}{3}$ **69.** $\dfrac{3}{2}$ **71.** $\varnothing$ **73.** answers may vary   **75.** 33%   **77.** 38.4 lb   **79.** answers may vary   **81.** no solution

83. $|x|=2$ **85.** $|2x-1|=4$ **87. a.** $c=0$ **b.** c is a negative number   **c.** c is a positive number

Mental Math **1.** D   **3.** C   **5.** A

Exercise Set 2.7 **1.** $\longleftrightarrow$ $;[-4,4]$ **3.** $\longleftrightarrow$ $;(1,5)$ **5.** $\longleftrightarrow$ $;(-5,-1)$ **7.** $\longleftrightarrow$ $;[-10,3]$

9. $\longleftrightarrow$ $;[-5,5]$ **11.** $\longleftarrow$ $;\varnothing$ **13.** $\longleftrightarrow$ $;[0,12]$ **15.** $\longleftarrow$ $;(-\infty,-3)\cup(3,\infty)$

17. $\longleftrightarrow$ $;(-\infty,-24]\cup[4,\infty)$ **19.** $\longleftrightarrow$ $;(-\infty,-4)\cup(4,\infty)$ **21.** $\longleftarrow$ $;(-\infty,\infty)$

23. $\left(-\infty, \frac{2}{3}\right) \cup (2, \infty)$ **25.** $\{0\}$ **27.** $\left(-\infty, -\frac{3}{8}\right) \cup \left(-\frac{3}{8}, \infty\right)$

29. $[-2, 2]$ **31.** $(-\infty, -1) \cup (1, \infty)$ **33.** $(-5, 11)$

35. $(-\infty, 4) \cup (6, \infty)$ **37.** $\varnothing$ **39.** $(-\infty, \infty)$ **41.** $[-2, 9]$

43. $(-\infty, -11] \cup [1, \infty)$ **45.** $(-\infty, 0) \cup (0, \infty)$ **47.** $(-\infty, \infty)$

49. $\left[-\frac{1}{2}, 1\right]$ **51.** $(-\infty, -3) \cup (0, \infty)$ **53.** $\varnothing$ **55.** $(-\infty, \infty)$

57. $\left(-\frac{2}{3}, 0\right)$ **59.** $(-\infty, -12) \cup (0, \infty)$ **61.** $[-1, 8]$ **63.** $\left[-\frac{23}{8}, \frac{17}{8}\right]$

65. $(-2, 5)$ **67.** $5, -2$ **69.** $(-\infty, -7] \cup [17, \infty)$ **71.** $-\frac{9}{4}$ **73.** $(-2, 1)$ **75.** $2, \frac{4}{3}$ **77.** $\varnothing$ **79.** $\frac{19}{2}, -\frac{17}{2}$

81. $\left(-\infty, -\frac{25}{3}\right) \cup \left(\frac{35}{3}, \infty\right)$ **83.** $\frac{1}{6}$ **85.** 0 **87.** $\frac{1}{3}$ **89.** -1.5 **91.** 0 **93.** $|x| < 7$ **95.** $|x| \leq 5$ **97.** answers may vary

99. $3.45 < x < 3.55$

Chapter 2 Review

1. 3 **3.** $-\frac{45}{14}$ **5.** 0 **7.** 6 **9.** all real numbers   **11.** $\varnothing$ **13.** -3 **15.** $\frac{96}{5}$ **17.** 32 **19.** 8 **21.** $\varnothing$

23. 2 **25.** -7 **27.** 52 **29.** 55 million viewers   **31.** No such odd integers exist.   **33.** 358 mi   **35.** 5 plants, $200   **37.** $r = \frac{C}{2\pi}$

39. $x = \frac{4y - 12}{5}$ **41.** $x = \frac{y - y_1 + mx_1}{m}$ **43.** $g = \frac{S - vt}{t^2}$ **45.** $P = \frac{I}{1 + rt}$ **47.** $h = \frac{3V}{\pi r^2}$ **49.** $T_2 = \frac{T_1 V_2}{V_1}$ **51.** $\left(\frac{290}{9}\right)°C \approx 32.2°C$

53. 16 packages   **55.** 58 mph   **57.** $(-\infty, -4]$ **59.** $(-17, \infty)$ **61.** $(-\infty, 4]$ **63.** $(-\infty, 1)$ **65.** $(2, \infty)$ **67.** $260° \leq C \leq 538°$

69. $1750 to $3750   **71.** $\left[-2, -\frac{9}{5}\right)$ **73.** $\left(-\frac{3}{5}, 0\right)$ **75.** $\left[-\frac{4}{3}, \frac{7}{6}\right]$ **77.** $(-\infty, \infty)$ **79.** $(5, \infty)$ **81.** $5, 11$ **83.** $-1, \frac{11}{3}$ **85.** $-\frac{1}{6}$

87. $\varnothing$ **89.** $1, 5$ **91.** $\varnothing$ **93.** $-10, -\frac{4}{3}$ **95.** $(-\infty, -4] \cup [1, \infty)$ **97.** $(-3, 3)$

99. $(-\infty, \infty)$ **101.** $\left(-\frac{1}{2}, 2\right)$ **103.** $\varnothing$

Chapter 2 Test

1. 10 **2.** 1 **3.** $\varnothing$ **4.** all real numbers   **5.** $-\frac{80}{29}$ **6.** $1, \frac{2}{3}$ **7.** $\varnothing$ **8.** $\frac{3}{2}$ **9.** $y = \frac{3x - 8}{4}$

10. $g = \frac{S}{t^2 + vt}$ **11.** $C = \frac{5}{9}(F - 32)$ **12.** $(5, \infty)$ **13.** $(-\infty, 2]$ **14.** $\left(\frac{3}{2}, 5\right]$ **15.** $(-\infty, -2) \cup \left(\frac{4}{3}, \infty\right)$ **16.** $(3, 7)$

17. $[-3, -1)$ **18.** $(-\infty, \infty)$ **19.** 9.6 **20.** 211,468 people   **21.** approximately 8 dogs   **22.** more than 850 sunglasses   **23.** $3542.27
24. Tokyo: 29.9 million; Mexico City: 27.8 million; New York: 14.6 million

Chapter 2 Cumulative Review

1. a. $\{2, 3, 4, 5\}$ **b.** $\{101, 102, 103, \dots\}$; Sec. 1.2, Ex. 3   **2. a.** $\{-2, -1, 0, 1, 2, 3, 4\}$

b. $\{4\}$; Sec. 1.2   **3. a.** 3 **b.** 5 **c.** -2 **d.** -8 **e.** 0; Sec. 1.2, Ex. 6   **4. a.** $-\frac{2}{3}$ **b.** 9 **c.** -1.5; Sec. 1.2   **5. a.** -14 **b.** -4

c. 5 **d.** -10.2 **e.** $-\frac{5}{21}$; Sec. 1.3, Ex. 1   **6. a.** 8 **b.** -7.2 **c.** $-\frac{3}{4}$; Sec. 1.3   **7. a.** 3 **b.** 5 **c.** $\frac{1}{2}$; Sec. 1.3, Ex. 7   **d.** -6 **e.** not a

real number   **8. a.** 6 **b.** $\frac{3}{7}$ **c.** 0 **d.** 10; Sec. 1.3   **9. a.** -2 **b.** 9 **c.** -1; Sec. 1.3, Ex. 11   **10. a.** 1 **b.** 2 **c.** 3; Sec. 1.3

11. a. $x + 5 = 20$ **b.** $2(3 + y) = 4$ **c.** $x - 8 = 2x$ **d.** $\frac{z}{9} = 3(z - 5)$; Sec. 1.4, Ex. 1   **12. a.** $>$ **b.** $=$ **c.** $>$; Sec. 1.4

13. $5 + 7x$; Sec. 1.4, Ex. 6   **14.** $5 \cdot (7x) = (5 \cdot 7)x = 35x$; Sec. 1.4   **15.** 2; Sec. 2.1, Ex. 1   **16.** -2; Sec. 2.1   **17.** all real numbers; Sec. 2.1,

Ex. 9   **18.** -4.25; Sec. 2.1   **19. a.** $3x + 3$ **b.** $12x - 3$; Sec. 2.2, Ex. 1   **20. a.** $3x + 3$ **b.** $12x + 4$; Sec. 2.2   **21.** $23, 49$; Sec. 2.2, Ex. 3

22. $11, 35$; Sec. 2.2   **23.** $y = \frac{2x + 7}{3}$ or $y = \frac{2x}{3} + \frac{7}{3}$; Sec. 2.3, Ex. 2   **24.** $x = \frac{10 + 4y}{7}$; Sec. 2.3   **25.** $b = \frac{2A - Bh}{h}$; Sec. 2.3, Ex. 3

26. $l = \frac{P - 2w}{2}$; Sec. 2.3   **27. a.** $[2, \infty)$ **b.** $(-\infty, -1)$ **c.** $(0.5\ 3]$; Sec. 2.4, Ex. 1

28. a. $(-\infty, -3]$ **b.** $[-2, 0.1)$; Sec. 2.4   **29.** $\left[\frac{5}{2}, \infty\right)$; Sec. 2.4, Ex. 5   **30.** $(3, \infty)$; Sec. 2.4

31. $(-\infty, \infty)$; Sec. 2.4, Ex. 7   **32.** $\varnothing$; Sec. 2.4   **33.** $\{4, 6\}$; Sec. 2.5, Ex. 1   **34.** $\{-2, -1, 0, 1, 2, 3, 4, 5\}$; Sec. 2.5   **35.** $(-\infty, 4)$; Sec. 2.5,
Ex. 2   **36.** $(-\infty, 3)$; Sec. 2.5   **37.** $\{2, 3, 4, 5, 6, 8\}$; Sec. 2.5, Ex. 6   **38.** $\varnothing$; Sec. 2.5   **39.** $(-\infty, \infty)$; Sec. 2.5, Ex. 8   **40.** $(-1, 0)$; Sec. 2.5
41. $2, -2$; Sec. 2.6, Ex. 1   **42.** $-5, 5$; Sec. 2.6   **43.** $24, -20$; Sec. 2.6, Ex. 3   **44.** $24, -36$; Sec. 2.6   **45.** 4; Sec. 2.6, Ex. 9   **46.** 2; Sec. 2.6
47. $[-3, 3]$; Sec. 2.7, Ex. 1   **48.** $(-\infty, -1) \cup (1, \infty)$; Sec. 2.7   **49.** $(-\infty, \infty)$; Sec. 2.7, Ex. 6   **50.** $\varnothing$; Sec. 2.7

CHAPTER 3 GRAPHS AND FUNCTIONS

Graphing Calculator Explorations

1. 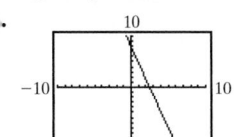 **3.** 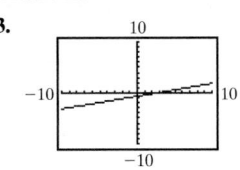 **5.** 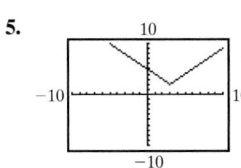 **7.**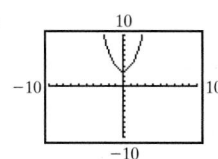

Mental Math **1.** $(5, 2)$ **3.** $(3, -1)$ **5.** $(-5, -2)$ **7.** $(-1, 0)$ **9.** QI **11.** QII **13.** QIII **15.** y-axis **17.** QIII **19.** x-axis

Exercise Set 3.1

1. Quadrant I **3.** Quadrant II **5.** Quadrant IV **7.** y-axis **9.** Quadrant III

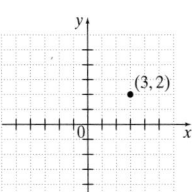 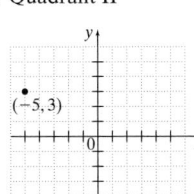 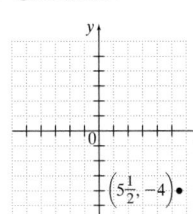 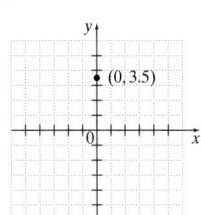 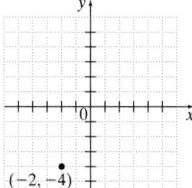

11. Quadrant IV **13.** x-axis **15.** Quadrant III **17.** no; yes **19.** yes; yes **21.** yes; yes **23.** yes; no **25.** yes; yes

27. linear **29.** linear **31.** linear **33.** not linear **35.** linear

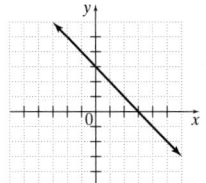 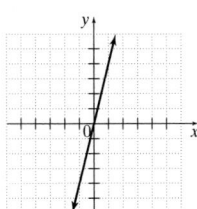 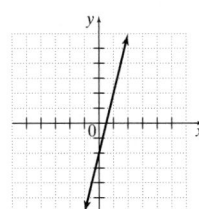 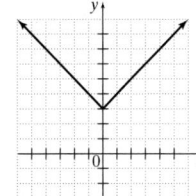 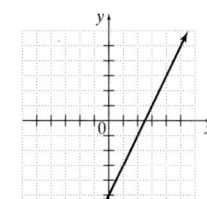

37. not linear **39.** not linear **41.** linear **43.** linear **45.** not linear

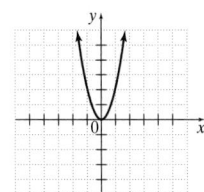 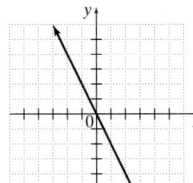 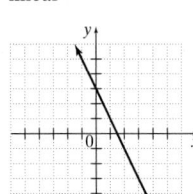 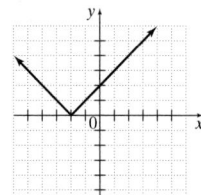

47. not linear **49.** not linear **51.** linear **53.** linear

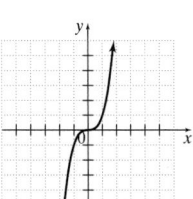 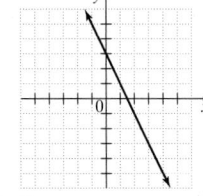 

55. -5 **57.** $-\dfrac{1}{10}$ **59.** $(-\infty, -5]$ **61.** $(-\infty, -4)$ **63.** B **65.** C **67.** 1991 **69.** answers may vary **71.**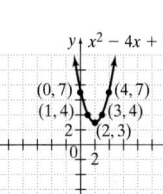

73. a. 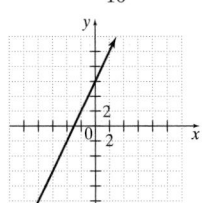 **b.** 14 in. year to year. **75.** $7000 **77.** $500 **79.** Depreciation is the same from year to year. **81.** 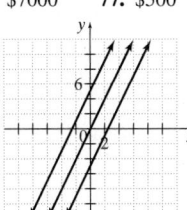 ; answers may vary. **83.** answers may vary

85. $y = -3 - 2x$;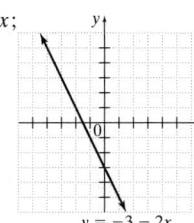

87. $y = 5 - x^2$;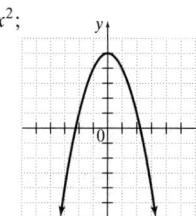

89.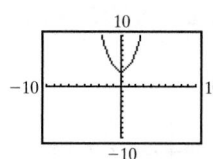

91.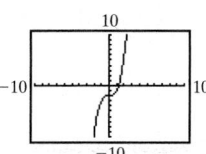

Graphing Calculator Explorations   **1.** 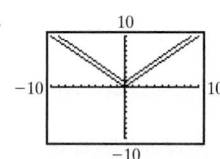   **3.** 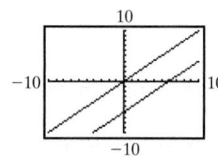   **5.**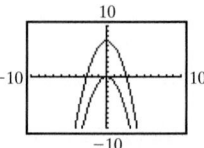

Exercise Set 3.2   **1.** domain: $\{-1, 0, -2, 5\}$; range: $\{7, 6, 2\}$; function   **3.** domain: $\{-2, 6, -7\}$; range: $\{4, -3, -8\}$; not a function

5. domain: $\{1\}$; range: $\{1, 2, 3, 4\}$; not a function   **7.** domain: $\left\{\frac{3}{2}, 0\right\}$; range: $\left\{\frac{1}{2}, -7, \frac{4}{5}\right\}$; not a function   **9.** domain: $\{-3, 0, 3\}$; range:

$\{-3, 0, 3\}$; function   **11.** domain: $\{-1, 1, 2, 3\}$; range: $\{2, 1\}$; function   **13.** domain: $\{$Colorado, Alaska, Delaware, Illinois, Connecticut, Texas$\}$; range: $\{6, 1, 20, 30\}$; function   **15.** domain: $\{32°, 104°, 212°, 50°\}$; range: $\{0°, 40°, 10°, 100°\}$; function   **17.** domain: $\{0\}$; range: $\{2, -1, 5, 100\}$; function   **19.** function   **21.** not a function   **23.** function   **25.** not a function   **27.** function   **29.** domain: $[0, \infty)$; range: $(-\infty, \infty)$; not a function   **31.** domain: $[-1, 1]$; range: $(-\infty, \infty)$; not a function   **33.** domain: $(-\infty, \infty)$; range: $(-\infty, -3] \cup [3, \infty)$; not a function   **35.** domain: $[2, 7]$; range $[1, 6]$; not a function   **37.** domain: $\{-2\}$; range: $(-\infty, \infty)$; not a function   **39.** domain: $(-\infty, \infty)$; range: $(-\infty, 3]$; function   **41.** answers may vary   **43.** yes   **45.** no   **47.** yes   **49.** yes   **51.** yes   **53.** no   **55.** 15   **57.** 38

59. 7   **61.** 3   **63. a.** 0   **b.** 1   **c.** -1 **65. a.** 246   **b.** 6   **c.** $\frac{9}{2}$ **67. a.** -5 **b.** -5 **c.** -5 **69. a.** 5.1   **b.** 15.5

c. 9.533   **71.** $(1, -10)$ **73.** $(4, 56)$ **75.** $f(-1) = -2$ **77.** $g(2) = 0$ **79.** $-4, 0$ **81.** 3   **83.** infinite number   **85. a.** $17.1 billion   **b.** $16.21 billion   **87.** $36.464 billion   **89.** $f(x) = x + 7$ **91.** 25π sq. cm   **93.** 2744 cu. in.   **95.** 166.38 cm   **97.** 163.2 mg   **99. a.** 95.99; per capita consumption of poultry was 95.99 lb in 2000.   **b.** 99.37 lb

101. $5, -5, 6$ 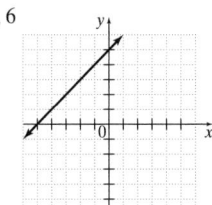   **103.** $2, \dfrac{8}{7}, \dfrac{12}{7}$ 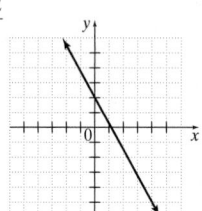   **105.** $0, 0, -6$ 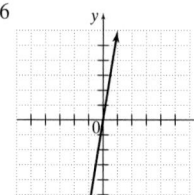   **107.** yes; 170 m

109. a. $-3s + 12$

b. $-3r + 12$

111. a. 132   **b.** $a^2 - 12$

113. answers may vary

Graphing Calculator Explorations

1. $y = \dfrac{x}{3.5}$ **3.** $y = -\dfrac{5.78}{2.31}x + \dfrac{10.98}{2.31}$ **5.** $y = |x| + 3.78$ **7.** $y = 5.6x^2 + 7.7x + 1.5$

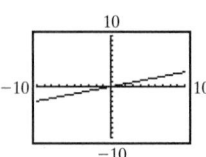   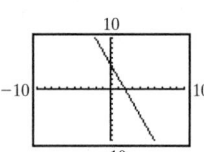   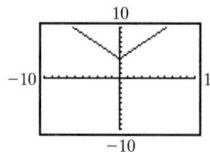   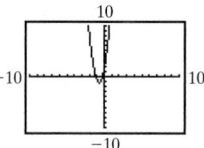

Exercise Set 3.3   **1.** 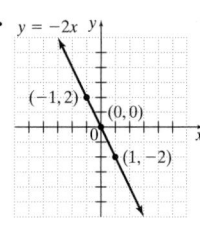   **3.** 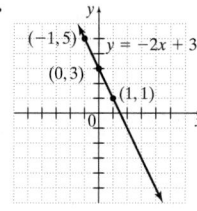   **5.** 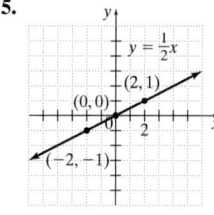   **7.**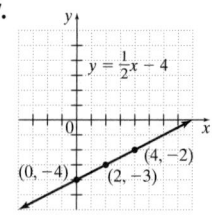

9. C   **11.** D   **13.** 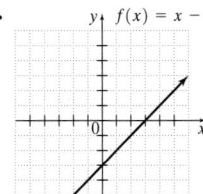   **15.** 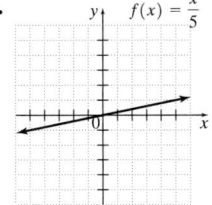   **17.** 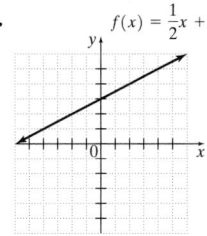   **19.**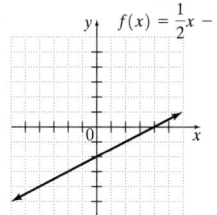

21. answers may vary   **23.** 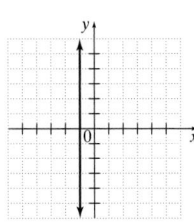   **25.** 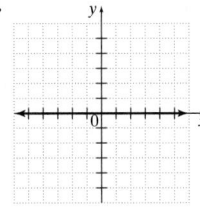   **27.**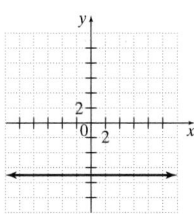

29. C   **31.** A   **33.** The vertical line $x = 0$ has y-intercepts.

35. 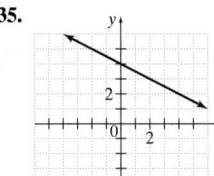   **37.** 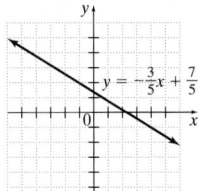   **39.** 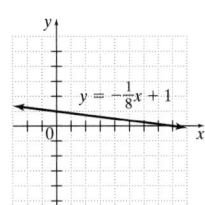   **41.** 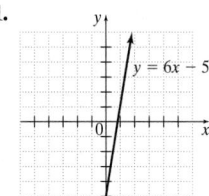   **43.**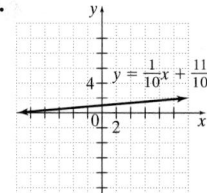

45. 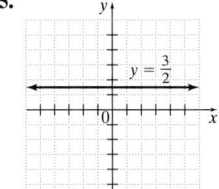   **47.** 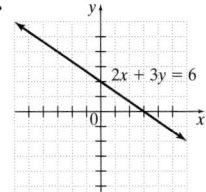   **49.** 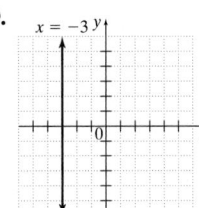   **51.** 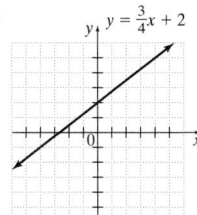   **53.**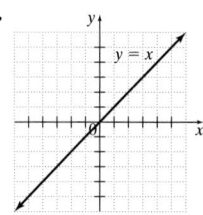

55. 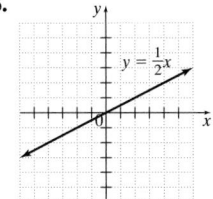   **57.** 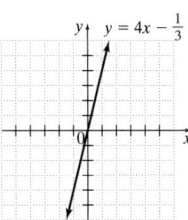   **59.**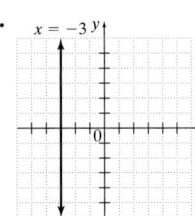

61. $9, -3$ **63.** $(-\infty, -4) \cup (-1, \infty)$

65. $\left[\dfrac{2}{3}, 2\right]$ **67.** $\dfrac{3}{2}$ **69.** 6 **71.** $-\dfrac{6}{5}$

73. a. $(0, 500)$; if no tables are produced, 500 chairs can be produced   **b.** $(750, 0)$; if no chairs are produced, 750 tables can be produced   **c.** 466 chairs

75. a. $64   **b.** 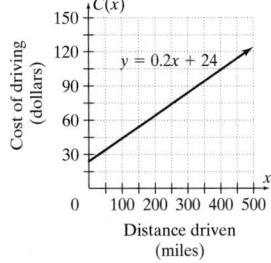   **c.** The line moves upward from left to right.   **77. a.** $1921.88   **b.** 2012   **c.** answers may vary

79. 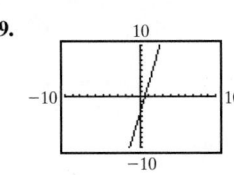   **81.**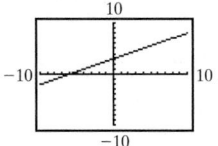

83. a. a line parallel to $-y = -4x$ but with x-intercept $(0, 2)$ **b.** a line parallel to $y = -4x$ but with x-intercept $(0, -5)$ **85.** B   **87.** A

Graphing Calculator Explorations   **1.** 18.4   **3.** −1.5   **5.** 14.0; 4.2, −9.4

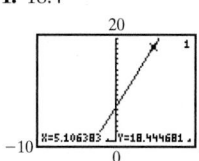   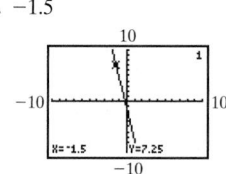   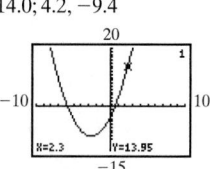

Mental Math   **1.** upward   **3.** horizontally

Exercise Set 3.4   **1.** $\frac{9}{5}$ **3.** $-\frac{7}{2}$ **5.** $-\frac{5}{6}$ **7.** $\frac{1}{3}$ **9.** $-\frac{4}{3}$ **11.** 0   **13.** undefined   **15.** 2   **17.** −1   **19.** l_2 **21.** l_2 **23.** l_2

25. $m = 5, b = -2$ **27.** $m = -2, b = 7$ **29.** $m = \frac{2}{3}, b = -\frac{10}{3}$ **31.** $m = \frac{1}{2}, b = 0$ **33.** A   **35.** B   **37.** undefined   **39.** 0

41. undefined   **43.** answers may vary   **45.** $m = -1, b = 5$ **47.** $m = \frac{6}{5}, b = 6$ **49.** $m = 3, b = 9$ **51.** $m = 0, b = 4$ **53.** $m = 7, b = 0$

55. $m = 0, b = 6$ **57.** slope is undefined, no y-intercept   **59.** neither   **61.** parallel   **63.** perpendicular   **65.** answers may vary   **67.** $\frac{3}{2}$

69. $-\frac{1}{2}$ **71.** $\frac{2}{3}$ **73.** approximately −0.12   **75. a.** $46,221.60   **b.** $m = 1545.4$; The annual income increases $1545.40 every year.

c. $b = 33{,}858.4$; At year $x = 0$, or 1997, the annual average income was $33,858.40.   **77. a.** $m = 24.5, b = 5.9$ **b.** The number of internet access

points increases by 24.5 thousand for every 1 year.   **c.** There were 5.9 thousand internet access points in 2002.   **79. a.** The yearly cost of tuition

increases $174.40 every 1 year.   **b.** The yearly cost of tuition in 1990 was $2074.38.   **81.** $-\frac{7}{2}$ **83.** $\frac{2}{7}$ **85.** $\frac{5}{2}$ **87.** $-\frac{2}{5}$ **89.** $\frac{2}{11}$

91. $\frac{3}{11}$ **93.** $\frac{4}{11}$ **95.** $y = -3x - 30$ **97.** $y = -8x - 23$ **99. a.** $(6, 20)$ **b.** $(10, 13)$ **c.** $-\frac{7}{4}$ or −1.75 yd per sec   **d.** $\frac{3}{2}$ or 1.5 yd per sec

101.   **103. a.**   **b.**   **c.** true

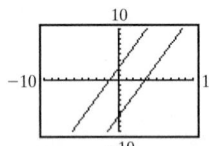   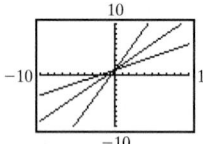   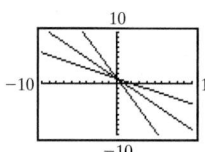

Mental Math   **1.** $m = -4, b = 12$ **3.** $m = 5, b = 0$ **5.** $m = \frac{1}{2}, b = 6$ **7.** parallel   **9.** neither

Exercise Set 3.5   **1.** $y = -x + 1$ **3.** $y = 2x + \frac{3}{4}$ **5.** $y = \frac{2}{7}x$

7.   **9.**   **11.**   **13.** $y = 3x - 1$ **15.** $y = -2x - 1$ **17.** $y = \frac{1}{2}x + 5$

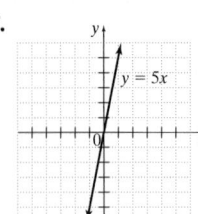   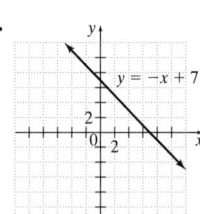   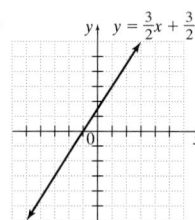 $y = \frac{3}{2}x + \frac{3}{2}$ **19.** $y = -\frac{9}{10}x - \frac{27}{10}$ **21.** $2x + y = 3$

23. $2x - 3y = -7$ **25.** $f(x) = 3x - 6$

27. $f(x) = -2x + 1$ **29.** $f(x) = -\frac{1}{2}x - 5$

31. $f(x) = \frac{1}{3}x - 7$ **33.** answers may vary   **35.** −2   **37.** 2

39. −2   **41.** $y = -4$ **43.** $x = 4$ **45.** $y = 5$ **47.** $f(x) = 4x - 4$ **49.** $f(x) = -3x + 1$ **51.** $f(x) = -\frac{3}{2}x - 6$ **53.** $2x - y = -7$

55. $f(x) = -x + 7$ **57.** $x + 2y = 22$ **59.** $2x + 7y = -42$ **61.** $4x + 3y = -20$ **63.** $x = -2$ **65.** $x + 2y = 2$ **67.** $y = 12$

69. $8x - y = 47$ **71.** $x = 5$ **73.** $f(x) = -\frac{3}{8}x - \frac{29}{4}$ **75. a.** $P(x) = 12{,}000x + 18{,}000$ **b.** $102,000   **c.** end of the ninth yr

77. a. $y = -1000x + 13{,}000$ **b.** 9500 Fun Noodles   **79. a.** $4834x + 133{,}300$ **b.** $176,806   **c.** every year, the median price of a

home increases by $4834.   **81. a.** $y = 29.5x + 757$ **b.** 875 thousand people   **83.** ——————⟶, $(-\infty, 14]$

14

85. ⟵——————, $\left[\frac{7}{2}, \infty\right)$ **87.** ⟵——————⟶ $\left(-\infty, -\frac{1}{4}\right)$ **89.** $-4x + y = 4$ **91.** $2x + y = -23$ **93.** $3x - 2y = -13$

$\frac{7}{2}$ $-\frac{1}{4}$

95.   **97.**   **99.** true

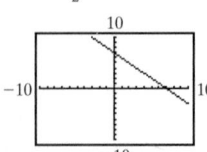   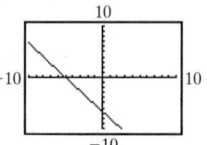

ntegrated Review **1.** 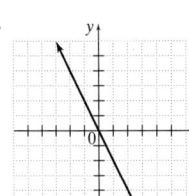 **2.** 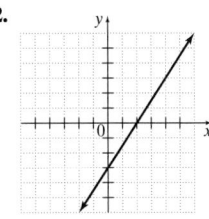 **3.** 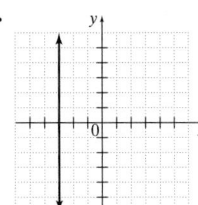 **4.**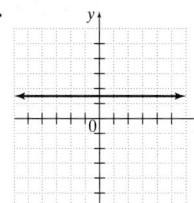

0 **6.** $-\dfrac{3}{5}$ **7.** $m = 3; (0, -5)$ **8.** $m = \dfrac{5}{2}; \left(0, -\dfrac{7}{2}\right)$ **9.** parallel **10.** perpendicular **11.** $y = -x + 7$ **12.** $x = -2$

3. $y = 0$ **14.** $y = -\dfrac{3}{8}x - \dfrac{29}{4}$ **15.** $y = -5x - 6$ **16.** $y = -4x + \dfrac{1}{3}$ **17.** $y = \dfrac{1}{2}x - 1$ **18.** $y = 3x - \dfrac{3}{2}$ **19.** $y = 3x - 2$

0. $y = -\dfrac{5}{4}x + 4$ **21.** $y = \dfrac{1}{4}x - \dfrac{7}{2}$ **22.** $y = -\dfrac{5}{2}x - \dfrac{5}{2}$ **23.** $x = -1$ **24.** $y = 3$

Exercise Set 3.6 **1.** 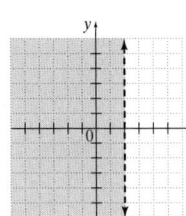 **3.** 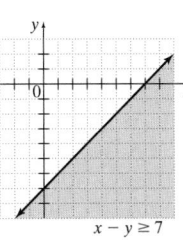 **5.** 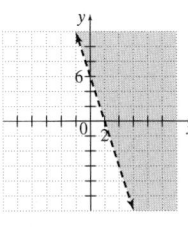 **7.**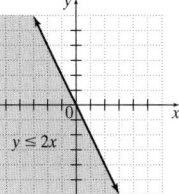

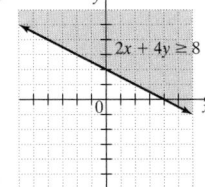 **11.** 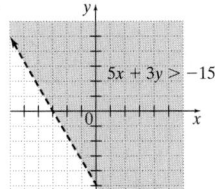 **13.** answers may vary **15.** 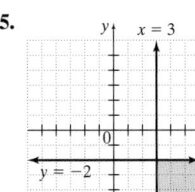 **17.**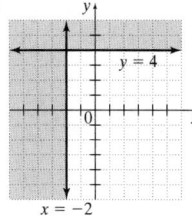

9. 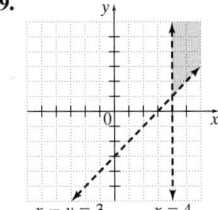 **21.** 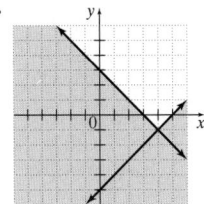 **23.** 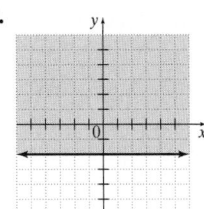 **25.** 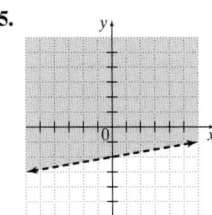 **27.**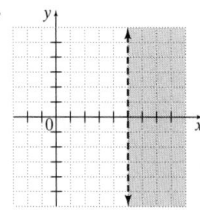

9. 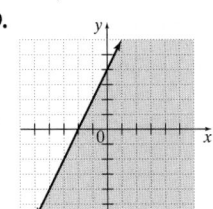 **31.** 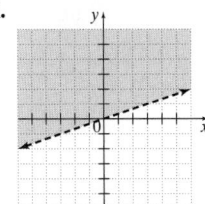 **33.** 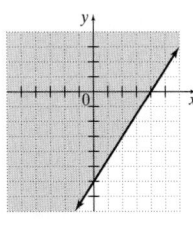 **35.** 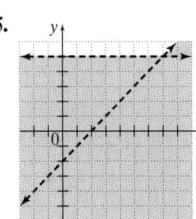 **37.**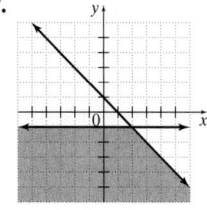

9. 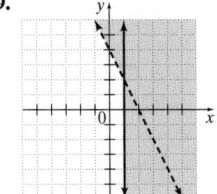 **41.** 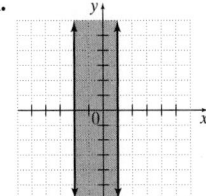 **43.** 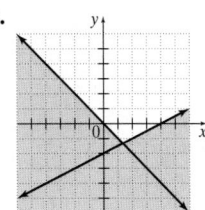 **45.**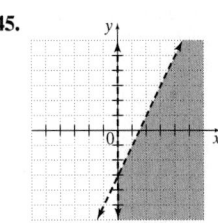

47. D **49.** A **51.** $x \geq 2$ **53.** $y \leq -3$ **55.** $y > 4$ **57.** $x < 1$ **59.** 8 **61.** -25 **63.** 16 **65.** $\dfrac{27}{125}$

67. domain: $[1, 5]$; range: $[1, 3]$; no **69.** $x \leq 20$ and $y \geq 10$. **71.**

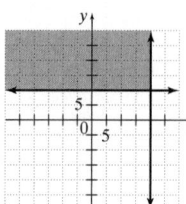 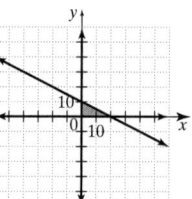

Chapter 3 Review

1. 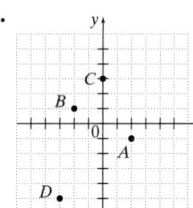 **3.** no, yes **5.** yes, yes **7.** linear 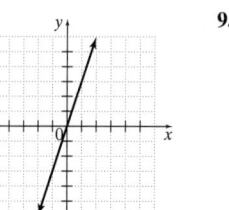 **9.** linear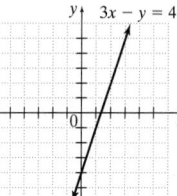

11. nonlinear 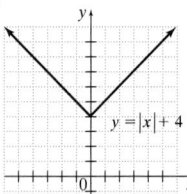 **13.** linear 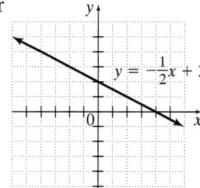 **15.** linear 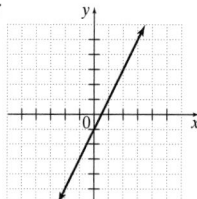 **17.** linear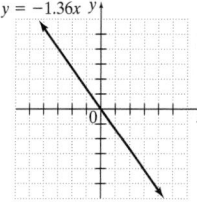

19. domain: $\left\{-\dfrac{1}{2}, 6, 0, 25\right\}$; range: $\left\{\dfrac{3}{4} \text{ or } 0.75, -12, 25\right\}$; function **21.** domain: $\{2, 4, 6, 8\}$; range: $\{2, 4, 5, 6\}$; not a function

23. domain: $(-\infty, \infty)$; range: $(-\infty, -1] \cup [1, \infty)$; not a function **25.** domain: $(-\infty, \infty)$; range: $\{4\}$; function **27.** -3 **29.** 18 **31.** -3

33. 381 lb **35.** 0 **37.** $-2, 4$

39. 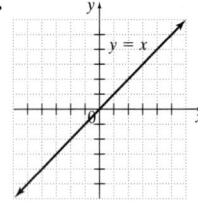 **41.** 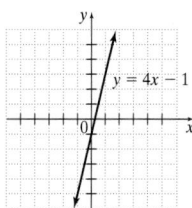 **43.** A **45.** D **47.** 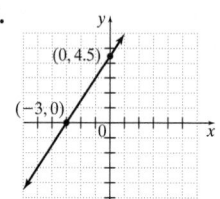 **49.**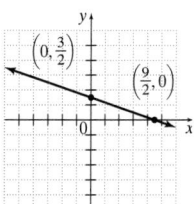

51. 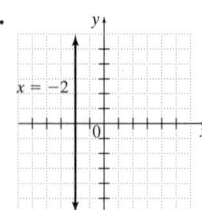 **53.** 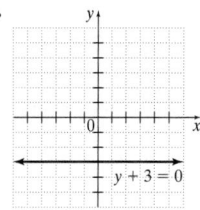 **55.** -3 **57.** $\dfrac{5}{2}$ **59.** $m = \dfrac{2}{5}, b = -\dfrac{4}{3}$ **61.** 0 **63.** l_2 **65.** l_2

67. a. $m = 0.3$; The cost increases by \$0.30 for each additional mile driven.
  b. $b = 42$; The cost for 0 miles driven is \$42.

69. parallel

71. 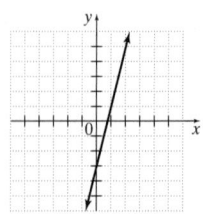 **73.** 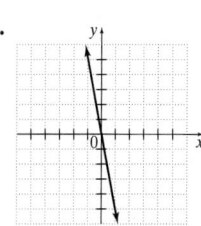 **75.** $x = -2$ **77.** $y = 5$ **79.** $2x - y = 12$ **81.** $11x + y = -52$ **83.** $y = -5$

85. $f(x) = -x - 2$ **87.** $f(x) = -\dfrac{3}{2}x - 8$ **89.** $f(x) = -\dfrac{3}{2}x - 1$

91. a. $y = \dfrac{17}{22}x + 43$ **b.** 52 million

3. 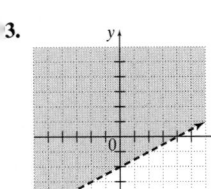 **95.** 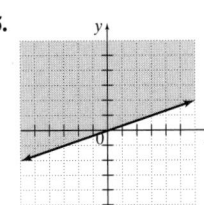 **97.** 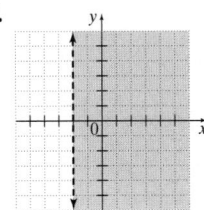 **99.**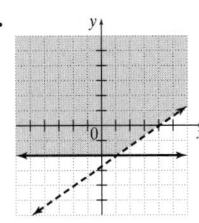

Chapter 3 Test 1. 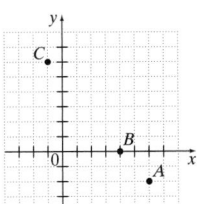 **2.** 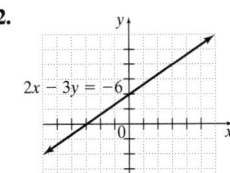 **3.** 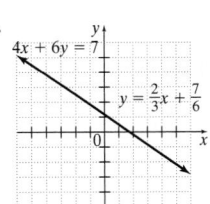 **4.**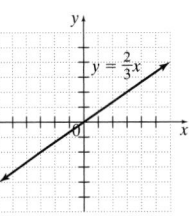

. 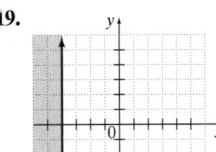 **6.** $-\dfrac{3}{2}$ **7.** $m = -\dfrac{1}{4}, b = \dfrac{2}{3}$ **8.** 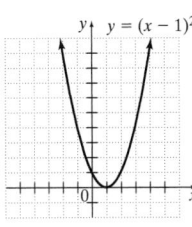 **9.** 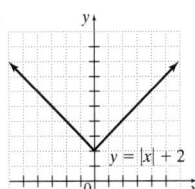 **10.** $y = -8$
11. $x = -4$
12. $y = -2$
13. $3x + y = 11$

14. $5x - y = 2$ **15.** $f(x) = -\dfrac{1}{2}x$ **16.** $f(x) = -\dfrac{1}{3}x + \dfrac{5}{3}$ **17.** $f(x) = -\dfrac{1}{2}x - \dfrac{1}{2}$ **18.** neither

19. 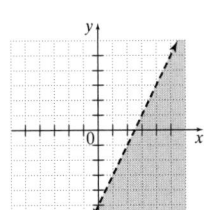 **20.** 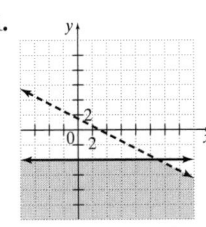 **21.**  **22.** domain: $(-\infty, \infty)$; range: $\{5\}$; function
23. domain: $\{-2\}$; range: $(-\infty, \infty)$; not a function
24. domain: $(-\infty, \infty)$; range: $[0, \infty)$; function
25. domain: $(-\infty, \infty)$; range: $(-\infty, \infty)$; function
26. a. \$22,892   **b.** \$28,016   **c.** 2008   **d.** The average yearly earnings for high school graduates increases \$732 per year.   **e.** The average yearly earnings for a high school graduate in 1996 was \$21,428.

Chapter 3 Cumulative Review 1. 41; Sec. 1.2, Ex. 2   **2. a.** -7 **b.** $\dfrac{5}{6}$ **c.** -13; Sec. 1.3   **3. a.** true   **b.** false   **c.** false

. false; Sec. 1.2, Ex. 5   **4. a.** 7   **b.** 0   **c.** $-\dfrac{1}{4}$; Sec. 1.2   **5. a.** -6 **b.** -7 **c.** -16 **d.** 20.5   **e.** $\dfrac{1}{6}$ **f.** 0.94

. -3; Sec. 1.3, Ex. 2   **6. a.** 7   **b.** 0   **c.** -10; Sec. 1.3   **7. a.** 9   **b.** $\dfrac{1}{16}$ **c.** -25 **d.** 25   **e.** -125 **f.** -125; Sec. 1.3, Ex. 6

8. a. distributive property   **b.** commutative property for addition; Sec. 1.4   **9. a.** $>$ **b.** $=$ **c.** $<$ **d.** $<$; Sec. 1.4, Ex. 2

10. a. 98   **b.** 98; Sec. 1.3   **11. a.** $\dfrac{1}{11}$ **b.** $-\dfrac{1}{9}$ **c.** $\dfrac{4}{7}$; Sec. 1.4, Ex. 5   **12.** 22; Sec. 1.3   **13.** 0.4; Sec. 2.1, Ex. 2   **14.** -17; Sec. 2.1

15. $\{\ \}$ or $\varnothing$; Sec. 2.1, Ex. 8   **16.** all real numbers; Sec. 2.1   **17.** 4; Sec. 2.2, Ex. 4   **18.** 4; Sec. 2.2   **19.** 86, 88 and 90; Sec. 2.2, Ex. 7

20. 69, 71, 73; Sec. 2.2   **21.** $\dfrac{V}{lw} = h$; Sec. 2.3, Ex. 1   **22.** $y = \dfrac{-7x + 21}{3}$ or $y = -\dfrac{7}{3}x + 7$; Sec. 2.3   **23.** $\{x | x < 7\}$ or $(-\infty, 7)$; ←———→ ;

Sec. 2.4, Ex. 2   **24.** $(-\infty, -26]$; Sec. 2.4   **25.** $\left(-\infty, -\dfrac{7}{3}\right]$; Sec. 2.4, Ex. 6   **26.** $(-25, \infty)$; Sec. 2.4   **27.** $\varnothing$; Sec. 2.5, Ex. 3   **28.** $(0, 8)$; Sec. 2.5

29. $\left(-\infty, \dfrac{13}{5}\right] \cup [4, \infty)$; Sec. 2.5, Ex. 7   **30.** $(-\infty, \infty)$; Sec. 2.5   **31.** $-2, \dfrac{4}{5}$; Sec. 2.6, Ex. 2   **32.** $1, -\dfrac{1}{5}$; Sec. 2.6   **33.** $\dfrac{3}{4}, 5$; Sec. 2.6, Ex. 8

34. $-\dfrac{1}{7}$; Sec. 2.6   **35.** $\left[-2, \dfrac{8}{5}\right]$; Sec. 2.7, Ex. 3   **36.** $[-2, 18]$; Sec. 2.7   **37.** $(-\infty, -4) \cup (10, \infty)$; Sec. 2.7, Ex. 5   **38.** $(-\infty, -4) \cup (-2, \infty)$

39. solutions: $(2, -6), (0, -12)$; not a solution $(1, 9)$; Sec. 3.1, Ex. 2   **40.** $m = -\dfrac{7}{2}$, y-intercept $(0, 5)$; Sec. 3.1   **41.** yes; Sec. 3.2, Ex. 3

42. no; Sec. 3.2   **43. a.** $\left(0, \dfrac{3}{7}\right)$ **b.** $(0, -3.2)$; Sec. 3.3, Ex. 3   **44.** $m = 3$; Sec. 3.4   **45.** $\dfrac{2}{3}$; Sec. 3.4, Ex.3   **46.** $x = -2$; Sec. 3.3

47. $y = \frac{1}{4}x - 3$; Sec. 3.5 Ex. 1   **48.** $y = -\frac{3}{4}$; Sec. 3.3   **49.** 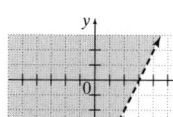   Sec. 3.6; Ex. 1   **50.** $x + y = 3$; Sec. 3.5

CHAPTER 4 SYSTEMS OF EQUATIONS

Graphing Calculator Explorations 1. $(2.11, 0.17)$ **3.** $(0.57, -1.97)$

Mental Math 1. B   **3.** A

Exercise Set 4.1 1. yes   **3.** no   **5.** yes

7. $(2, -1)$ 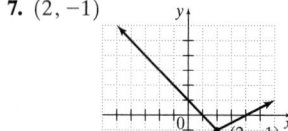   **9.** $(1, 2)$ 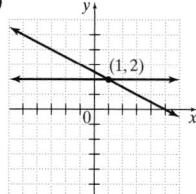   **11.** $\varnothing$ 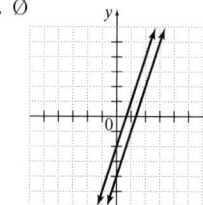   **13.** No; answers may vary   **15.** $(2, 8)$
17. $(0, -9)$ **19.** $(1, -1)$ **21.** $(-5, 3)$
23. $\left(\frac{5}{2}, \frac{5}{4}\right)$ **25.** $(1, -2)$ **27.** $(9, 9)$
29. $(7, 2)$ **31.** $\varnothing$
33. $\{(x, y) \mid 3x + y = 1\}$

35. $\left(\frac{3}{2}, 1\right)$ **37.** $(2, -1)$ **39.** $(-5, 3)$ **41.** $\{(x, y) \mid 3x + 9y = 12\}$ **43.** $\varnothing$ **45.** $\left(\frac{1}{2}, \frac{1}{5}\right)$ **47.** $(8, 2)$ **49.** $\{(x, y) \mid x = 3y + 2\}$

51. $\left(-\frac{1}{4}, \frac{1}{2}\right)$ **53.** $(3, 2)$ **55.** $(7, -3)$ **57.** $\varnothing$ **59.** $(3, 4)$ **61.** $(-2, 1)$ **63.** $(1.2, -3.6)$ **65.** true   **67.** false   **69.** $6y - 4z = 25$

71. $x + 10y = 2$ **73.** 5000 DVDs; $21   **75.** supply greater than demand   **77.** $(1875; 4687.5)$ **79.** makes money

81. for x-values greater than 1875   **83.** answers may vary; One possibility: $\begin{cases} -2x + y = 1 \\ x - 2y = -8 \end{cases}$

85. a. Consumption of red meat is decreasing while consumption of poultry is increasing.   **b.** $(17, 108)$ **c.** In the year 2015, red meat and poultry consumption will each be about 108 pounds per person.   **87.** $\left(\frac{1}{4}, 8\right)$ **89.** $\left(\frac{1}{3}, \frac{1}{2}\right)$ **91.** $\left(\frac{1}{4}, -\frac{1}{3}\right)$ **93.** $\varnothing$

Exercise Set 4.2 1. A, B, C, D   **3.** Yes; answers may vary.   **5.** $(-1, 5, 2)$ **7.** $(-2, 5, 1)$ **9.** $(-2, 3, -1)$
11. $\{(x, y, z) \mid x - 2y + z = -5\}$ **13.** $\varnothing$ **15.** $(0, 0, 0)$ **17.** $(-3, -35, -7)$ **19.** $(6, 22, -20)$ **21.** $\varnothing$ **23.** $(3, 2, 2)$
25. $\{(x, y, z) \mid x + 2y - 3z = 4\}$ **27.** $(-3, -4, -5)$ **29.** $\left(0, \frac{1}{2}, -4\right)$ **31.** $(12, 6, 4)$ **33.** 15 and 30   **35.** 5   **37.** $-\frac{5}{3}$
39. answers may vary   **41.** answers may vary   **43.** $(1, 1, -1)$ **45.** $(1, 1, 0, 2)$ **47.** $(1, -1, 2, 3)$ **49.** answers may vary

Exercise Set 4.3 1. 10 and 8   **3. a.** Enterprise class: 1101 ft; Nimitz class: 1092 ft   **b.** 3.67 foot ball fields   **5.** plane: 520 mph; wind: 40 mph   **7.** 20 qt of 4%; 40 qt of 1%   **9.** United Kingdom; 27,720 students; Spain: 12,292 students   **11.** 9 large frames; 13 small frames   **13.** -10 and -8 **15.** 2005   **17.** tablets: $0.80; pens: $0.20   **19.** speed of plane: 630 mph; speed of wind: 90 mph   **21. a.** answers may vary but notice the slope of each function   **b.** 2006   **23.** 28 cm; 28 cm; 37 cm   **25.** 600 mi   **27.** $x = 75; y = 105$ **29.** 625 units
31. 3000 units   **33.** 1280 units   **35. a.** $R(x) = 450x$ **b.** $C(x) = 200x + 6000$ **c.** 24 desks   **37.** 2 units of Mix A; 3 units of Mix B; 1 unit of Mix C   **39.** 5 in.; 7 in.; 10 in.   **41.** 18, 13, and 9   **43.** 151 free throws; 215 two-point field goals; 39 three-point field goals
45. $x = 60; y = 55; z = 65$ **47.** $5x + 5z = 10$ **49.** $-5y + 2z = 2$ **51.** 1980: 300,000; 2001: 1,400,000   **53.** $a = 3, b = 4, c = -1$

55. $a = 15\frac{5}{6}, b = -10\frac{5}{6}, c = 1065$; 2250 students in 2009

Integrated Review 1. C   **2.** D   **3.** A   **4.** B   **5.** $(1, 3)$ **6.** $\left(\frac{4}{3}, \frac{16}{3}\right)$ **7.** $(2, -1)$ **8.** $(5, 2)$ **9.** $\left(\frac{3}{2}, 1\right)$ **10.** $\left(-2, \frac{3}{4}\right)$

11. $\varnothing$ **12.** $\{(x, y) \mid 2x - 5y = 3\}$ **13.** $(-1, 3, 2)$ **14.** $(1, -3, 0)$ **15.** $\varnothing$ **16.** $\{(x, y, z) \mid x - y + 3z = 2\}$ **17.** $\left(2, 5, \frac{1}{2}\right)$

18. $\left(1, 1, \frac{1}{3}\right)$ **19.** 19 and 27   **20.** 70°; 70°; 100°; 120°

Exercise Set 4.4   **1.** $(2, -1)$ **3.** $(-4, 2)$ **5.** $\emptyset$ **7.** $\{(x, y)|3x - 3y = 9\}$ **9.** $(-2, 5, -2)$ **11.** $(1, -2, 3)$ **13.** $(4, -3)$ **15.** $(2, 1, -1)$ **17.** $(9, 9)$ **19.** $\emptyset$ **21.** $\emptyset$ **23.** $(1, -4, 3)$ **25.** function   **27.** not a function   **29.** -13 **31.** -36 **33.** 0 **35. a.** end of 1984   **b.** black-and-white sets; microwave ovens; The percent of households owning black-and-white television sets is decreasing and the percent of households owning microwave overs is increasing; answers may vary   **c.** in 2002   **d.** no; answers may vary   **37.** answers may vary

Exercise Set 4.5   **1.** 26   **3.** -19 **5.** 0   **7.** $(1, 2)$ **9.** $\{(x, y)|3x + y = 1\}$ **11.** $(9, 9)$ **13.** 8   **15.** 0   **17.** 54

19. $(-2, 0, 5)$ **21.** $(6, -2, 4)$ **23.** 16   **25.** 15   **27.** $\dfrac{13}{6}$ **29.** 0   **31.** 56   **33.** $(-3, -2)$ **35.** $\emptyset$ **37.** $(-2, 3, -1)$

39. $(3, 4)$ **41.** $(-2, 1)$ **43.** $\{(x, y, z)|x - 2y + z = -3\}$ **45.** $(0, 2, -1)$ **47.** $6x - 18$ **49.** $9x - 15$

51.
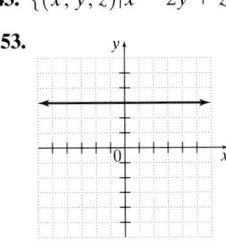
  53.
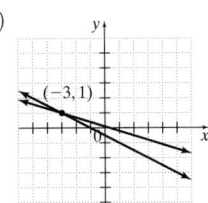
  55. 5   **57.** 0   **59.**

+	−	+	−
−	+	−	+
+	−	+	−
−	+	−	+

  61. -125 **63.** 24

Chapter 4 Review   **1.** $(-3, 1)$
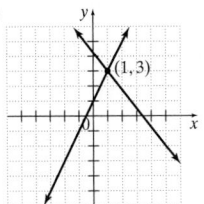
  3. $\emptyset$ **5.** $\left(3, \dfrac{8}{3}\right)$
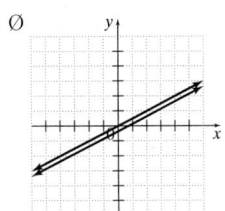
  7. $(2, 0, 2)$

9. $\left(-\dfrac{1}{2}, \dfrac{3}{4}, 1\right)$

11. $\emptyset$

13. $(1, 1, -2)$

15. 10, 40, and 48   **17.** 58 mph, 65 mph   **19.** 20 liters of 10% solution, 30 liters of 60% solution   **21.** 17 pennies, 20 nickels, and 16 dimes

23. Two sides are 22 cm each; third side is 29 cm.   **25.** $(-3, 1)$ **27.** $\left(-\dfrac{2}{3}, 3\right)$ **29.** $\left(\dfrac{5}{4}, \dfrac{5}{8}\right)$ **31.** $(1, 3)$ **33.** $(1, 2, 3)$ **35.** $(3, -2, 5)$

37. $(1, 1, -2)$ **39.** -17 **41.** 34   **43.** $\left(-\dfrac{2}{3}, 3\right)$ **45.** $(-3, 1)$ **47.** $\emptyset$ **49.** $(1, 2, 3)$ **51.** $(2, 1, 0)$ **53.** $\emptyset$

Chapter 4 Test   **1.** 34   **2.** -6 **3.** $(1, 3)$
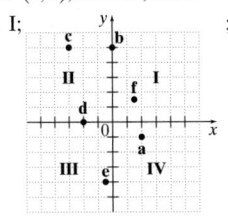
  4. $\emptyset$ **5.** $(2, -3)$ **6.** $\{(x, y)|10x + 4y = 10\}$

7. $(-1, -2, 4)$ **8.** $\emptyset$ **9.** $\left(\dfrac{7}{2}, -10\right)$
10. $(2, -1)$ **11.** $(3, -1, 2)$
12. $\{(x, y)|x - y = -2\}$ **13.** $(5, -3)$

14. $(-1, -1, 0)$ **15.** 53 double rooms and 27 single rooms   **16.** 5 gal of 10%, 15 gal of 20%   **17.** 800 packages   **18.** $23°, 45°, 112°$

Chapter 4 Cumulative Review   **1. a.** true   **b.** true; Sec. 1.2, Ex. 4   **2. a.** false   **b.** true; Sec. 1.2   **3. a.** 6   **b.** -7; Sec. 1.3, Ex. 3

4. a. -5 **b.** -24; Sec. 1.3   **5. a.** -8 **b.** $-\dfrac{1}{5}$ **c.** 9.6; Sec. 1.4, Ex. 4   **6. a.** $\dfrac{1}{5}$ **b.** $-\dfrac{3}{2}$; Sec. 1.4   **7. a.** $6x + 3y$

b. $-3x + 1$ **c.** $0.7ab - 1.4a$; Sec. 1.4, Ex. 8   **8. a.** $21x - 14y + 28$ **b.** $2s + 3t$; Sec. 1.4   **9. a.** $-2x + 4$ **b.** $8yz$ **c.** $4z + 6.1$; Sec. 1.4, Ex. 11   **10. a.** $7y^2 + 3$ **b.** $2.2x + 1.2$; Sec. 1.4   **11.** -4; Sec. 2.1, Ex. 3   **12.** 0; Sec. 2.1   **13.** -4; Sec. 2.1, Ex. 7   **14.** all real numbers; Sec. 2.1   **15.** 25 cm, 62 cm, 62 cm; Sec. 2.2, Ex. 6   **16.** $100°, 100°, 110°, 50°$; Sec. 2.2   **17.** $\{x|x \geq -10\}$![number line at −10]; Sec. 2.4, Ex. 3   **18.** $(0, \infty)$; Sec. 2.4   **19.** $(-3, 2)$; Sec 2.5, Ex. 4   **20.** $(-2, 1)$; Sec. 2.5   **21.** $1, -1$; Sec. 2.6, Ex. 4   **22.** $1, 9$; Sec. 2.6

23. $(4, 8)$; Sec. 2.7, Ex. 2   **24.** $(-\infty, -3) \cup (2, \infty)$; Sec. 2.7   **25. a.** IV   **b.** y-axis   **c.** II   **d.** x-axis   **e.** III

f. I;
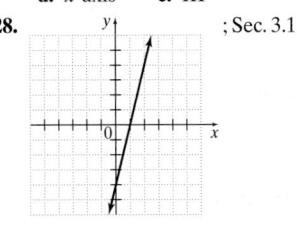
; Sec. 3.1, Ex. 1   **26. a.** III   **b.** IV   **c.** y-axis; Sec. 3.1   **28.** ![graph]; Sec. 3.1

27. yes; Sec. 3.2, Ex. 3

29. a. 5 **b.** 1 **c.** 35 **d.** -2; Sec 3.2, Ex. 7 **30. a.** 75 **b.** 12; Sec. 3.2

31. 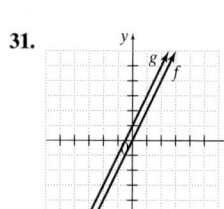 ; Sec. 3.3, Ex. 1 **32.** $m = \dfrac{3}{2}$; Sec. 3.4 **33.** slope: $\dfrac{3}{4}$; y-intercept: $(0, -1)$; Sec 3.4, Ex. 4

34. $m = 0$, y-intercept: $(0, 2)$; Sec. 3.4 **35. a.** parallel **b.** neither; Sec. 3.4, Ex. 8

36. $y = \dfrac{1}{5}x - 9$; Sec. 3.5 **37.** $f(x) = \dfrac{5}{8}x - \dfrac{5}{2}$; Sec. 3.5, Ex. 5 **38.** $y = -2x + 2$; Sec. 3.5

39. 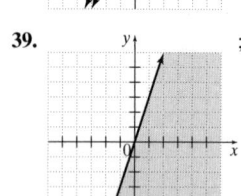 ; Sec. 3.6, Ex. 2 **40.** ; Sec. 3.6 **41. a.** yes **b.** no; Sec 4.1, Ex. 1 **42.** $(-1, 3)$; Sec. 4.2

43. $(-4, 2, -1)$; Sec. 4.2, Ex. 1 **44.** $(-1, 2, 5)$; Sec. 4.3

45. $(-1, 2)$; Sec. 4.4, Ex. 1 **46.** $\varnothing$; Sec. 4.2

CHAPTER 5 EXPONENTS, POLYNOMIALS, AND POLYNOMIAL FUNCTIONS

Graphing Calculator Explorations **1.** 6×10^{43} **3.** 3.796×10^{28}

Mental Math **1.** $\dfrac{5}{xy^2}$ **3.** $\dfrac{a^2}{bc^5}$ **5.** $\dfrac{x^4}{y^2}$

Exercise Set 5.1 **1.** 4^5 **3.** x^8 **5.** $-140x^{12}$ **7.** $-20x^2y$ **9.** $-16x^6y^3p^2$ **11.** -1 **13.** 1 **15.** 6 **17.** answers may vary

19. a^3 **21.** x **23.** $-13z^4$ **25.** $-6a^4b^4c^6$ **27.** $\dfrac{1}{16}$ **29.** $\dfrac{1}{x^8}$ **31.** $\dfrac{5}{a^4}$ **33.** $\dfrac{1}{x^7}$ **35.** $4r^8$ **37.** 1 **39.** $\dfrac{13}{36}$ **41.** 9 **43.** x^{16}

45. $10x^{10}$ **47.** $\dfrac{1}{z^3}$ **49.** y^4 **51.** $\dfrac{3}{x}$ **53.** -2 **55.** r^8 **57.** $\dfrac{1}{x^9y^4}$ **59.** $\dfrac{b^7}{9a^7}$ **61.** $\dfrac{6x^{16}}{5}$ **63.** 3.125×10^7 **65.** 1.6×10^{-2}

67. 6.7413×10^4 **69.** 1.25×10^{-2} **71.** 5.3×10^{-5} **73.** 7.783×10^8 **75.** 7.37×10^5 **77.** 1.41×10^9 **79.** 1.0×10^{-3}
81. 0.0000000036 **83.** 93,000,000 **85.** 1,278,000 **87.** 7,350,000,000,000 **89.** 0.000000403 **91.** 200,000,000 **93.** 4,900,000,000

95. 100 **97.** $\dfrac{27}{64}$ **99.** 64 **101.** $\dfrac{1}{16}$ **103.** answers may vary **105. a.** x^{2a} **b.** $2x^a$ **c.** x^{a-b} **d.** x^{a+b} **e.** $x^a + x^b$ **107.** 7^{13}

109. 7^{-11} **111.** x^{7a+5} **113.** x^{2t-1} **115.** x^{4a+7} **117.** z^{6x-7} **119.** x^{6t-1} **121.** x^{3a+9}

Mental Math **1.** x^{20} **3.** x^9 **5.** y^{42} **7.** z^{36} **9.** z^{18}

Exercise Set 5.2 **1.** $\dfrac{1}{9}$ **3.** $\dfrac{1}{x^{36}}$ **5.** $\dfrac{1}{y^5}$ **7.** $9x^4y^6$ **9.** $16x^{20}y^{12}$ **11.** $\dfrac{c^{18}}{a^{12}b^6}$ **13.** $\dfrac{y^{15}}{x^{35}z^{20}}$ **15.** $\dfrac{1}{125}$ **17.** x^{15} **19.** $\dfrac{8}{x^{12}y^{18}}$

21. $\dfrac{y^{16}}{64x^5}$ **23.** $\dfrac{64}{p^9}$ **25.** $-\dfrac{1}{x^9a^9}$ **27.** $\dfrac{x^5y^{10}}{5^{15}}$ **29.** $\dfrac{1}{x^{63}}$ **31.** $\dfrac{343}{512}$ **33.** $16x^4$ **35.** $-\dfrac{y^3}{64}$ **37.** $4^8x^2y^6$ **39.** 64 **41.** $\dfrac{x^4}{16}$ **43.** $\dfrac{1}{y^{15}}$

45. $\dfrac{x^9}{8y^3}$ **47.** $\dfrac{16a^2b^9}{9}$ **49.** $\dfrac{3}{8x^8y^7}$ **51.** $\dfrac{1}{x^{30}b^6c^6}$ **53.** $\dfrac{25}{8x^5y^4}$ **55.** $\dfrac{2}{x^4y^{10}}$ **57.** 1.45×10^9 **59.** 8×10^{15} **61.** 4×10^{-7} **63.** 3×10^{-1}

65. 2×10^1 **67.** 1×10^1 **69.** 8×10^{-5} **71.** 1.1×10^7 **73.** $8.877840909 \times 10^{20}$ **75.** 2×10^{-3} sec **77.** 6.232×10^{-11} cu. m

79. $-3m - 15$ **81.** $-3y - 5$ **83.** $-3x + 5$ **85.** x^{4b+14} **87.** x^{-3y+1} **89.** c^{6a+9} **91.** y^{26a+1} **93.** $9y^{12a-2}$ **95.** y^{3b-a}

97. $x^{-3a-3b}y^{b-a}$ **99.** $\dfrac{15y^3}{x^8}$ sq. ft **101.** 1.331928×10^{13} **103.** no **105.** 83 people per sq.mi **107.** 3.9 **109.** 4.5 times

Graphing Calculator Explorations **1.** $x^3 - 4x^2 + 7x - 8$ **3.** $-2.1x^2 - 3.2x - 1.7$ **5.** $7.69x^2 - 1.26x + 5.3$

Exercise Set 5.3 **1.** 0 **3.** 2 **5.** 3 **7.** degree 1; binomial **9.** degree 2; trinomial **11.** degree 3; monomial **13.** degree 3;

none of these **15.** answers may vary **17.** 57 **19.** 499 **21.** 1 **23.** $-\dfrac{11}{16}$ **25.** 989 ft **27.** 477 ft **29.** $6y$ **31.** $11x - 3$

47. $-2x^2 - 4x + 15$ **49.** $4x - 13$ **51.** $x^2 + 2$ **53.** $12x^3 + 8x + 8$ **55.** $7x^3 + 4x^2 + 8x - 10$ **57.** $-18y^2 + 11yx + 14$
59. $-x^3 + 8a - 12$ **61.** $5x^2 - 9x - 3$ **63.** $-3x^2 + 3$ **65.** $8xy^2 + 2x^3 + 3x^2 - 3$ **67.** $7y^2 - 3$ **69.** $5x^2 + 22x + 16$
71. $\frac{3}{4}x^2 - \frac{1}{3}x^2y - \frac{8}{3}x^2y^2 + \frac{3}{2}y^3$ **73.** $-q^4 + q^2 - 3q + 5$ **75.** $15x^2 + 8x - 6$ **77.** $x^4 - 7x^2 + 5$ **79.** $\frac{1}{3}x^2 - x + 1$ **81.** 202 sq. in.
83. a. 284 ft **b.** 536 ft **c.** 756 ft **d.** 944 ft **e.** answers may vary **f.** 19 sec **85.** $80,000 **87.** $40,000 **89.** A **91.** D
93. $15x - 10$ **95.** $-2x^2 + 10x - 12$ **97.** $3x^{2a} + 2x^a + 0.7$ **99.** $4x^{2y} + 2x^y - 11$ **101.** $(6x^2 + 14y)$ units **103.** $4x^2 - 3x + 6$
105. $-x^2 - 6x + 10$ **107.** $3x^2 - 12x + 13$ **109.** $15x^2 + 12x - 9$ **111. a.** $2a - 3$ **b.** $-2x - 3$ **c.** $2x + 2h - 3$ **113. a.** $4a$
b. $-4x$ **c.** $4x + 4h$ **115. a.** $4a - 1$ **b.** $-4x - 1$ **c.** $4x + 4h - 1$ **117. a.** 1017 stations **b.** 3806 stations **c.** 331 stations
d. answers may vary **119. a.** 3.1 million SUVs **b.** 5.8 million SUVs **121. a.** $1622 **b.** $3198 **c.** $6087 **d.** No, $f(x)$ is not linear.

Graphing Calculator Explorations **1.** $x^2 - 16$ **3.** $9x^2 - 42x + 49$ **5.** $5x^3 - 14x^2 - 13x - 2$

Exercise Set 5.4 **1.** $-12x^5$ **3.** $12x^2 + 21x$ **5.** $-24x^2y - 6xy^2$ **7.** $-4a^3bx - 4a^3by + 12ab$ **9.** $2x^2 - 2x - 12$
11. $2x^4 + 3x^3 - 2x^2 + x + 6$ **13.** $15x^2 - 7x - 2$ **15.** $15m^3 + 16m^2 - m - 2$ **17.** answers may vary **19.** $x^2 + x - 12$
21. $10x^2 + 11xy - 8y^2$ **23.** $3x^2 + 8x - 3$ **25.** $9x^2 - \frac{1}{4}$ **27.** $x^2 + 8x + 16$ **29.** $36y^2 - 1$ **31.** $9x^2 - 6xy + y^2$ **33.** $9b^2 - 36y^2$
35. $16b^2 + 32b + 16$ **37.** $4s^2 - 12s + 8$ **39.** $x^2y^2 - 4xy + 4$ **41.** answers may vary **43.** $2x^3 + 2x^2y + x^2 + xy - x - y$
45. $x^4 - 8x^3 + 24x^2 - 32x + 16$ **47.** $x^4 - 625$ **49.** $9x^2 + 18x + 5$ **51.** $10x^5 + 8x^4 + 2x^3 + 25x^2 + 20x + 5$ **53.** $49x^2 - 9$
55. $9x^3 + 30x^2 + 12x - 24$ **57.** $16x^2 - \frac{2}{3}x - \frac{1}{6}$ **59.** $36x^2 + 12x + 1$ **61.** $x^4 - 4y^2$ **63.** $-30a^4b^4 + 36a^3b^2 + 36a^2b^3$
65. $2a^2 - 12a + 16$ **67.** $49a^2b^2 - 9c^2$ **69.** $m^2 - 8m + 16$ **71.** $9x^2 + 6x + 1$ **73.** $y^2 - 7y + 12$
75. $2x^3 + 2x^2y + x^2 + xy - x - y$ **77.** $9x^4 + 12x^3 - 2x^2 - 4x + 1$ **79.** $12x^3 - 2x^2 + 13x + 5$ **81.** $a^2 - 3a$
83. $a^2 + 2ah + h^2 - 3a - 3h$ **85.** $b^2 - 7b + 10$ **87.** -2 **89.** $\frac{3}{5}$ **91.** function **93. a.** $a^2 + 2ah + h^2 + 3a + 3h + 2$
b. $a^2 + 3a + 2$ **c.** $2ah + h^2 + 3h$ **95.** $30x^2y^{2n+1} - 10x^2y^n$ **97.** $x^{3a} + 5x^{2a} - 3x^a - 15$ **99.** $\pi(25x^2 - 20x + 4)$ sq. km
101. $(8x^2 - 12x + 4)$ sq. in. **103. a.** $6x + 12$ **b.** $9x^2 + 36x + 35$; one operation is addition, the other is multiplication. **105.** $5x^2 + 25x$
107. $x^4 - 4x^2 + 4$ **109.** $x^3 + 5x^2 - 2x - 10$

Mental Math **1.** 6 **3.** 5 **5.** x **7.** $7x$

Exercise Set 5.5 **1.** a^3 **3.** y^2z^2 **5.** $3x^2y$ **7.** $5xz^3$ **9.** $6(3x - 2)$ **11.** $4y^2(1 - 4xy)$ **13.** $2x^3(3x^2 - 4x + 1)$
15. $4ab(2a^2b^2 - ab + 1 + 4b)$ **17.** $(x + 3)(6 + 5a)$ **19.** $(z + 7)(2x + 1)$ **21.** $(x^2 + 5)(3x - 2)$ **23.** answers may vary
25. $(a + 2)(b + 3)$ **27.** $(a - 2)(c + 4)$ **29.** $(x - 2)(2y - 3)$ **31.** $(4x - 1)(3y - 2)$ **33.** $3(2x^3 + 3)$ **35.** $x^2(x + 3)$
37. $4a(2a^2 - 1)$ **39.** $-4xy(5x - 4y^2)$ **41.** $5ab^2(2ab + 1 - 3b)$ **43.** $3b(3ac^2 + 2a^2c - 2a + c)$ **45.** $(y - 2)(4x - 3)$
47. $(2x + 3)(3y + 5)$ **49.** $(x + 3)(y - 5)$ **51.** $(2a - 3)(3b - 1)$ **53.** $(6x + 1)(2y + 3)$ **55.** $(n - 8)(2m - 1)$ **57.** $3x^2y^2(5x - 6)$
59. $(2x + 3y)(x + 2)$ **61.** $(5x - 3)(x + y)$ **63.** $(x^2 + 4)(x + 3)$ **65.** $(x^2 - 2)(x - 1)$ **67.** $55x^7$ **69.** $125x^6$ **71.** $x^2 - 3x - 10$
73. $x^2 + 5x + 6$ **75.** $y^2 - 4y + 3$ **77.** none **79.** a **81.** $I(R_1 + R_2) = E$ **83.** $x(x + 40)$ sq. in. **85. a.** $h(t) = -16(t^2 - 14)$
b. 160 ft **c.** answers may vary **87.** $y^n(3 + 3y^n + 5y^{7n})$ **89.** $3x^{2a}(x^{3a} - 2x^a + 3)$

Mental Math **1.** 5 and 2 **3.** 8 and 3

Exercise Set 5.6 **1.** $(x + 3)(x + 6)$ **3.** $(x - 8)(x - 4)$ **5.** $(x + 12)(x - 2)$ **7.** $(x - 6)(x + 4)$ **9.** $3(x - 2)(x - 4)$
11. $4z(x + 2)(x + 5)$ **13.** $2(x + 18)(x - 3)$ **15.** $\pm 5, \pm 7$ **17.** $(5x + 1)(x + 3)$ **19.** $(2x - 3)(x - 4)$ **21.** prime polynomial
23. $(2x - 3)^2$ **25.** $2(3x - 5)(2x + 5)$ **27.** $y^2(3y + 5)(y - 2)$ **29.** $2x(3x^2 + 4x + 12)$ **31.** $(x + 7z)(x + z)$ **33.** $(2x + y)(x - 3y)$
35. $(x - 4)(x + 3)$ **37.** $2(7y + 2)(2y + 1)$ **39.** $(2x - 3)(x + 9)$ **41.** $\pm 8, \pm 16$ **43.** $(x^2 + 3)(x^2 - 2)$ **45.** $(5x + 8)(5x + 2)$
47. $(x^3 - 4)(x^3 - 3)$ **49.** $(a - 3)(a + 8)$ **51.** $x(3x + 4)(x - 2)$ **53.** $(x - 27)(x + 3)$ **55.** $(x - 18)(x + 3)$ **57.** $3(x - 1)^2$
59. $(3x + 1)(x - 2)$ **61.** $(4x - 3)(2x - 5)$ **63.** $3x^2(2x + 1)(3x + 2)$ **65.** $3(a + 2b)^2$ **67.** prime polynomial **69.** $(2x + 13)(x + 3)$
71. $(3x - 2)(2x - 15)$ **73.** $(x^2 - 6)(x^2 + 1)$ **75.** $x(3x + 1)(2x - 1)$ **77.** $(4a - 3b)(3a - 5b)$ **79.** $(3x + 5)^2$
81. $y(3x - 8)(x - 1)$ **83.** $2(x + 3)(x - 2)$ **85.** $(x + 2)(x - 7)$ **87.** $(2x^3 - 3)(x^3 + 3)$ **89.** $2x(6y^2 - z)^2$ **91.** $x^2 - 9$
93. $4x^2 + 4x + 1$ **95.** $x^3 - 8$ **97. a.** 576 ft; 672 ft; 640 ft; 480 ft **b.** answers may vary **c.** $-16(t + 4)(t - 9)$ **99.** $(x^n + 8)(x^n + 2)$
101. $(x^n - 6)(x^n + 3)$ **103.** $(2x^n + 1)(x^n + 5)$ **105.** $(2x^n - 3)^2$ **107.** $x^2(x + 5)(x + 1)$ **109.** $3x(5x - 1)(2x + 1)$

Exercise Set 5.7 **1.** $(x + 3)^2$ **3.** $(2x - 3)^2$ **5.** $3(x - 4)^2$ **7.** $x^2(3y + 2)^2$ **9.** $(x + 5)(x - 5)$ **11.** $(3 + 2z)(3 - 2z)$
13. $(y + 9)(y - 5)$ **15.** $4(4x + 5)(4x - 5)$ **17.** $(x + 3)(x^2 - 3x + 9)$ **19.** $(z - 1)(z^2 + z + 1)$ **21.** $(m + n)(m^2 - mn + n^2)$
23. $y^2(x - 3)(x^2 + 3x + 9)$ **25.** $b(a + 2b)(a^2 - 2ab + 4b^2)$ **27.** $(5y - 2x)(25y^2 + 10yx + 4x^2)$ **29.** $(x + 3 + y)(x + 3 - y)$
31. $(x - 5 + y)(x - 5 - y)$ **33.** $(2x + 1 + z)(2x + 1 - z)$ **35.** $(3x + 7)(3x - 7)$ **37.** $(x - 6)^2$ **39.** $(x^2 + 9)(x + 3)(x - 3)$
41. $(x + 4 + 2y)(x + 4 - 2y)$ **43.** $(x + 2y + 3)(x + 2y - 3)$ **45.** $(x - 6)(x^2 + 6x + 36)$ **47.** $(x + 5)(x^2 - 5x + 25)$
49. prime polynomial **51.** $(2a + 3)^2$ **53.** $2y(3x + 1)(3x - 1)$ **55.** $(2x + y)(4x^2 - 2xy + y^2)$ **57.** $(x^2 - y)(x^4 + x^2y + y^2)$
59. $(x + 8 + x^2)(x + 8 - x^2)$ **61.** $3y^2(x^2 + 3)(x^4 - 3x^2 + 9)$ **63.** $(x + y + 5)(x^2 + 2xy + y^2 - 5x - 5y + 25)$

65. $(2x - 1)(4x^2 + 20x + 37)$ **67.** 5   **69.** $-\dfrac{1}{3}$ **71.** 0   **73.** 5   **75.** $\pi R^2 - \pi r^2 = \pi(R + r)(R - r)$

77. $x^3 - y^2x = x(x + y)(x - y)$ **79.** $c = 9$ **81.** $c = 49$ **83.** $c = \pm 8$ **85. a.** $(x + 1)(x^2 - x + 1)(x - 1)(x^2 + x + 1)$
b. $(x + 1)(x - 1)(x^4 + x^2 + 1)$ **c.** answers may vary   **87.** $(x^n + 6)(x^n - 6)$ **89.** $(5x^n + 9)(5x^n - 9)$ **91.** $(x^{2n} + 25)(x^n + 5)(x^n - 5)$

Integrated Review

1. $2y^2 + 2y - 11$ **2.** $-2z^4 - 6z^2 + 3z$ **3.** $x^2 - 7x + 7$ **4.** $7x^2 - 4x - 5$ **5.** $25x^2 - 30x + 9$ **6.** $x - 3$
7. $2x^3 - 4x^2 + 5x - 5 + \dfrac{8}{x + 2}$ **8.** $4x^3 - 13x^2 - 5x + 2$ **9.** $(x - 4 + y)(x - 4 - y)$ **10.** $2(3x + 2)(2x - 5)$
11. $x(x - 1)(x^2 + x + 1)$ **12.** $2x(2x - 1)$ **13.** $2xy(7x - 1)$ **14.** $6ab(4b - 1)$ **15.** $4(x + 2)(x - 2)$ **16.** $9(x + 3)(x - 3)$
17. $(3x - 11)(x + 1)$ **18.** $(5x + 3)(x - 1)$ **19.** $4(x + 3)(x - 1)$ **20.** $6(x + 1)(x - 2)$ **21.** $(2x + 9)^2$ **22.** $(5x + 4)^2$
23. $(2x + 5y)(4x^2 - 10xy + 25y^2)$ **24.** $(3x - 4y)(9x^2 + 12xy + 16y^2)$ **25.** $8x^2(2y - 1)(4y^2 + 2y + 1)$
26. $27x^2y(xy - 2)(x^2y^2 + 2xy + 4)$ **27.** $(x + 5 + y)(x^2 + 10x - xy - 5y + y^2 + 25)$ **28.** $(y - 1 + 3x)(y^2 - 2y + 1 - 3xy + 3x + 9x^2)$
29. $(5a - 6)^2$ **30.** $(4r + 5)^2$ **31.** $7x(x - 9)$ **32.** $(4x + 3)(5x + 2)$ **33.** $(a + 7)(b - 6)$ **34.** $20(x - 6)(x - 5)$
35. $(x^2 + 1)(x - 1)(x + 1)$ **36.** $5x(3x - 4)$ **37.** $(5x - 11)(2x + 3)$ **38.** $9m^2n^2(5mn - 3)$ **39.** $5a^3b(b^2 - 10)$
40. $x(x + 1)(x^2 - x + 1)$ **41.** prime   **42.** $20(x + y)(x^2 - xy + y^2)$ **43.** $10x(x - 10)(x - 11)$ **44.** $(3y - 7)^2$
45. $a^3b(4b - 3)(16b^2 + 12b + 9)$ **46.** $(y^2 + 4)(y + 2)(y - 2)$ **47.** $2(x - 3)(x^2 + 3x + 9)$ **48.** $(2s - 1)(r + 5)$ **49.** $(y^4 + 2)(3y - 5)$
50. prime   **51.** $100(z + 1)(z^2 - z + 1)$ **52.** $2x(5x - 2)(25x^2 + 10x + 4)$ **53.** $(2b - 9)^2$ **54.** $(a^4 + 3)(2a - 1)$ **55.** $(y - 4)(y - 5)$
56. $(c - 3)(c + 1)$ **57.** $A = 9 - 4x^2 = (3 + 2x)(3 - 2x)$

Graphing Calculator Explorations

1. $-3.562, 0.562$ **3.** $-0.874, 2.787$ **5.** $-0.465, 1.910$

Mental Math

1. $3, -5$ **3.** $3, -7$ **5.** $0, 9$

Exercise Set 5.8

1. $-3, \dfrac{4}{3}$ **3.** $\dfrac{5}{2}, -\dfrac{3}{4}$ **5.** $-3, -8$ **7.** $\dfrac{1}{4}, -\dfrac{2}{3}$ **9.** $1, 9$ **11.** $\dfrac{3}{5}, -1$ **13.** 0   **15.** $6, -3$ **17.** $\dfrac{2}{5}, -\dfrac{1}{2}$
19. $\dfrac{3}{4}, -\dfrac{1}{2}$ **21.** $-2, 7, \dfrac{8}{3}$ **23.** $0, 3, -3$ **25.** $2, 1, -1$ **27.** answers may vary   **29.** $-\dfrac{7}{2}, 10$ **31.** $0, 5$ **33.** $-3, 5$ **35.** $-\dfrac{1}{2}, \dfrac{1}{3}$
37. $-4, 9$ **39.** $\dfrac{4}{5}$ **41.** $-5, 0, 2$ **43.** $-3, 0, \dfrac{4}{5}$ **45.** $\varnothing$ **47.** $-7, 4$ **49.** $4, 6$ **51.** $-\dfrac{1}{2}$ **53.** $-4, -3, 3$ **55.** $-5, 0, 5$
57. $-6, 5$ **59.** $-\dfrac{1}{3}, 0, 1$ **61.** $-\dfrac{1}{3}, 0$ **63.** $-\dfrac{7}{8}$ **65.** $\dfrac{31}{4}$ **67.** 1   **69. a.** incorrect   **b.** correct   **c.** correct   **d.** incorrect
71. -11 and -6 or 6 and 11   **73.** 75 ft   **75.** 105 units   **77.** 12 cm and 9 cm   **79.** 2 in.   **81.** 10 sec   **83.** width: $7\dfrac{1}{2}$ ft; length: 12 ft
85. 10 in. sq. tier   **87.** 9 sec   **89.** E   **91.** F   **93.** B   **95.** $(-3, 0), (0, 2)$; function   **97.** $(-4, 0), (0, 2), (4, 0), (0, -2)$; not a function
99. answers may vary   **101.** $\left\{-3, -\dfrac{1}{3}, 2, 5\right\}$ **103.** No; answers may vary.   **105.** answers may vary. Ex.: $f(x) = x^2 - 13x + 42$
107. answers may vary. Ex.: $f(x) = x^2 - x - 12$

Chapter 5 Review

1. 4   **3.** -4 **5.** 1   **7.** $-\dfrac{1}{16}$ **9.** $-x^2y^7z$ **11.** $\dfrac{1}{a^9}$ **13.** $\dfrac{1}{x^{11}}$ **15.** $\dfrac{1}{y^5}$ **17.** -3.62×10^{-4} **19.** 410,000
21. $\dfrac{a^2}{16}$ **23.** $\dfrac{1}{16x^2}$ **25.** $\dfrac{1}{8^{18}}$ **27.** $-\dfrac{1}{8x^9}$ **29.** $\dfrac{-27y^6}{x^6}$ **31.** $\dfrac{xz}{4}$ **33.** $\dfrac{2}{27z^3}$ **35.** $2y^{x-7}$ **37.** -2.21×10^{-11} **39.** $\dfrac{x^3y^{10}}{3z^{12}}$ **41.** 5
43. $12x - 6x^2 - 6x^2y$ **45.** $4x^2 + 8y + 6$ **47.** $8x^2 + 2b - 22$ **49.** $12x^2y - 7xy + 3$ **51.** $x^3 + x - 2xy^2 - y - 7$ **53.** 58
55. $x^2 + 4x - 6$ **57.** $(6x^2y - 12x + 12)$ cm   **59.** $-12a^2b^5 - 28a^2b^3 - 4ab^2$ **61.** $9x^2a^2 - 24xab + 16b^2$ **63.** $15x^2 + 18xy - 81y^2$
65. $x^4 + 18x^3 + 83x^2 + 18x + 1$ **67.** $16x^2 + 72x + 81$ **69.** $16 - 9a^2 + 6ab - b^2$ **71.** $(9y^2 - 49z^2)$ sq. units   **73.** $16x^2y^{2z} - 8xy^zb + b^2$ **75.** $8x^2(2x - 3)$ **77.** $2ab(3b + 4 - 2ab)$ **79.** $(a + 3b)(6a - 5)$ **81.** $(x - 6)(y + 3)$
83. $(p - 5)(q - 3)$ **85.** $x(2y - x)$ **87.** $(x - 4)(x + 20)$ **89.** $3(x + 2)(x + 9)$ **91.** $(3x + 8)(x - 2)$ **93.** $(15x - 1)(x - 6)$
95. $3(x - 2)(3x + 2)$ **97.** $(x + 7)(x + 9)$ **99.** $(x^2 - 2)(x^2 + 10)$ **101.** $(x + 9)(x - 9)$ **103.** $6(x + 3)(x - 3)$
105. $(4 + y^2)(2 + y)(2 - y)$ **107.** $(x - 7)(x + 1)$ **109.** $(y + 8)(y^2 - 8y + 64)$ **111.** $(1 - 4y)(1 + 4y + 16y^2)$
113. $2x^2(x + 2y)(x^2 - 2xy + 4y^2)$ **115.** $(x - 3 - 2y)(x - 3 + 2y)$ **117.** $(4a - 5b)^2$ **119.** $\dfrac{1}{3}, -7$ **121.** $0, 4, \dfrac{9}{2}$ **123.** $0, 6$
125. $-\dfrac{1}{3}, 2$ **127.** $-4, 1$ **129.** $0, 6, -3$ **131.** $0, -2, 1$ **133.** $-\dfrac{15}{2}, 7$ **135.** 5 sec

Chapter 5 Test

1. $\dfrac{1}{81x^2}$ **2.** $-12x^2z$ **3.** $\dfrac{3a^7}{2b^5}$ **4.** $-\dfrac{y^{40}}{z^5}$ **5.** 6.3×10^8 **6.** 1.2×10^{-2} **7.** 0.000005   **8.** 0.0009
9. $-5x^3 - 11x - 9$ **10.** $-12x^2y - 3xy^2$ **11.** $12x^2 - 5x - 28$ **12.** $25a^2 - 4b^2$ **13.** $36m^2 + 12mn + n^2$ **14.** $2x^3 - 13x^2 + 14x - 4$
15. $4x^2y(4x - 3y^3)$ **16.** $(x - 15)(x + 2)$ **17.** $(2y + 5)^2$ **18.** $3(2x + 1)(x - 3)$ **19.** $(2x + 5)(2x - 5)$ **20.** $(x + 4)(x^2 - 4x + 16)$
21. $3y(x + 3y)(x - 3y)$ **22.** $6(x^2 + 4)$ **23.** $2(2y - 1)(4y^2 + 2y + 1)$ **24.** $(x + 3)(x - 3)(y - 3)$ **25.** $4, -\dfrac{8}{7}$ **26.** $-3, 8$
27. $-\dfrac{5}{2}, -2, 2$ **28.** $(x + 2y)(x - 2y)$ **29. a.** 960 ft   **b.** 953.44 ft   **c.** 11 sec

Chapter 5 Cumulative Review   **1. a.** 3   **b.** 1   **c.** 2; Sec. 1.3, Ex. 8   **2. a.** 4   **b.** 3   **c.** 2; Sec. 1.3   **3.** 1; Sec. 2.1, Ex. 4

4. 8; Sec. 2.1   **5.** $11,607.55; Sec. 2.3, Ex. 4   **6.** 3 gals; Sec. 2.3   **7. a.** $\left\{ x \middle| x \le \dfrac{3}{2} \right\}$ **b.** $\{x | x > -3\}$; Sec. 2.4, Ex. 8

   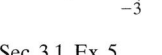

8. $\{x | x \le -5\}$; Sec. 2.4   **11.** 0; Sec. 2.6, Ex. 5   **15.** 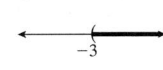   ; Sec. 3.1, Ex. 5   **16.** 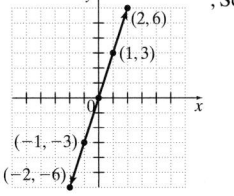   ; Sec. 3.1

$\xrightarrow{\quad}$, $(-\infty, -5]$ **12.** $-4, 4$; Sec. 2.6

9. $\left[-9, -\dfrac{9}{2} \right]$; Sec. 2.5, Ex. 5   **13.** $\varnothing$; Sec. 2.7, Ex. 4

14. $(-\infty, \infty)$; Sec. 2.7

10. $\left(-1, \dfrac{1}{3} \right]$; Sec. 2.5

17. no; Sec. 3.2, Ex. 4   **19.** 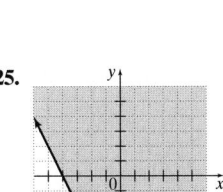   ; Sec. 3.3, Ex. 6   **20.** 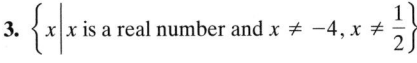   ; Sec. 3.3   **21.** 0; Sec. 3.4, Ex. 7   **22.** -2; Sec. 3.4

18. 24; Sec. 3.2   **23.** $y = 3$; Sec. 3.5, Ex. 7   **24.** $x = -3$; Sec. 3.5

25. 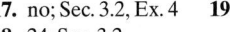   ; Sec. 3.6, Ex. 4   **26.** $y = 3$; Sec. 3.6   **27.** $\left(-4, \dfrac{1}{2} \right)$; Sec. 4.1, Ex. 3   **28.** $(2, 0)$; Sec. 4.1   **29.** $\left(\dfrac{1}{2}, 0, \dfrac{3}{4} \right)$; Sec. 4.2, Ex. 3

30. $(-3, -4, -5)$; Sec. 4.2   **31.** 7, 11; Sec. 4.3, Ex. 2   **32.** 37.5 oz. of 20% solution; 12.5 oz of 60% solution; Sec. 4.3

33. $\varnothing$; Sec. 4.4, Ex. 2   **34.** $(5, 2)$ **35.** $(1, -2, -1)$; Sec. 4.5, Ex. 4   **36.** $(-3, -2, 5)$; Sec. 4.5   **37. a.** 7.3×10^5

b. 1.04×10^{-6}; Sec. 5.1, Ex. 8   **38. a.** 8.25×10^6 **b.** 3.46×10^{-5}; Sec. 5.1   **39. a.** $\dfrac{y^6}{4}$ **b.** x^9 **c.** $\dfrac{49}{4}$

d. $\dfrac{y^{16}}{25x^5}$; Sec. 5.2, Ex. 3   **40. a.** $\dfrac{a^3}{64}$ **b.** $\dfrac{1}{a^4}$ **c.** $\dfrac{27}{8}$ **d.** $\dfrac{b^{17}}{9a^6}$; Sec. 5.2   **41.** 4; Sec. 5.3, Ex. 3

42. $-2x^2 - 5x$; Sec. 5.3   **43. a.** $10x^9$ **b.** $-7xy^{15}z^9$; Sec. 5.4, Ex. 1   **44. a.** $12y^8$ **b.** $-6a^5b^3c^4$; Sec. 5.4   **45.** $17x^3y^2(1 - 2x)$; Sec. 5.5,

Ex. 3   **46.** $3xy(2x + y)(2x - y)$; Sec. 5.7   **47.** $(x + 2)(x + 8)$; Sec. 5.6, Ex. 1   **48.** $(5a - 1)(a + 3)$; Sec. 5.6   **49.** $-5, \dfrac{1}{2}$; Sec. 5.8, Ex. 2

50. $4, -\dfrac{2}{3}$; Sec. 5.8

CHAPTER 6   RATIONAL EXPRESSIONS

Graphing Calculator Explorations   **1.** $\{x | x$ is a real number and $x \ne -2, x \ne 2\}$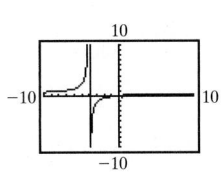

3. $\left\{ x \middle| x \text{ is a real number and } x \ne -4, x \ne \dfrac{1}{2} \right\}$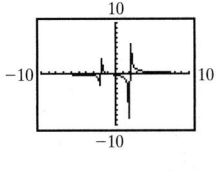

Exercise Set 6.1   **1.** $\dfrac{10}{3}, -8, -\dfrac{7}{3}$ **3.** $-\dfrac{17}{48}, \dfrac{2}{7}, -\dfrac{3}{8}$ **5.** $\{x | x$ is a real number$\}$ **7.** $\{t | t$ is a real number and $t \ne 0\}$

9. $\{x | x$ is a real number and $x \ne 7\}$ **11.** $\left\{ x \middle| x \text{ is a real number and } x \ne \dfrac{1}{3} \right\}$ **13.** $\{x | x$ is a real number and $x \ne -2, x \ne 0, x \ne 1\}$

15. $\{x | x$ is a real number and $x \ne 2, x \ne -2\}$ **17.** answers may vary   **19.** $\dfrac{4}{3}$ **21.** -2 **23.** $\dfrac{x + 1}{x - 3}$ **25.** $\dfrac{2(x + 3)}{x - 3}$ **27.** $\dfrac{3}{x}$

29. $\dfrac{x + 1}{x^2 + 1}$ **31.** $\dfrac{1}{2(q - 1)}$ **33.** $x - 4$ **35.** $-x^2 - 5x - 25$ **37.** $\dfrac{4x^2 + 6x + 9}{2}$ **39.** D   **41.** $-\dfrac{2}{3x^3y^2}$ **43.** $\dfrac{4}{ab^6}$ **45.** $\dfrac{1}{4a(a - b)}$

47. $\dfrac{(x + 2)(x + 3)}{4}$ **49.** $\dfrac{3}{2(x - 1)}$ **51.** $\dfrac{4a^2}{a - b}$ **53.** $\dfrac{2(x + 3)(x - 3)}{5(x^2 - 8x - 15)}$ **55.** $\dfrac{x + 2}{x + 3}$ **57.** $\dfrac{3b}{a - b}$ **59.** $\dfrac{3a}{a - b}$ **61.** $\dfrac{1}{4}$ **63.** -1

65. $\dfrac{8}{3}$ **67.** $\dfrac{8(a - 2)}{3(a + 2)}$ **69.** $\dfrac{8}{x^2y}$ **71.** $\dfrac{(y + 5)(2x - 1)}{(y + 2)(5x + 1)}$ **73.** $\dfrac{5(3a + 2)}{a}$ **75.** $\dfrac{5x^2 - 2}{(x - 1)^2}$ **77.** $\dfrac{7}{5}$ **79.** $\dfrac{1}{12}$ **81.** $\dfrac{11}{16}$

83. $\dfrac{5}{x-2}$ sq. m **85. a.** $\{x\,|\,0 \le x < 100\}$ **b.** \$42,857.14 **c.** \$150,000; \$400,000 **d.** \$900,000; \$1,900,000; \$9,900,000; answers may vary

87. answers may vary **89.** $\dfrac{(x+2)(x-1)^2}{x^5}$ ft. **91.** $0, \dfrac{20}{9}, \dfrac{60}{7}, 20, \dfrac{140}{3}, 180, 380, 1980;$

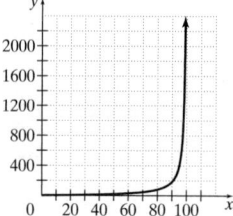

93. $2x^2(x^n + 2)$ **95.** $\dfrac{1}{10y(y^n + 3)}$ **97.** $\dfrac{y^n + 1}{2(y^n - 1)}$

Mental Math **1.** A, B **3.** C **5.** $\dfrac{12}{y}$ **7.** $\dfrac{35}{y^2}$

Exercise Set 6.2 **1.** $-\dfrac{3}{x}$ **3.** $\dfrac{x+2}{x-2}$ **5.** $x-2$ **7.** $\dfrac{1}{2-x}$ **9.** $\dfrac{4x}{x+5}$ ft; $\dfrac{x^2}{x^2 + 10x + 25}$ sq. ft **11.** $35x$ **13.** $x(x+1)$

15. $(x+7)(x-7)$ **17.** $6(x+2)(x-2)$ **19.** $(3x-1)(x+2)$ **21.** $(a+b)(a-b)^2$ **23.** $-4x(x+3)(x-3)$

25. answers may vary **27.** $\dfrac{17}{6x}$ **29.** $\dfrac{35-4y}{14y^2}$ **31.** $\dfrac{-13x+4}{(x+4)(x-4)}$ **33.** $\dfrac{2x+4}{(x-5)(x+4)}$ **35.** 0 **37.** $-\dfrac{x}{x-1}$ **39.** $\dfrac{-x+1}{x-2}$

41. $\dfrac{y^2 + 2y + 10}{(y+4)(y-4)(y-2)}$ **43.** $\dfrac{5(x^2 + x - 4)}{(3x+2)(x+3)(2x-5)}$ **45.** $\dfrac{x^2 + 5x + 21}{(x-2)(x+1)(x+3)}$ **47.** $\dfrac{-2x+5}{2(x+1)}$ **49.** $\dfrac{2(x^2 + x - 21)}{(x+3)^2(x-3)}$

51. $\dfrac{3}{x^2 y^3}$ **53.** $-\dfrac{5}{x}$ **55.** $\dfrac{25}{6(x+5)}$ **57.** $\dfrac{-2x-1}{x^2(x-3)}$ **59.** $\dfrac{2ab - b^2}{(a+b)(a-b)}$ **61.** $\dfrac{2x+16}{(x+2)^2(x-2)}$ **63.** $\dfrac{5a+1}{(a+1)^2(a-1)}$

65. answers may vary **67.** answers may vary **69.** $\dfrac{2x^2 + 9x - 18}{6x^2}$ **71.** $\dfrac{4}{3}$ **73.** $\dfrac{4a^2}{9(a-1)}$ **75.** 4 **77.** $\dfrac{6x}{(x+3)(x-3)^2}$

79. $-\dfrac{4}{x-1}$ **81.** $-\dfrac{32}{x(x+2)(x-2)}$ **83.** 10 **85.** $4 + x^2$ **87.** 10 **89.** 2 **91.** 3 **93.** 5 m **95.** $\dfrac{3}{2x}$ **97.** $\dfrac{4-3x}{x^2}$

99. $\dfrac{1-3x}{x^3}$ **101.** 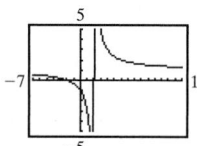 **103.**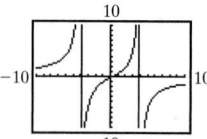

Exercise Set 6.3 **1.** 4 **3.** $\dfrac{7}{13}$ **5.** $\dfrac{4}{x}$ **7.** $\dfrac{9(x-2)}{9x^2 + 4}$ **9.** $2x + y$ **11.** $\dfrac{2(x+1)}{2x-1}$ **13.** $\dfrac{2x+3}{4-9x}$ **15.** $\dfrac{1}{x^2 - 2x + 4}$ **17.** $\dfrac{x}{5x-10}$

19. $\dfrac{x-2}{2x-1}$ **21.** $\dfrac{x}{2-3x}$ **23.** $-\dfrac{y}{x+y}$ **25.** $-\dfrac{2x^3}{y(x-y)}$ **27.** $\dfrac{2x+1}{y}$ **29.** $\dfrac{x-3}{9}$ **31.** $\dfrac{1}{x+2}$ **33.** $\dfrac{xy^2}{x^2 + y^2}$ **35.** $\dfrac{2b^2 + 3a}{b(b-a)}$

37. $\dfrac{x}{(x+1)(x-1)}$ **39.** $\dfrac{1+a}{1-a}$ **41.** $\dfrac{x(x+6y)}{2y}$ **43.** $\dfrac{5a}{2a+4}$ **45.** $5xy^2 + 2x^2y$ **47.** $\dfrac{xy}{2x+5y}$ **49.** $\dfrac{x^2 y^2}{4}$ **51.** $-9x^3 y^4$

53. $-4, 14$ **55.** $\dfrac{770a}{770 - s}$ **57.** a, b **59.** $\dfrac{1+x}{2+x}$ **61.** $x^2 + x$ **63.** $\dfrac{x-3y}{x+3y}$ **65.** $3a^2 + 4a + 4$ **67. a.** $\dfrac{1}{a+h}$ **b.** $\dfrac{1}{a}$

c. $\dfrac{\dfrac{1}{a+h} - \dfrac{1}{a}}{h}$ **d.** $\dfrac{-1}{a(a+h)}$ **69. a.** $\dfrac{3}{a+h+1}$ **b.** $\dfrac{3}{a+1}$ **c.** $\dfrac{\dfrac{3}{a+h+1} - \dfrac{3}{a+1}}{h}$ **d.** $\dfrac{-3}{(a+h+1)(a+1)}$

Exercise Set 6.4 **1.** $2a + 4$ **3.** $3ab + 4$ **5.** $2y + \dfrac{3y}{x} - \dfrac{2y}{x^2}$ **7.** $x^2 + 2x + 1$ **9.** $(x^4 + 2x^2 - 6)$ m **11.** $x + 1$ **13.** $2x - 8 + \dfrac{1}{x+1}$

15. $x - \dfrac{1}{2}$ **17.** $2x^2 - \dfrac{1}{2}x + 5$ **19.** $(3x - 7)$ in. **21.** $\dfrac{5b^5}{2a^3}$ **23.** $x^3 y^3 - 1$ **25.** $a + 3$ **27.** $2x + 5$ **29.** $4y - 6y^2$

31. $2x + 23 + \dfrac{130}{x-5}$ **33.** $10x + 3y - 6x^2 y^2$ **35.** $2x + 4$ **37.** $y + 5$ **39.** $2x + 3$ **41.** $2x^2 - 8x + 38 - \dfrac{156}{x+4}$ **43.** $3x + 3 - \dfrac{1}{x-1}$

45. $-2x^3 + 3x^2 - x + 4$ **47.** $3x^3 + 5x + 4 - \dfrac{2x}{x^2 - 2}$ **49.** $x - \dfrac{5}{3x^2}$ **51.** $=$ **53.** $=$ **55.** $(-9, -1)$ **57.** $(-\infty, -8] \cup [1, \infty)$

59. 4 **61.** 372 **63.** answers may vary **65.** $x^3 + \dfrac{5}{3}x^2 + \dfrac{5}{3}x + \dfrac{8}{3} + \dfrac{8}{3(x-1)}$ **67.** $\dfrac{3}{2}x^3 + \dfrac{1}{4}x^2 + \dfrac{1}{8}x - \dfrac{7}{16} + \dfrac{1}{16(2x-1)}$

69. $x^3 - \dfrac{2}{5}x$ **71.** $5x - 1 + \dfrac{6}{x}; x \ne 0$ **73.** $7x^3 + 14x^2 + 25x + 50 + \dfrac{102}{x-2}; x \ne 2$ **75.** answers may vary

Exercise Set 6.5   **1.** $x + 8$ **3.** $x - 1$ **5.** $x^2 - 5x - 23 - \dfrac{41}{x - 2}$ **7.** $4x + 8 + \dfrac{7}{x - 2}$ **9.** 3   **11.** 73   **13.** -8

15. $x^2 + \dfrac{2}{x - 3}$ **17.** $6x + 7 + \dfrac{1}{x + 1}$ **19.** $2x^3 - 3x^2 + x - 4$ **21.** $3x - 9 + \dfrac{12}{x + 3}$ **23.** $3x^2 - \dfrac{9}{2}x + \dfrac{7}{4} + \dfrac{47}{8\left(x - \frac{1}{2}\right)}$

25. $3x^2 + 3x - 3$ **27.** $3x^2 + 4x - 8 + \dfrac{20}{x + 1}$ **29.** $x^2 + x + 1$ **31.** $x - 6$ **33.** 1   **35.** -133 **37.** 3   **39.** $-\dfrac{187}{81}$ **41.** $\dfrac{95}{32}$

43. answers may vary   **45.** $-\dfrac{5}{6}$ **47.** 2   **49.** 54   **51.** $(x - 1)(x^2 + x + 1)$ **53.** $(5z + 2)(25z^2 - 10z + 4)$ **55.** $(y + 2)(x + 3)$

57. $x(x + 3)(x - 3)$ **59.** $(x + 3)(x^2 + 4) = x^3 + 3x^2 + 4x + 12$ **61.** 0   **63.** $x^3 + 2x^2 + 7x + 28$ **65.** $(x - 1)$ m

Exercise Set 6.6   **1.** 72   **3.** 2   **5.** 6   **7.** $2, -2$ **9.** Ø   **11.** $-\dfrac{28}{3}$ **13.** 3   **15.** -8 **17.** 3   **19.** Ø   **21.** 1   **23.** 3

25. -1 **27.** 6   **29.** $\dfrac{1}{3}$ **31.** $-5, 5$ **33.** 3   **35.** 7   **37.** Ø   **39.** $\dfrac{4}{3}$ **41.** -12 **43.** $1, \dfrac{11}{4}$ **45.** $-5, -1$ **47.** $-\dfrac{7}{5}$ **49.** 5

51. length, 15 in.; width, 10 in.   **53.** 10%   **55.** 25–29 and 30–34   **57.** 6785 inmates   **59.** 800 pencil sharpeners   **61.** $\dfrac{1}{9}, -\dfrac{1}{4}$ **63.** $3, 2$

65. 1.39   **67.** -0.08 **69.** 1, 2   **71.** $-3, -\dfrac{3}{4}$ **73.**   **75.**

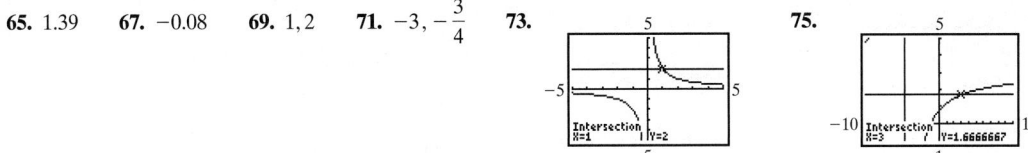

Integrated Review   **1.** $\dfrac{1}{2}$ **2.** 10   **3.** $\dfrac{1 + 2x}{8}$ **4.** $\dfrac{15 + x}{10}$ **5.** $\dfrac{2(x - 4)}{(x + 2)(x - 1)}$ **6.** $-\dfrac{5(x - 8)}{(x - 2)(x + 4)}$ **7.** 4   **8.** 8   **9.** -5

10. $-\dfrac{2}{3}$ **11.** $\dfrac{2x + 5}{x(x - 3)}$ **12.** $\dfrac{5}{2x}$ **13.** -2 **14.** $-\dfrac{y}{x}$ **15.** $\dfrac{(a + 3)(a + 1)}{a + 2}$ **16.** $\dfrac{-a^2 + 31a + 10}{5(a - 6)(a + 1)}$ **17.** $-\dfrac{1}{5}$ **18.** $-\dfrac{3}{13}$

19. $\dfrac{4a + 1}{(3a + 1)(3a - 1)}$ **20.** $\dfrac{-a - 8}{4a(a - 2)}$ or $-\dfrac{a + 8}{4a(a - 2)}$ **21.** $-1, \dfrac{3}{2}$ **22.** $\dfrac{x^2 - 3x + 10}{2(x + 3)(x - 3)}$ **23.** $\dfrac{3}{x + 1}$ **24.** $\{x \mid x$ is a real number and

$x \neq 2, x \neq -1\}$ **25.** -1 **26.** $\dfrac{22z - 45}{3z(z - 3)}$ **27. a.** $\dfrac{x}{5} - \dfrac{x}{4} + \dfrac{1}{10}$ **b.** Write each rational expression term so that the denominator is the

LCD, 20.   **c.** $\dfrac{-x + 2}{20}$ **28. a.** $\dfrac{x}{5} - \dfrac{x}{4} = \dfrac{1}{10}$ **b.** Clear the equation of fractions by multiplying each term by the LCD, 20.   **c.** -2 **29.** b

30. d   **31.** d   **32.** a   **33.** d

Exercise Set 6.7   **1.** $C = \dfrac{5}{9}(F - 32)$ **3.** $I = A - QL$ **5.** $R = \dfrac{R_1 R_2}{R_1 + R_2}$ **7.** $n = \dfrac{2S}{a + L}$ **9.** $b = \dfrac{2A - ah}{h}$ **11.** $T_2 = \dfrac{P_2 V_2 T_1}{P_1 V_1}$

13. $f_2 = \dfrac{f_1 f}{f_1 - f}$ **15.** $L = \dfrac{n\lambda}{2}$ **17.** $c = \dfrac{2L\omega}{\theta}$ **19.** 1 and 5   **21.** 5   **23.** 4.5 gal   **25.** 3643 women   **27.** 15.6 hr   **29.** 10 min

31. 200 mph   **33.** 15 mph   **35.** -8 and -7 **37.** 36 min   **39.** 45 mph; 60 mph   **41.** 5.9 hr   **43.** 2 hr   **45.** 135 mph   **47.** 12 mi

49. $2\dfrac{2}{9}$ hr   **51.** $\dfrac{7}{8}$ **53.** $1\dfrac{1}{2}$ min   **55.** 63 mph   **57.** 1 hr   **59.** 2 hr   **61.** $\{6\}$ **63.** $\{22\}$ **65.** answers may vary; 60 in. or 5 ft

67. 6 ohms   **69.** $\dfrac{1}{R} = \dfrac{1}{R_1} + \dfrac{1}{R_2} + \dfrac{1}{R_3}; R = \dfrac{15}{13}$ ohms

Mental Math   **1.** direct   **3.** joint   **5.** inverse   **7.** direct

Exercise Set 6.8   **1.** $y = kx$ **3.** $a = \dfrac{k}{b}$ **5.** $y = kxz$ **7.** $y = \dfrac{k}{x^3}$ **9.** $y = \dfrac{kx}{p^2}$ **11.** $k = \dfrac{1}{5}; y = \dfrac{1}{5}x$ **13.** $k = \dfrac{3}{2}; y = \dfrac{3}{2}x$

15. $k = 14; y = 14x$ **17.** $k = 0.25; y = 0.25x$ **19.** 4.05 lb   **21.** $P = 566{,}222$ tons   **23.** $k = 30; y = \dfrac{30}{x}$ **25.** $k = 700; y = \dfrac{700}{x}$

27. $k = 2; y = \dfrac{2}{x}$ **29.** $k = 0.14; y = \dfrac{0.14}{x}$ **31.** 54 mph   **33.** 72 amps   **35.** divided by 4   **37.** $x = kyz$ **39.** $r = kst^3$

41. $k = \dfrac{1}{3}; y = \dfrac{1}{3}x^3$ **43.** $k = 0.2; y = 0.2\sqrt{x}$ **45.** $k = 1.3; y = \dfrac{1.3}{x^2}$ **47.** $k = 3; y = 3xz^3$ **49.** 22.5 tons   **51.** 15π cu. in.

53. 90 hp   **55.** 800 millibars   **57.** $C = 12\pi$ cm; $A = 36\pi$ sq. cm   **59.** $C = 14\pi$ m; $A = 49\pi$ sq. m   **61.** 6   **63.** 2   **65.** $\dfrac{1}{5}$ **67.** $\dfrac{5}{11}$

69. multiplied by 2   **71.** multiplied by 4

73.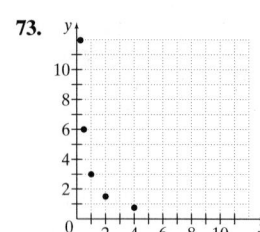

75.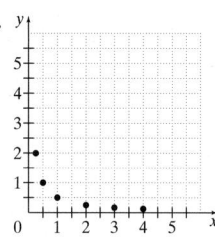

Chapter 6 Review

1. $\{x \mid x \text{ is a real number}\}$ **3.** $\{x \mid x \text{ is a real number and } x \neq 5\}$ **5.** $\{x \mid x \text{ is a real number and } x \neq 0, x \neq -8\}$

7. $\dfrac{x^2}{3}$ **9.** $\dfrac{9m^2p}{5}$ **11.** $\dfrac{1}{5}$ **13.** $\dfrac{1}{x-1}$ **15.** $\dfrac{2(x-3)}{x-4}$ **17. a.** \$119   **b.** \$77   **c.** decrease   **19.** $\dfrac{2x^3}{z^3}$ **21.** $\dfrac{2}{5}$ **23.** $\dfrac{1}{6}$

25. $\dfrac{3x}{16}$ **27.** $\dfrac{3c^2}{14a^2b}$ **29.** $\dfrac{(x+4)(x+5)}{3}$ **31.** $\dfrac{7(x-4)}{2(x-2)}$ **33.** $-\dfrac{1}{x}$ **35.** $\dfrac{8}{9a^2}$ **37.** $\dfrac{6}{a}$ **39.** $60x^2y^5$ **41.** $5x(x-5)$ **43.** $\dfrac{2}{5}$

45. $\dfrac{2}{x^2}$ **47.** $\dfrac{1}{x-2}$ **49.** $\dfrac{5x^2 - 3y^2}{15x^4y^3}$ **51.** $\dfrac{-x+5}{(x+1)(x-1)}$ **53.** $\dfrac{2x^2 - 5x - 4}{x-3}$ **55.** $\dfrac{3x^2 - 7x - 4}{(3x-4)(9x^2 + 12x + 16)}$

57. $-\dfrac{12}{x(x+1)(x-3)}$ **59.** $\dfrac{14x - 40}{(x+4)^2(x-4)}$ **61.** $\dfrac{2}{3}$ **63.** $\dfrac{2}{15 - 2x}$ **65.** $\dfrac{y}{2}$ **67.** $\dfrac{20x - 15}{10x^2 - 4}$ **69.** $\dfrac{5xy + x}{3y}$ **71.** $\dfrac{1+x}{1-x}$

73. $\dfrac{x-1}{3x-1}$ **75.** $-\dfrac{x^2+9}{6x}$ **77. a.** $\dfrac{3}{a+h}$ **b.** $\dfrac{3}{a}$ **c.** $\dfrac{\dfrac{3}{a+h} - \dfrac{3}{a}}{h}$ **d.** $\dfrac{-3}{a(a+h)}$ **79.** $\dfrac{9b^2z^3}{4a}$ **81.** $\dfrac{3}{b} + 4b$

83. $2x^3 - 4x^2 + 7x - 9 + \dfrac{6}{x+2}$ **85.** $x^2 - 1 + \dfrac{5}{2x+3}$ **87.** $3x^2 + 6$ **89.** $3x^2 - \dfrac{5}{2}x - \dfrac{1}{4} - \dfrac{5}{8\left(x + \dfrac{3}{2}\right)}$ **91.** $x^2 + 3x + 9 - \dfrac{54}{x-3}$

93. $3x^3 - 6x^2 + 10x - 20 + \dfrac{50}{x+2}$ **95.** -9323 **97.** $\dfrac{365}{32}$ **99.** 6   **101.** 2   **103.** $\dfrac{3}{2}$ **105.** $\dfrac{5}{3}$ **107.** $-\dfrac{1}{3}, 2$ **109.** $a = \dfrac{2A - hb}{h}$

111. $R = \dfrac{E - Ir}{I}$ **113.** $A = \dfrac{HL}{k(T_1 - T_2)}$ **115.** 7   **117.** -10 and -8 **119.** 12 hr   **121.** 490 mph   **123.** 8 mph   **125.** 4 mph

127. 9   **129.** 3.125 cu. ft

Chapter 6 Test

1. $\{x \mid x \text{ is a real number and } x \neq 1\}$ **2.** $\{x \mid x \text{ is a real number and } x \neq -3, x \neq -1\}$ **3.** $-\dfrac{7}{8}$ **4.** $\dfrac{x}{x+9}$ **5.** $\dfrac{5}{3x}$

6. $\dfrac{x+2}{2(x+3)}$ **7.** $-\dfrac{4(2x+9)}{5}$ **8.** -1 **9.** $\dfrac{5x-2}{(x-3)(x+2)(x-2)}$ **10.** $\dfrac{-x+30}{6(x-7)}$ **11.** $\dfrac{3}{2}$ **12.** $\dfrac{1}{5}$ **13.** $\dfrac{64}{3}$ **14.** $\dfrac{4xy}{3z} + \dfrac{3}{z} + 1$

15. $2x^2 - x - 2 + \dfrac{2}{2x+1}$ **16.** $4x^3 - 15x^2 + 45x - 136 + \dfrac{407}{x+3}$ **17.** 91   **18.** $\dfrac{2}{7}$ **19.** 3   **20.** $x = \dfrac{7a^2 + b^2}{4a - b}$ **21.** 5   **22.** $\dfrac{6}{7}$ hr

23. 16   **24.** 9   **25.** 256 ft

Chapter 6 Cumulative Review

1. a. $8x$ **b.** $8x + 3$ **c.** $x \div -7$ or $\dfrac{x}{-7}$ **d.** $2x - 1.6$; Sec. 1.2, Ex. 8

2. a. $x - \dfrac{1}{3}$ **b.** $5x - 6$ **c.** $8x + 3$ **d.** $\dfrac{7}{2 - x}$; Sec. 1.2   **3.** 2; Sec. 2.1, Ex. 5   **4.** 7; Sec. 2.1   **5.** 2013 and after; Sec. 2.4, Ex. 9

6. 82; Sec. 2.4   **7.** $\varnothing$; Sec. 2.6, Ex. 7   **8.** $\varnothing$; Sec. 2.6   **9.** -1; Sec. 2.7, Ex. 8   **10.** $\left(\infty, -\dfrac{5}{3}\right] \cup \left[\dfrac{11}{3}, \infty\right)$; Sec. 2.7

11. 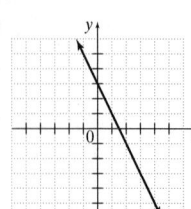 ; Sec. 3.1, Ex. 4   **12.** 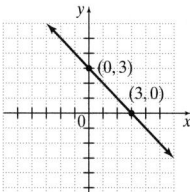 ; Sec. 3.1   **13. a.** function
b. not a function
c. function; Sec. 3.2, Ex. 2

14. a. -2 **b.** -20 **c.** $-\dfrac{10}{9}$; Sec. 3.2

15. 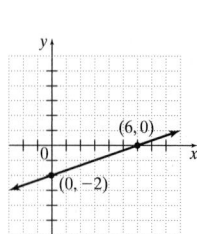 ; Sec. 3.3, Ex. 4   **16.** 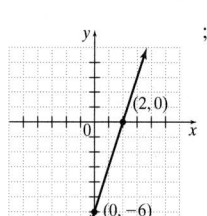 ; Sec. 3.3   **17.** $y = -3x - 2$; Sec. 3.5, Ex. 4

18. $f(x) = \dfrac{1}{2}x + \dfrac{7}{2}$; Sec. 3.5

19. 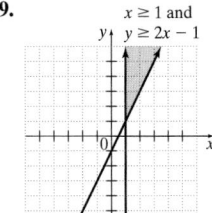 $x \geq 1$ and $y \geq 2x - 1$; Sec. 3.6, Ex. 3   **20.** 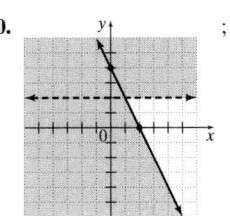 ; Sec. 3.6   **21.** $(0, -5)$; Sec. 4.1, Ex. 6   **22.** $(3, 4)$; Sec. 4.1   **23.** $\emptyset$; Sec. 4.2, Ex. 2   **24.** $(2, 1, 1)$; Sec. 4.2   **25.** $30°, 110°, 40°$; Sec. 4.3, Ex. 6   **26.** Paper, \$3.80; folders, \$5.25; Sec. 4.3   **27.** $(1, -1, 3)$; Sec. 4.4, Ex. 3   **28.** $(0, 5, 4)$; Sec. 4.4

29. a. 1   **b.** -1 **c.** 1   **d.** 2; Sec. 5.1, Ex. 3   **30. a.** $\frac{7}{12}$ **b.** -6 **c.** $\frac{1}{x^3}$; Sec. 5.1   **31. a.** $4x^b$ **b.** y^{5a+6}; Sec 5.2, Ex. 5

32. a. $48a^{2a}$ **b.** y^{10b+3}; Sec. 5.2   **33. a.** 2   **b.** 5   **c.** 1   **d.** 6   **e.** 0; Sec. 5.3, Ex. 1   **34.** $2x^2 + 6x + 4$; Sec. 5.3

35. $9 + 12a + 6b + 4a^2 + 4ab + b^2$; Sec. 5.4, Ex. 9   **36.** $16 + 24x - 8y + 9x^2 - 6xy + y^2$; Sec. 5.4   **37.** $(b - 6)(a + 2)$; Sec 5.5, Ex. 7

38. $(x - 5)(y + 2)$; Sec. 5.5   **39.** $2(n^2 - 19n + 40)$; Sec. 5.6, Ex. 4   **40.** $(2x - 5)(3x + 7)$; Sec. 5.6   **41.** $(x + 2 + y)(x + 2 - y)$; Sec. 5.7, Ex. 5   **42.** $(2x + 3y - 1)(2x - 3y - 1)$; Sec. 5.7   **43.** $-2, 6$; Sec. 5.8, Ex. 1   **44.** $0, -\frac{1}{3}, 3$; Sec. 5.8   **45.** $\frac{1}{5x - 1}$; Sec. 6.1, Ex. 2

46. a. domain: $(-\infty, \infty)$ range: $[-4, \infty)$ **b.** x-intercepts: $(-2, 0), (2, 0)$ y-intercepts: $(0, -4)$ **c.** there is no such point   **d.** $(0, -4)$
e. $-2, 2$ **f.** between $x = -2$ and $x = 2$ **g.** $-2, 2$; Sec. 3.2   **47.** $\frac{5k^2 - 7k + 4}{(k + 2)(k - 2)(k - 1)}$; Sec. 6.2, Ex. 4   **48.** $\frac{8a + 6}{(a + 2)(a - 2)}$; Sec. 6.2
49. -2; Sec. 6.6, Ex. 2   **50.** -4; Sec. 6.6

CHAPTER 7   RATIONAL EXPONENTS, RADICALS, AND COMPLEX NUMBERS

Mental Math   1. D   **3.** D

Exercise Set 7.1   1. 10   **3.** $\frac{1}{2}$ **5.** 0.01   **7.** -6 **9.** x^5 **11.** $4y^3$ **13.** 2.646   **15.** 6.164   **17.** 14.142   **19.** 4

21. $\frac{1}{2}$ **23.** -1 **25.** x^4 **27.** $-3x^3$ **29.** -2 **31.** not a real number   **33.** -2 **35.** x^4 **37.** $2x^2$ **39.** $9x^2$ **41.** $4x^2$

43. 8   **45.** -8 **47.** $2|x|$ **49.** x **51.** $|x - 5|$ **53.** $|x + 2|$ **55.** -11 **57.** $2x$ **59.** y^6 **61.** $5ab^{10}$ **63.** $-3x^4y^3$

65. a^4b **67.** $-2x^2y$ **69.** $\frac{5}{7}$ **71.** $\frac{x}{2y}$ **73.** $-\frac{z^7}{3x}$ **75.** $\frac{x}{2}$ **77.** $\sqrt{3}$ **79.** -1 **81.** -3 **83.** $\sqrt{7}$

85. $[0, \infty)$; 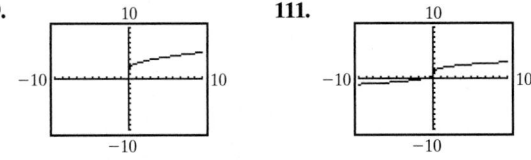   **87.** $[3, \infty)$; 0, 1, 2, 3   **89.** $(-\infty, \infty)$;   **91.** $(-\infty, \infty)$; 0, 1, -1, 2, -2

93. $-32x^{15}y^{10}$ **95.** $-60x^7y^{10}z^5$ **97.** $\frac{x^9y^5}{2}$ **99.** answers may vary   **101.** 13   **103.** 18   **105.** 1.69 sq. m   **107.** answers may vary

109. 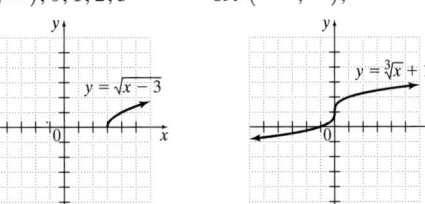   **111.**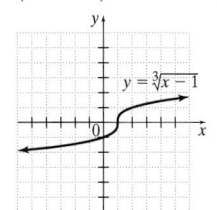

Mental Math   1. A   **3.** C   **5.** B   **7.** B   **9.** B

Exercise Set 7.2   1. 7   **3.** 3   **5.** $\frac{1}{2}$ **7.** 13   **9.** $2\sqrt[3]{m}$ **11.** $3x^2$ **13.** -3 **15.** -2 **17.** 8   **19.** 16   **21.** not a real number

23. $\sqrt[5]{(2x)^3}$ **25.** $\sqrt[4]{(7x + 2)^2}$ **27.** $\frac{64}{27}$ **29.** $\frac{1}{16}$ **31.** $\frac{1}{16}$ **33.** not a real number   **35.** $\frac{1}{x^{1/4}}$ **37.** $a^{2/3}$ **39.** $\frac{5x^{3/4}}{7}$

41. answers may vary   **43.** $a^{7/3}$ **45.** x **47.** $3^{5/8}$ **49.** $y^{1/6}$ **51.** $8u^3$ **53.** $-b$ **55.** $27x^{2/3}$ **57.** $y - y^{7/6}$ **59.** $2x^{5/3} - 2x^{2/3}$
61. $4x^{2/3} - 9$ **63.** $x^{8/3}(1 + x^{2/3})$ **65.** $x^{1/5}(x^{1/5} - 3)$ **67.** $x^{-1/3}(5 + x)$ **69.** $\sqrt{x}$ **71.** $\sqrt[3]{2}$ **73.** $2\sqrt{x}$ **75.** $\sqrt{xy}$ **77.** $\sqrt[15]{y^{11}}$
79. $\sqrt[12]{b^5}$ **81.** $\sqrt{a}$ **83.** $\sqrt[6]{432}$ **85.** $\sqrt[15]{343y^5}$ **87.** $25 \cdot 3$ **89.** $16 \cdot 3$ or $4 \cdot 12$ **91.** $8 \cdot 2$ **93.** $27 \cdot 2$ **95.** 1509 calories
97. 97.2 million   **99.** $a^{1/3}$ **101.** $x^{1/5}$ **103.** 1.6818   **105.** 5.6645   **107.** $\dfrac{t^{1/2}}{u^{1/2}}$

Exercise Set 7.3   **1.** $\sqrt{14}$ **3.** 2   **5.** $\sqrt[3]{36}$ **7.** $\sqrt{6x}$ **9.** $\sqrt{\dfrac{14}{xy}}$ **11.** $\sqrt[4]{20x^3}$ **13.** $\dfrac{\sqrt{6}}{7}$ **15.** $\dfrac{\sqrt{2}}{7}$ **17.** $\dfrac{\sqrt[4]{x^3}}{2}$ **19.** $\dfrac{\sqrt[3]{4}}{3}$

21. $\dfrac{\sqrt[4]{8}}{x^2}$ **23.** $\dfrac{\sqrt[3]{2x}}{3y^4\sqrt[3]{3}}$ **25.** $\dfrac{x\sqrt{y}}{10}$ **27.** $\dfrac{\sqrt{5x}}{2y}$ **29.** $-\dfrac{z^2\sqrt[3]{z}}{3x}$ **31.** $4\sqrt{2}$ **33.** $4\sqrt[3]{3}$ **35.** $25\sqrt{3}$ **37.** $2\sqrt{6}$ **39.** $10x^2\sqrt{x}$
41. $2y^2\sqrt[3]{2y}$ **43.** $a^2b\sqrt[4]{b^3}$ **45.** $y^2\sqrt{y}$ **47.** $5ab\sqrt{b}$ **49.** $-2x^2\sqrt[5]{y}$ **51.** $x^4\sqrt[3]{50x^2}$ **53.** $-4a^4b^3\sqrt{2b}$ **55.** $3x^3y^4\sqrt{xy}$ **57.** $5r^3s^4$
59. $\sqrt{2}$ **61.** 2   **63.** 10   **65.** x^2y **67.** $24m^2$ **69.** $\dfrac{15x\sqrt{2x}}{2}$ or $\dfrac{15x}{2}\sqrt{2x}$ **71.** $2a^2\sqrt[4]{2}$ **73.** $14x$ **75.** $2x^2 - 7x - 15$ **77.** y^2
79. $-3x - 15$ **81.** $x^2 - 8x - 16$ **83. a.** 20π sq. cm   **b.** 211.57 sq. ft   **85. a.** 3.8 times   **b.** 2.9 times   **c.** answers may vary

Mental Math   **1.** $6\sqrt{3}$ **3.** $3\sqrt{x}$ **5.** $12\sqrt[3]{x}$ **7.** $2\sqrt{11}$ **9.** $8\sqrt{13}$ **11.** $10\sqrt[3]{2x}$

Exercise Set 7.4   **1.** $-2\sqrt{2}$ **3.** $10x\sqrt{2x}$ **5.** $17\sqrt{2} - 15\sqrt{5}$ **7.** $-\sqrt[3]{2x}$ **9.** $5b\sqrt{b}$ **11.** $\dfrac{31\sqrt{2}}{15}$ **13.** $\dfrac{\sqrt[3]{11}}{3}$ **15.** $\dfrac{5\sqrt{5x}}{9}$
17. $14 + \sqrt{3}$ **19.** $7 - 3y$ **21.** $6\sqrt{3} - 6\sqrt{2}$ **23.** $-23\sqrt[3]{5}$ **25.** $2b\sqrt{b}$ **27.** $20y\sqrt{2y}$ **29.** $2y\sqrt[3]{2x}$ **31.** $6\sqrt[3]{11} - 4\sqrt{11}$
33. $4x\sqrt[4]{x^3}$ **35.** $\dfrac{2\sqrt{3}}{3}$ **37.** $\dfrac{5x\sqrt[3]{x}}{7}$ **39.** $\dfrac{5\sqrt{7}}{2x}$ **41.** $\dfrac{\sqrt[3]{2}}{6}$ **43.** $\dfrac{14x\sqrt[3]{2x}}{9}$ **45.** $15\sqrt{3}$ in.   **47.** $\sqrt{35} + \sqrt{21}$ **49.** $7 - 2\sqrt{10}$
51. $3\sqrt{x} - x\sqrt{3}$ **53.** $6x - 13\sqrt{x} - 5$ **55.** $\sqrt[3]{a^2} + \sqrt[3]{a} - 20$ **57.** $6\sqrt{2} - 12$ **59.** $2 + 2x\sqrt{3}$ **61.** $-16 - \sqrt{35}$ **63.** $x - y^2$
65. $3 + 2x\sqrt{3} + x^2$ **67.** $5x - 3\sqrt{15x} - 3\sqrt{10x} + 9\sqrt{6}$ **69.** $2\sqrt[3]{2} - \sqrt[3]{4}$ **71.** $-4\sqrt[6]{x^5} + \sqrt[3]{x^2} + 8\sqrt[3]{x} - 4\sqrt{x} + 7$
73. $x + 24 + 10\sqrt{x - 1}$ **75.** $2x + 6 - 2\sqrt{2x + 5}$ **77.** $x - 7$ **79.** $\dfrac{7}{x + y}$ **81.** $2a - 3$ **83.** $\dfrac{-2 + \sqrt{3}}{3}$ **85.** $22\sqrt{5}$ ft; 150 sq. ft
87. a. $2\sqrt{3}$ **b.** 3   **c.** answers may vary   **89.** answers may vary

Mental Math   **1.** $\sqrt{2} - x$ **3.** $5 + \sqrt{a}$ **5.** $7\sqrt{5} - 8\sqrt{x}$

Exercise Set 7.5   **1.** $\dfrac{\sqrt{14}}{7}$ **3.** $\dfrac{\sqrt{5}}{5}$ **5.** $\dfrac{\sqrt[3]{6}}{2}$ **7.** $\dfrac{4\sqrt[3]{9}}{3}$ **9.** $\dfrac{3\sqrt[3]{2x}}{4x}$ **11.** $\dfrac{3\sqrt[3]{2x}}{2x}$ **13.** $\dfrac{2\sqrt{x}}{x}$ **15.** $\dfrac{3\sqrt{3a}}{a}$ **17.** $\dfrac{3\sqrt[3]{4}}{2}$
19. $\dfrac{2\sqrt{21}}{7}$ **21.** $\dfrac{\sqrt{10xy}}{5y}$ **23.** $\dfrac{3\sqrt[4]{2}}{2}$ **25.** $\dfrac{2\sqrt[4]{9x}}{3x^2}$ **27.** $\dfrac{5a\sqrt[5]{4ab^4}}{2a^2b^3}$ **29.** $-2(2 + \sqrt{7})$ **31.** $\dfrac{7(3 + \sqrt{x})}{9 - x}$ **33.** $-5 + 2\sqrt{6}$
35. $\dfrac{2a + 2\sqrt{a} + \sqrt{ab} + \sqrt{b}}{4a - b}$ **37.** $-\dfrac{8(1 - \sqrt{10})}{9}$ **39.** $\dfrac{x - \sqrt{xy}}{x - y}$ **41.** $\dfrac{5 + 3\sqrt{2}}{7}$ **43.** $\dfrac{5}{\sqrt{15}}$ **45.** $\dfrac{6}{\sqrt{10}}$ **47.** $\dfrac{2x}{7\sqrt{x}}$
49. $\dfrac{5y}{\sqrt[3]{100xy}}$ **51.** $\dfrac{2}{\sqrt{10}}$ **53.** $\dfrac{2x}{11\sqrt{2x}}$ **55.** $\dfrac{7}{2\sqrt[3]{49}}$ **57.** $\dfrac{3x^2}{10\sqrt[3]{9x}}$ **59.** $\dfrac{6x^2y^3}{\sqrt{6z}}$ **61.** answers may vary   **63.** $\dfrac{-7}{12 + 6\sqrt{11}}$
65. $\dfrac{3}{10 + 5\sqrt{7}}$ **67.** $\dfrac{x - 9}{x - 3\sqrt{x}}$ **69.** $\dfrac{1}{3 + 2\sqrt{2}}$ **71.** $\dfrac{x - 1}{x - 2\sqrt{x} + 1}$ **73.** 5   **75.** $-\dfrac{1}{2}, 6$ **77.** 2, 6   **79.** $r = \dfrac{\sqrt{A\pi}}{2\pi}$
81. answers may vary

Integrated Review   **1.** 9   **2.** -2 **3.** $\dfrac{1}{2}$ **4.** x^3 **5.** y^3 **6.** $2y^5$ **7.** $-2y$ **8.** $3b^3$ **9.** 6   **10.** $\sqrt[4]{3y}$ **11.** $\dfrac{1}{16}$
12. $\sqrt[5]{(x + 1)^3}$ **13.** y **14.** $16x^{1/2}$ **15.** $x^{5/4}$ **16.** $4^{11/15}$ **17.** $2x^2$ **18.** $\sqrt[4]{a^3b^2}$ **19.** $\sqrt[4]{x^3}$ **20.** $\sqrt[6]{500}$ **21.** $2\sqrt{10}$
22. $2xy^2\sqrt[4]{x^3y^2}$ **23.** $3x\sqrt[3]{2x}$ **24.** $-2b^2\sqrt[5]{2}$ **25.** $\sqrt{5x}$ **26.** $4x$ **27.** $7y^2\sqrt{y}$ **28.** $2a^2\sqrt[3]{3}$ **29.** $2\sqrt{5} - 5\sqrt{3} + 5\sqrt{7}$
30. $y\sqrt[3]{2y}$ **31.** $\sqrt{15} - \sqrt{6}$ **32.** $10 + 2\sqrt{21}$ **33.** $4x^2 - 5$ **34.** $x + 2 - 2\sqrt{x + 1}$ **35.** $\dfrac{\sqrt{21}}{3}$ **36.** $\dfrac{5\sqrt[3]{4x}}{2x}$ **37.** $\dfrac{13 - 3\sqrt{21}}{5}$
38. $\dfrac{7}{\sqrt{21}}$ **39.** $\dfrac{3y}{\sqrt[3]{33y^2}}$ **40.** $\dfrac{x - 4}{x + 2\sqrt{x}}$

Graphing Calculator Explorations   **1.** 3.19   **3.** $\varnothing$ **5.** 3.23

PHOTO CREDITS

Contents Reuters Media, Inc./Corbis/Bettmann, © Kevin Fleming/CORBIS, W.A. Harewood/Getty Images, Inc./Liaison, © Jason Hawkes/CORBIS, Index Stock Imagery, Inc., © Gregg Stott/Masterfile Corporation, Whitney, Frank/Getty Images, Inc./Image Bank, Mark Gibson/Mark and Audra Gibson Photography/© Gibson Stock Photography, © David R. Frazier/David R. Frazier Photolibrary, Inc. www.drfphoto.com, Superstock Royalty Free, © David Young Wolff/PhotoEdit Inc.

Chapter 1 Reuters Media, Inc./Corbis/Bettmann, (p.2) Sepp Seitz/Woodfin Camp & Associates, (p.3) © Rachel Epstein/PhotoEdit, (p.7) Boeing Commercial Airplane Group/Courtesy of The Boeing Company

Chapter 2 © Kevin Fleming/CORBIS, (p.62) AP/Wide World Photos, (p.65) Michael Newman/PhotoEdit, (p.67) Jeremy Woodhouse/Getty Images, Inc./Photodisc, (p.69) © David Jennings/The Image Works, (p.69) Jeff Robbins/AP/Wide World Photos, (p.78) Georgia, Fredrica/Photo Researchers, Inc., (p.81) Jeffrey Stevensen Studio, (p.90) © Spencer Ainsley/The Image Works

Chapter 3 W.A. Harewood/Getty Images, Inc./Liaison, (p.133) © Bonn Sequenz/Imapress/The Image Works, (p.149) © Mark Richards/PhotoEdit, (p.155) Masterfile Corporation, (p.156) AGE Fotostock America, Inc., (p.179) Bob Daemmrich/Bob Daemmrich Photography, Inc., (p.185) Bill Bachmann/Photo Researchers, Inc., (p.191) © Mark Richards/PhotoEdit, (p.210) David Young Wolff/PhotoEdit Inc.

Chapter 4 © Jason Hawkes/CORBIS, (p.216) © Lon C. Diehl/PhotoEdit Inc., (p.244) SuperStock, Inc., (p.245) © James Leynse/CORBIS/SABA Press Photos, Inc., (p.246) © Armando Arorizo/ZUMA/Corbis, (p.246) AP/Wide World Photos, (p.247) Pierre Tremblay/Masterfile Corporation, (p.262) T.A.Wiewandt/DRK Photo

Chapter 5 Index Stock Imagery, Inc., (p.281) Corbis Digital Stock, (p.283) Chris Butler/Science Photo Library, (p.283) © Rudi Von Briel/PhotoEdit Inc., (p.290) John Lemker/Animals Animals/Earth Scenes, (p.351) Getty Images, Inc./Photodisc

Chapter 6 © Gregg Stott/Masterfile Corporation, (p.376) Guirard, Greg/Getty Images Inc./Image Bank, (p.392) Pictor/Image State/International Stock Photography Ltd., (p.392) Kelly-Mooney Photography/Corbis/Bettmann, (p.411) Spike Mafford/Getty Images Inc./Photodisc, (p.416) Rob Melnychuk/Getty Images Inc./Photodisc, (p.417) Amy C. Etra/PhotoEdit, (p.418) John Serafin, (p.422) Michael Gadomski/Photo Researchers, Inc., (p.427) Richard A. Cooke III/Getty Images Inc./Stone Allstock, (p.429) © Ken Welsh/AGE Fotostock America, Inc.

Chapter 7 Whitney, Frank/Getty Images, Inc./Image Bank. (p.463) © Susan Findlay/Masterfile Corporation, (p.494) Steve Gottlieb/Getty Images Inc./Taxi

Chapter 8 Mark Gibson/Mark and Audra Gibson Photography/© Gibson Stock Photography, (p.525) Tony Freeman/PhotoEdit, (p.528) David Parker/Science Photo Library/Photo Researchers, Inc., (p.538) Dr. Chikaraishi/National Institute for Fusion Science, (p.538) © Shane Pedersen/Wildlight Photo Agency, (p.544) © ZEFA/Masterfile Corporation, (p.547) Tim Flach/Getty Images Inc./Stone Allstock, (p.547) Arthur S. Aubry Photography/Getty Images Inc./Photodisc, (p.576) Robert Harding/Robert Harding World Imagery, (p.582) AP/Wide World Photos

Chapter 9 © David R. Frazier/David R. Frazier Photolibrary, Inc. www.drfphoto.com, (p.612) © I and I/Masterfile Corporation, (p.612) Peter Arnold, Inc., (p.613)Getty Images Inc./Photodisc, (p.637) © Weiss/Sunset/Animals Animals/Earth Scenes

Chapter 10 Superstock Royalty Free

Chapter 11 © David Young Wolff/PhotoEdit Inc.

READ THIS LICENSE CAREFULLY BEFORE OPENING THIS PACKAGE. BY OPENING THIS PACKAGE, YOU ARE AGR
ING TO THE TERMS AND CONDITIONS OF THIS LICENSE. IF YOU DO NOT AGREE, DO NOT OPEN THE PACKA
PROMPTLY RETURN THE UNOPENED PACKAGE AND ALL ACCOMPANYING ITEMS TO THE PLACE YOU OBTAIN
THEM. THESE TERMS APPLY TO ALL LICENSED SOFTWARE ON THE DISK EXCEPT THAT THE TERMS FOR USE
ANY SHAREWARE OR FREEWARE ON THE DISKETTES ARE AS SET FORTH IN THE ELECTRONIC LICENSE LOC
ED ON THE DISK:

Single PC Site License

1.   GRANT OF LICENSE and OWNERSHIP: The enclosed computer programs and any data ("Software")
licensed, not sold, to you by Pearson Education, Inc. publishing as Pearson Prentice Hall ("We" or the "Company") in considera
of your adoption of the accompanying Company textbooks and/or other materials, and your agreement to these terms. You own
the disk(s) but we and/or our licensors own the Software itself. This license allows instructors and students enrolled in the course u
the Company textbook that accompanies this Software (the "Course") to use and display the enclosed copy of the Software o
unlimited number of computers, for academic use only, so long as you comply with the terms of this Agreement. You may make
copy for back up only. We reserve any rights not granted to you.

2.   USE RESTRICTIONS: You may <u>not</u> sell or license copies of the Software or the Documentation to others.
may not transfer, distribute or make available the Software or the Documentation. You may not reverse engineer, disassemble, dec
pile, modify, adapt, translate or create derivative works based on the Software or the Documentation. You may be held legally res
sible for any copying or copyright infringement that is caused by your failure to abide by the terms of these restrictions.

3.   TERMINATION: This license is effective until terminated. This license will terminate automatically without no
from the Company if you fail to comply with any provisions or limitations of this license. Upon termination, you shall destroy
Documentation and all copies of the Software. All provisions of this Agreement as to limitation and disclaimer of warranties, lin
tion of liability, remedies or damages, and our ownership rights shall survive termination.

**4.   DISCLAIMER OF WARRANTY: THE COMPANY AND ITS LICENSORS MAKE <u>NO</u> WARRANTIES AB(
THE SOFTWARE, WHICH IS PROVIDED "<u>AS-IS</u>." IF THE DISK IS DEFECTIVE IN MATERIALS OR WORKMANSHIP, YO
ONLY REMEDY IS TO RETURN IT TO THE COMPANY WITHIN 30 DAYS FOR REPLACEMENT UNLESS THE COMPA
DETERMINES IN GOOD FAITH THAT THE DISK HAS BEEN MISUSED OR IMPROPERLY INSTALLED, REPAIR
ALTERED OR DAMAGED. THE COMPANY DISCLAIMS ALL WARRANTIES, EXPRESS OR IMPLIED, INCLUDING WI
OUT LIMITATION, THE IMPLIED WARRANTIES OF MERCHANTABILITY AND FITNESS FOR A PARTICULAR P
POSE. THE COMPANY DOES NOT WARRANT, GUARANTEE OR MAKE ANY REPRESENTATION REGARDING
ACCURACY, RELIABILITY, CURRENTNESS, USE, OR RESULTS OF USE, OF THE SOFTWARE.**

**5.   LIMITATION OF REMEDIES AND DAMAGES: IN NO EVENT, SHALL THE COMPANY OR ITS EMPL
EES, AGENTS, LICENSORS OR CONTRACTORS BE LIABLE FOR ANY INCIDENTAL, INDIRECT, SPECIAL OR CO1
QUENTIAL DAMAGES ARISING OUT OF OR IN CONNECTION WITH THIS LICENSE OR THE SOFTWARE, INCLUD1
WITHOUT LIMITATION, LOSS OF USE, LOSS OF DATA, LOSS OF INCOME OR PROFIT, OR OTHER LOSSES SUSTA1
AS A RESULT OF INJURY TO ANY PERSON, OR LOSS OF OR DAMAGE TO PROPERTY, OR CLAIMS OF THIRD PART
EVEN IF THE COMPANY OR AN AUTHORIZED REPRESENTATIVE OF THE COMPANY HAS BEEN ADVISED OF
POSSIBILITY OF SUCH DAMAGES.** SOME JURISDICTIONS DO NOT ALLOW THE LIMITATION OF DAMAGES IN C
TAIN CIRCUMSTANCES, SO THE ABOVE LIMITATIONS MAY NOT ALWAYS APPLY.

6.   GENERAL: THIS AGREEMENT SHALL BE CONSTRUED IN ACCORDANCE WITH THE LAWS
THE UNITED STATES OF AMERICA AND THE STATE OF NEW YORK, APPLICABLE TO CONTRACTS MADE IN N
YORK, AND SHALL BENEFIT THE COMPANY, ITS AFFILIATES AND ASSIGNEES. This Agreement is the complete
exclusive statement of the agreement between you and the Company and supersedes all proposals, prior agreements, oral or wri
and any other communications between you and the company or any of its representatives relating to the subject matter. If you a
U.S. Government user, this Software is licensed with "restricted rights" as set forth in subparagraphs (a)-(d) of the Comme
Computer-Restricted Rights clause at FAR 52.227-19 or in subparagraphs (c)(1)(ii) of the Rights in Technical Data and Comp
Software clause at DFARS 252.227-7013, and similar clauses, as applicable.

Should you have any questions concerning this agreement or if you wish to contact the Company for any reason, please contact in
ing: Customer Service Pearson Prentice Hall, 200 Old Tappan Road, Old Tappan NJ 07675.

Minimum System Requirements

Windows	Macintosh
Pentium II 300 MHz processor	Power PC G3 233 MHz or better
Windows 98 or later	Mac OS 9.x or 10.x
64 MB RAM	64 MB RAM
800 x 600 resolution	800 x 600 resolution
8x or faster CD-ROM drive	8x or faster CD-ROM drive
QuickTime 6.0 or later	QuickTime 6.0 or later